.JAPAN

D0198821

Author Alan Booth was born in London in 1946. He has an honors degree from Birmingham University and did postgraduate research at the Shakespeare Institute. He won the Birmingham Post Prize for Poetry in 1967.

He came to Japan in 1970 and has walked the length of the country, a journey described in his 1985 *The Roads to Sata*. Alan Booth has won four PATA literary prizes, including Best Story (Any Language) in 1982. He was for 11 years a Japanese film critic for the *Asahi Evening News*, and is a regular contributor to journals both inside and outside Japan.

Alan Booth lives in Tokyo with his wife, Sok-Chzeng, and daughter, Mirai.

Photographer Ken Straiton was born in Toronto, Canada, in 1949. After graduating from the University of Waterloo, Ontario, he moved in 1973 to Vancouver to study architecture.

His interests soon led him toward film-making at the Simon Fraser Film Workshop, and while there he became increasingly interested in photography. Today he focuses on corporate work and feature stories, commuting between Tokyo, where he has lived since 1982, and the rest of the world.

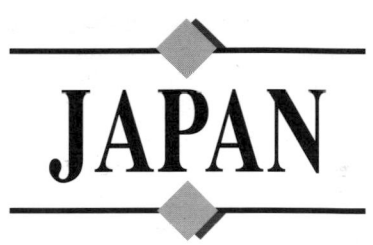

JAPAN

Alan Booth

Photography by Ken Straiton

Hong Kong

Grateful acknowledgement is made to the following authors and publishers
for permissions granted:

Atlantic Monthly Press and Andre Deutsch Limited for
Pictures from the Water Trade, © 1985 by John David Morley

Grove Press for
'Human Ashes' by Katsuzo Oda
and
Teach Us to Outgrow our Madness by Kenzburō Oe

Penguin Books Ltd for
Zen in the Art of Archery by Eugen Herrigel, translated by R F C Hull,
© 1953 by Routledge & Kegan Paul
and
The Japan Diaries of Richard Gordon Smith
edited by Victoria Manthorpe, © 1986 by J Austin and E A Tudge

Random House Inc and Martin Secker & Warburg Ltd for
The Tale of Genji by Murasaki Shikibu, English translation
© 1976 by Edward G Seidensticker. Reprinted by permission of Alfred A Knopf Inc
and
The Master of Go by Yasunari Kawabata, © 1972 by Alfred A Knopf

Distribution in the United Kingdom, Ireland, Europe and certain Commonwealth countries
by Hodder and Stoughton, Mill Road, Dunton Green, Sevenoaks, Kent TN13 2YA

Editor: David Price
Series Editor: Claire Banham
Illustrations Editor: Caroline Robertson
Map Artwork: Bai Yiliang
Design: Unity Design Studio
Cover Concept: Raquel Jaramillo and Aubrey Tse
Photographs by Ken Straiton/Pacific Press Service, with additional contributions by
Altfield Gallery (104, 105 above); Wayne Brothers (201); Nigel Hicks (4–5, 34–35,
186–187); Mike Yamashita/Pacific Press Service (220); woodblock print (30–31)
courtesy of the Board of Trustees of the Victoria and Albert Museum London; Wattis Fine
Art (105 below).

British Library Cataloguing in Publication Data has been applied for.

Production House: Twin Age Limited, Hong Kong
Printed in Hong Kong by Sing Cheong Printing Co. Ltd.

Contents

Special Topics

Maps

Excerpts

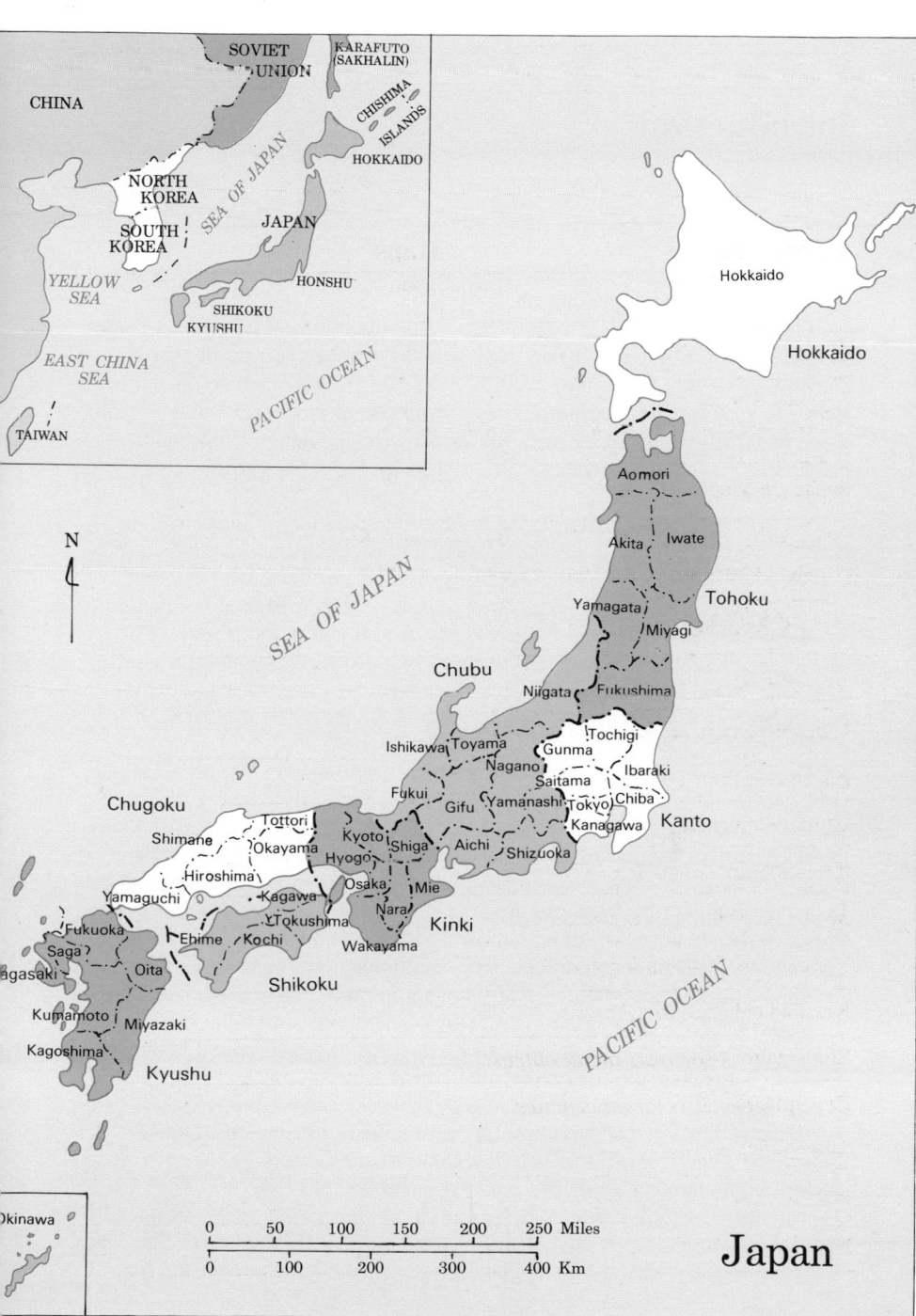

Japan

Introduction

More thorough nonsense must be spoken and written about Japan than about any comparably developed nation.

On the congested Washington Metro a newly returned traveller remarks to his fellow passengers, 'If you think this is crowded, you should see the subways in Tokyo. There they employ attendants to push people on and off trains because Japanese commuters are too polite to push each other'. And a guide to Japan published recently for the American business community informs its readers that Japanese office workers begin each working day with a tea ceremony.

As with all the most misleading myths, there is a tiny grain of truth in both these extraordinary statements, sufficient to throw the credulous completely off balance. During Tokyo rush hours, white-gloved station employees can indeed be seen pushing people onto jam-packed trains, but social decorum is not among their reasons. And it is true that a male office worker arriving at his desk in the morning will probably be served a small cup of green tea by a female office worker who thereby discharges the main part of her job; but this has as little to do with the tea ceremony as an office outing to the pub has to do with a royal garden party.

One of the difficulties of coming to grips with Japan is that myths about Japanese quaintness die so very hard. Ever since the 'discovery' of Japan by the West, Western visitors have gone out of their way to emphasize as many of the unfamiliar aspects of Japanese life as they could, partly because by doing so they made their own stay there sound all the more intrepid. And ever since the discovery by Japanese government and business circles that Western trade negotiators and others are willing to be fobbed off with such lines as 'You can't understand the way we do things because you are not Japanese', the mythmaking fraternity has multiplied to plague proportions.

Of course the foreign visitor to Japan wants to see unfamiliar things; if he didn't he would have gone to Brighton. His delight in the vertical neon signs of Ginza is genuine, and made possible by the fact that he can't read them. A British poet's enthusiastic comparison of Japanese conversation to the twittering of birds is tolerated because neither he nor his readers can understand a single word that is being said. Where the foreign traveller in Japan is concerned, ignorance is the best guarantee of bliss.

The most difficult myths to dispel are those concocted by the Japanese themselves: for example, the curious and universally credited myth that Japan is a small country. Of Japan's four main islands, the largest, Honshu, is slightly larger than all of Great Britain; Hokkaido is about the size of Austria; Kyushu is exactly the size of Denmark; and Shikoku is a little smaller than Wales. The climate and vegetation of northern Hokkaido are subarctic, while those of southern Kyushu are subtropical (in fact, Japan's southernmost island, Iriomote, lies a bare one degree north of the Tropic of Cancer). If this is a small country, then most of the other countries in the world must be classified as microscopic.

Or there is the equally pervasive belief in Japan's 'uniqueness', a quality taken for granted whenever Japanese people attempt to define their country and the ways in which it differs from everyone else's. For example: 'Japan has four seasons. Japan is unique. Therefore no other country has four seasons.' Or: 'The Japanese language is subtle and poetic. Japan is unique. Therefore all other languages are crude and merely "logical".' These and similar articles of faith can be encountered at all levels of the social spectrum —in unthinking youths for whom they are reinforced nightly by television quiz shows, as well as in educated 'opinion makers' who write books 'proving' the Japanese to be totally unlike all other human beings. This class of literature is called *nihonjinron* (literally, 'Japanese People Discussions'), examples of which regularly rank among the nation's best sellers.

Naturally enough, these facts of Japanese life can exert a somewhat negative influence on the long-term foreign resident or the Japanese specialist who takes his field of study seriously. But the short-term visitor is more likely to find them enchanting than otherwise. They are ideal subjects with which he can regale fellow passengers on congested Washington trains and, if you don't understand a word of it, *nihonjinron* must sound disarmingly like the twittering of birds.

From 1639 to 1854 Japan maintained a policy of national seclusion (*sakoku*—literally 'closed country'), when Japanese citizens were forcibly prevented from travelling abroad and foreigners who found their way to Japan were either sent packing or beheaded. Within the country a strict military dictatorship ensured social conformity at all levels, the price of peace and unity being a conspicuous absence of personal freedoms. For example, the authorities operated a series of barrier gates on all of the main feudal highways at which tolls were collected, thus seriously discouraging travel between regions, particularly among the impecunious. Most people born into the peasant or farming classes spent their entire lives within a few miles of the place where they were born, with the possible exception—once and once only—of a pilgrimage to the Grand Shrine at Ise.

This de facto restriction of movement had two main results, both of which can still be strongly felt. The first was an almost mystical attachment to one's 'home country' (*furusato*—a word that has no real equivalent in English, implying both the place where a person was actually born and the place to which he feels the strongest spiritual ties). Regional identity is still an important fact of life in modern Japan and, for all the official stress upon homogeneity and the never-ending litany of 'We Japanese', local diversity—whether of dialect, diet, music, produce or custom—is a major and continuing source of pride.

The second result was that travel to distant parts of the country obtained an aura of romance which has hardly diminished in modern times. The great feudal highways, particularly the Tokaido which ran from Edo (Tokyo) to Kyoto and Osaka, were among the best-loved settings for stories, plays and legends. The *michiyuki* (literally, 'Going Along the Road') was an essential scene in most popular Kabuki and puppet plays, and usually depicted the flight of a pair of doomed lovers down some impossibly picturesque thoroughfare, strewn with cherry blossoms and overshadowed by the pristine cone of Mount Fuji. Recently this aura of romance found its way into the slogans used in two campaigns mounted by the national railways to persuade people to spend their holidays exploring distant parts of the country. The slogans were 'Discover Japan' and 'Exotic Japan' (both, incidentally, couched in English so as to imbue them with the same degree of dreamy unreality as was conveyed by the cherry blossoms and Fuji's cone).

With postwar affluence has come a large-scale boom in leisure travel, and domestic tourism is one of the most flourishing industries in the nation. For the foreign visitor, this state of affairs has both advantages and disadvantages. The chief advantage is that, with an infrastructure so comprehensively and efficiently developed, he will rarely experience any difficulty in obtaining information about, and then reaching, a chosen destination, and his problem once there will hardly ever be lack of accommodation but rather a plethora out of which to choose. The disadvantage is that, unless he is unusually fortunate, he is likely to find himself viewing some spot noted for its tranquillity and remoteness in the company of half the population of Osaka.

What is the best time of year to visit Japan? Skiing and other winter sports now form a sizeable chunk of the booming tourist industry, and the most reliable months for these are January and February. The most popular resorts do not yet employ white-gloved attendants to push skiers in and out of chair lifts but, at weekends and during holidays, congestion falls not far short of rush-hour density. Local festivals provide a colourful reason for visiting provincial cities, and the thickest concentration of these occurs in August, during the Buddhist observance of *O-Bon*, sometimes called the 'Festival of the Dead', when the spirits of departed ancestors are thought to return to the homes of their families, who dance and provide other diversions to entertain them. Family members who have moved to the great cities often go back to the towns and villages where they were born to celebrate O-Bon, making mid-August the peak travel period of the year. Between August 8 and 18 (or thereabouts, depending on the distribution of weekends) long-distance trains carry up to twice their normal capacity of passengers and seats on domestic

flights are usually unavailable unless booked well in advance. Beaches near major cities are so popular with bathers on August Sundays that, almost without fail, the Monday morning papers report between 20 and 30 drownings.

New Year is, for most people, a family celebration, but increasing numbers of 'nuclear families', not tied to home by the presence of older relatives, seize the opportunity to spend a few days away, often at a hot-spring resort. Hotels and inns at the more popular tourist destinations may receive New Year reservations up to a year in advance, dooming spur-of-the-moment plans by foreign visitors to likely frustration. This is even truer of the week beginning 29 April and ending 5 May, known as 'Golden Week' because it contains no fewer than three national holidays: 29 April , Greenery Day *(Midori-no-Hi)*, originally Emperor Hirohito's birthday, retained as a national holiday and named for the former emperor's interest in biology, 3 May (Constitution Day) and 5 May (The Boys' Festival, now more equably known as Children's Day). It is becoming the custom for people to take the whole week off work and make it the high point of their travelling year. Nowadays, too, more and more Japanese people are using the leisure time available at New Year, Golden Week and O-Bon for taking trips abroad, so that international flights into and out of Japan are as fully booked as domestic flights. Visitors arriving in Japan with open tickets and expecting to make last-minute reservations home during these periods could end up staying longer than they bargained for.

In addition to these three weeks of airport, hotel and railway upheaval, the Japanese have traditionally regarded three short periods of the year as the best times for organizing outings to noted beauty spots. The first of these is the cherry-blossom season, which starts in Kyushu in early March, reaches Tokyo around the beginning of April, and ends in northern Honshu in May. The moon is said to be at its best in early autumn, so September was traditionally a month for organizing moon-viewing parties, a recreation now sadly lapsed. And the often spectacular colouring of the leaves in late autumn makes October and November favourite months for trips to lakes or mountain spas.

Many people would advise against travelling during the rainy season (called *tsuyu* or *baiu*; for most of the country early June to mid-July), but the misty precipitation characteristic of this time of year can enhance some destinations—the gardens of Kyoto temples, for instance—and, in any case, the rainy season usually includes stretches of up to a week when the whole country basks in completely rainless summer weather. Meteorologists insist that there is a second rainy season (*shurin*) during late September and early October, but this period is more obviously characterized by the late typhoons that blow up through the South China Sea and bring torrential downpours to much of southern Japan, especially the Ryukyu islands and Kyushu. It is certainly not a time of misty precipitation; rather of the dispersal of rooftiles and the washing away of grandmothers.

An all-year-round phenomenon is the supposed difficulty raised by the 'language barrier', though this tends to weigh more heavily on the Japanese consciousness than it does on that of the average foreign visitor. It is not many years since the Japan Tourist Bureau did its best to persuade people with foreign faces not to stay at country inns and lodging houses, citing the 'language barrier' as the reason. And the proprietors of the country inns themselves would often fly into mild panics and pretend to be full or closed or under a demolition order when faced with the possibility that a guest might have to ask the way to the bathroom by pointing his finger rather than engaging his host in a ten-minute discussion. Happily, things have changed for the better and, though one can still encounter reluctance to accept foreign visitors at some places, there is nowadays a much wider acceptance of the fact that people who have taken the considerable trouble to reach, say, the interior of Shikoku will in all likelihood not be expecting to find water beds, tenderloin steaks and an innkeeper with a degree in modern languages.

Practically all Japanese people educated in the postwar period have studied English for at least six years at school, and practically none can speak a sensible word of it. This is less their fault than the fault of an educational system which has seized upon the intricacies of English grammar and lexis as a perfect means of testing rote memory and willingness to submit to grinding discipline for the sake of social advancement. Grammar is taught as though it were a series of algebraic equations and vocabulary is introduced with little concern for its potential usefulness in everyday life but with every consideration for its likely occurrence in examination papers. That young people resent learning English and leave school thinking that foreigners and their languages are colossal jokes is hardly surprising.

Needless to say, the visitor who confines his stay to Western-style hotels and does all his booking through major travel agents will find English speakers on the staffs of both, so considerations of language will not much worry him. But the more adventurous visitor, provided he is amply supplied with time and patience, will likely discover that the 'language barrier' is a more formidable obstacle in the imagination than it is in reality.

Quite aside from questions of language, many foreign visitors have returned from their trips to Japan brimming with praise for the helpfulness and honesty of the people they have encountered, and few of their tales are exaggerated. The personal honesty of the Japanese (when they are not filing income tax returns) is, quite rightly, proverbial. Visitors have left their handbags on the back seats of taxis and had them returned within the hour by drivers who have turned off their meters and taken time off work to cruise the streets looking for the owners. Foreign tourists have dropped their wallets in station taxi queues and gone to the station lost property offices hours, or even days, later to find that their wallets have been handed in with the contents intact. The only glaring exceptions to this rule are umbrellas and bicycles, which, no matter how much they cost and no matter how many combination locks protect them, tend to be viewed as fair game for anyone in urgent need of either.

As for helpfulness, it has been the common experience of travellers, particularly in remoter areas, that no sooner have they opened their guidebooks or maps to consult them than someone has approached and asked if he could help. If a visitor has solicited directions, he has frequently found that the person he asked has left whatever he was doing and accompanied the visitor to his destination, sometimes inviting him for coffee on the way. I have walked past houses in remote rural areas and had the owners run out to summon me inside for a cup of tea. I have knocked at a door to ask the way and spent the rest of the afternoon sitting on the veranda drinking beer. Visitors who shun encounters of this kind because they pay too much attention to mutterings about language barriers do themselves a serious disfavour. And besides, if you speak three words of Japanese you will be rapturously applauded for your linguistic mastery. It is only when you are approaching competence that you will be frowned upon as a threat to the national polity.

It seems hardly necessary to emphasize the limitations of a book of this kind. It has often been said that a festival takes place somewhere in Japan every day of the year. There are countless little shrines and temple that no guidebook will ever mention. They may boast no valuable statuary nor any special historical associations, but a combination of circumstance, location, age and atmosphere can turn any one of them into the high point of a visitor's stay. And the unspoiled, little-visited parts of the Japanese countryside still hugely outnumber the famous spots singled out for full-throttle tourist spoliation. The Inland Sea National Park alone contains more than a thousand islands.

Other limitations the book has imposed on itself. It recommends no hotels or restaurants; it does not give advice on how best to waste the nighttime hours; it provides no details of rail, road or air connections to the places it describes. Visitors in need of this sort of information can find themselves inundated with it, if they choose, within minutes of arrival. A lot of it is available free from their hotel information desk or from any large travel agent. See page 238 for most of the reliable sources.

This guide's approach is regional. The Kanto (including Tokyo) and Kinki (including Nara and Kyoto) regions occupy the longest sections because they are the places where most foreign visitors to Japan spend the greatest amount of time, but more than half the book is concerned with other, often remoter, destinations. Each region is introduced by some general remarks aimed at providing the reader with background information on history and geography, as well as with some idea of a district's character and reputation. Following this, the main sights and attractions of each region are described, prefecture by prefecture (the nine regions are divided into a total of 47 prefectures). A prefectural approach has the disadvantage that some notable tourist spots (like the Fuji-Hakone-Izu National Park) spread over two or more prefectures; so that the reader is obliged to look in several different parts of the book for a comprehensive description of what he will see there, though his task is simplified by cross-references. However, this inconvenience is outweighed by the fact that much of the tourist information available within Japan is organized at a prefectural level. Each prefecture has its own tourist offices and these publish many of the brochures, maps and other material available. A prefectural approach facilitates the use of information from local sources to amplify and complement the descriptions and opinions contained in this book.

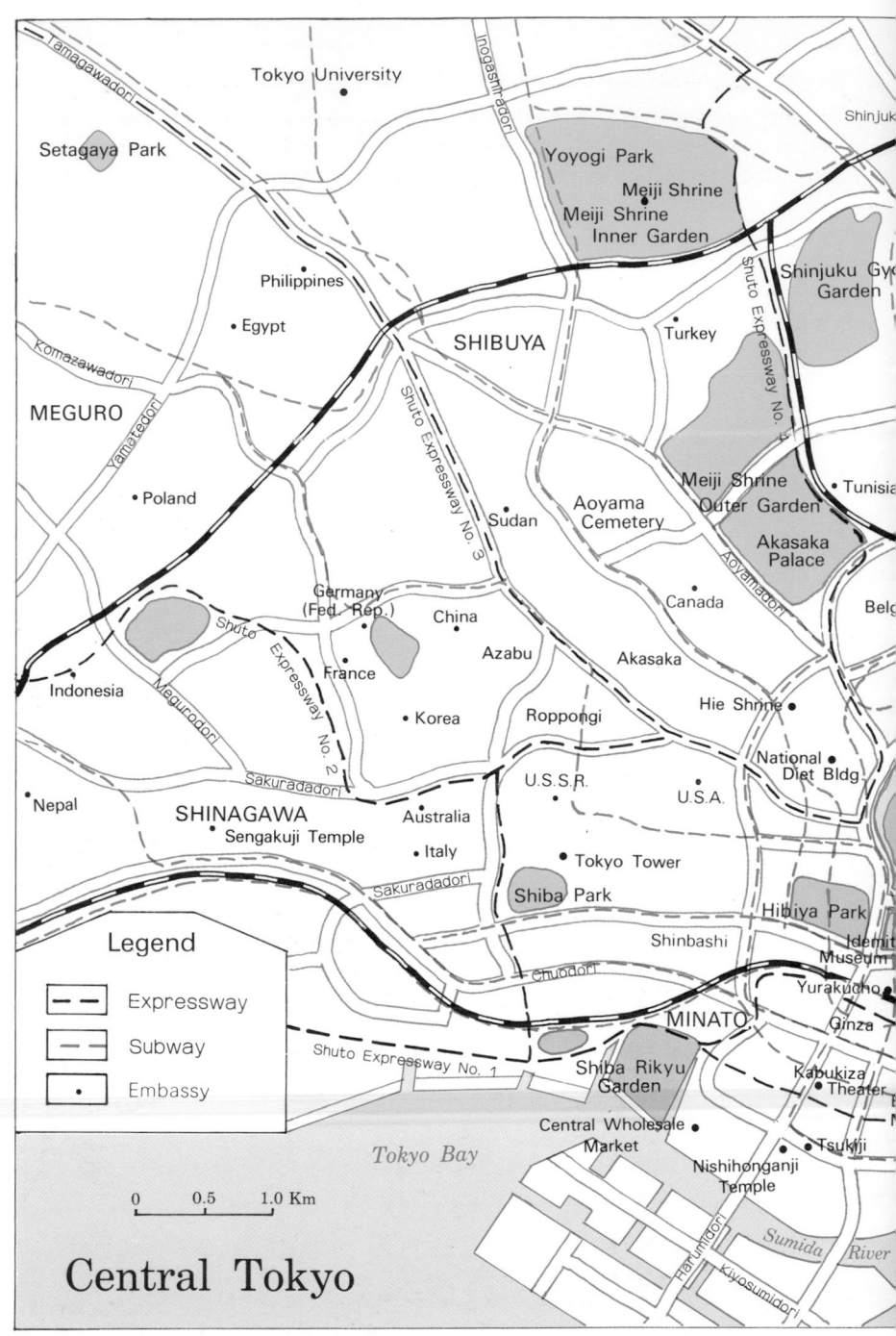

Central Tokyo

Legend

- – – – Expressway
- —— Subway
- • Embassy

0   0.5   1.0 Km

Tamagawadori
Inogashiradori
Tokyo University
Shinjuk
Setagaya Park
Yoyogi Park
Meiji Shrine
Meiji Shrine Inner Garden
Shinjuku Gy Garden
Komazawadori
Philippines
• Egypt
Turkey
Shuto Expressway No. 4
MEGURO
SHIBUYA
Yamatedori
Shuto Expressway No. 3
Meiji Shrine Outer Garden
• Tunisia
• Poland
• Sudan
Aoyama Cemetery
Akasaka Palace
Aoyamadori
Germany (Fed. Rep.)
China
Canada
Belg
France
Azabu
Akasaka
Shuto Expressway No. 2
Meguro dori
• Korea
Roppongi
Hie Shrine •
Indonesia
Sakuradadori
National • Diet Bldg
• Nepal
U.S.S.R.
U.S.A.
SHINAGAWA
Sengakuji Temple
Australia
• Italy
• Tokyo Tower
Hibiya Park
Sakuradadori
Shiba Park
Shinbashi
Idemit Museum
Chuodori
Yurakucho •
MINATO
Ginza
Shuto Expressway No. 1
Shiba Rikyu Garden
Kabukiza • Theater
Central Wholesale Market
• Tsukiji
Tokyo Bay
Nishihonganji Temple
Harumidori
Sumida River
Kiyosumidori

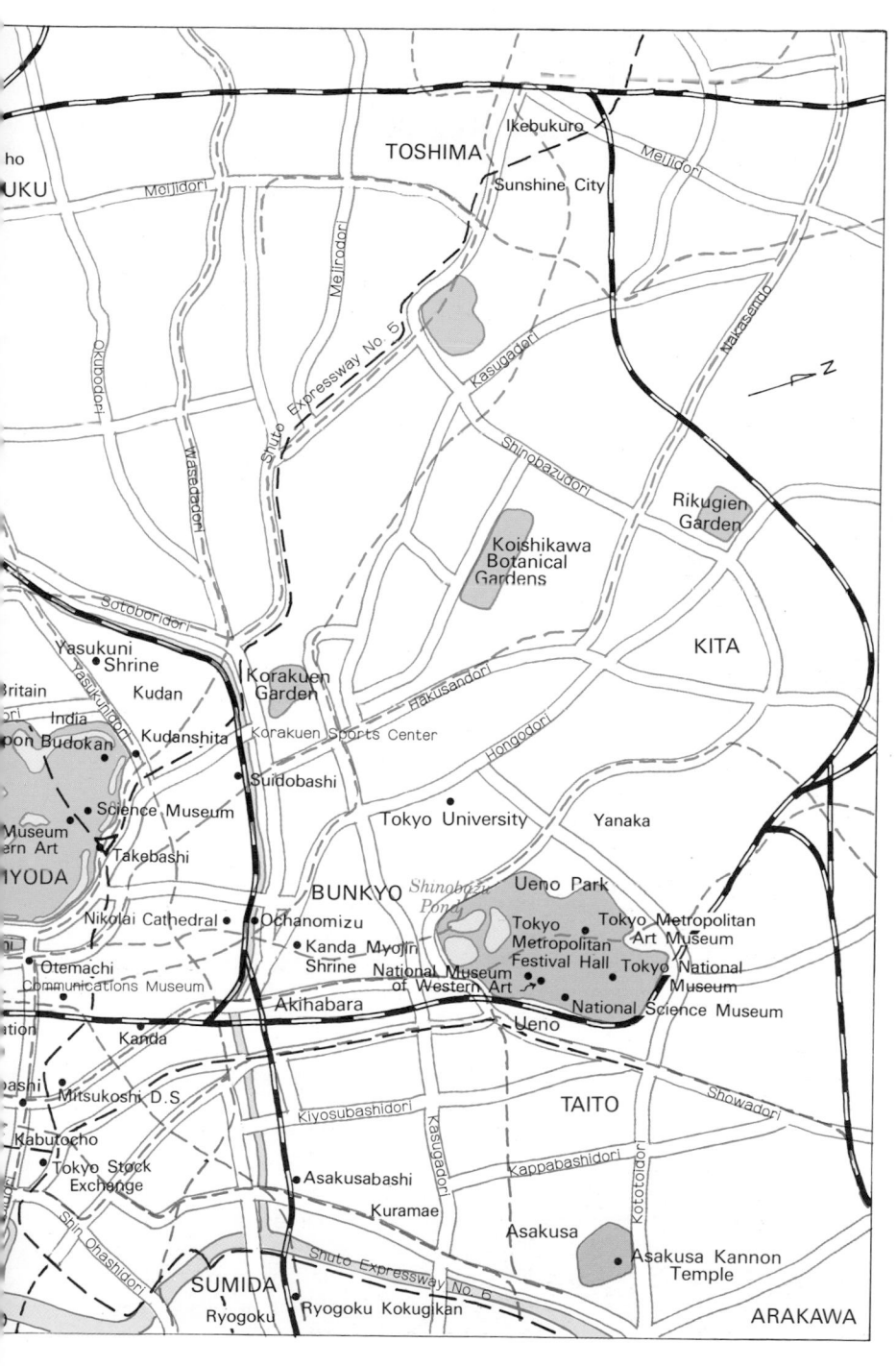

Tokyo and the Kanto Region

Tokyo: History, Size, Crowds, Chaos, Character

When in 1721 the eighth Tokugawa shogun's super-efficient bureaucracy conducted the first of its nationwide censuses, it discovered that the city of Edo (now called Tokyo) had a population approaching 1.3 million. Eighty-two years earlier, the eighth shogun's second cousin had ordered that Japan be closed to practically all foreign contact, so by 1721 information about other countries cannot have been very up-to-date nor very readily available. Possibly, then, not even the super-efficient bureaucracy realized that, on the evidence of its first mammoth head-count, Edo was the most populous city on earth and had probably been so for at least half a century. If it had known that, the bureaucracy would certainly have advertised the fact with great relish, since statistical demonstrations of ways in which Japan outshines all other countries, in whatever field of human activity, have long been a national hobby.

Since 1603, when the Tokugawa shogunate was founded, Edo had been the shogun's administrative centre and the site of the shogun's own castle, but it was not Japan's official capital. The official capital was Kyoto, where the emperor maintained his infinitely sophisticated and totally powerless court. And so it remained until 1868, when the Tokugawa shogunate finally collapsed and the new government, with the present emperor's great-grandfather nominally at its head, renamed Edo Tokyo (Eastern Capital), thus confirming in name what, for two and a half centuries, the city had been in fact.

Accounts of the origins and rise of the Eastern Capital often imply that, until the first Tokugawa shogun, Ieyasu, decided to situate his government there, the place was a swampy little village; but this is fanciful, and suggests that the authors are somehow confusing Tokyo with Kuala Lumpur. Edo had been a power base of sorts since 1457, when Lord Ota Dokan built a fortress there—which for a time enjoyed a reputation as the strongest fortress in the Kanto region, the pivot of three major highways that were to play a fundamental role in the social and economic development of Japan. These highways were the Tokaido (joining Edo to Kyoto, and extending to Osaka), the Koshukaido (from Edo to Kofu in today's Yamanashi prefecture) and the Oshukaido (which began at Edo and went north into the unpoliced wilds of the Tohoku region). By the end of the 16th century, the fortress had fallen into disrepair but Ieyasu's decision to site his administrative seat there was hardly the example of preternatural longsightedness that his admirers pretend.

It is as well to begin a description of Tokyo aimed at the short-term visitor with at least this much ancient history, since the city today boasts few visible relics of anything older than the Second World War, and these first paragraphs can remain in the visitor's mind as an evocation of things that he will see little sign of.

Certainly, the so-called 'Edo period' (1603–1867) is alive and well on television. Almost every televised example of what the Japanese call *chambara* (swashbuckling action adventures) is set in the colourful, crowded city of Edo during the two and a half busy centuries when the shogun held sway there. The popularity of the Edo period among T.V. viewers probably owes something to the enforced absence of foreigners (the few who turn up are either crucified or beheaded, thus greatly increasing their entertainment value) and it owes something, too, to the inflexible class structure maintained throughout feudal times, a structure wherein everyone knew at a glance both his own place and everybody else's, and was thus rarely at a loss about how to comport himself with the people he encountered—a situation woefully different today, with uncrucified foreigners turning up on all sides and the sons and daughters of company executives wearing torn jeans and 'Prick Up' tee-shirts.

Edo was also the city in which a non-aristocratic Japanese urban culture first came into its own. The city's great entertainments—its fairs, its festivals, its licensed quarters, its Kabuki theatre—flourished in response to the earthy demands of a newly powerful and ebullient merchant class. This—now that the values of the marketplace have eclipsed forever the once dominant mores of the samurai—adds hugely to the ongoing popularity of the Edo period, making it and the city that gave it its name both symbols of an imagined egalitarianism.

But the visitor—whether Japanese or non-Japanese—who comes to Tokyo in search of the old Edo is doomed to disappointment. Few cities on earth change as rapidly and as constantly as Tokyo does; and while the visitor from any other part of Japan is liable to list among his first impressions of Tokyo its vast size, its vast population and the vast amount of chaos generated by the apparent lack of any form of rational town planning, the long-term resident is more likely to characterize the city by the frequency and abruptness of the changes that continually overtake its various districts.

Tokyo is still, by many measures, the largest city in the world. Its size is officially given as 2,145 square kilometres (1,341 square miles), almost twice that of Greater London. This is the figure for the total metropolitan area, including the 23 inner wards and the 26 outer sub-cities. But Tokyo has no green belt, and the urban sprawl extends uninterrupted well beyond the metropolitan boundaries and into the neighbouring prefectures of Kanagawa, Saitama and Chiba, much of whose residential space is occupied by daily commuters to the capital. The traveller between Tokyo and Yokohama, for example, will be quite unable to determine merely by looking out of his train, bus or taxi window when he leaves one and enters the other, and this applies equally to the commuter from Chiba city or one of the 'bed-towns' in

A Simple Prayer

"Ho-ke-kyō!"

My uguisu is awake at last, and utters his morning prayer. You do not know what an uguisu is? An uguisu is a holy little bird that professes Buddhism. All uguisu have professed Buddhism from time immemorial; all uguisu preach alike to men the excellence of the divine Sutra.

"Ho-ke-kyō!"

In the Japanese tongue, Ho-ke-kyō; in Sanskrit, Saddharma-Pundarika: The Sutra of the Lotus of the Good Law, *the divine book of the Nichiren sect. Very brief, indeed, is my little feathered Buddhist's confession of faith—only the sacred name reiterated over and over again like a litany, with liquid bursts of twittering between.*

"Ho-ke-kyō!"

Only this one phrase, but how deliciously he utters it! With what slow amorous ecstasy he dwells upon its golden syllable!

It hath been written: "He who shall keep, read, teach, or write this Sutra shall obtain eight hundred good qualities of the Eye. He shall see the whole Triple Universe down to the great hell Aviki, and up to the extremity of existence. He shall obtain twelve hundred good qualities of the Ear. He shall hear all sounds in the Triple Universe—sounds of gods, goblins, demons, and beings not human."

"Ho-ke-kyō!"

A single word only. But it is also written: "He who shall joyfully accept but a single word from this Sutra, incalculably greater shall be his merit than the merit of one who should supply all beings in the four hundred thousand Asankhyeyas of worlds with all the necessaries for happiness."

Lafcadio Hearn, Glimpses of Unfamiliar Japan, *1894*

Saitama. The population of Tokyo is usually stated to be in the region of 12 million but, given that the sprawl far exceeds the capital's administrative boundaries, this is a somewhat artificial figure too. If the populations of the indistinguishably adjoining areas are included, the figure more than doubles; which means that something like a quarter of Japan's total population (which now stands at about 123 million) lives within an area that, for practical purposes, we must call Greater Tokyo.

In terms of population density, Tokyo is nowhere near as badly off today as it was when the shogun's bureaucracy conducted its 1721 census (a fact which may supply a modicum of comfort to the visitor struggling through Shinjuku Station at eight o'clock on a weekday morning). In 1721, Tokyo had a total area of 70 square kilometres (43 square miles) and an overall population density of about 18,500 per square kilometre. Today, if we accept for the sake of argument the official metropolitan figures, the overall density is about 5,500 per square kilometre—positively thin on the ground when you take into account the advent of high-rise buildings. But, of course, populations are never evenly spread, and in 1721 the unevenness perfectly reflected the painful inequities of Japan's feudal class system. More than 66 percent of Edo's land area was owned by the lords and their samurai retainers, and only about 12.5 percent by the far more populous trading class. As a result, in the tradesmen's areas (particularly in parts of what is nowadays Chuo ward) population density reached a horrendous 70,000 per square kilometre. That is about what it reaches in Hongkong today, but in Hongkong people's residences are stacked vertically for 12 or 20 storeys, whereas in old Edo they were all stuck down in the mud. The sheer difficulty of shifting your weight from one foot to the other without mangling the hem of your neighbour's kimono must have been an ever-present worry, and perhaps the high degree of overcrowding among a class of people destined to become the prime shapers of post-feudal Japan contributed greatly to the absence among them of a 'Western' sense of privacy, as well as to the development of elaborate forms of social lubrication (incessant bowing, ultra-polite language, ritualized gift giving, maintenance of a rigid hierarchical order, the accepted difference between what you say and what you really think); forms that helped to stave off the permanent tension that such overcrowding could easily have given rise to. Today the most densely populated ward in Tokyo is Toshima (about 20,000 per square kilometre), which is, not coincidentally, a ward that contains a large number of high-rise housing developments.

As for chaos: it is hard to imagine a more thoroughly mind-numbing introduction to any city in the world than to take the limousine bus from the New Tokyo International Airport at Narita to one of its downtown destinations. The bus travels along some 70 kilometres (43 miles) of concrete expressway which, once the narrow agricultural belt around Narita itself has been passed, is flanked on both sides for as far as the eye can see, and the disturbed brain conceive, by an uninterrupted vista of grey ferroconcrete offices, factories, docks, warehouses and huge characterless housing developments containing tiny apartments which the Japanese, without any irony call 'mansions'. At night the sea of neon and fluorescent-lit windows can have a magical attraction, particularly when the skyscrapers of West Shinjuku float into sight. In daylight, the chief effect is one of horror tinged with whimsy (the whimsy being nowadays enhanced by the fairy-tale spires of Tokyo's Disneyland, which appear breifly on the left-hand side). No two roads seem to run in compatible directions, no two buildings seem to face the same way or to have the same number of storeys or to have been designed with any thought for their surroundings. It is often noted, both by local and foreign observers, that Japanese people tend to promote the ideal of uniformity in their dress, speech, education and behaviour; but uniformity is the very last impression one receives from Tokyo's buildings. The buildings surrounding a well-planned European plaza or flanking a well-laid-out avenue can seem wedded to each other. Tokyo's buildings seem at war with each other. Each is a little island, paying no attention whatever to its neighbours, devouring their sunlight, blocking their approaches, maintaining a ferocious independence in what the architects clearly regarded as hostile territory, or no-man's land at best

Most Japanese city roads, streets, lanes and avenues have no names, and those of Tokyo are not exceptions. Areas have names, and within these areas blocks are numbered, and within these blocks sub-blocks, and within sub-blocks buildings. But because the roads that surround the blocks strike out and fork in all directions, the blocks are seldom uniform, so the numbers are not necessarily sequential. Some sources derive glee from further horrifying newcomers with the assertion that numbers are assigned to houses not according to their topographical position in a street or block, but according to the (unremembered) date when they were built. This is a nice idea, but fanciful—at least nowadays. Numbers are assigned in as logical a manner as the circumstances permit, which is hardly logical at all. It is somewhat like trying to assign sequential numbers to the leaves of a large tree. They are never regularly arranged and are constantly either falling or sprouting, just as Japanese houses and offices are constantly being ripped down and re-erected. (When Japanese people buy a house they generally tear it down and build a new one immediately, their principal expense and investment being in the land, not in the building). The newcomer can derive some comfort from the fact that life-long residents of Tokyo are obliged— just like himself—to find their way about by means of little maps scribbled on the backs of envelopes. Addresses are normally given only when postal communication is likely. Otherwise your chief recourse is the scribbled map—turn left at the public bath, right at the Chinese restaurant, cross four traffic lights and enquire at the police box.

It is not as though Japanese planners lacked experience in laying out a logically organized city. Kyoto (laid out in 792) had been deliberately modelled on the ancient Chinese capital of Chang'an: its blocks perfectly uniform, its streets intersecting at right angles and aligned with the cardinal points of the compass. Why did planners not follow this familiar example when laying out the shogun's de facto capital of Edo in 1603? One answer is that the land was more hilly. Another is that to have designed Edo along the lines of imperial Kyoto would have been a direct affront to the emperor and an obvious challenge to his, and Kyoto's, fancied pre-eminence. If this is so, it would also account for the fact that no logical replanning was undertaken after the great fire of 1657 (which destroyed half the city's buildings and killed a quarter of its residents) or after any one of the 97 major fires that devastated Edo throughout the 17th, 18th and early 19th centuries (and for which the residents came to feel a curious affection: fires and brawls were called 'the flowers of Edo'). But it does not explain why no extensive replanning took place after the Great Kanto Earthquake of 1923 or the immensely destructive fire-bomb raids of March 1945, since by the time those calamities occurred Tokyo was Japan's capital in name as well as in fact, the shogun had long since disappeared into history and the emperor now made his home there. Some Japanese commentators have tried to suggest that Tokyo is an especially 'Japanese' city precisely because it has never been rigidified in a 'Western' manner. They point to what they see as a similar victory of the Japanese spirit in the carefully preserved 'naturalness' of a Japanese garden versus the straight paths and regimented flower-beds of, say, Versailles. Tokyo is quintessentially Japanese, they suggest, because it has developed 'organically', like cirrhosis of the liver.

Quite apart from fires, earthquakes, bombs, and the fact that many of the buildings in the capital's residential districts are still constructed of timber, and so are as prone to conflagration, typhoon damage and natural degeneration as they ever were, rapid changes are the lifeblood of Tokyo people. From their earliest history the Edokko, the true 'sons of Edo'— particularly the merchants and artisans—were famous for their love of the brash and the new, for fashions and fads, for discarding the outmoded without so much as a sigh and for welcoming novelties, the more striking and unlikely the better.

At the very beginning of the 17th century the Edokko were already busily changing the basic topography of their city by reclaiming huge areas of the bay on which it stands—a practice that has continued virtually uninterrupted to the present day. Much of Chuo, Koto and Edogawa wards stands on land reclaimed from the sea, as do the entire Port of Tokyo, the generators of the Tokyo Electric Company, Haneda Airport (until 1978 Tokyo's only international airport, today the terminus for most domestic flights), Tokyo's largest rubbish tip (endearingly named Yumenoshima—'Island of Dreams') and dozens of other major facilities, both commercial and residential. The latest development project is an undersea road tunnel planned to cross the entire width of the bay from Kawasaki in Kanagawa prefecture to Kisarazu in Chiba prefecture.

Inland, Tokyo's propensity for change is enormously aided by the fact that the city has no single centre. Rather, it has a multiplicity of sub-centres, each with its own distinct and still evolving character, each striving to outdo the others in atmosphere and attractions. This too has been a largely unplanned development, since the briefest glance at a map of the city is enough to reveal that the topographical 'centre' of old Edo—and the intended centre of Tokyo—was the Imperial Palace (formerly the shogun's castle), isolated and grandly surrounded by its moats and walls and still flanked by untypically wide roads and rare plaza-like spaces. During the Edo period, the shogun's castle was the hub of government and the chief focus of attention for all the provincial lords who were forced by the shogun to spend alternate years in the capital so as to prevent them being long enough in their own distant fiefs to foment rebellion. (In the years when the lords were allowed to live in their own fiefs, family members were obliged to remain in Edo under what amounted to a system of legalized hostage-taking). But even during these centuries, the capital had more than this one awe-inspiring centre. For the merchants and artisans, the 'centre' of Edo lay about a kilometre and a half east of the castle, in the most densely populated area of the city. This 'centre' was the Nihonbashi Bridge, and it was recognized as such by the bureaucracy to the extent that distances between the capital and all other points were measured from there (it was over the Nihonbashi Bridge that the major trunk roads entered Edo, but the system of measuring distances from there is curious when you consider how jealously the shogun guarded most other prerogatives; you would expect all distances to have been measured from the dais on which he sat, but perhaps this was also part of a deliberate policy of not offending the emperor).

The main modern sub-centres grew up as a result of private enterprise's taking advantage of the flood of commuter traffic which began shortly after the war. Private railway companies, unable to purchase land for their terminuses in the already congested central areas of the city, were forced to build them an average of just over five kilometres (three miles) away from the castle, in an arc marking the western boundary of what became the Yamanote loop line (see page 226). Because land this distant from the centre was still comparatively cheap, the companies diversified their investments into department stores, theatres and other facilities: the nuclei of today's sub-centres. The Seibu, Keio and Odakyu companies developed Shinjuku, once a simple staging point on journeys west, today the capital's liveliest district, served by a massively complex railway station through which two

million people pass each day—the equivalent of the entire population of Paris. The Tokyu company developed Shibuya, now a major shopping and entertainment area, the site of NHK's (the National Broadcasting Corporation's) headquarters and the pools and stadiums built for the 1964 Olympics. And the Seibu and Tobu companies developed Ikebukuro, not so fashionable as Shibuya nor so frantic as Shinjuku, but the chief shopping and entertainment district of Tokyo's most densely populated ward. The other two major terminuses on the Yamanote loop line—Tokyo and Ueno—both serve mainly lines that have only recently been privatized and predate the postwar boom in sub-centres. Both lie much nearer the palace, in what was Edo proper rather than its outskirts. Tokyo station is close both to the city's major business and banking areas, Otemachi and Marunouchi, and to the traditional, but now sadly eclipsed, shopping and entertainment districts of Ginza and Shinbashi. Ueno is the site of a major park as well as several of Tokyo's principal art museums and concert halls.

Unless they are bent on some special errand, such as the purchase of electrical equipment or the study of industrial robots, most short-term visitors are likely to want to gain three things during their stay in Tokyo: a sense of the city's history, a sense of its importance and function as the nation's capital and as the richest and arguably the most powerful city in Asia, and a sense of its elusive and multi-faceted spirit. The following sections deal in turn with each of these ambitions.

Historical Tokyo

The point has already been made that comparatively little remains in modern Tokyo to recall its colourful feudal-era past. Perishable wooden buildings, natural and man-made disasters have conspired to rob it of visible remains. In addition, an understandable desire to put the disastrous military adventures of the 1930s and '40s firmly out of mind has resulted in a tendency among many Japanese people to ignore—and sometimes actively to dislike—their own history. Where T.V. dramas treat historical subjects, they almost invariably turn them into fairyland fantasies: class distinctions disappear, old Edo bursts at the seams with impossibly dashing Robin Hoods, dictatorship—even military dictatorship—is always benevolent.

The centre of Edo-era military dictatorship was the shogun's castle, now the **Imperial Palace** constructed on the site of Ota Dokan's 15th-century fortress. The palace itself, having been destroyed during the war, was rebuilt in ferroconcrete in 1968 (the visitor had better accustom himself quickly to the idea of ancient buildings having been rebuilt in recent times, since it is true of most of Japan's castles, and many of her most impressive temples and shrines). The massive stone walls, however, are original and typical of Japanese feudal-era fortifications. The emperor and his consort live today in a fairly modest building not visible from outside the walls. There is, naturally, no public admission to the palace, but the outer garden is open regularly and it is occasionally possible to obtain from influential acquaintances invitations to Gagaku and Bugaku (ancient court music and dance) performances staged in a special auditorium within the walls by the Imperial Court Orchestra. Otherwise, entrance is restricted to two days annually— 2nd January and 23 December (the Emperor's Birthday, on both of which the emperor and members of his family wave to the crowds gathered below from behind the bulletproof glass of their balcony.

The visitor who has been to, say, Windsor Castle or the historical residences of other European crowned heads, may be surprised and perhaps disappointed by the sobriety (some might say dreariness) of the external aspect of the Japanese emperor's palace and by the complete absence of any such colourful ritual as the Changing of the Guard. But it will be as well for him to accustom himself quite quickly to this idea too: that understatement, relative smallness of scale and a love of the monochrome and low-key are at the root of much of what the Japanese have traditionally considered worthy of admiration.

Though every feudal lord maintained a residence in Edo, and though these together accounted for more than two-thirds of the city's total land area, none of these residences has survived. Most of the city's modern parks, major hotels and university campuses have been built on the grounds that these residences occupied, so the visitor can at least get some idea of where they once stood. **Tokyo University**, for example, stands on land once owned by the lords of Kaga (modern Ishikawa prefecture), a fitting location since Tokyo University (or Todai as it is usually known) is the most prestigious seat of learning in the country and Kaga was the richest fief.

Edo was a city of rivers and canals, comparable, so some observers reckoned, to Amsterdam or Venice. Just as the visitor can obtain an idea of where the residences of lords once stood by searching out parks, universities and hotels, so he can get a notion of where the rivers and canals once ran by looking at elevated expressways, since many of these have been built on the concreted-over courses of old waterways. One or two stretches of the waterways survive intact, such as that at **Ochanomizu** where the **Kanda River** joins the outer moat of the palace. The name 'Ochanomizu' means, charmingly enough, 'water for making tea', though putting the water here to that particular use today would likely result in a lengthy period of hospitalization (and, conveniently enough, one of Tokyo's many hospitals, Ikashikadai, is situated on the very bank). For a glimpse of how pleasant Edo's waterways must have been in feudal days, the visitor with time to spare can take the orange Chuo Line 20 kilometres (12 miles) out to Mitaka Station, from which a brief taxi ride will bring him to a point where the **Tama** (Jewel) **Canal**, though surrounded by unremitting suburban greyness, is still shaded

by trees and lined with pleasant rural-like paths. The canal here proved so irresistibly attractive to the novelist Dazai Osamu that in 1948 he drowned himself in it.

Most people in search of the old Edo go first to **Asakusa**. Asakusa is—or rather, was—the centrepiece of what Tokyo people affectionately call the *shitamachi* (the 'low city'). It is definitely to the shitamachi—the old overcrowded tradesmen's area—that a visitor should go in his quest for as much of the spirit of old Edo as survives; though it is no longer quite so definite that he should concentrate his quest in Asakusa. Asakusa has enjoyed several heydays. From 1657 until prostitution was officially outlawed in 1958, it was the site of the **Yoshiwara**, the largest licensed quarter in the country, which in turn spawned all kinds of other, less private forms of entertainment. In the early modern period Asakusa remained the quintessential Edokko district, boasting every imported and novel delight that the fad-mad son of Edo could possibly crave. It was the site of Japan's first 'skyscraper'—the red-brick 'Twelve Storeys', destroyed in the great earthquake of 1923, which had incorporated the country's first elevator. It was the site of Japan's first cinemas, dance halls and cabarets. As late as the mid-1970s Asakusa was still the nightlife capital of the shitamachi, with its stalls, restaurants and *minyo sakaba* (eating and drinking establishments where live folk music and dances are performed). Then, in the 1980s, the blight of change overtook it. The Kokusai Theatre was torn down and replaced by the modern Asakusa View Hotel. *Oiwake* (Crossroads), one of the largest and liveliest of the minyo sakaba was closed, and the entire area began a not-yet-completed transformation from entertainment quarter to business district.

Asakusa's showpiece is **Sensoji** Temple, also called **Asakusa Kannon** Temple (Kannon is the Goddess of Mercy). It is one of the oldest temples in the capital, with records dating from the seventh century, but, like so many other landmarks, it was completely destroyed during the Second World War and rebuilt in ferroconcrete in 1958 (a tumultuous year for both temple and prostitutes). Among the temple's attractions are the rows of small shops (*Nakamise*) within its precincts, that sell traditional items such as dolls, cakes, clogs, kimonos and oiled-paper umbrellas. Visitors fortunate enough to be in Asakusa on 17 and 18 May (or the nearest weekend) will find the **Sanja Matsuri** in full swing. This is one of the capital's largest and most impressive festivals, and during its two days the spirit of old Edo comes as close to resurrection as it ever will. Though radical change is a way of life in Tokyo, the city's three main festivals—this, the **Sanno Matsuri** (15 June of even-numbered years) and the **Kanda Matsuri** (15 May of odd-numbered years)—remain a good deal more authentic, in externals as well as in spirit, than are many of the large provincial celebrations.

Like most of the city's other waterways, the **Nihonbashi River**, spanned by the famous measuring-point bridge (the present bridge dates from 1911), is largely obscured by an elevated expressway, and **Nihonbashi** itself is today best known as the site of the large **Mitsukoshi Department Store**, the forerunner of which was founded here in 1673.

Kanda, whose 17th-century **Myojin Shrine** (rebuilt in 1934) hosts one of the three great festivals already mentioned, is best known for its bookshops. Some of these specialize in second-hand foreign-language books, as well as old maps and prints, and many restrict their stock to specific subject areas such as philosophy and religion. For some reason, Kanda has also become the capital's chief retail centre for ski equipment. (It is worth pointing out that, as was traditionally the case in many Asian cities, whole areas of the shitamachi tend to specialize in the retailing of a single kind of commodity. Thus, **Akihabara**, next-door to Kanda, is the place to go for electrical equipment, **Asakusabashi** for paper ornaments, **Tawaramachi**, next-door to Asakusa, for lacquered Buddhist altars, **Kappabashi**, next-door to Tawaramachi, for kitchen utensils and plastic food.)

Tsukiji is the place to go for fresh fish and sushi, owing to the fact that it contains the city's largest wholesale fish market, formally inaugurated there in 1935. Visitors are allowed into the market, but they must go very early in the morning to see anything worth seeing, and they must make up their minds not to be offended by porters cursing them in loud voices if they happen to be standing in the path of a ton of bleeding tuna.

Ueno boasts Japan's oldest Western-style zoo, the **Tokyo National Museum** (the largest museum in Japan), the **Tokyo Metropolitan Art Gallery**, the **National Museum of Western Art**, and the **National Science Museum**, as well as one of Tokyo's leading concert halls, housed in the **Bunka Kaikan** (Culture Centre). It is pleasing to think that working-class Ueno has become such a culturally-minded spot, since the railway terminus is the main arriving point for itinerant labourers from the depressed rural north, and Tokyo sophisticates used to congregate around the station for the humour to be derived from listening to the arriving bumpkins' outlandish accents. Ueno Park is a favourite place for cherry-blossom viewing in late March or early April, a traditional pastime that requires a delicate sensitivity to the transient beauties of nature and an extremely indelicate constitution capable of handling the massive amounts of sake and beer whose rapid consumption the transient blossoms inspire. Nearby is the lotus-shrouded **Shinobazu Pond** with its little island dedicated to the goddess Benten, who in some ways is the presiding deity of the whole city since it was she who led Lord Ota Dokan to found the first Edo Castle.

None of these places has very many visible relics of the feudal age, but the Edo spirit was a bustling, clamorous, out-to-turn-a-quick-trick spirit that can still be found in the narrow shopping streets, markets and nightlife

districts for which some of the shitamachi areas are noted.

The Edo age lives visibly on in the rituals, costumes, hairstyles and atmosphere associated with the national sport of sumo wrestling, and it is no coincidence that the mecca of sumo, the **Kokugikan**, lies in the shitamachi district of **Ryogoku**. Three 15-day tournaments are held here each year, in January, May and September. (There are six annual tournaments altogether; the others are held at Osaka in March, Nagoya in July and Fukuoka in November.) The former sumo mecca, abandoned in 1984, lies just across the **Sumida River** in **Kuramae**, and has been turned into a plant for treating sewage.

For a more subdued shitamachi, the visitor might turn to the **Yanaka** area, famous for its many small, quiet temples. In most cases nowadays one must look for the old Edo atmosphere not in buildings or objects, but in the lifestyle of shitamachi residents. Yanaka is one of the last areas where something of the atmosphere of the old city can still be said to linger, even when its streets are empty.

Away from the shitamachi, in the more fashionable, middle-class areas of Tokyo that lie within the Yamanote loop line, the chief landmarks of historical interest include three large shrines and one not very large temple.

The **Hie Shrine** in **Akasaka** hosts the already-mentioned Sanno Matsuri and, sometimes on summer evenings, performances of classical Noh dramas (which, when given by torchlight, are called *Takigi Noh*). The shrine was founded here at the same time as the first Edo castle was founded, with the object of protecting the castle's inhabitants. It was completely destroyed in the air raids of 1945, and rebuilt in 1959 (not, happily, in ferroconcrete). It is dedicated to Sanno Gongen, the tutelary deity of Mount Hiei outside Kyoto (see page 102), where its parent shrine is situated and from which it takes its name.

The **Meiji Shrine** in **Harajuku** is dedicated to the flesh-and-blood person of the Emperor Meiji, the present emperor's great-grandfather, who gave his name both to the restoration of 1868, which propelled Japan into the modern era, and to the first period of that era (1868–1911). The shrine was completed in 1920, destroyed in 1945, restored in 1958, and its **Inner Garden** is famous for the irises that bloom there in June. That a human being should be enshrined and receive prayers like those offered to a god is not at all unusual. It happens in the West, too, with saints; but in Japan the deified human may have spent a life completely undedicated to religion in any shape or form, and the reverence accorded his spirit falls somewhere in the shadowy territory between worship and simple secular respect.

Still, this reverence is at the root of the controversy surrounding the third historically interesting shrine, the **Yasukuni Shrine** in **Kudan**, which has survived intact since 1869 and which is dedicated to Japan's war dead. Part of the problem is that the war dead enshrined here include some of those who were executed by the occupation authorities as Class-A war criminals, men like the wartime leader, Tojo Hideki. The second part of the problem is that in recent years, the prime minister and members of his cabinet, ignoring protests from such widely differing sources as Japanese Christians and the government of the People's Republic of China, have taken to visiting the Yasukuni Shrine, just as leaders in other countries visit secular cenotaphs and the tombs of unknown soldiers. Critics purport to see in this a dangerous blurring of the separation of religion from state which is guaranteed under the (American-drafted) postwar constitution. On occasions when the prime minister has declined to visit the shrine he has been criticized for succumbing to foreign pressure, so the whole business has become for him a kind of ceremonial Catch 22. The Yasukuni Shrine is also known for its cherry blossoms—often associated in poems and in the popular imagination with young men who die in battle (cherry blossoms that perish after so brief a life were the theme of the kamikaze pilots' marching song)—and blossom-viewers at Yasukuni tend not to get falling-down drunk under them.

Sengakuji Temple in **Shinagawa** is famous for its connection with the 47 loyal retainers of Lord Asano Naganori, whose graves it contains, and who were responsible for the best known and most admired incident in Edo-era history. Their lord was a young man from the provinces who overlooked the necessity of presenting expensive gifts to an older lord, Kira Yoshinaka, who had been assigned to instruct him in the intricacies of court etiquette. Kira insulted Asano, goading him into drawing his sword in anger within the precincts of the shogun's castle, for which unpardonable breach of the peace Asano was sentenced to commit ritual suicide (*hara-kiri*—'belly-slitting'—more properly called *seppuku*). Forty-seven of his most loyal samurai, now masterless (the word for a masterless samurai is *ronin*—the same word applied today to students who fail to gain admission to universities and spend a rootless year in cram schools waiting for the next set of entrance examinations), swore to avenge their lord's death, which they did on a snowy night in 1702. They attacked Kira's residence (400 metres from the present sumo stadium in Ryogoku), killed and decapitated him, bore his head to Sengakuji, their lord's family temple, washed it in the well which still stands in the precincts, and offered it to Asano's departed spirit. Since vendettas were strictly forbidden by law, they were sentenced, despite the widespread adulation their act had earned them, to commit *seppuku* themselves, and each calmly took his own life. The adulation has not much abated. Their exploit is the subject of one of the most perennially popular Kabuki plays, *Chushingura* (The Treasury of Loyal Retainers), and visitors to Sengakuji Temple will still find their graves decked with flowers and wreathed with incense smoke. It is interesting to note that the only other Kabuki play of comparable fame, *Kanjincho* (see page 154), also treats of the unswerving devotion of a loyal subject for his feudal lord, a theme that

Japanese Theatre

The earliest forms of Japanese theatre were simple dances of a pastoral kind, that survive at some festivals, and of a religious and ceremonial kind, that survive in the shrine dances called *Kagura*. As Buddhist and other cultural influences improved the intellectual life of the aristocracy, a more complex ritual and narrative drama developed which, in the 14th century, was refined into the form called *Noh*.

About 240 Noh plays continue to be performed on stages and in a style not much different from that of six centuries ago. Some Western sources refer to them as 'operas', some as 'ballets', but both those terms are misleading. Noh is a slow moving, subtly lyric drama, some of which is danced and much of which is chanted. A small musical ensemble and chorus accompanies the performance, and there are usually no more than three protagonists, with female parts taken by masked male actors. The themes are often from classical Japanese literature and many plays treat of Zen-inspired subjects, such as the transience of human glory. The masks and gorgeously embroidered kimonos make the Noh an almost hypnotizing experience even if the language is beyond the listener (and it is well beyond the average modern Japanese). There are several Noh theatres in Tokyo, the newest being the National Noh Theatre (*Kokuritsu Nohgakudo*).

Kyogen are 'comic interludes' performed between or before the more sombre Noh. Kyogen depend far more for their effect on dialogue than do Noh plays and, though they are shorter and much livelier, their verbal base as well as the absence of masks and exquisite costumes limits their interest for a non-Japanese-speaking visitor.

Kabuki is a melodramatic and often spectacular theatre form that evolved in the 17th century to satisfy the earthier and more extravagant tastes of the newly powerful urban merchants. As in the Noh, female parts are taken by male performers, some of whom achieve a popularity similar to that of film stars. With its revolving stage, its stunning costumes and scenery and its dances and full orchestral accompaniment, it is the most easily approachable form of 'classical' Japanese drama for the casual Western visitor. It is also the most popular form among modern Japanese audiences, though the majority of people never see it except on television. In Tokyo it is performed regularly at the *Kabukiza* and at the National Theatre (*Kokuritsu Gekijo*).

Fans of the *Bunraku* puppet theatre are inclined to rave about the 'magic' moment when they forget the presence of the highly visible puppeteers and begin to believe that the dolls are alive, making it sound like a version of the Indian rope trick. Bunraku is a drama of great skill and concentration on detail, and it has a fine, strong repertoire of plays (the dramatist often called 'the Shakespeare of Japan', Chikamatsu Monzaemon, wrote primarily for puppets). Whether it also has the power to move and thrill must remain a question of personal taste and experience.

(Preceding page) Kabuki actor in bravura pose; a popular subject with nineteenth-century ukiyoe *(woodblock print) fanciers.*

clearly moves the spirits of Japanese audiences today as it did when lords were lords and subjects were subjects.

Institutional Tokyo

Tokyo Tower (height 333 metres or 1,092 feet), a transmitting station for local television broadcasts, owes much to the example of Monsieur Eiffel's contraption though, being newer (it was built in 1958), it is imbued with less romance. It and the souvenir stalls that cram it attest to the ongoing attraction which idiotic novelties exert on Tokyo people. From the higher of its two observation floors, on a clear day, a breathtakingly comprehensive view of Tokyo and its environs can be obtained, so a trip up the tower is a perfect way for the visitor to disorient himself.

The red-brick west (Marunouchi-side) facade of **Tokyo Station**, built in 1914, survived the war and is today one of the most famous 20th-century architectural landmarks in the city. From time to time it is threatened with demolition, but each time conservationist-minded citizens flock to its defence in sufficient numbers for a reprieve to be granted. The Nichigeki Music Hall in **Yurakucho** was not so fortunate and is the most recent of the capital's well-known landmarks to vanish, having been replaced by a vast prison-like building called **Yurakucho Mullion**, housing newspaper offices, banks, a concert hall, five cinemas and two department stores. As the walls of Kuala Lumpur jail are adorned with colourful murals, so the external wall of this edifice boasts a clock that chimes and opens to reveal cherubs who dance the hours.

The **Tokyo Stock Exchange** in **Kabutocho**, opened in 1878 and now, in terms of market capitalization, the largest stock exchange in the world, is included on a number of guided tours of the city.

The grimly monumental-looking **National Diet Building** (*Kokkaigijido*) in **Kasumigaseki** was completed in 1936 and also, somewhat surprisingly, survived the war. It contains the Upper and Lower Houses of Japan's national legislature (the House of Councillors and the House of Representatives). Admission is not easily obtained.

Equally monumental is Tokyo's **Disneyland** in **Urayasu**, to which admission is only a problem for the impecunious. Since it opened in April 1983 it has become one of the chief sightseeing destinations in East Asia. Some tourists, particularly from neighbouring Asian countries, make it the main object of their visit, and there is an express bus service direct from Narita Airport. It offers attractions and rides closely modelled on those of its parent park in California, as well as the quite unforgettable experience of hearing *Deibii Kuroketto* (Davy Crockett) sung in Japanese. Visitors to Disneyland should be forewarned of the long periods of queueing necessary to gain admission to even the less popular attractions. For each of the more popular, even on a day of pouring rain, you can find yourself waiting without shelter for up to two hours, and to visit the park on a summer weekend, or during school or national holidays, is to court a large degree of frustration. The frustration is not relieved by the fact that Urayasu, where the park is situated, is among the greyest and gloomiest of Tokyo's suburbs (it is actually just across the prefectural border in Chiba) so, if you give up on Disneyland, there is absolutely nothing else to do there for amusement.

Before Disneyland opened, Tokyo's best known amusement park was **Korakuen**, next door to Suidobashi Station, which now looks sadly shabby by comparison. It is still jam-packed on many a summer evening since it houses the new home stadium of Japan's most popular baseball club, the Yomiuri Giants, most of whose fixtures are night games so that they can be televised live during peak viewing hours (at least up to 9.24 p.m., when they are often brusquely cut off as the sponsor changes, regardless of the state of play). The new stadium boasts Japan's first 'airdome', known as the 'Big Egg', completely roofing both field and stands.

The **Nippon Budokan** in Kudan, opposite the Yasukuni Shrine, was built immediately prior to the Tokyo Olympics in 1964 as a mecca for the martial arts (its name means 'Martial Arts Hall') but has achieved greater prominence as a venue for large-scale rock concerts. The first of these was given by the Beatles in June 1966, since when many leading Western rock bands have performed there. On nights when concerts are scheduled, the exits of Kudanshita station are crowded with disreputable-looking ticket touts whose only connection with martial arts is likely to be the ownership of a set of knuckledusters.

NHK's Broadcasting Centre stands a short walk from Shibuya or Harajuku stations. Like the BBC in Britain, NHK is publicly funded through the collection of licence fees and is thus free from commercial pressures and, in theory at least, from government influence. A sightseeing tour of some of NHK's facilities, including the largest T.V. studio in the world, is on the itinerary of many school trips to the capital. **NHK Hall**, next-door, is the home of the NHK Symphony Orchestra.

Tokyo boasts many special-interest museums in addition to those in Ueno. The **National Museum of Modern Art** is in **Takebashi**, near the headquarters of the *Mainichi Shinbun* newspaper. The **Japan Science Museum** is close to the Nippon Budokan. The **Communications Museum** is a short walk from Tokyo Station's red-brick facade. Some large business corporations who pride themselves on being patrons of the arts also operate museums and galleries. Two of the best known of these are the **Idemitsu Gallery**, also near the Marunouchi side of Tokyo Station, and the **Bridgestone Museum of Art**, not far away on the other side. Major department stores have also become leading contenders in the patron-of-the-

arts stakes and most visiting foreign exhibitions are displayed at one or other of these.

But it is not primarily the viewing of foreign art that keeps Tokyo's department stores so crowded. Visits to department stores for the purpose of shopping (window- or actual) are the leading leisure-time activity in the capital, and on weekends or just before the two main annual gift-giving seasons (midsummer and end of the year) the most popular stores—such as Shinjuku's **Isetan**, **Odakyu** and **Keio**, Nihonbashi's **Mitsukoshi** and Shibuya's **Tokyu** and **Seibu**—can become as dauntingly choked with people as rush-hour trains. The degree to which department stores have become leisure-time magnets is certainly a measure of Japan's new-won affluence, but it is also a measure of how completely novel the affluence still seems to many Japanese people. It is almost as though Tokyo's residents regarded affluence itself as one of their forever passing fads: if we don't throng department stores now, they'll have disappeared before we know it. Despite the intense competition among stores, they tend to be laid out in a very similar manner with the emphasis on predictability. Restaurants and galleries are invariably at the top and food halls invariably in the basement. Some have recreation facilities for children on their roofs (and recreation facilities for adults, in summer, in the inviting form of beer gardens). With the rise in value of the yen, the free samples offered by department-store food halls have begun to attract budget-conscious travellers from abroad to the extent that where to obtain a free gourmet lunch is now among the most frequent questions posed to tourist information officers. Free samples still abound, but sales staff are becoming less generous and a good deal more eagle-eyed.

A fashionable alternative to ordinary department-store shopping, particularly popular with the moping young, is the 'fashion building', often architecturally striking, that houses designer boutiques, a café bar or two, a chic restaurant, and other leisure facilities such as theatres and exhibition halls. Among the best known such centres are **Parco** in Shibuya, **La Foret** in Harajuku, the **Axis Building** in Roppongi, and the **Spiral Building** in Aoyama. Falling somewhere between the monolithic familiarity of the older-style department store (in fact it contains a branch of Mitsukoshi) and the newer, more gimmicky eclecticism of the 'fashion building' is the **Sunshine City** complex in Ikebukuro, at 60 storeys the second tallest building in Japan (after the new Tokyo City Hall, see page 48), boasting a museum, a hotel, a planetarium and an aquarium. Major trade fairs are also staged here.

Then there are the buildings that house Japan's new religious organizations. The postwar period has seen an extraordinary boom in new religious sects and cults (see page 75), and some of these have become rich enough to encase their spiritual aspirations in remarkable earthly containers. Among the most outwardly striking are the headquarters of the **Reiyukai**

(Companions of the Spirits) near Tokyo Tower, housed in a 1975 building which looks like a Chaldaean ziggurat, and the Arabian-Nights-and-pink-mushroom inspired minarets of the headquarters of the **Rissho Koseikai** (Society to Foster the Establishment of Righteousness) in the suburban ward of **Suginami**, some four kilometres (2.5 miles) west of Shinjuku. Older foreign-looking religious landmarks include the **Tsukiji Honganji** Temple near the wholesale fish market, whose present building was completed in 1935 and purports to have been inspired by ancient Hindu architecture, and the Russian Orthodox **Nikolai Cathedral** in Ochanomizu, which dates from 1884 except for its dome, the original of which was a victim of the 1923 earthquake.

Fluid Tokyo

Most visitors will have heard of (the) **Ginza**, which takes its name from a silver mint that used to stand in the area. Some guides still call it 'Tokyo's fabulous Ginza', thereby helping to sustain a myth that no longer has much basis in reality. Ginza has major department stores, cinemas, the **Kabukiza** theatre, some expensive designer shops and many small picture galleries in its back streets. Some of Tokyo's priciest restaurants and watering holes are there, the latter used mainly for the expense-account pampering of business associates (Japanese corporate entertainment spending now runs to a higher annual total than the government's budget for education). But Ginza has had to endure the ever-threatening ravages of change and, for sheer excitement, it has been eclipsed by brasher, newer pleasure centres such as Shinjuku and Roppongi.

Bordering Ginza on the southwest is **Shinbashi**, once also a favoured pleasure spot, particularly famous for its *geisha* who could sometimes be glimpsed as they rode through the narrow streets in rickshaws (*jinrikisha*—literally, 'person-powered vehicles'). Both rickshaws and geisha are today endangered species, and Shinbashi, too, has been eclipsed. Perhaps the most entertaining nightlife in the Ginza area nowadays—for those without massive expense accounts anyway—is to be found under and around the railway arches in **Yurakucho**, near Ginza's northwest corner. In times of poverty and hardship, such as followed the defeat of 1945, the arches beneath elevated railways provided shelter to people made homeless by bombs and other disasters. Gradually, whole communities grew up under the arches, with food and drink stalls (*yatai*) to cater to them. As prosperity returned, some of the yatai owners, hustled along by the winds of change, transformed their stalls into permanent bars and eating places, still wedged under the thundering tracks. Today, along parts of the Yamanote loop line and a great deal of the Chuo Line, the arches and immediately adjacent streets harbour some of Tokyo's least pretentious and most reasonably priced places to eat and

An Intimate Retreat

s the Europeans never go there, the "Maison de la Grue" has retained its meticulous Japanese daintiness; I slip my shoes off as I enter, and two servants, as I appear, fall upon all fours, noses to the floor, following the pure etiquette of other days, which I had thought lost. On the first floor, in a large white room which is empty and resonous, they settle me on the floor, upon cushions of black velvet, and prostrate themselves anew to take my orders. I desire to hire for one hour a Geisha, that is, a girl musician, and a Maiko, that is, a dancing girl. . .

Enters first a frail creature, a diminutive girl-child, in long robe of crepe, mouse grey, with a rose sash, rose of the peach blossom, knotted behind, and of which the bows are like the wings of a quaint butterfly which had settled there. It is Mademoiselle Matsuko, the musician, who now prostrates herself; chance has served me well, for she is dainty and pretty.

Then appears the most strange little being that I have ever seen in my wanderings through the world, half doll and half cat, one of those that at first sight impress by the very excess of their bizarrerie, which you never forget again. She advances, smiling from the corners of her bridled eyes; her head, the size of your fist, is poised, and seems unreal, on a child's neck, a neck too long and too thin; and her tiny nothingness of a body is lost in the folds of an extravagant dress, hugely flowered with great gilded chrysanthemums. It is Mademoiselle April-Shower, the dancing girl, who also prostrates herself.

She admits to thirteen, but, so small is she, so tiny, so slender, that I should allow her scarcely eight, were it not for the expression of her cajoling quizzical eyes where, between too very childish smiles, there flits, furtively, a little precocious femininity, a little bitterness. However, the little thing is delicious to look at in its draperies of farthest Asia, amazing, unlike anything else, indefinable, and sexless.

I am no longer bored or lonely; I have met the plaything which I have, vaguely perhaps, desired all my life: a little talking cat.

Before their performance begins, I must do the honours of my miniature banquet for my two inimitable little guests; so knowing from of old what are good manners in Japan, I myself wash, in a bowl of hot water, brought for the purpose, the miniature cup out of which I have drunk, pour into it a few drops of saké, and offer it in turn to the two mousmés; they pretend to drink, I pretend to empty the bowl after them, and we exchange ceremonious reverences: etiquette is preserved.

And now the guitar preludes. The little cat rises, in the folds of its marvellous robe; from the depths of the lacquer box it draws out masks; it chooses itself a face which it carefully conceals, fastens it over its own comic mask with its back turned to me, and then abruptly shows itself again!. . .Oh, but the surprise!. . .where is it, my tiny cat? It has become a fat common creature, with an air of such astonishment, so ingenuous and so silly, that I cannot restrain myself from bursting into laughter. And it dances, with a calculated clumsiness that is really great art.

A fresh transformation, another dive into the mischief-box, choice of a new mask rapidly attached, and a new apparition to make one shudder. . . Now it is an old, old hag, the colour of a corpse, with eyes at once greedy and dead whose expression is beyond bearing. It dances, bent double, crouching; the thing still has the arms of a child, and all the time winnows the air, the great sleeves waving like bat's wings. And the guitar sobs on deep notes a sinister tremolo. . . When the mousmé then, her dance ended, lets fall her hideous mask to make her bow one finds her delicious little face, by contrast, the more exquisite.

This is the first time that in Japan I have come under a spell. . . I shall often return to the "Maison de la Grue."

Pierre Loti, Madame Prune, *1905*
translated by S.R.C. Plimsoll

and drink. Those at Yurakucho are the best known and most centrally located. Some cater mainly to manual workers, some are ritzier and not quite so inexpensive as they might appear from the outside.

Shinjuku is an area crisply divided by its station. On the west side stand the new skyscrapers of 'Tokyo's Manhattan'—the head offices of major corporations such as Mitsui, Sumitomo and KDD, flashy hotels like the Keio Plaza, Hilton and Century Hyatt, and the new City Hall, at 243 metres one of the tallest buildings in Japan. On winter nights, when the wind gusts between these huge cold obelisks, West Shinjuku can seem a desolate place, and yet the novelty of having so many tall buildings clustered together in one small area has clearly struck a chord in the Tokyo residents' novelty-loving soul. In a dreadful 1987 disaster film, Tokyo is threatened by a cloud of electrically-charged smog and has to be rescued single-handed by a young municipal engineer. In the film the heart of the city—the first sight to stand revealed when the cloud disperses, the violins soar, and the rays of the sun break through again—is not the Imperial Palace nor the National Diet Building, but West Shinjuku's skyscrapers.

On the east side of the station stands the rabbit-warren of streets lined with bars, coffee shops, restaurants, cinemas, amusement arcades, pinball and mahjong parlours, sex shows and cabarets that give Shinjuku its name for sleaze, bustle and loose living. **Kabukicho**, northeast of the station, has no connection whatever with classical theatre. It is Tokyo's brashest nightlife district with a heavy emphasis on sexual titillation. Since the area is largely controlled by the *yakuza* (organized crime syndicates), its character and reputation have earned it some criticism, particularly from the proprietors of neighbouring toy shops and so on. But, like all other parts of the city—indeed, of the whole country—it is a perfectly safe area to stroll around at any time of the day or night, the only dangers being to one's eardrums and mental and moral equilibrium.

Roppongi is sometimes referred to in trendy tabloids as 'Gaijin Gulch'—*gaijin* (literally 'outside person') being the Japanese word for a foreigner. It is an area of loud, colourful bars, restaurants, coffee shops and discotheques frequented by foreigners and by young Japanese ladies who wish to acquire foreign boyfriends in order to parade them before their acquaintances (though not before their families) as status symbols, akin to multi-system video tape recorders. The Almond Coffee Shop at the corner of Roppongi Crossing is probably the best-known coffee shop in Tokyo, not because it possesses any outstanding attractions (in fact it is supremely dull), but because the corner on which it stands is the second most famous place for arranging to meet people. The most famous meeting place is the statue of Hachiko outside the north exit of Shibuya Station. Hachiko was a dog who died after waiting seven years for her master; a fact which the visitor, if he had not had drummed into him the lesson of Japan's incomparable efficiency, might take for a comment on

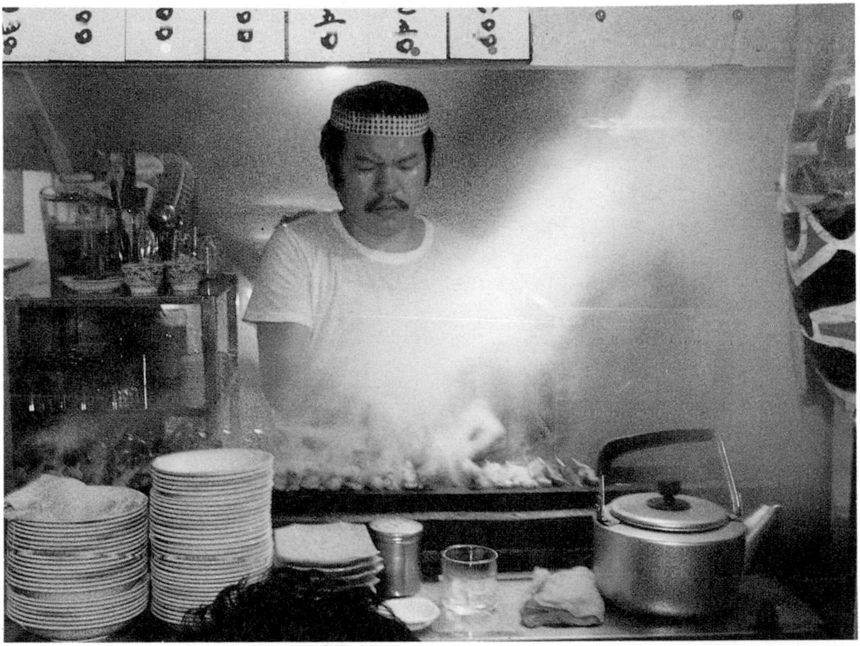

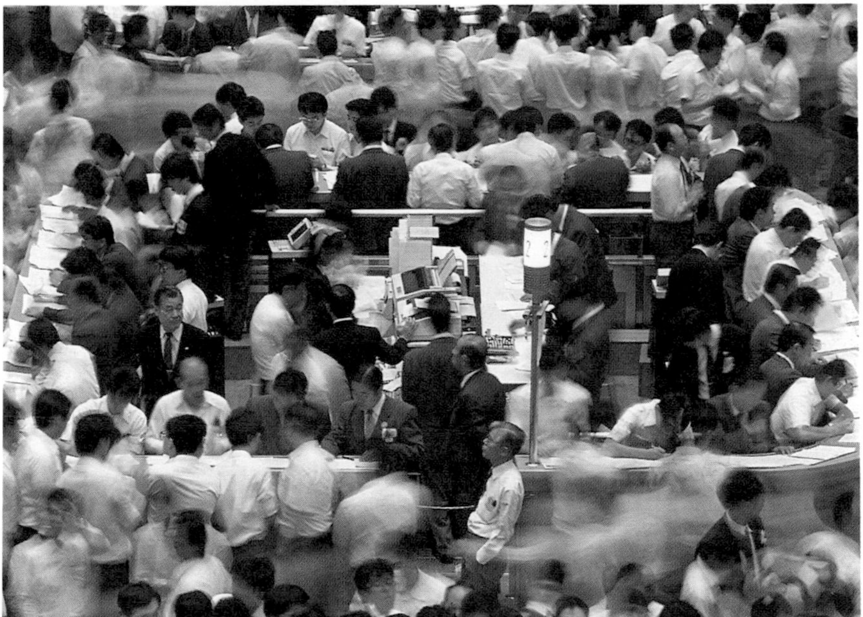

Japanese habits of punctuality, at least outside the business sphere. Next-door to Roppongi is **Azabu**, less lively at night, but the home of many well-heeled foreigners and an area known for its boutiques and café-bars.

Akasaka used to offer Roppongi some competition as a young people's nighttime entertainment area, but its competitiveness has diminished. Change has overtaken it. Its most famous discotheque (Mugen) closed in 1987, and like Asakusa (with which, owing to the similarity of the two names, visitors sometimes confuse it), it is turning into a business district.

The young people's principal daytime entertainment area is nowadays **Harajuku**, where, incongruously enough, the solemn Meiji Shrine stands, as though to remind the place of forgotten virtues. Harajuku is newly famous for its 2,000 or so trendy clothing boutiques, selling items that look as though they were designed for 7-year-olds to chirruping throngs of 17-year-olds with as much money to spend as their grandparents' generation used not to accumulate until they were 70-year-olds. On Sundays in the streets of Harajuku and in nearby **Yoyogi Park**, fantastically-dressed young people dance to rock music supplied by large portable cassette players. These are the *Takenoko Zoku* (the 'Bamboo Shoot Tribe'), who began their career as a daring scion of the counter culture and who now, caught up in Tokyo's infectious passion for bizarre novelty, are a tourist attraction and an institution.

Tokyo's Islands

Equally bizarre, to anyone not familiar with the workings of Japanese city halls, is the discovery that the Tokyo metropolitan area includes a number of tiny remote rural islands which have as little in common with the lifestyle of the capital as today's Kabukicho has with Kabuki. The most easily accessible of these are the **Izu Islands**, off the southeast coast of the Izu Peninsula (see page 135), most of which form a part of the Fuji-Hakone-Izu National Park. The islands are **Oshima** (population 11,000), whose **Mount Mihara** erupted so violently in 1986 that the entire island had to be evacuated, **Toshima** (population 280), **Niijima** (population 3,600, including nearby **Shikinejima**), **Kozujima** (population 2,200), **Miyakejima** (population 4,400), at present a centre of controversy owing to the government's insistence that an airstrip be built there from which U.S. forces can conduct night training flights, a plan that is being pushed forward despite the opposition of 80 percent of the islanders, **Mikurajima** (population 200) and **Hachijojima** (population 10,000). (*Shima* or *-jima* means island). These islands provide attractive opportunities for hiking, camping, fishing, bathing and experiencing eruptions and anti-government demonstrations.

Even more remote are the **Ogasawara Islands** (sometimes referred to by English-language sources as the Bonin Islands), lying more than 900 kilometres (560 miles) south of the capital, to which nevertheless they have belonged since 1968 when, four years earlier than Okinawa, they reverted to Japan from U.S. control. The inhabited islands are **Chichijima** (population 1,300) and **Hahajima** (population 280) and together with some outlying uninhabited islands they form the **Ogasawara National Park**. Further south still are the three specks called **Iojima** (or Iwojima or, on some charts and maps, The Volcanic Islands), which have a total population of 60 and are principally famous for having been the scene of fierce land fighting between Japanese and American troops during the early months of 1945. To reach even the closest of the Ogasawara group from Tokyo takes almost two days by ferry and the service is infrequent, so these islands, though fascinating from the point of view of history and administrative anomaly, are unlikely to figure on most visitors' itineraries.

The Rest of the Kanto Region

The **Kanto** region, of which Tokyo is the heart, also contains the prefectures of **Kanagawa, Saitama, Gunma, Tochigi, Ibaraki** and **Chiba**. 'Kanto' means 'East of the Barrier', the barrier being the Hakone Mountains, the major natural obstacle along the Tokaido Highway which joined this eastern district to the older capitals in the west. The Kanto is a relatively flat area, its plain being the broadest in Japan, rising in Gunma and Tochigi to the southern slopes of the Mikuni Mountains.

The prefectural capital of **Kanagawa** is **Yokohama** (population 2.9 million), today the second largest city in Japan and one of the first ports opened to foreign commerce following the end of Japan's self-imposed feudal isolation. It was opened in 1859, since when the city has been home to a tenaciously-rooted foreign community, whose wealthier members live mainly on the heights known as 'The Bluff', where the original foreign concession was located. As a result—and because it remains the second largest foreign trading port in Japan (after Kobe)—Yokohama, together with Kobe and Nagasaki which also had early foreign communities, is known for its 'cosmopolitan' atmosphere. By this is not meant that it can be compared with the sort of melting pot that, say, San Francisco is, nor in its short history could it ever be. But it has its own Chinatown, where the cuisine in the restaurants is as authentic as one is likely to find in Japan. It has a **Foreigner's Cemetery** *(Gaijin Bochi)* and another cemetery for British and Commonwealth war dead. Several of the Kanto area's leading international schools are also situated in Yokohama, the majority of them established by Christian religious orders.

Jealous efforts have been made by the Yokohama authorities to see that

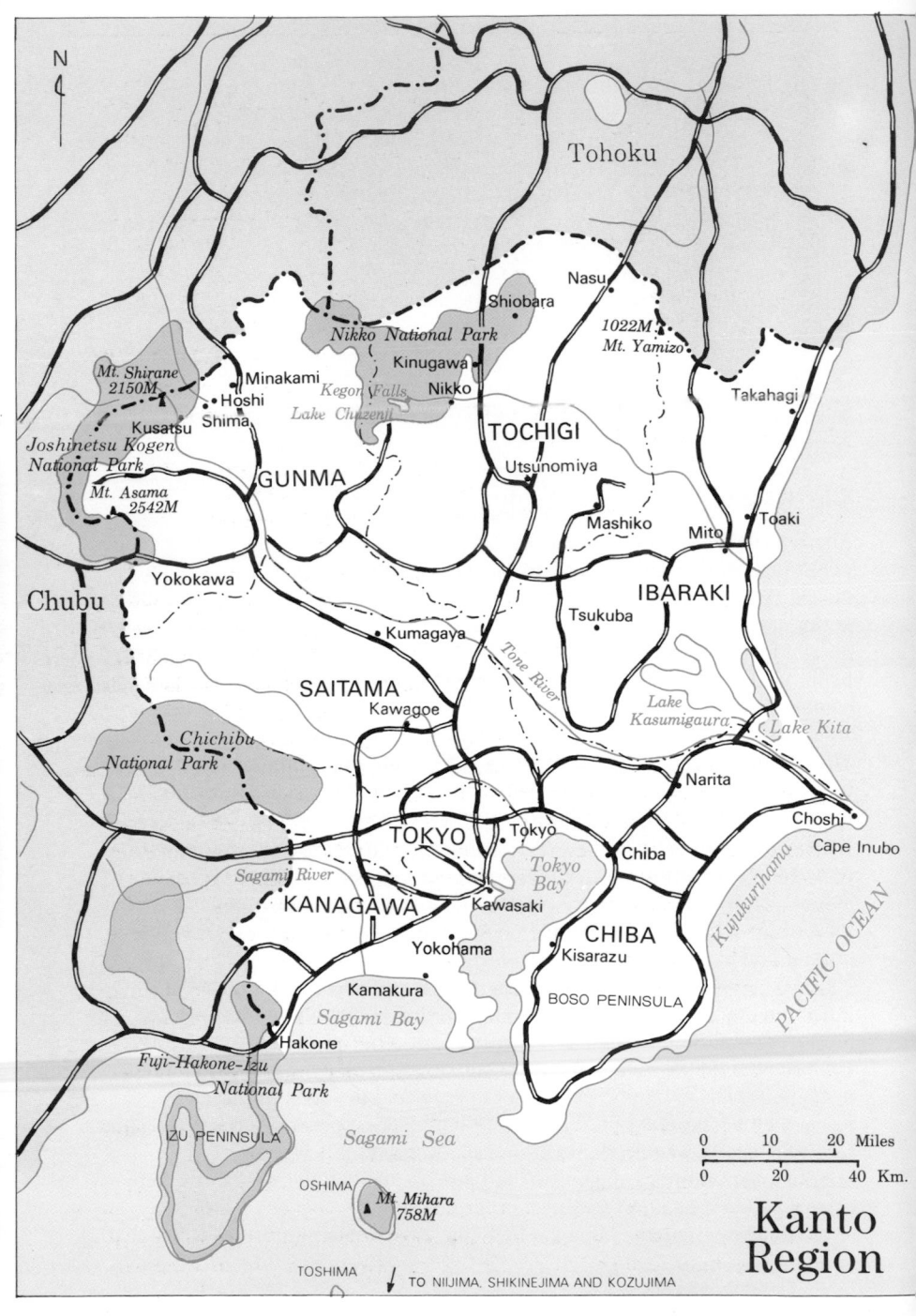

Kanto
Region

their city does not lag too far behind its larger fad-loving neighbour in leisure facilities. The **Motomachi** shopping street is famous even in Tokyo, and the **Takashimaya** department store and **Diamond Shopping Centre**, next-door to Yokohama Station, are quite the rivals of similar stores in the capital. Yokohama strikes the visitor arriving from Tokyo as a comparatively clean, up-to-date, pleasantly laid-out city (at least spasmodically), where some priority is still given to matters like the preservation of greenery and the provision of areas where a pedestrian can walk without ending up under a truck. There are some pleasant walks around Yokohama Stadium at **Sakuragicho** and the passenger harbour, near where the **Silk Museum** is to be found. One can live a lifetime in Tokyo and quite forget that it is on the coast, whereas in Yokohama the ocean is always there and still an encouragement to romance.

But for visitors with time to spare for only one of Kanagawa's cities—particularly for visitors interested in history, art, architecture or simply atmosphere—by far the more rewarding destination is the historic city of **Kamakura**.

For almost a century and a half Kamakura was the de facto capital of Japan, and the era of its supremacy (1192–1333) is known as the 'Kamakura Period'. Its supremacy came about because of the fierce rivalry between two powerful military clans, the Heike (or Taira) and the Genji (or Minamoto). From the middle of the 12th century the Heike controlled the court in Kyoto and were the real power in the country. But in 1180 the head of the Genji, Yoritomo, began raising an army in the Kanto region to move against the Heike and, largely because of its perfect defensive position with hills on three sides and sea on the fourth, Kamakura became Yoritomo's headquarters. In 1185 the Heike were finally overthrown. The tale of their defeat and scattered flight is one of the great sources of dramatic and poetic literature in Japan, firmly attesting to the Japanese preference for noble failure over clever triumph. Today, many remote villages in widely different parts of Japan still proudly claim to have been settled by Heike survivors; nowhere are such claims made on behalf of the victorious Genji. In 1192 Yoritomo was proclaimed shogun and the military government that he established in Kamakura, and which was maintained after his death by descendents of his father-in-law, lasted until forces loyal to the emperor attacked Kamakura in 1333, defeated the military regents there, and restored power to Kyoto.

Kamakura (present population 173,000) is a seaside town, and its dusty beach is jam-packed on fine summer weekends with thousands upon thousands of young people, who have mostly come down from Tokyo. But it is principally Kamakura's historical landmarks that will occupy the attention of the short-term visitor. Visitors arriving by train from Tokyo (the journey takes only an hour) can get off one stop before Kamakura, at Kita (North)

Kamakura, in order to visit **Engakuji** Temple, a major centre of Rinzai Zen Buddhism, founded in 1282 and largely restored after the 1923 earthquake. The temple is in a hilly area (the hills around Kamakura contain many pleasant walks and small, out-of-the-way temples) and is well known for its long and picturesque flights of steps, one of which leads up to a belfry in which hangs the largest temple bell in the city, cast in 1301. The Buddhist scholar and explicator, Suzuki Daisetz, whose work is well known abroad and was partly responsible for the popularity—and almost total misunderstanding—that Zen Buddhism achieved among hippies and others in the 1960s lived near this temple until his death in 1966. He is buried across the road in the small temple of **Tokeiji**, formerly a convent famous for having offered sanctuary to women seeking divorce or merely refuge from belligerent husbands, a tradition that continued into the early years of this century.

In Kamakura proper (to which the visitor can easily walk from Kita Kamakura, though the road is loud and dusty) the two chief historical showpieces are the **Tsurugaoka Hachiman Shrine** (founded on this site in 1191, rebuilt in 1828) and the 11.4-metre (37.5-foot) high **Daibutsu** (Great Buddha) cast in bronze in 1252, which stands in the precincts of **Kotokuin** Temple. This is one of two famous Great Buddhas in Japan, the other—larger and five centuries older—being housed at Todaiji Temple in Nara (see page 77). Some prefer the Kamakura Buddha simply because it is open to the sky, although it was originally enclosed in a structure that was destroyed by a tidal wave in 1495. A similar tidal wave on a summer Sunday today would bury the Buddha under a mound of gangly bathers. In the precincts of the Tsurugaoka Hachiman Shrine stand a vermilion drumbridge that visitors may clamber across at the risk of a severely twisted ankle and a famous and ancient gingko tree, from behind which, according to legend, an assassin leaped out in 1219 to lop off the head of Yoritomo's second son, the assassin later being identified as his victim's own nephew. In September each year the shrine hosts an exhibition of mounted archery (*yabusame*) which can be very exciting if you are lucky enough, or tall enough, to be able to see it over the countless heads of jostling spectators.

Kamakura abounds in smaller, quieter temples that amply repay the leisurely stroller's attention. Three of the best-known are **Sugimotoji**, founded in 734, long before Kamakura figured on anyone's map of the nation's power structure, and famous for its statues of Kannon, the Goddess of Mercy; **Hasedera**, also famous for its massive statue of Kannon as well as for the thousand or so tiny statues of Jizo, the Buddhist guardian of children, which have led to the temple being associated specifically with the welfare of infants, born and unborn; and **Hokokuji**, founded in 1334 and famous for its carefully nurtured bamboo grove, viewable upon the paying of an admission charge that includes a bowl of ceremonial tea.

Among the most popular and accessible hot-spring resorts for residents of Tokyo is **Hakone** at the extreme southwestern tip of Kanagawa prefecture; part of the **Fuji-Hakone-Izu National Park**. During the Edo period, Hakone was the site of the shogun's principal barrier gate along the Tokaido highway, and there is a small museum dedicated to this institution. Because it is so accessible, Hakone has been enthusiastically developed by entrepreneurs and consortiums who clearly believe that the ideal weekend in the country is one spent gazing out of the window of a 12-storey hotel at a vista of other 12-storey hotels. Hakone is popular with not terribly adventurous honeymooners, and more popular still among the organizers of even less adventurous company outings. Many of Hakone's hotels earn most of their income not from couples or families, but from large groups, such as associations of traders, who arrive en masse in hired buses and get as helplessly drunk as they can in the shortest possible space of time. This is called experiencing nature.

Saitama prefecture, more than half of which has been invaded by the northern reaches of Greater Tokyo's industrial and residential sprawl, has little in the way of sightseeing attractions to offer the short-term visitor. In the hilly west of the prefecture lies part of the **Chichibu-Tama National Park**, easily reached from Tokyo and famous for its woods and gorges, though the more interesting parts of the park lie still further west in Yamanashi prefecture. Closer to Tokyo, the town of **Kawagoe** (population 259,000) contains some fairly old wattle-and-daub buildings, mostly shops and tradesmen's houses.

Due north of Saitama lies **Gunma** prefecture, where the great Kanto plain peters out into a more typical Japanese landscape of mountains rising steeply to heights of more than 2,000 metres (6,500 feet). Gunma has some notable hot-spring resorts, the most devastatingly overdeveloped being **Minakami**, just south of the border with Niigata, but many are on a smaller scale and offer a more traditional environment in which to relax. Among these are **Kusatsu**, famous as one of the hottest spas in Japan (so hot that ablutions in some of the town's bathhouses are strictly organized and timed by a 'bathmaster', **Shima**, and **Hoshi**, which possesses a cathedral-like wooden bathhouse that makes up for its lack of outdoor bathing facilities. During the more peaceful years of his life, Admiral Yamamoto Isoroku, the commander of the Imperial Navy who died when his plane was shot down in the Solomon Islands in 1943, used to stay at Hoshi, and his namecard is proudly preserved at the front office of the resort's only ryokan. For visitors with little time to venture into the countryside, Gunma's hot springs, all reachable from Tokyo in three or four hours, provide a relaxing sampler, and they also provide a good cross-section of traditional hot-spring styles. At Kusatsu the whole of the little town is given over to the serious enjoyment of bathing and there are many ryokans, bathhouses and bars

to choose from, while the single ryokan at Hoshi lies on the edge of
quiet wooded hills, 20 minutes by taxi from the nearest bus stop. The
energetic visitor can walk over the hills from Hoshi to Shima, a tramp
of several hours.

Continuing clockwise round the edge of the Kanto plain, one comes to
Tochigi prefecture, whose uplands also boast some fine hot springs. The
most easily accessible is **Kinugawa** and, because it is so easily accessible
(two hours from Asakusa by Tobu-Line express), it has become a slightly
shabbier version of Hakone. Better are the resorts that cluster on the plateaus
of **Shiobara** and **Nasu**. Another famous military leader, General Nogi
Maresuke, the chief architect of Japan's victory in the Russo-Japanese War of
1904–5, used to stay at **Omaru**, a short taxi ride from the main Nasu spa. The
single ryokan there preserves the room he stayed in as a museum, and it
contains a striking formal photograph of the general and his wife taken
shortly before their quiet suicides (the general's in the traditional samurai
manner by disembowelment) committed at their Tokyo residence on the
occasion of the funeral of Emperor Meiji.

A short distance from the prefectural capital of **Utsunomiya**, at the
northern extremity of the Kanto plain, stands the small town of **Mashiko**
(population 22,000), the object of a day-trip from Tokyo for many visitors
interested in traditional ceramics. Mashiko is the best-known centre for the
manufacture of folk pottery in the Kanto region, and has been so since shortly
after 1924, when the potter Hamada Shoji, who was designated a 'Living
National Treasure' in 1955, established his most famous kiln there.
Previously, Japanese connoisseurs had tended to disregard the merits of the
traditional coarse-glazed pots of the rural areas (just as connoisseurs of
painting had scorned woodblock prints), preferring the finer Chinese-inspired
product of kilns like Kutani in Fukui prefecture. But attitudes gradually
changed as a result of the success of the *mingei undo* (folk-craft movement)
of the 1920s and '30s, which aimed to restore dignity and economic viability
to various traditional rural arts, and in which Hamada and the English potter
Bernard Leach were highly influential. Mashiko pottery (when not an
exhibition piece from the kiln of one of the best-known potters) is
comparatively inexpensive, and its heavy but subtle glazes with their abstract
designs and natural colours lend themselves well to modern Western-style
place settings. Mashiko today is far more of a mecca for souvenir-hunting
tourists than a haven for reclusive potters bent on preserving traditional skills,
but commercial independence for the artist was as much an aim of the mingei
undo as was the injection of new life into lapsing arts, so Hamada would
presumably find little to complain about.

But most visitors to Tochigi will head straight for **Nikko** and its famous **Toshogu Shrine**, the mausoleum of Ieyasu, the founder of the Tokugawa shogunate. The mausoleum was completed in 1636 and the immense expenditure of money and effort lavished on it is apparent at a glance 'lavish' being the operative word, since the gaudy, gilded and lacquered structures clearly fly in the teeth of those canons of Japanese aesthetics whose chief concern is with subtlety and understatement. By any standards, the place is an exercise in excess. The mausoleum was built to specifications laid down by Ieyasu himself and is thus one of the world's most spectacular testaments to megalomania. With its flashy colours and hectic cramming in of exotic detail, it seems far more Chinese in appearance and inspiration than does any other shrine or temple in Japan, even those of far earlier date which actually acknowledge the debt they owe to continental methods and tastes. One cannot help but see a rich irony in this when one recalls the extreme xenophobia displayed by the regime that Ieyasu founded, even as the building of the Toshogu Shrine was in progress. Japanese guidebooks and brochures intended for foreigners rarely fail to quote the famous saying about Nikko (possibly coined by the ancestors of the entrepreneurs who developed Hakone), *Nikko o mizushite 'kekko' to iunakare,* which these publications invariably translate as 'Never say "splendid" until you've seen Nikko', but which might equally accurately be rendered, 'See Nikko and say you've had enough!'

On 17 and 18 May (the same dates as Tokyo's Sanja Matsuri) Nikko's 'Procession of a Thousand Armed Men' marches along a one-kilometre route between the picturesque cryptomeria trees that line the approaches to the mausoleum. The participants are dressed in costumes and armour of the early Edo period and annually attract more than 100,000 spectators interested in fancy-dress parades.

A 50-minute bus ride from Nikko lies **Lake Chuzenji**, and the visitor who is planning an overnight stay in the Nikko area might welcome the comparative serenity of the lakeside after the florid self-aggrandizement of the Tokugawas. In summer, serenity is not an easy commodity to discover at Chuzenji, since its location so close to one of Japan's foremost tourist attractions has led to its development as a busy resort in its own right, where boating, water-skiing and lake- and river-fishing are all available to the energetic. The vicinity of the lake is well known for its waterfalls, the most famous being the **Kegon Fall**, about 100 metres (327 feet) high, formerly a favourite spot for romantically-motivated suicides.

Ibariki (or **Ibaragi**) prefecture has Japan's second largest freshwater lake in **Lake Kasumigaura**, but this is not a developed tourist attraction, mainly owing to the industrial exploitation that the prefecture's flatness and proximity to Tokyo early inflicted on it. It is, by and large, a drab prefecture, formerly known for its mines and for the grim, warlike nature of its people (not for nothing did Yoritomo choose to raise his army in the Kanto region), and today Ibaraki is the home of a coastal industrial belt with massive port facilities and the largest oil refinery in the world, as well as Japan's Atomic Energy Research Institute and atomic power stations at **Tokai** village (the bombings of Hiroshima and Nagasaki have left many Japanese people with what they call a 'nuclear allergy', and this allergy finds expression both in popular opposition to atomic energy in any form and in the government's carefully maintined pretence that U.S. Naval vessels with nuclear capability do not bring their armaments into Japan). The prefectural capital is **Mito** (population 216,000), which posesses one of the 'Three Most Beautiful Landscape Gardens in Japan' called **Kairakuen**, completed in 1843. For the other two celebrated gardens see Kanazawa (page 151) and Okayama (page 163). At **Tsukuba** stands the recently built 'Academic New Town' or 'Science City', in 1985 the site of a six-month-long scientific and technological exposition, and now a leading research and development centre, featuring the world's largest particle accelerator. Visitors interested in accelerating particles should head there without delay.

    Chiba prefecture has gained recognition among international travellers due to the siting of Tokyo's New International Airport at **Narita**. Visitors with longish waits in transit at Narita might consider a trip by bus or taxi into Narita city (population 68,000), and particularly to **Shinshoji** Temple, a large complex founded in the tenth century, which belongs to the Shingon sect of Buddhism, famous for its rigorous asceticism. Among the outward manifestations of this are fasting, pouring icy water over one's naked body in the middle of winter, and walking 100 times round the main hall of Shinshoji rubbing beads and reciting sutras, a practice visitors can see at all times of the year. The street leading up to Shinshoji is lined with shops selling traditional items such as handicrafts, sweets and rice crackers, and is a cheaper source of last-minute souvenirs than are the shops in the airport.

    The **Boso Peninsula** is flattish and has little to offer the sightseer other than the famous **Kujukurihama** (Ninety-Nine-League Beach) which is actually 57 kilometres (35 miles) long and lies along the peninsula's east coast. The lighthouse at **Cape Inubo** in the city of **Choshi** provided the last sight of the homeland to early emigrants bound by ship across the Pacific to the United States or South America, and has thus achieved a small degree of romance.

    Other destinations suitable for one- or two-day trips from Tokyo include Mount Fuji and its five lakes and the Izu Peninsula. These are dealt with on pages 135–138.

Nara, Kyoto and the Kinki Region

The Ancient Capitals, Their History, Their Primary

The **Kinki** (Around the Capital) region consists of the 'urban prefectures' of **Kyoto** and **Osaka**, and the ordinary prefectures of **Nara**, **Shiga**, **Mie**, **Wakayama** and **Hyogo**. The distinction between 'prefecture' (*ken*) and 'urban prefecture' (*fu*), of which Kyoto and Osaka are Japan's only examples, may conceivably have some meaning for the bureaucrats who dreamed it up, but it is of no earthly use to anyone else, and in the case of Kyoto is downright misleading, since the outlying parts of this 'urban prefecture' are as rural as anywhere else in the region. Perhaps the distinction was awarded Kyoto simply as a means of setting it apart from most of the rest of the country, but history and art have achieved that goal without the need for any bureaucratic fiddling. Another potential source of confusion where nomenclature is concerned is that the whole area is more commonly referred to as **Kansai** (West of the Barrier), just as Kanto is East of the Barrier (see page 51). *Kinki* is a term more often found in official designations than in ordinary speech, but it serves as a useful reminder of the central role that the region played in Japan's development as a nation.

No single word has more powerful associations for the Japanese people than the word *Yamato*, written with two ideograms that mean, literally, 'Great Harmony' or 'Great Us'. It is a poetic, spirit-stirring name for Japan and the Japanese race (as Albion is for England and the English), implying especially a purity unsullied by external influences. *Yamato* was the name of the great battleship that set out for Okinawa four months before the end of the Second World War in a last-ditch effort to turn the tide, and which carried only enough fuel for the outward journey—an example of heroic, unpragmatic self-sacrifice that the Japanese deem typical of their spirit at its most wholesome. *Yamato* was also the name of the first political power base—or court, or state—in Japan, said to have been established in the Nara basin by the legendary Emperor Jimmu in 660 BC. Historians treat this date as a complete fiction, and regard the Yamato state as having existed much later—between the third and seventh centuries AD—but it still represented the first attempt to unify the country under a single rule and was 'pure' in that its culture predated the tremendous continental influences—in particular those deriving from the introduction of Buddhism—which were to play such a crucial role in shaping Japanese society in later centuries.

The capital of the Yamato state was moved from place to place with the passing of each ruler, and little trace of the sites of these earliest power bases remains, though most, if not all, were located in what is today Nara prefecture. But in 710, by which time the Buddhist religion had become the most important influence on the life, art and intellectual aspirations of Japan, the court and bureaucratic machinery had grown so cumbersome that the need for a more stable base was felt, and a permanent capital was established at Nara city. Nara (then called **Heijokyo**—Capital of the Peaceful Fortress) remained the capital until 784 and, in the three-quarters of a century during which it held that position, the unification of the country continued, with imperial forces pushing north into the wild regions occupied by tribes such as the Ainu, who were racially quite different from the founders of the Yamato state. In 784 the particularly energetic Emperor Kammu, said to have grown wary of the power and political ambitions of Nara's belligerent Buddhist priesthood, ordered a new capital built at Nagaoka, out from under the intimidating shadow of the great temples, and eight years later, his passion for pristine horizons still seemingly undimmed, he began laying out yet another new capital a few kilometres to the northeast. The court was trundled to this newest site in 794 and the city that sprang up around it was known at first as **Heiankyo** (Capital of Tranquillity), and then as **Kyoto** (simply, Capital City). Kyoto remained the imperial capital of Japan for more than a thousand years.

There is a fashion among some foreign residents of Japan who play host to visitors from abroad to steer them away from the old capitals of the Kansai on the grounds that 'everyone goes there'. More knowledgeable than 'everyone', these residents prefer to direct their guests toward thatch-roofed lodging houses in remote rural areas or microphone-equipped bars where salaried workers sing pop songs to each other, so that their guests can experience the 'real' Japan. There is no doubt that microphone-equipped bars can harbour an abundance of delights. There is no doubt, either, that unless the visitor is tremendously lucky or presciently choosy in his timing, he will have to share the chief sights of the old capitals with large crowds of other sightseers. But nor can there be any doubt in a sane mind that the cities of Nara and Kyoto together arc the cradle, nursery and full-blown flower of Japanese culture. To avoid them or omit them for want of time is an act of stupendous folly.

Among the 'everyone' who crowd the chief sights of Nara and Kyoto are the hordes of Japanese schoolchildren who are taken there on educational visits. Naturally enough, those two historical cities are the chief focus of many of the school trips which are included in the standard syllabus for junior and senior high school pupils—a fact that can prove an unlooked-for irritation to the foreign visitor since a good proportion of the pupils will find the sight of him quite as remarkable as any of the historical monuments they have been taken to see, and will comment to this effect in loud and giggly voices. One solution is to try to time your visit so that it coincides with one of the longer school holidays—the months of July and August, and the weeks on either side of the New Year. A drawback to this plan is that Nara and Kyoto (Kyoto especially) lie in a basin, and are thus subject to more extreme temperature highs and lows than are hilly or coastal regions. In midsummer

Strong Medicine

Some of their medicinal preparations are very remarkable, producing most singular effects. Of these there is one spoken of by Titsingh, who saw its application and its consequences; and from some of the officers of our own expedition we have heard of this preparation, of which, we believe, they have brought home specimens. Titsingh thus writes:

"Instead of enclosing the bodies of the dead in coffins of a length and breadth proportionate to the stature and bulk of the deceased, they place the body in a tub, three feet high, two feet and a half in diameter at the top, and two feet at bottom. It is difficult to conceive how the body of a grown person can be compressed into so small a space, when the limbs, rendered rigid by death, cannot be bent in any way. The Japanese to whom I made this observation told me that they produced the result by means of a particular powder called Dosia, which they introduce into the ears, nostrils, and mouth of the deceased, after which, the limbs, all at once, acquire astonishing flexibility. As they promised to perform the experiment in my presence, I could not do otherwise than suspend my judgment, lest I should condemn, as an absurd fiction, a fact which, indeed, surpasses our conceptions, but may yet be susceptible of a plausible explanation, especially by galvanism, the recently discovered effects of which also appeared at first to exceed the bounds of credulity. The experiment accordingly took place in the month of October, 1783, when the cold was pretty severe. A young Dutchman having died in our factory at Dezima, I directed the physician to cause the body to be washed and left all night exposed to the air, on a table placed near an open window, in order that it might become completely stiff. Next morning, several Japanese, some of the officers of our factory, and myself, went to examine the corpse, which was as hard as a piece of wood. One of the interpreters, named Zenby, drew from his bosom a santock, or pocket-book, and took out of it an oblong paper, filled with a coarse powder resembling sand. This was the famous Dosia powder. He put a pinch into the ears, another pinch into the nostrils, and a third into the mouth; and presently, whether from the effect of this drug, or of some trick which I could not detect, the arms, which had before been crossed over the breast, dropped of themselves, and in less than twenty minutes by the watch, the body recovered all its flexibility.

"I attributed this phenomenon to the action of some subtle poison, but was assured that the Dosia powder, so far from being poisonous, was a most excellent medicine in child-bearing, for diseases of the eyes, and for other maladies. An infusion of this powder, taken even in perfect health, is said to have virtues which cause it to be in great request among the Japanese of all classes. It cheers the spirits and refreshes the body. It is carefully tied up in a white cloth and dried, after being used, as it will serve a great number of times before losing its virtues.

"The same infusion is given to people of quality when at the point of death; if it does not prolong life, it prevents rigidity of the limbs; and the body is not exposed to the rude handling of professional persons, a circumstance of some consequence in a country where respect for the dead is carried to excess. I had the curiosity to procure some of this powder, for which I was obliged to send to Kidjo, or the nine provinces, to the temples of the Sintoos, which enjoy the exclusive sale of it, because they practice the doctrine of Kobou–Daysi, its inventor. The quantity obtained in consequence of my first application was very small, and even this was a special favor of the priests, who otherwise never part with more than a single pinch at a time."

Commodore M C Perry, Narrative of The Expedition of an American Squadron to The China Seas and Japan, *1856*

Kyoto is uncomfortably hot and in January it is tingly cold. In July Kyoto is crowded for another reason (the **Gion Matsuri**—see page 98), and on New Year's Eve and the three days following, some of the major shrines and temples become so congested that it is hard enough to squeeze through their gates, let alone enjoy their sights. But the visitor prepared to put up with the frostiness of late December or mid-January to mid-February will usually find himself rewarded with at least a whiff of that tranquillity for which the city was originally named.

Though Nara and Kyoto (only half an hour apart by express) are often linked as a single historical 'package', the two cities are very different in character and the visitor should approach them in very different frames of mind. It is part of the object of what follows to suggest some of the differences between the two, particularly those differences that dictate the peculiar kind of beauty that each contains.

Nara

Nara's beauty is monumental, and resides in such qualities as size, strength and symmetry. It is a spacious, public beauty; a beauty amid which to congregate and applaud. Though Nara (present population 298,000) is the older of the two great capitals, and though many of its treasures owe their origins and forms to the influences of continental Asia (these having found their way to Nara, via T'ang China and Korea, along the Silk Road), it is still a city with which a Western visitor can feel an immediate kinship. Mostly, this is because the chief sights of the city centre—the temples of Todaiji and Kofukuji and the Kasuga Shrine—lie on the edges of open parkland, through which the visitor can stroll and in which he can enjoy the sort of panoramic vista that is crucial to most Western ideas of what constitutes an attractive place.

With Buddhism came, for the first time, a fully-developed means of writing down language (the Japanese script is wholly borrowed or adapted from the Chinese—see page 234) and, as with the religious institutions of the West during the dark and early middle ages, the Buddhist temples of the Nara period were the principal repositories of learning and culture. It is thus fitting that the chief surviving monuments of Nara's greatness are not palaces or mansions, but the massive brooding religious edifices that were the apex of its intellectual, as well as of its outward, glory.

The visitor arriving from Kyoto by the rapid and comfortable Kintetsu Line express emerges from Kintetsu Nara station to find himself within 200 metres of Kofukuji Temple, which has occupied this site since the year of Nara's founding and whose five-storey pagoda is one of the city's most immediately recognizable landmarks. But his patience will be repaid if the visitor postpones his visit to Kofukuji for the moment and instead takes a bus or taxi some four kilometres (2.5 miles) west to **Yakushiji**, a temple almost as old, and which provides a more illuminating introduction to Nara's temple architecture.

Yakushiji (named after the Buddha of Healing) was founded on this site in 718 and, like so many of Japan's historical monuments, has been largely destroyed and rebuilt several times. This is immediately obvious from the spanking new condition of two of the temple's freshly restored buildings, the Kondo (Golden Hall), completed in 1976, and the West Pagoda, completed in 1981. The old Yamato state had maintained relations with China, but there had been no large-scale attempt to imitate continental civilization. This changed with the introduction of Buddhism in the mid-sixth century, and from the time of Japan's first great lawgiver, Prince Shotoku, Chinese manners, learning, customs, writing, architecture and most other arts were imported with as much fervour as have been the habits and inventions of the West in modern times. The two restored structures in Yakushiji are quite unlike anything else standing in Nara today and, like Nikko on a brasher and more baroque scale, they seem to contradict those canons of Japanese taste wherein the subdued and the monochrome are accorded pride of place. Many Japanese visitors to Yakushiji, though quick to admire the craftsmanship and dedication to tradition that have raised these new structures, are equally quick to express a preference for the stark, age-darkened buildings like the East Pagoda (said to date from the temple's founding), which, they like to infer, are somehow more 'Japanese'. The bright primary colours of the new structures strike them as distinctly Chinese in flavour—which, of course, they are, being perfectly faithful to the temple's seventh-century Chinese-inspired design. So it is worth keeping in mind, when making the rounds of Nara's temples, that they were all once as brightly decorated as these two parts of Yakushiji are. Having made a start with freshly painted buildings, the visitor will perhaps have a sharper eye for the traces of red that can still be found, say, on the rafters of the Great Buddha Hall in Todaiji, and this sharper eye may help in turn to sharpen his imagination so that he sees the great temples not only as they stand brooding and dark today, but as they once stood.

Behind the East Pagoda is another very old building which has miraculously survived more than eight centuries: the Toindo (East Temple Hall), erected in 1285, in which stands the bronze statue of Sho-Kannon (the original manifestation of the Goddess of Mercy), cast at the end of the seventh century, probably in Korea, and presented as a gift to the Japanese emperor by the King of Paekche. Other fine statues, including that of Yakushi Nyorai, the Buddha of Healing who gives the temple its name, are kept in the Kondo.

A second reason for choosing Yakushiji as the springboard for a tour of Nara is that an old Nara-period road begins just outside its north gate, and the visitor with time and a taste for leisurely strolls can follow this road a little

over three kilometres (1.8 miles) to the formerly great temple of Saidaiji, passing as he strolls two of the ancient capital's most important historical monuments.

The first of these, which he reaches within minutes of leaving Yakushiji, is **Toshodaiji**, perhaps the most exquisite of all Nara's temples. Here, more than anywhere else, one blesses the centuries that have worn away the reds and greens and blues and golds, and left the almost-black of the wood and the crisp white of the plaster and wide gravel paths to reveal without the distraction of colour the temple's perfect architectural harmonies. 'Toshodaiji' means 'Temple of the One who was Invited and Brought from China' and was founded in 759 by the Chinese priest Chien Chen (Jian Zhen), whom the Japanese call Ganjin. In 742 Chien Chen was invited by envoys of the Japanese emperor to visit Japan in order to instruct the priests there. Chien Chen was forbidden to leave China by imperial decree and his various attempts, one of which ended in shipwreck, occupied 11 years and cost him his sight. The hardships Chien Chen underwent in his efforts to reach Nara are a measure not only of his determination and stoicism, but of the hazards of eighth-century sea travel, even at a time when Japan was particularly anxious to preserve and strengthen the umbilical cord that precariously joined it to the continent. It has been estimated that, in Chien Chen's time, fully half the ships that set out to cross the sea between China and Japan either turned back or were lost.

The first sight that greets the visitor as he enters Toshodaiji through the Great South Gate is one of the most striking he will see in all Nara: the Kondo, or main hall, which has survived intact from the date of the temple's founding and must rank as one of the most beautifully proportioned buildings in the world. Much of its strength derives from the eight great pillars that support its roof along the south facade, lending a peculiar sense of weight and rootedness to the entire compound, and making one wonder whether the architectural heritage of classical Greece was not among the many influences that found their way along the Silk Road. Among the statues housed in the Kondo is a seated dry-lacquer figure of the sombre Buddha of the Law (Vairocana), said to have been made by two of the Chinese artist-priests who accompanied Chien Chen to Nara. The flanking statues are all by Chinese sculptors.

Most of the other originally Nara-period structures in the compound—the lecture hall, the drum tower—have a simplicity and grace and a way of complementing each other to create a completely satisfying aesthetic whole that is not matched in any other Nara temple, with the possible exception of Horyuji. At the very back of the compound, away from the main buildings and beyond a small lotus-pond, stands the unassuming grave of blind Chien Chen the founder, who never saw the material loveliness of the temple he established and so never knew how great a legacy his adopted country had received from him.

The old road now crosses the Kintetsu railway line and turns north again to lead the stroller past the southeast corner of the key-hole shaped island and lake that mark the tomb of Emperor Suinin, one of the semi-legendary Yamato-era or pre-Yamato rulers, said to have lived for 139 years and to have reigned as emperor for a full century (29 BC–AD 70), dates and figures that all attest to the early and energetic development of the fairy story. But the tomb is genuine enough, and so is the fact that it houses the remains of a notable ancient ruler (alone perhaps, since the custom of retainers immolating themselves on the deaths of their lords is said to have ended in Suinin's reign). Six more of these mysterious key-hole shaped burying grounds lie a little over a kilometre northeast of here, beyond the site of the now vanished imperial palace, and there are many more near Osaka and throughout the old Yamato basin. A small controversy has developed around these tombs owing to the reluctance of the authorities to consent to their being excavated. The authorities state, quite credibly, that the tombs should be left alone in order not to disturb the august spirits of those for whom they were built. But critics have suggested that this reluctance is due more to a fear of what might be found if the tombs were systematically examined. Such excavations as have taken place (mostly at later tomb sites in Kyushu) have revealed paintings very similar to tomb frescoes that exist in Korea and, so critics charge, the Japanese establishment (particularly that part of it that spends so much of its time 'proving' the uniqueness and racial purity of Japanese people) would likely suffer embarrassment if too many early links with the 'inferior' culture of Korea were uncovered.

But this controversy need not detain the stroller, indifferent as he is bound to be to spurious claims of cultural and racial uniqueness, and if he continues north for about another kilometre, the old road will bring him finally to the gate of **Saidaiji**, 'The Great Temple in the West', founded here in 765 and formerly of a scale to compare with Todaiji, 'The Great Temple in the East', which it was built to complement. It is now much reduced in size and grandeur and none of its present buildings is earlier than 18th century.

The three-kilometre (1.8-mile) stroll described above, with visits to Yakushiji and Toshodaiji, could well occupy the best part of a day. Visitors with less time to spare might squeeze it into a morning and then, from Saidaiji station, take the Kintetsu Line two stops to the Nara terminus and continue their tour of the chief sights of Nara with visits to Kofukuji, Todaiji and the Kasuga Shrine.

Kofukuji was moved to this site in 710 (some of the city's temples were originally founded elsewhere and re-established in Nara after it had become the capital), and its chief buildings, including the famous five-storey pagoda, were rebuilt, after repeated destruction by fire, in the early 15th century. Kofukuji means 'Happiness-Producing Temple', an appropriate name in that

The Opening Game

*T*he Master got up. A folded fan in his hand, he suggested a warrior readying his dirk. He seated himself at the board. The fingers of his left hand in the overskirt of his kimono, his right hand lightly clenched, he raised his head and looked straight before him. Otaké seated himself opposite. After bowing to the Master he took the bowl of black stones from the board and placed them at his right. He bowed again and, motionless, closed his eyes.

'Suppose we begin,' said the Master.

His voice was low but intense, as if he were telling Otaké to be quick about it. Was he objecting to the somewhat histrionic quality of Otaké's behaviour, was he eager to do battle? Otaké opened his eyes and closed them again. During the sessions at Itō he read the Lotus Sutra *on mornings of play, and he now seemed to be bringing himself to order through silent meditation. Then, quickly, there came a rap of stone on board. It was twenty minutes before noon.*

Would it be a new opening or an old, a hoshi *or a* komoku? *The world was asking whether Otaké would mount a new offensive or an old. Otaké's play was conservative, at R–16, in the upper right-hand corner; and so one of the mysteries was solved.*

His hands on his knees, the Master gazed at the opening komoku. *Under the gaudy camera lights his mouth was so tightly closed that his lips protruded, and the rest of us seemed to have left his world. This was the third match I had seen the Master play; and always, when he sat before the Go board, he seemed to exude a quiet fragrance that cooled and cleaned the air around him.*

After five minutes he seemed about to play.

Yasunari Kawabata, The Master of Go
translated by Edward G Seidensticker

its pagoda and main hall were built to house a powerful regiment of benevolent Buddhas, including the Buddha of Compassion (Amida), the Buddha of Healing (Yakushi), the Historical Buddha (Sakyamuni) and the Buddha of the Future (Miroku Bosatsu). But the temple's most arresting sculpture is the slender and exquisitely human three-faced and six-armed Ashura, which dates from the early eighth century and is kept today with most of Kofukuji's other treasures in the temple's ferroconcrete museum. One can't help wondering how much happiness their removal from 15th-century wood to 1950s ferroconcrete produced in the Buddhas.

A stroll east from Kofukuji through Nara Park takes the visitor past excavations that have uncovered the foundations of a solid Nara-period road, to the **Nara National Museum**. By this time the visitor cannot help but have noticed the famous **Nara deer**, who graze at large through the park and the precincts of the temples and shrines that surround it, and who may already have attempted to relieve him of half the items he is carrying (those who congregate in the approaches to Todaiji's Great Buddha Hall are most adept at this, having continual daily practice from the tourists who feed them rice crackers bought at the nearby souvenir stalls). The connection between deer and Buddhism is a long one, and owes much to the supposedly gentle nature of these animals—fitting symbols for a faith that, unlike Islam and Christianity, has usually refrained from aggressive proselytizing or from seeking converts by force. The Historical Buddha's first sermon was preached in a deer park at Varanasi in India, the first place he entered after obtaining his enlightenment. As the visitor continues east and reaches the beginning of the long and picturesque flight of stone steps that leads up to the **Kasuga Shrine**, he will notice that bas-relief sculptured deer form a repeated motif on the stone lanterns that line these steps. The shrine is dedicated to Shinto gods, not to any manifestation of the Buddha (see page 75), but the deer's presence here is a clear testament to the accommodating line taken by both faiths since Buddhism arrived in Japan. In fact, the Kasuga Shrine was originally linked to Kofukuji by virtue of the fact that both were ancestral places of worship for the Fujiwara family, the real power behind the throne from the mid-ninth to the mid-eleventh centuries, and among the Shinto shrine's official functions was protection of the Buddhist temple. The deer came to be regarded as incarnations of the many local deities and of the Fujiwara ancestors themselves. Each year in mid-October a ceremonial horn-cropping takes place in a compound erected to the right of the long flight of steps.

The Kasuga Shrine (whose name is written with ideograms that mean 'Spring Day') is in fact a complex consisting of four small shrines, each of which is dedicated to a different deity—two of these being legendary ancestors of the flesh-and-blood Fujiwaras. That gods should father human descendants is, of course, not uncommon; it happens throughout Greek mythology, and the best-known Japanese example is that of the imperial family who, until the present emperor's father renounced his divinity following the defeat of 1945, claimed direct descent from the Sun Goddess, Amaterasu Omikami. For centuries the Kasuga Shrine buildings were demolished and rebuilt every 20 years, a practice of ritual renewal that continues today at the Grand Shrine of Ise (see page 103). The chief structures of the main Kasuga Shrine were last rebuilt in the mid-17th century and those of the next-door **Kasuga-Wakamiya Shrine** in the mid-19th. Many of the shrine buildings have rows of metal lanterns hanging from their eaves. These are lit twice a year, together with the stone lanterns that flank the steps, on 3 February (traditionally a date on which the dark spirits of winter are ceremonially banished) and on 15 August, when the lantern lighting takes on an added significance owing to this date marking the (mainly Buddhist) Festival of the Dead (see page 121).

In its situation among steep wooded hills, deriving most of its attraction not from grandly monumental architecture but from the pleasantness of its sylvan setting, the Kasuga Shrine presents a sharp contrast to most of the Nara-period temples with their clean, flat compounds and crisp, Chinese geometry. As such, it helps to delineate a crucial difference between the Nara-period Buddhist temple and the Shinto shrine, and between the faiths that inspired them. Pre-Zen Buddhist temples preserve a teaching, or a moral system, or ideas such as 'salvation' and 'law'; but Shinto shrines are the signposts to a non-didactic spirit-in-nature, a spirit that lodges not so much in the man-made structures as in the trees and hills and rocks and waterfalls to which the structures were built to pay homage. This is not always true. It is not true, for example, of the Meiji and Yasukuni Shrines in Tokyo which were erected specifically to honour the souls of newly-dead men. Nor is it true of such bureaucratically-inspired examples of shrine-building as the 'Heian Shrine' in Kyoto. And there are many Buddhist temples of a later date than the Nara period which draw their chief outward beauty from a sense of being wedded to their surroundings. But if the visitor will keep in mind the difference between an ordered 'teaching' and an unconfinable 'spirit-in-nature', it will help him to appreciate better both the different functions and characters of the temples and shrines he visits, as well as the fact that the two were never mutually contradictory or exclusive.

For a sight of one more exquisite example of Nara-period sculpture, very different in character from the meditating Buddhas, the visitor can walk south along a short woodland path that leads from the precincts of the Kasuga Shrine, across a modern road, to the temple of **Shinyakushiji** (New Yakushiji), which stands down a winding back street that ends in rice paddies. This temple, like Saidaiji, is greatly reduced from its former splendour, but in a dark, stable-like hall it houses an image of the Buddha of Healing, from which it takes its name, surrounded by clay statues of the

Religion in Japan

It is sometimes said that the modern Japanese are the most secular-minded nation in the world. Nevertheless, a recent nationwide survey revealed that 95,860,000 Japanese people regard themselves as adherents of the Shinto faith; 87,750,000 are Buddhists; and 2,020,000 profess to be Christians. In a country whose total population is just over 123 million, it is clear that a large number of those surveyed are hedging their bets.

Shinto (literally 'the Way of the Gods') derives from the animistic cults that pre-dated Buddhism in Japan. Where these survive in their most original forms (the rural northeast and Okinawa), one still finds older country people consulting female shamans. Shinto's vast pantheon inhabits mountains, rivers and waterfalls, and some of the gods, but by no means all, concern themselves with human welfare. The myths of the founding of the nation and the divine descent of the imperial family were early incorporated into the faith, and from them specifically derives the nationalistic aspect of Shinto which shaped much of the social climate in the 1930s and '40s. An observance such as *hatsumode* (the first prayer of the new year) is far more an affirmation of Japaneseness than an expression of any form of supernatural belief.

Buddhism was introduced into Japan from Korea and China in the sixth century and was officially adopted as the state religion during the Nara period (710–94). Buddhism and Shinto were never in serious conflict and complemented rather than opposed each other, with Shinto deities coming to be regarded as the protectors of Buddhist temples. An attempt to separate the two faiths was made at the beginning of the Meiji period when Buddhism was disestablished and Shinto (or the nationalistic face of it) came to monopolize state support. Since the war, with freedom of religion guaranteed under the postwar constitution, they have partly resumed their complementary roles: Shinto ceremonies often accompany early infancy and marriage, while Buddhism looks after the dead.

Perhaps to counter the oppressive weight of unalloyed materialism, the postwar period has seen a remarkable proliferation of 'new religions', many of which could be better described as new Buddhist or Shinto sects. The best-known and most powerful is the *Sokagakkai* (founded in 1930), a lay splinter group of Nichiren Buddhism, which now claims a Japanese membership of 10 million and another million worldwide. The group has a 'political wing' in the form of the *Komeito* (Clean Government Party), with an established presence in the Diet. Until 1979 the president of Sokagakkai was the humourless, silk-suited, limousine-chauffered Ikeda Daisaku, regarded by his followers as an embodiment of the Buddha.

For comments on the relationship between Shinto and Buddhism, and for an outline of the development of Buddhism in Japan, see the sections on Nara and Kyoto. For a brief account of the introduction and persecution of Christianity, see the section on Kyushu.

Twelve Guardian Generals who defend the Buddha's law. Many of these are justly celebrated, but the outstanding sculpture is that of the fierce, teeth-baring **Basara**, whose right hand holds a sword and the fingers of whose left hand are curiously and tensely poised. Buddhist mythology has its figures of terror just as it has its embodiments of sublime peace, and, unlike those in the Christian myths, the figures of terror are often on the side of right.

The visitor can now head north again, past **Sagiike** (The Heron Pond) and back through the park to **Todaiji** Temple, easily the most visited temple in Nara on account of its containing the 16.2-metre-high (54-foot) bronze **Daibutsu** (Great Buddha), larger than the similar statue in Kamakura, and housed in a structure (the **Daibutsuden**, or Great Buddha Hall) which is the largest wooden building on earth. The striking proportions of this building are best appreciated if you approach it, as most visitors do, through the **Nandaimon** (Great South Gate), itself a huge structure that dates from 1199.

Todaiji was founded in 745 and its chief object of worship, the bronze Buddha, was completed in 749, having been cast under the supervision of a Korean metalworker named Kimimaro. The great fires that have twice reduced the Buddha Hall to ashes—once in 1180, once in 1567—were both deliberate acts of war in the millennium-long struggle for supremacy between power-hungry warlords; a struggle in which the priestly orders were often embroiled, even when they did not willingly embroil themselves. The great bronze Buddha had already had his head knocked off by an earthquake in 855. During the fire of 1180 he lost it again together with his right arm, and during that of 1567 he lost it a disorienting third time. He was restored to his present state in 1692, and the hall was rebuilt on a somewhat smaller scale than it had originally possessed in 1709, and again extensively renovated in 1914. That the Great Buddha seems to lack the ageless serenity of many of the finest Nara temple sculptures can, of course, be blamed on the vicissitudes of war and earthquakes, on decapitation and emergency surgery. But, disasters apart, if sculptures like Kofukuji's Ashura and the Buddha of the Future in Chuguji have anything to communicate beyond an infinite capacity for love, it is that size alone, even size as momentarily overpowering as this, is a barren quality without the deeper mystery carved into those figures' faces; a mystery of which the great bronze Buddha has little visible trace.

On the heights to the east of the Daibutsuden, beyond the belfry, are the **Nigatsudo** (Hall of the Second Moon) and **Sangatsudo** (Hall of the Third Moon—'moon', in these cases, meaning the months of the old lunar calendar). The present Nigatsudo dates from 1669 and from its platform the viewer can see the distant five-storey pagoda of Kofukuji rising above the rooftiles and trees of the Todaiji complex. The Nigatsudo is the site of an important annual two-week-long ritual called **O-Mizutori** (Water-Drawing), which takes its name from the climactic event enacted each year on 12 March—the drawing up of water from the well below the building. This is preceded by a nighttime procession of priests, each carrying a large brightly blazing pine torch, who, when they reach the platform of the Nigatsudo, swing and shake their torches to produce a massive shower of sparks and embers that wraps the entire building in flame. This ceremony, dating back to the mid-eighth century, is the most hallowed in the old capital and is, in origin, a combination of purification ritual (the flames purging the temple of winter spirits) and absolution from sin, symbolized by the gift of sacred water. Many of Nara's annual observances involve the use of fire; another famous ritual being the spectacular grass-burning on **Mount Wakakusa** (Mount Young-Grass), above the Kasuga Shrine, which takes place each year on 15 January (Coming-of-Age Day).

Northwest of the Daibutsuden stands the log-cabin-like **Shosoin** repository, in which are—or were—stored some of the outstanding treasures of the Nara period, many of them, like the masks and five-stringed lute, providing crystal clear evidence of the extent to which the Silk Road brought foreign cultural influences and artifacts to early Japan from as far away as the Middle East and, perhaps, the Mediterranean. These treasures are not usually on public display, owing, so the authorities maintain, to their fragility. But they are exhibited annually for a brief time during the safely unhumid weather of autumn.

In Nara Prefecture

One of the most important temples associated with the old capital stands not in the city of Nara itself, but some 14 kilometres (8.5 miles) southwest of it. This is the temple complex of **Horyuji**, the oldest existing temple in Japan, founded by Prince Shotoku in 607, a bare 20 years after the official espousal of Buddhism, destroyed by fire in 670 and rebuilt at about the time that Nara became the capital. As an example of T'ang Chinese religious architecture Horyuji is unrivalled in the world, and its treasure house and neighbouring nunnery contain two of the most superb sculptures the visitor will ever see.

The larger west compound is the one the visitor enters first, with its main hall (Kondo) and five-storey pagoda (reassembled after the Second World War using the original eighth-century timbers) arranged to right and left of the gateway after the Korean fashion (many of the craftsmen employed in the temple's construction were Korean), rather than one behind the other as was usual in China. Both these buildings contain treasures—the Kondo has several bronze statues of Buddhas, including Sakyamuni (The Historical Buddha) and Yakushi, cast at, or shortly after, the time of Horyuji's founding, notable for their unmysterious, naively complacent expressions. The pagoda contains clay bas-reliefs of scenes from the Buddha's life, death and ascension to paradise.

But for Horyuji's most riveting sculptured treasure the visitor must go to the 20th-century treasure house, where he will see among many other things, if he is lucky (since it is not always displayed), the tall, impossibly slender form of **Kudara Kannon** with its sublime, still somehow homely features. The origins of this statue are a mystery. It has been claimed for a seventh-century Japanese sculptor of Korean descent, but also for the artists of southern China and the Korean kingdom of Paekche (the Japanese name for which was 'Kudara'). A modern mystery is why the curators of this treasure house have stuck the statue behind reflecting glass, a plan that makes the full appreciation of its lovely face a practical impossibility. Another celebrated image of Kannon (the Goddess of Mercy) is housed in the **Yumedono** (Hall of Dreams), the beautiful octagonal pavilion at the centre of the east compound. This statue has been ascribed to no less an artist than Prince Shotoku himself, and has been worshipped since shortly after his death as the repository of his soul. The statue is rarely on public view.

A few dozen metres from the Hall of Dreams is the nunnery of **Chuguji**, originally the home of Prince Shotoku's mother. In its modern treasure hall stands arguably the finest piece of sculpture in Japan, the wooden, incense-blackened **Miroku Bosatsu** (Buddha of the Future), whose distinctly feminine aspect has also caused the figure to be identified with the Goddess of Mercy. The only comparably beautiful statue of Miroku Bosatsu is the one in Koryuji Temple in Kyoto (see page 84) which has not the softness of the Chuguji figure, but is more purely androgynous. The Chuguji figure is also attributed by legend to Prince Shotoku, though the complete irrelevance of its provenance cannot but strike the awed visitor who looks long enough at its softly shining face. It doesn't matter who carved it. It is sufficient that such a perfect thing exists.

Perhaps the most satisfying thing about the finest Nara sculptures—this, the Ashura, the Kudara Kannon—is the degree to which they communicate to the viewer a seeming longing to inspire in him the same perfect calm that inspires them. Their chief aim is not to be merely beautiful, but actively to pass on the quality that sustains their beauty. Compare this accessibility with the defiant loftiness of, say, Michelangelo's David, who stares away over his magnificently untouchable shoulder as though the viewer were completely beneath his contempt. There is no contempt, no cold magnificence, in the faces of these Nara figures. Rather, they seem like encouraging relatives (the *homeliness* of the Kudara Kannon; she is just like somebody's auntie!) who derive a palpable pleasure from the viewer's confidence in their concern.

If the reflecting glass of Horyuji's treasure house proved an irritant, how much more so will the tape-recorded commentary switched faithfully on every 10 or 12 minutes by the lady custodian of Chuguji's Miroku Bosatsu. This worthy person has responded in the past to requests that the tape

recorder be turned off, but always with a puzzled frown, and the visitor who threatens her with physical violence does so at the risk of his soul. Besides, the visitor had better accustom himself to tape-recorded commentaries before he sets out to view the chief sights of Kyoto, otherwise he could end up leaving old unsullied Yamato in a straitjacket.

Within easy strolling distance of Horyuji stand the two small unfrequented temples of **Horinji** and **Hokkiji**, both founded in the seventh century. Hokkiji is remarkable for its lovely three-storey pagoda which survives in its original state.

The mountainous **Yoshino** area, in the south of Nara prefecture, an area famous for its cryptomeria and cherry blossoms, is part of the **Yoshino-Kumano National Park** (see also page 107).

Kyoto

When in the West we speak of 'a beautiful city', we often have in our minds a place which, viewed from some point of vantage, presents a pleasing overall prospect. Kyoto is not like that at all. If your first sight of Kyoto is from the platform where the bullet train deposits you, its superficial ugliness can move you to despair. Kyoto's beauty is not like Nara's—monumental, expansive, public. Kyoto's beauty is elusive and has to be sought out with patience and forethought.

Partly this is because Kyoto has continued to grow and flourish as a living city, while Nara has tended to settle reclusively into the sombre business of being a museum. Modern city growth has on all sides threatened the peace and loveliness of old Kyoto—threatened, but not extinguished. Nara's claim on the visitor's attention has often to do with size—the great bronze Buddha, the extent of the compounds of Todaiji and Horyuji, the largest wooden building on earth. But the best of what Kyoto has to offer is often small in scale and of a delicacy that the encroachment of raucous modernity seems always to underline, and sometimes enhance—the rock garden at the Daisenin, the Shisendo hermitage, the Jakkoin nunnery, a single gate, a single patch of crumbling wall, the window of a doll shop that contains for its display one single, painstakingly chosen doll.

You cannot enjoy Kyoto from a point of vantage (even from such traditional points of vantage as Mount Hiei or the platform of Kiyomizu Temple), let alone from the top of the banal lighthouse-shaped tower of the Kyoto Tower Hotel. You have to go down among the narrow back streets where the old and the new clash so echoingly and begin ferreting out the private corners of that beauty which is the heritage of Kyoto's privacy-minded people.

In three or four days, the diligent, sensitive visitor might come close to understanding and appreciating what, for want of a more properly descriptive term, we shall have to call the 'heart' of Nara. But to come within striking distance of the 'heart' of Kyoto would take as many years, and even then the discovered 'heart' would be an unashamedly private invention, as different from the next man's image of 'the real' Kyoto as you are different from him. I hope that the visitor will not mind my being completely subjective in the advice I have to give.

The advice is in two parts. In the first part I shall briefly describe most of the famous sights of Kyoto which any bus tour will take the visitor to see, and on which I urge him, with little more than personal prejudice for a reason, not to spend more than half his total time. In the second part I shall try to point him in the direction of other sights (some equally famous, some largely ignored) where I have found and been able to enjoy some vestige of what I regard as the 'real' Kyoto beauty. I cannot guarantee that the visitor will find that beauty there in equal measure for, as well as being a private matter, the charm of this old city is almost wholly dependent on such unpredictable factors as the weather, the season, the time of day, and whether or not the visitor is in love. Part of the beauty of the great monuments of Nara lies in the impression of strength they convey. But the private, elusive beauty of Kyoto is far less vigorous a thing, and it is easily spoiled. Talk too loud, look too hard, think too much, and it is gone.

Kyoto: The Skin

Kyoto (present population 1.5 million) contains about 20 percent of all Japan's listed national treasures—an embarrassment of riches—so the chief problem for a visitor with limited time is one of choice. Perhaps his best means of approaching the famous sights in this first section is to allow convenience of location to make the choice for him. It doesn't really matter in what order he sees these things, only that he get round as many as interest him and still leave himself time to follow at least some of the suggestions in the next section. The temples and shrines are introduced here roughly in the order of their founding.

Heian is the name given to the period, almost four centuries long, between the establishment of the capital at Heiankyo (Kyoto) in 794 and the removal of real power to Kamakura in 1185 (see page 53). It was, for the privileged classes, an age of elegance and sophistication, derived from the manners and interests of the still preeminent imperial court. The clearest legacy of the period is Kyoto's grid-like street plan, modelled on that of the T'ang Chinese capital of Chang'an. Directions to Kyoto's taxi drivers often consist in naming the intersections of major thoroughfares (as in New York), and the main east-west avenues are still numbered one to nine.

The style of architecture on which it is based requires that the **Heian Shrine** be mentioned early, though it is not a Heian shrine at all but a late

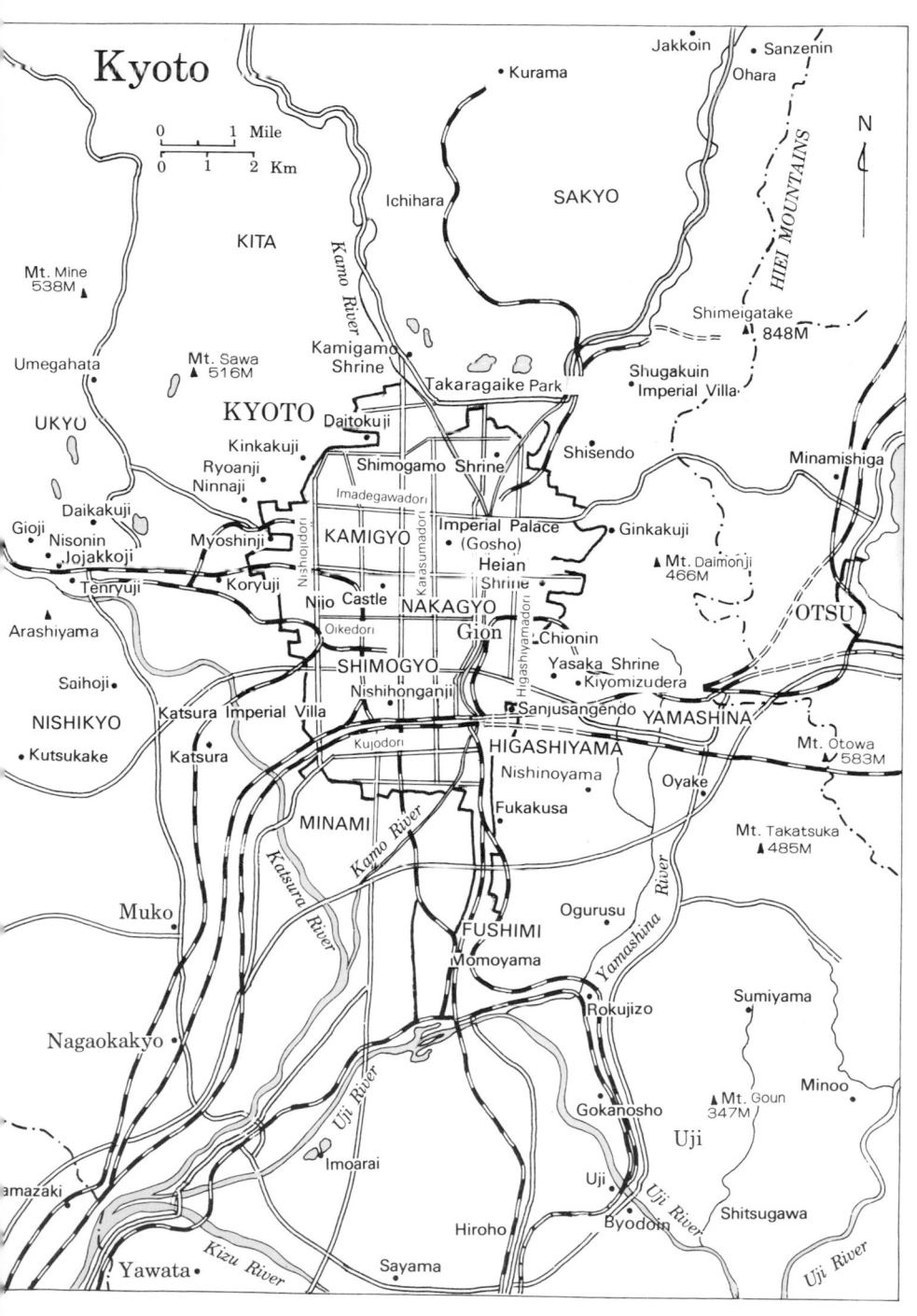

19th-century replica of the earliest imperial palace in Kyoto, built to a scale of about half the size of the original on former parkland in 1895 to commemorate the 1,100th anniversary of the city's founding. It possesses, in consequence, the spiritual depth of a stage set for an extravagant production of Gilbert and Sullivan's *The Mikado,* an operetta already a decade old when the 'Heian Shrine' first opened its gates.

The **Yasaka Shrine**, on the other hand, is genuinely Heian in origin, though its present buildings were constructed in the mid-17th century. Its location in **Gion** (it is sometimes called the 'Gion Shrine'), which is the old theatre and entertainment quarter of the city, well-known for its geisha, has given this particular religious edifice a not unattractive atmosphere of worldly bustle, especially on New Year's Eve, when a bonfire is lit in the shrine compound, and people can be seen strolling through the precincts twirling in their hands the smouldering strings with which, traditionally, they would have kindled the first hearth fire of the new year. The shrine's most famous annual observance occurs in July and is Kyoto's best-known festival (see Gion Matsuri page 98).

Of the principal temples within the city proper, **Koryuji** is the oldest, having been established during the time of Prince Shotoku, in 622, long before Kyoto became the capital. Its main hall still dates from 1165, but the visitor's attention will be chiefly claimed by the exquisite late-sixth or early-seventh-century statue of **Miroku Bosatsu** (The Buddha of the Future), the first piece of sculpture ever designated a National Treasure, which is housed today in the temple's modern museum. Opinions differ as to which of the two similarly posed statues is the finer, this or the one in Chuguji (see page 79). Chuguji's may strike the viewer as the more accessibly human, while this in Koryuji seems to hover tantalizingly between the human and the purely spiritual. The story is told of a student who, during the days (not so long ago) when the statue was less rigorously protected than it is now, was so captivated by its beauty that he leaned across to caress it and accidently broke off one of the delicate fingers of its right hand. Horrified at the enormity of what he had done, and prevented by sheer terror from confessing, he carried the finger around in his pocket for several days while the country went into an uproar and the police conducted a frantic search. Eventually he plucked up the courage to hand the finger over to the authorities, who restored the statue and placed it behind the carefully guarded plate glass where it meditates today on how to effect the salvation of mankind. The student's salvation was quick to arrive, and he became something of a folk hero, more admired for his love of the ethereally beautiful than frowned on for his folly.

Visitors interested in folly will find the **Toei Eiga Mura** (Film Village), a stone's throw from Koryuji, entirely to their taste. Here they can see how one of the major Japanese film companies goes grandly and energetically about the task of reducing the country's history to a series of swashbuckling

confrontations between baddies who speak out of the corners of their mouths and goodies who speak with their quivering chins tucked back into their Adam's apples.

Of temples founded after Kyoto became the capital, **Kiyomizudera** (Pure Water Temple, taking its name from a spring on the steep hillside where it stands) is among the most famous and ancient, having been established here in 798. Most of the present structures date from the 17th century. The temple's chief architectural feature—and main tourist attraction—is the stilted platform on which the main hall stands, commanding a view over part of the city. Below the platform, paths disappear into the wooded hillside, affording a short, but pleasant stroll. Kiyomizudera is approached along a street lined with shops that sell, among other souvenirs, examples of the pottery to which the temple has given its name. The district has been famous for its ceramics since it was settled by Korean potters brought back to Japan following the campaigns in Korea during the 1590s.

Ninnaji Temple was founded in 888, but most of its buildings have been reconstructed (several during the last hundred years) in the style of the late 16th century, so it is not typical of the period of its founding, although it preserves an atmosphere of calm elegance better than do its more famous neighbours, Ryoanji and Kinkakuji. This temple is a recognized centre for the gentle arts of tea ceremony and flower arrangement and, throughout feudal times, the head priest was a member of the imperial family.

During the Kamakura period (see page 53), when political power shifted for the first time to the Kanto region, Kyoto, though still a seething hotbed of plot and counterplot, was thrown back to a large extent on cultural and philosophical pursuits, such as the assimilation of several new schools of Buddhism, all Japanese in origin. These included the 'Pure Land' sect founded by Honen, the 'True Pure Land' sect founded by Shinran, and the 'Nichiren' sect, named after its highly egotistical founder, Nichiren, regarded, on his own recognizance, as an incarnation of the Buddha. Each of these new Japanese sects was, in one way or another, an attempt to popularize and simplify the hitherto esoteric doctrines of the adopted continental faith. But the most important artistic development within Japanese Buddhism during this period came once again from the continent. This was the introduction from China of Zen (Ch'an) Buddhism toward the end of the 12th century.

For the most striking example of original Kamakura-period architecture in Kyoto one turns to **Sanjusangendo**, a long wooden structure built in 1266, and belonging to **Myohoin** Temple, which was actually founded in Heian times. Inside, the entire 118-metre (390-foot) length of the hall forms a vast exhibition platform for 1,001 statues of the Goddess of Mercy which are among the most breathtaking sights in the city—not because of their beauty, but because of their sheer massed numbers. In the gallery behind the main exhibition, through which the visitor passes before reaching the exit, stand some genuinely moving sculptured figures, in particular that of the praying woman, **Mawara-nyo**, and of the lean, bearded hermit, **Basu**. Since 1606 the building's long veranda has been the site of a famous annual archery contest, still held on 15 January (Coming of Age Day, a national holiday). The name Sanjusangendo means 'Hall of Thirty-Three Spaces' and refers to the number of gaps between its supporting pillars.

Another, even larger, Kamakura-period temple is the **Chion-in**, the earliest of whose present buildings dates from the 17th century. The temple's massive bell was cast at about the same time, and is a major attraction for visitors to Kyoto on New Year's Eve when, throughout the country, temple bells ring out the 108 sins of the old year. The Chion-in bell is so huge that the priest appointed to strike it (an exhausting business, so the priests relieve each other very frequently) must throw the whole weight of his body at the bell, being hoisted off the ground by the momentum of the heavy wooden striker in a somewhat unpriestly display of trapezery.

The collapse of the military government in Kamakura and the return of political power to Kyoto marked the beginning of the Muromachi period (1333–1568), an era so plagued by civil wars and armed rivalry between supporters of the court, of the powerful Ashikaga family (for much of the era de facto rulers of the nation), and of numerous provincial lords, that the latter half is also known as the Sengoku period or 'Period of the Country at War'. Nevertheless, the chief architectural monuments of these centuries are particularly noted for their elegance and refinement.

Rokuonji Temple, far better known as **Kinkakuji** (The Temple of the Golden Pavilion), was the retreat of the third Ashikaga shogun, Yoshimitsu, who entered the priesthood on his retirement in 1394 and subsequently both built the famous pavilion and laid out the temple's large garden. The pavilion was intended as an expression of the earthly wealth and power of the retired shogun's family rather than as a monument to religious zeal—just as was, more than two centuries later, Ieyasu's Toshogu Shrine at Nikko (see page 59) so a comparison between the two buildings provides an illuminating lesson in the decline of aesthetic taste from Ashikagas to Tokugawas. The original pavilion was completely destroyed by arson in 1950, and this astonishing act of vandalism forms the climax of Mishima Yukio's 1956 novel, *Kinkakuji,* in which the author suggests that the culprit, a Buddhist acolyte, destroyed the pavilion partly out of an inability to tolerate the existence of so perfect an object of beauty in an imperfect, ugly world. The present pavilion, completed in 1955, is a replica of the original.

Ginkakuji (The Temple of the Silver Pavilion) was built almost a century after the construction of its golden forebear, in 1488. It was built by Yoshimitsu's grandson, the eighth Ashikaga shogun, Yoshimasa, not as a place to retire to but as a distraction from the cares of office. Yoshimasa

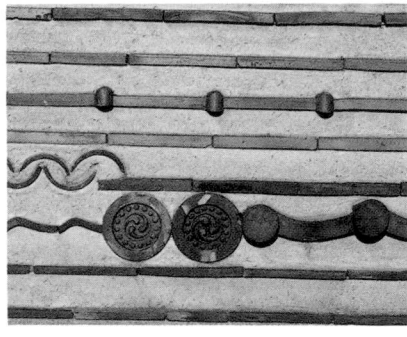

made his pavilion a centre for the refined hobbies to which he was addicted—tea ceremony, painting and flower arrangement—and to his consequent neglect of the affairs of government can be attributed the beginning of his family's fall from power. The Mount-Fuji-shaped sand hill, which is the most striking object in the pavilion's famous garden, has often been praised as an example of Zen artistry and has always struck this observer as supremely silly.

But for the most famous example of Zen artistry in Kyoto one must go to **Ryoanji** Temple, founded in 1473, whose garden of 15 rocks and raked sand has come, perhaps more than any other single work, to symbolize the simplicity and metaphysical profundity to which Zen art aspires, or, more often, professes. Do these rocks 'represent' islands in an ocean? Or mountain peaks above a sea of cloud? Or tigers carrying their cubs across a river? Or are they just boulders scattered randomly about a patch of flat sand which has been raked in a finicky way? The visitor will wish he knew. He may also wish he knew how the monks manage to rake the sand into those circles without leaving footprints. And, if he stays longer than five minutes, he will also wish he knew why a temple whose introductory pamphlet invites visitors to sit down and meditate quietly on the profundities of its garden plays an endless tape-loop of explanatory babble designed to prevent them doing any such thing.

The three decades between the end of the Muromachi period and the beginning of the Edo period (see page 20) form the brief Azuchi-Momoyama period (1568–1600), during which the long era of civil war was gradually forced to a close, and the warring provinces brought to heel, by the unifying policies of two ruthless and powerful warlords, Oda Nobunaga and Toyotomi Hideyoshi. Between them they created the conditions on which Ieyasu could found the strong centralized government of the Tokugawas. Painting and other arts continued to flourish, but the period has not added much to the Kyoto visitor's itinerary. The **Nishi** (West) **Honganji** Temple dates from 1591, and the **Higashi** (East) **Honganji** Temple from 1602. Both are large temples of the 'True Pure Land Sect' founded by Shinran, and are popular with visitors, not so much on account of their intrinsic architectural merits (though Nishi Honganji is highly regarded), but on account of their proximity to Kyoto station.

The chief architectural legacy of the Edo period is secular, not religious. The most accessible example of it is **Nijo Castle**, begun in 1569 by Nobunaga, but much expanded in 1601–3 by Ieyasu, who used it as his Kyoto residence, the first real permanent evidence of the heights of power he had attained. Visitors to Tokyo who were disappointed by the Imperial Palace's lack of glamour may find their disappointment assuaged somewhat by the spacious gardens and interior grandeur of Nijo Castle (Nijo means simply 'Second Avenue', the name of the thoroughfare where it is located), though the exterior is hardly less sombre. An explanatory tape-loop boasts endlessly of the castle's size—33 rooms, 800 tatami mats, 3,300 square metres (3,950 square yards)—and many of its ceilings and panels are decorated with a richness which foreshadows the baroque extravagance that was eventually to dictate the form of the Nikko mausoleum. An interesting architectural innovation is the 'nightingale' floor, constructed so as to emit a low squeaking sound when anyone walks across it. It was designed to afford the shogun's bodyguards warning of the approach of possible intruders and one marvels that it did not drive the permanent staff of the shogun's household completely barmy.

The **Katsura Imperial Villa** (built in 1624) and the **Shugakuin Imperial Villa** (built in 1659) attest to the fine things that emperors could create and inspire when they didn't have to bother themselves with governing. Katsura is famous for the restrained beauty of its architecture and possesses a lovely garden, while Shugakuin, situated on the lowest slopes of Mount Hiei, has an attractive rusticity that must have made it a perfect setting for the tea ceremonies regularly conducted there. These villas are only open to visitors who have made prior application to the Imperial Household Agency, and then only when they consent to be shown round by a talkative official guide. Applications can be made through offices of the Japan Travel Bureau and should be filed at least a week in advance.

Kyoto's most spacious landmark is the **Gosho** (Imperial Palace), originally built here in 1790, destroyed in 1854, rebuilt in 1855. Its outer gardens are always open for the visitor to stroll through, but entrance to the palace itself is subject to the same restrictions as is entrance to the imperial villas (except that applications may be accepted at 24 hours' notice instead of a week's). The palace is the starting point of the procession which forms the basis of the Aoi Matsuri (see page 98) in May.

Kyoto: The Bones

And now, having made the rounds of these monuments, many of them outstandingly beautiful, the visitor may feel compelled to ask in what way they are not the elusively 'real' Kyoto. What is it that they lack? Here, the author falls back, as he warned he would, on personal predilection. They lack little or nothing in terms of material splendour. No temple I am about to mention has a statue that remotely matches in loveliness Koryuji's Miroku Bosatsu. None has a building so striking, and so strikingly filled, as Sanjusangendo. None has the aura of wealth and power that hangs over the Golden and Silver Pavilions or Nijo Castle. None has a view so famous and so wide as that from Kiyomizudera. It follows that, in this author's view at least, the hard-to-define but distinctive Kyoto beauty resides in something other than statuary, striking buildings, wealth and worldly power and

20-year-olds celebrate their coming of age with a shrine visit on Adult's Day (January 15). The arrows are bought for luck.

92

wide-ranging prospects. For statuary and striking buildings, one should really go to Nara; for the display of worldly riches to Nikko; for vast eye-pleasing prospects to the mountains. Kyoto's beauty resides, I think, in a particular kind of atmosphere; in the sensation of uncomplicated peace for which the city was first named.

I have not stressed up to now the *kind* of Buddhism practised in the temples this guide has described because a book of this nature, and of these limitations, is obviously no place for a discourse on the many Buddhist sects and the complexities of their widely differing ideas and practices. Yet, it is impossible to point the visitor toward the particular atmosphere of tranquillity that distinguishes the temples I am now going to recommend he visit without at least attempting to say something about the way in which Zen Buddhism differs from other forms.

Up to the beginning of the Kamakura period Buddhism had developed in a more or less straight line from the esoteric (*mikkyo*) forms introduced from China and Korea. The main Japanese sects, *Shingon* (Koryuji, Ninnaji) and *Tendai* (Kiyomizudera, Sanjusangendo) based their worship mainly on complex rituals and on the teachings found in the ancient mandalas and sutras, teachings to which secret or semi-secret formulas were sometimes believed to hold the key. The founding of the purely Japanese schools of Buddhism during the Kamakura period can be seen as a populist reaction against the entrenched mysticism of this earliest kind of Buddhism. The new sects maintained that a knowledge of esoteric formulas was unnecessary, and that the unlettered had as much chance of achieving everlasting peace in the Buddha's 'Western Paradise' as did the most learned and deeply initiated among the clergy, merely through the profession of faith. This profession might take the form of simple prayers or the repetition of the Buddha's name, comparable to the Pater Nosters and Ave Marias of Catholicism. The notion of 'salvation' fostered by these sects is also akin to the Christian notion of Heaven, and the Buddha and his incarnations came to be regarded as 'saviours', shouldering the responsibility for dragging mankind out of sin and propelling him into paradise on the strength of 'I believe'.

Zen, introduced from China, proposed a completely different view of man's place and destiny. No supernatural intervention was going to 'save' man; indeed 'salvation', in the sense of admission to a happy afterlife, was not man's chief object. His object was present enlightenment (*satori*), which was obtainable only through discipline of body and mind, a discipline for which he was himself wholly responsible. Through enlightenment man would come to understand the nature of existence and his relationship with all else that lived or was inanimate. He would lose his ego — that most damaging commodity which kept him from a knowledge and enjoyment of true peace— and see that in his insignificance still dwelt the essential Buddha-nature. Man himself is Buddha. Hence Zen's overriding concern with the here-and-now,

with the transient present, not some dreamed-of future glory. Enlightenment does not lurk behind pearly gates. Like Kyoto's elusive beauty, it must be actively sought for—in a rice field, on a mountain top, in a freezing cold temple corridor. 'The truth is everywhere. The truth is where we are,' wrote Dogen, the founder of the Soto sect of Zen. 'One step separates earth from heaven.'

Though Chinese in origin, the Zen teachings achieved their finest and most lasting fruits in Japan. Among these fruits is the distinctive atmosphere of peace and simplicity that pervades Kyoto's Rinzai Zen temples, and is, I believe, directly related to Zen's reverence for the here-and-now, and not for subservience to, or ultimate union with, a godhead that moves in mysterious ways. The two main Japanese Zen sects, Rinzai and Soto, differ in the kinds of discipline they encourage, but are united in their determination to remove the barriers of mind that keep man from his potential enlightenment. The oneness of the human and the natural (a quality seen by many as a prerequisite for 'Japaneseness' in the arts) is the mainstay of the unassuming beauty that characterizes these temples and that clearly differentiates them from, say, the great religious buildings of Nara. You could remove all the natural objects—rocks and trees and moss—from the vicinity of almost any of the great law-preserving temples in Nara, or from Sanjusangendo or Kiyomizudera for that matter, and the places would still be awesome and grand. But if you removed those links with nature from the compounds of Daitokuji or Myoshinji or Saihoji, you would strike at their very essence.

If the visitor has been to see all of the sights mentioned in the previous section, he has already visited three Rinzai Zen Temples: Kinkakuji, Ginkakuji and Ryoanji. **Daitokuji** (founded in 1324) and **Myoshinji** (founded in 1337) are the largest Rinzai Zen centres in Kyoto, but they differ from those of the first section in two important ways. First, they are not single temples as Ryoanji is, but large clusters of smaller temples, each jealously guarding the sense of privacy which this author at least finds essential to the 'real' Kyoto beauty. Second, they have not opened themselves up to tourism to the extent that those in the first section have. This may sound elitist, but it is possible to argue that the sheer fuss made of, say, Ryoanji's rock-and-sand garden has lessened, rather than heightened, its impact on the viewer. You approach it half expecting a shock of revelation, whereas it would likely impress you far more deeply if you could come on it unawares. In Daitokuji and Myoshinji you can stroll down quiet paths, linger at gates leading to empty temple gardens, and come completely unawares on many small corners of private loveliness. Most of the temples within the complexes are not open to the public. Those that are open include, in Daitokuji, the **Daisenin**, also famous for its rock-and-sand garden, the **Hoshunin, Sangenin, Ryogenin, Zuihoin, Kotoin** and **Obaiin**, and, in Myoshinji, the **Taizoin** (the suffixes -*ji* and -*in* both mean 'temple', -*in* usually denoting a smallness of scale).

Saihoji, another Rinzai Zen temple, founded in 1339, is sometimes called **Kokedera** (Moss Temple) on account of its spacious garden lushly carpeted with various species of moss. Until 1977 admission to this temple was unrestricted, with the result that large crowds of trampling sightseers began seriously to endanger the very sight for which the temple was famous. Admission is now only granted to visitors with prior permission. There is a waiting list and the number of visitors per day is strictly limited. If you are lucky enough to obtain permission, you will be doubly lucky if it has rained shortly before—or even during—your visit since, after a rain, the moss is at its most luminescent.

It would, of course, be wrong to suggest that early 14th-century Rinzai Zen Temples have a complete monopoly on peace and solitude. Kyoto has other quiet corners where these qualities may be found and enjoyed. If the visitor has devoted most of a day—as he surely should—to Daitokuji, Myoshinji and (with luck) Saihoji, he might end it by relaxing for an hour at the **Shisendo** hermitage, an unassuming little retreat built in 1631 by the poet Ishikawa Jozan, and the possessor of a carefully tended garden on the edge of wild woodland.

A second day could profitably be spent in the **Arashiyama** area of western Kyoto, beginning at the Heian-period temple of **Daikakuji**, formerly a villa belonging to the Emperor Saga who retired there in 823. Emperor Saga was a poet by inclination and hobby, and he so preferred this outlying rural suburb (called Saga) to the capital's bustling centre that he took it for his posthumous name. Daikakuji reminds one a little of Ninnaji, with its maze of covered walkways and corridors but, unlike the raked bare spaces at Ninnaji, the spaces between the walkways at Daikakuji are crowded with overgrown plant-life, reminders of its location in the rural wilds. The temple overlooks a small lake.

Strolling toward the Rinzai Zen complex of **Tenryuji**, founded in 1340, the visitor can turn right just before he reaches it to begin a walk that will take him along narrow rural lanes to several small, comparatively secluded temples. First, he comes to the tiny cottage where the 17th-century poet Kyorai lived, and where he will find the poet's grave. Further on stands the steep hilly Muromachi-period temple of **Jojakkoji**, further still the Kamakura-period **Nisonin** and, finally, at the end of the visitor's stroll, the tiny but lovely Heian-period thatch-roofed temple of **Gioji**, named after the Lady Gio who was loved in her youth by the great Heike leader, Taira no Kiyomori, and who in later life became a nun and spent her last days in this tranquil spot at the foot of Mount Atago.

At least part of a third day can be spent in the northeastern suburb of **Ohara**, where the two chief attractions are both Heian-period temples. The larger is the **Sanzenin**. The smaller, and more poignantly connected, is the

98

*(Preceding page) The garden of the Jakkoin nunnery,
Ohara, Kyoto. Bone-penetrating peace.*

little nunnery called **Jakkoin**, famous as the retreat of Kenreimonin, the daughter of Kiyomori and mother of the eight-year-old Emperor Antoku,who plunged into the sea with her son when defeat for the Heike became certain at the climax of the decisive sea battle of Dannoura in 1185. Antoku was drowned, but Kenreimonin was rescued by her enemies and ended her days here, a nun. It is hard to imagine a more perfectly peaceful place to spend the last years of one's life, away from the clamour of court and war. Like Gioji, the Jakkoin possesses everything implied by the 'real' Kyoto beauty— privacy, tranquillity, and the unmistakable note of sadness which comes with the realization that such places are so lovely because they are so few.

The visitor can easily combine a trip to Ohara with an excursion to Mount Hiei and the Enryakuji Temple complex (see page 102).

Festive Kyoto

I have said nothing at all about Kyoto's thriving modernity, because I have assumed that it will not be what the visitor is primarily looking for. But Kyoto is a bustling, fashion-conscious city with its own subway, major department stores and well-known shopping street (**Kawaramachi**). For night life, the small streets behind the Kawaramachi-Shijo (Fourth Avenue) intersection offer the most interesting possibilities. The **Minamiza**, Kyoto's Kabuki theatre, is located near Shijo station. Running north to south between Shijo and Sanjo (Third Avenue) is the narrow street called **Pontocho**, famous in the past—and lingeringly today—for its ultra-sophisticated geisha clubs and restaurants. These line the alley, unassuming almost to the point of invisibility, behind their opaque slatted windows, guarded by exquisitely refined, unforgiving, unbudgeable matrons who, unless the visitor has been invited by a very rich and very trusted client, will not allow him to cross the the threshold for love—or, even, for money.

The principal festivals in Kyoto are, on 15 May the **Aoi** (Hollyhock) **Matsuri**; in July the **Gion Matsuri**; and on 22 October the **Jidai Matsuri** (Festival of the Ages). The first and last of these are mainly spectator-oriented costume parades. The Aoi Matsuri (dating from the sixth century and thought by some to be the oldest festival in the world) begins at the Gosho and proceeds to the two Kamo Shrines (**Shimogamo Jinja** and **Kamigamo Jinja**) where an imperial messenger presents a sacred horse. The participants wear costumes modelled on those of the Heian period, and the event commemorates the successful attempt by Emperor Kinmei in 553 to placate the local gods who had grown impatient at the impiety of the people (or, more likely, their espousal of Buddhism) and were flooding the area with violent storms. The Gion Matsuri dates from the ninth century and commemorates the end of the great plague of 869. Large floats topped with halberds (symbolizing protection) process through the city, culminating in a parade on 17 July. The Jidai Matsuri had its origin in the same tide of 19th-century bureaucratic enthusiasm that gave birth to the Heian Shrine. Participants wear costumes modelled on those of the various ages of Kyoto's history, from Heian to Meiji, and march to the Gosho from the Heian Shrine. On the same night (22 October) the little village of **Kurama**, some 12 kilometres (7 miles) north of Kyoto and easily reached on the Keifuku Line, celebrates a spectacular fire festival, the *Kurama no Hi Matsuri,* in which participants carry huge pine torches through the little streets of the village and drag them, as they disintegrate dangerously, up the steps of the village shrine. The torches, like the Gion halberds, are symbols of the gods' protective favours, though at the festival's climax they are so boisterously handled that one wonders how the village survives its own protection.

In Kyoto Prefecture

In the city of **Uji** (population 153,000), about 12 kilometres (7.5 miles) south of Kyoto, stands the **Byodoin** Temple, originally a private villa of the Fujiwara family, which became a temple in 1052. The main hall is known as the 'Hall of the Phoenix' both because of the shape of the whole structure, like a bird with outspread wings, and because of the bronze ornaments that top it. It is regarded as the finest example of Heian temple architecture to remain standing in its original state.

Otherwise, the principal sightseeing attraction in Kyoto, outside the prefectural capital, is located on the Japan Sea coast. This is the sand bar, a little over 3 kilometres (1.8 miles) in length, which stretches across the **Bay of Miyazu** and is called **Amanohashidate** (The Floating Bridge of Heaven). The Japanese love to arrange things—their natural wonders included—in categories that reflect a strict hierarchical order, and Amanohashidate has gone down in the ledgers as one of the 'Three Most Beautiful Scenic Views' in the country. (For the other two, see Matsushima on page 120 and Miyajima on page 160.) One can walk the length of the sand bar, pleasantly wooded with pine trees, or take a sightseeing cruise around it. But, traditionally, the finest view of it is obtained from the heights of **Kasamatsu Park** on the northern side of the bay, where visitors stand on one of three small stone benches with their backs to the sand bar, bend down and look at it through their open legs. This curious method of looking at a landscape is said to create in the viewer the impression that the bridge is truly floating in space. It is also likely to create in the foreign visitor not forewarned of the custom the impression that he has wandered unawares into the grounds of the prefectural mental asylum.

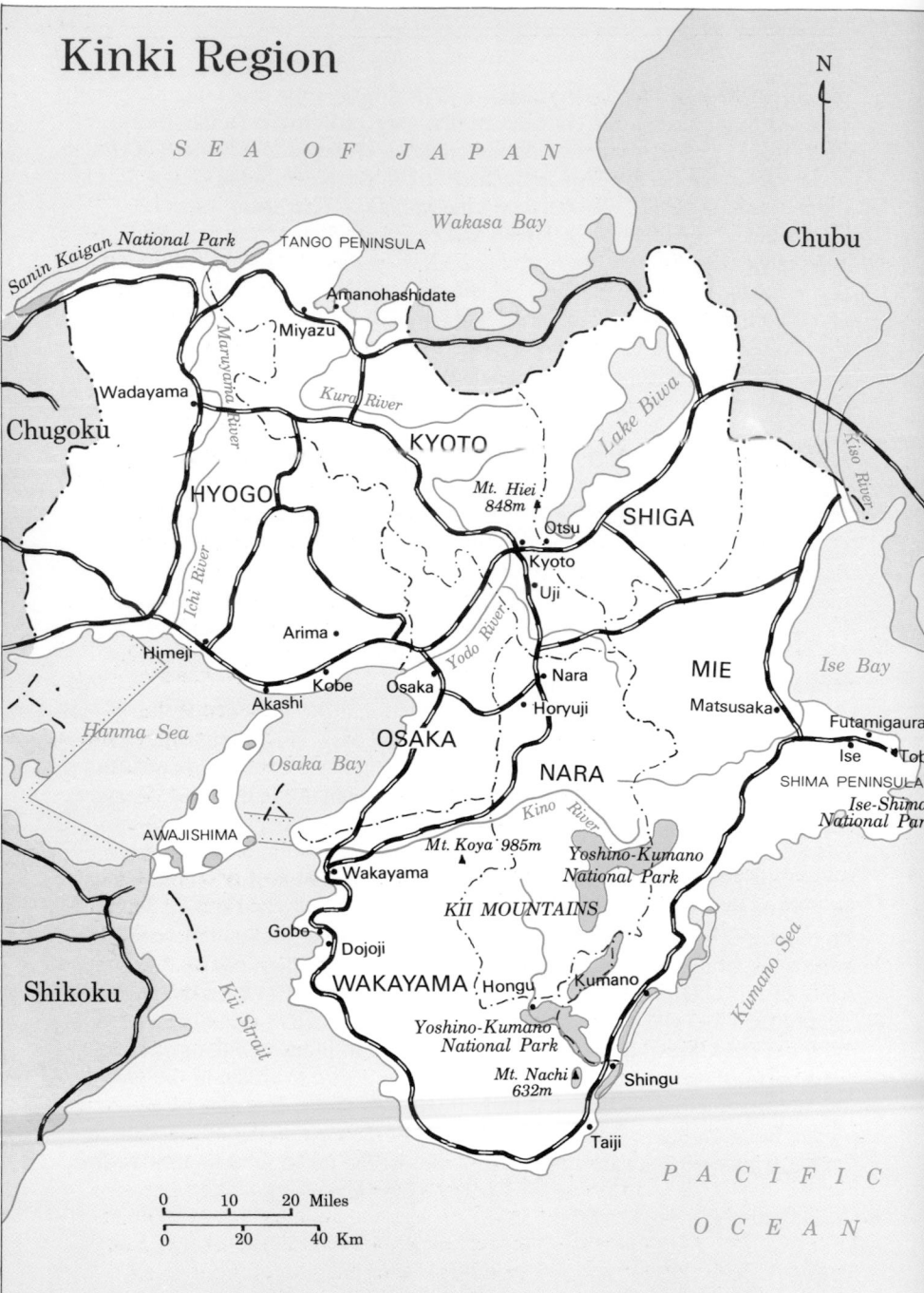

Kinki Region

N

SEA OF JAPAN

Wakasa Bay

Chubu

Sanin Kaigan National Park

TANGO PENINSULA

Amanohashidate

Miyazu

Maruyama River

Kura River

Wadayama

KYOTO

Lake Biwa

Kiso River

Chugoku

HYOGO

Mt. Hiei
848m

Otsu

SHIGA

Kyoto

Uji

Ichi River

Arima

Yodo River

MIE

Ise Bay

Himeji

Kobe

Osaka

Nara

Akashi

Harima Sea

Horyuji

Matsusaka

Futamigaura

OSAKA

Ise

Tob

Osaka Bay

NARA

SHIMA PENINSULA

*Ise-Shima
National Par*

AWAJISHIMA

Mt. Koya 985m

*Yoshino-Kumano
National Park*

Wakayama

Kino River

Kumano Sea

KII MOUNTAINS

Shikoku

Gobe

Dojoji

WAKAYAMA   Hongu

Kumano

Kii Strait

*Yoshino-Kumano
National Park*

Mt. Nachi
632m

Shingu

Taiji

PACIFIC

OCEAN

0   10   20 Miles
0   20   40 Km

The Rest of the Kinki Region

Osaka (population 2.7 million) was the site of the 1970 World Exposition, an event that, together with the 1964 Tokyo Olympics, catapulted Japan onto the modern international stage and squarely into the modern preoccupation with being 'truly international' that has plagued the country ever since. At the time of Expo '70, Osaka was the second largest city in Japan, and it is now the third, having been topped by Yokohama. It is an almost exclusively, and exhaustingly, commercial city, its hotels and public buildings geared for conferences and trade fairs; and it is hard to know what the uncommercial visitor might do there, apart from spend his entire time crawling between the thousands of bars that crowd the city's southern quarter. He could go to see the reconstructed ferroconcrete seven-storey **Osaka Castle**, the original of which was subjected to a famous siege by Ieyasu in 1615, and thus treat himself, perhaps for the first and only time in his life, to the sight of a feudal fortress with elevators. Or he could visit **Shitennoji** Temple, which boasts of being the oldest in Japan, in order to admire the 1950s craftsmanship displayed in its reconstructed buildings. He could shop in the huge intimidating-looking department stores around **Umeda** Station or in the garish underground arcades. If it is 24 or 25 July, he could go to the **Tenmangu Shrine** to find the **Tenjin Matsuri** in full swing—one of Japan's largest merchants' festivals, and a rival in liveliness to Tokyo's Sanja Matsuri. If Bunraku puppet plays are scheduled for performance at the **National Bunraku Theatre** of Osaka, he could take the opportunity to witness this unique form of theatre—the elevation of *waza* (skill) and *kata* (form) above all considerations of content and meaning. Or, at the misnamed **Shin-Kabukiza** (New Kabuki theatre), he could sample Osaka's other major contribution to theatrical art, *manzai*—quick-fire verbal comedy routines usually performed in screeching voices by teams of two comedians dressed in loud check jackets. Then, his throat dry from vicarious screeching, he could stroll through **Dotonbori**, the city's major nightlife area, and wash some of the dust and carbon monoxide, at least temporarily, out of his throat.

Osaka's chief contribution to Japanese life has been the unapologetic, cut-throat mercantile instinct. To the T.V. generation the city has also contributed an aggressively blunt style of speech and behaviour, which some profess to find endearing. Osakans specialize in calling a spade a spade. Tokyo bureaucrats are more likely to call a spade an item of Earth-Realigning Equipment. The citizens of Kyoto would likely call one an Honourable Moon-in-the-Water-Stirring Altering-of-the-Ineffable-Landscape Device. No two neighbouring cities could offer a greater contrast in the mechanics of voice production than do Kyoto and Osaka—the cultivated, gently sibilant, birdlike tones of Kyoto, where the men all sound disturbingly like women, and the throaty chin-thrusting rasps of Osaka, where a lot of the women sound disturbingly like men and the men sound like bulldozers.

The rivalry between Osaka–Kobe, the commercial and industrial heartland of the Kansa, and Tokyo–Yokohama, the equivalent in the Kanto, is deeply entrenched, and has been intensified by Osaka's yielding second-city status to Yokohama. A large new airport is being constructed on a man-made island in Osaka Bay, and this could help nudge the pendulum back west. In the meantime, unless the visitor is studying the economic implications of tonsillitis, he is probably better off elsewhere.

About a fifth of the total area of **Shiga** prefecture is occupied by Japan's largest lake, **Lake Biwa**, named, because of a faint similarity in shape, after the ancient lute-like instrument called the *biwa* (see page 132). Like anything statistically outstanding (largest, longest, oldest and so on), Lake Biwa has attracted the scrutiny of ledger-compiling bureaucrats. Those of the 15th century were responsible for designating eight points around the lake's shoreline the 'Eight Beautiful Views of Omi' (Omi is an old name for the locality), while those of the 20th century, with a bravado typical of the period of postwar optimism, named the entire area a 'Quasi-National Park' (*Kokutei-koen*, as opposed to *Kokuritsu-koen*, 'National Park'). For meaningful differences between National Parks and Quasi-National Parks, consult your nearest town hall official. Those interested in putting the aesthetic sensibilities of the bureaucratic mind to the test will want to know that the 'Eight Beautiful Views of Omi' were: Mount Hira, Katata, Karasaki, Miidera Temple, Awazu, Seta, Ishiyama and Yabase. The southern end of the lake is very tourist-oriented, with boat trips and other activities centering on **Otsu** (population 215,000), the prefectural capital. The west shore is less developed, but served by both trains and sightseeing buses. **Hikone**, on the east shore, has a well-preserved early 17th-century castle.

On the border between Shiga and Kyoto prefectures lies **Mount Hiei**, easily accessible from Kyoto via cable car and the Eizan Line of the Keifuku Railway. On the heights of the mountain, just on the Shiga side, stands the **Enryakuji Temple** complex, which predates Kyoto by six years, having been founded here in 788. It is a sprawling set of impressive buildings joined by pleasant hilltop walks. The monks of Enryakuji were notoriously bellicose, making frequent armed forays into Kyoto until as late as the 16th century, at which time the entire temple complex was destroyed by the powerful warlord Oda Nobunaga. Most of the present buildings are thus of comparatively recent date.

The names of certain of the cities and rural areas of Mie prefecture have become household words because of the particular industries that have grown up in them. **Yokkaichi**'s petrochemical complexes will not long detain the visitor, but **Matsusaka**'s beer-fed cattle produce some of the finest and most expensive meat in the country, so Matsusaka beef has become synonymous with gourmet eating and extravagant household spending. Further south, among the intricate fjords of **Ago Bay**, the visitor will find himself at the centre of Japan's cultured pearl industry, pioneered by Kokichi Mikimoto at the turn of the last century. Some 1,000 tons of cultured pearls are now produced here annually. Long before Mikimoto, the warmish, shallow sea around the **Shima Peninsula** provided an ideal theatre of operations for Japan's famous white-clad *ama* (women divers), who can still sometimes be seen operating from boats in which their husbands lounge chain-smoking. Their principal prey is agar-agar, *wakame* (a species of seaweed) and, occasionally, abalone and lobster, depending on the season. It was these ideal conditions that Mikimoto exploited and, today, the chief monuments to his success stand some 20 kilometres (12.5 miles) north of the bay in the small city of **Toba** (population 29,000), where there is a Mikimoto Museum and, on **Pearl Island** in the city's harbour, a model pearl farm open to visitors, who have included Queen Elizabeth II of Great Britain. The coast west of Ago Bay is pleasantly unspoiled.

But not all the cultured pearls, beef steaks and women divers in the world should keep the visitor from what must be his chief destination in Mie prefecture—**Ise Jingu**, The Grand Shrine of Ise, the most revered Shinto shrine in Japan and an object of pilgrimage for people from all over the country, regardless of wealth or class, for some 1,300 years. Even during the later feudal period (when the shogun's efficient police made unrestricted travel an impossibility for the aristocracy, let alone for the rigidly controlled lower classes), a farmer or an artisan might still hope to visit Ise once before he died—the only decent break from labour he would ever know; the journey of a lifetime.

To see Ise after seeing the Toshogu Shrine at Nikko is like clawing one's way out of a bath of lukewarm treacle and plunging naked into a pool of clear, cold water. Ise Jingu stands in a forest of cedar trees, and has two chief centres, or compounds, the Inner (**Naiku**) and Outer (**Geku**) shrines, about six kilometres (3.7 miles) apart. The first is dedicated to the Sun Goddess, Amaterasu Omikami, the second to the God of Plenty. The most reliable estimates of when the shrines were founded date the Inner to the fourth century and the Outer toward the end of the fifth. The Inner Shrine is the more revered since it houses the sacred Mirror (a part of the imperial regalia consisting of Mirror, Sword and Jewel) which, according to legend, was brought down to earth by the Sun Goddess's grandson. Many shrines throughout Japan house mirrors, and this is their great archetype. The visitor will not see it. In fact, he will be hard put to crane his neck to glimpse the building that houses it. Whether he is Japanese or foreign, aristocrat or artisan, he will not (unless he is a member of, or emissary from, the imperial family) be permitted closer than the outermost of the four wooden fences that surround and protect each of the two main compounds. The mystery is all.

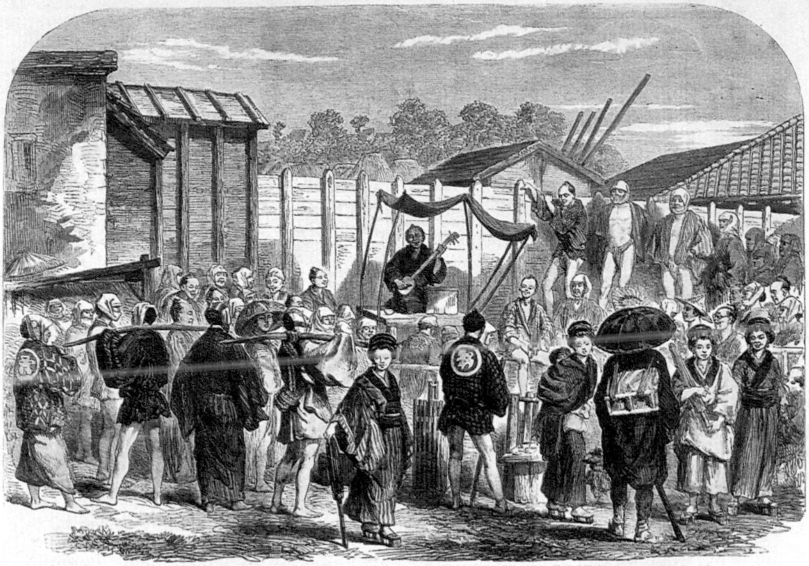

SKETCHES IN JAPAN BY OUR SPECIAL ARTIST THE STORYTELLER (A DAILY SCENE) IN YOKOHAMA.

SKETCHES FROM JAPAN: TRAVELLING IN THE KAGO.

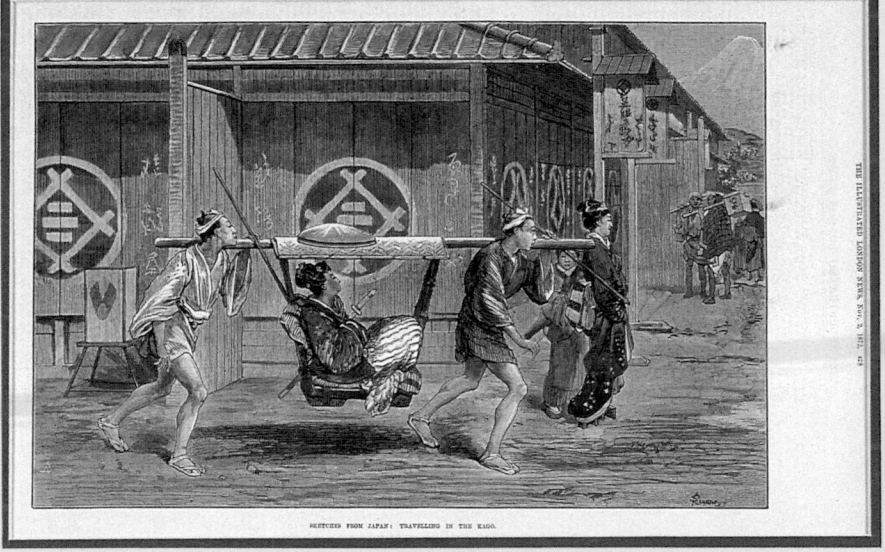

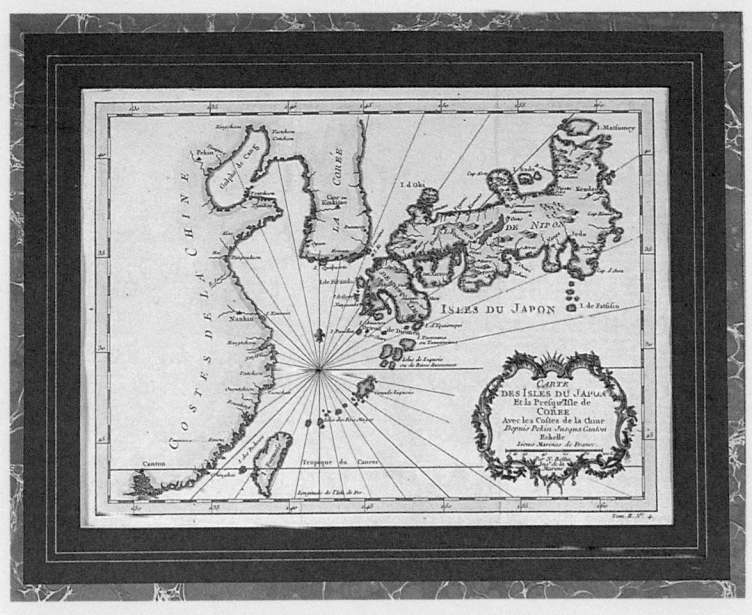

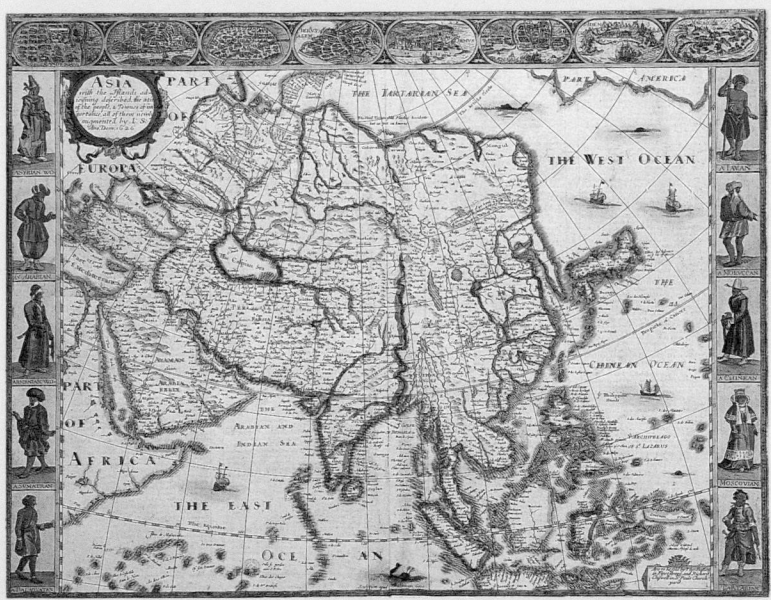

Without the mystery the gods crumple, the legends turn to ash in the mouth, Japan descends to the unspeakable level of a merely human-founded nation, like any other.

And yet perhaps the mystery is not quite all, for there is a pleasing uncluttered external purity about the structures themselves, even the vision-impeding fences. 'Mystery' in connection with religious buildings conjures up, maybe, in the minds of most Westerners, an image of deep crypts or dark gargoyled corners. But Ise is all light and air and plain, unpainted cypress wood, doweled and jointed in the oldest style known, without the use of nails.

For the foreign visitor, the deepest mystery surrounding Ise may well lie in the remarkable fact that, every 20 years, both the Inner and Outer shrines are completely demolished and rebuilt in exactly the same manner and proportions on the adjacent sites that until then have stood empty save for one small structure that houses the base of the 'heart pillar', said to date from the shrines' founding, and which is incorporated into each rebuilding in order to emphasize the continuity of spirit. The practice of demolishing and rebuilding shrines every 20 years was mentioned earlier in connection with the Kasuga Shrine in Nara (see page 73), where it has been discontinued. It survives famously at Ise, and it would be hard to think of a more perfect symbol for the alliance of continuity and novelty that has characterized the progress of Japanese tradition through the centuries. At each rebuilding (the last was completed in 1973), the old shrine structures offer models for the new, the new are fresh reworkings of the old, and the whole costly, time-consuming practice testifies not only to the survival of extraordinary practical skills but of the impulse that first led to the enshrinement of the Sun Goddess's mirror. More than in a merely old building one feels, if one is Japanese, the rekindling of the ancient pride in being a race set apart, a pride that the disasters of war and defeat have done little to diminish. Besides which, the repeated rebuildings offer this lesson to the foreign visitor, equally pertinent when viewing other famous monuments in Japan: that 'age' may be less a matter of years marching by than of the atmosphere and associations that the marching years carry with them.

On the coast just outside the city of Ise, at **Futamigaura**, stand the often photographed **Meoto Iwa** (Wedded Rocks). These are two naturally occuring offshore rocks that have been joined together by a straw rope and signposted as holy by the construction of a small *torii* gate. Their holiness derives partly from the idea that they represent the god Izanagi and the goddess Izanami, the mythical creators of the Japanese islands, but more especially from the animistic impulse which imbues all nature with a sentient and sacred spirit.

The **Kii Peninsula** is made up of the three prefectures of Nara, Mie and

Wakayama, in the southern half of which, straddling the border with Mie, is the area called **Kumano**, part of the Yoshino-Kumano National Park. This area has long been regarded as the abode of a multitude of gods, and its three major shrines, known collectively as the **Kumano Shrines**, are located at **Nachi, Hongu** and **Shingu**. These shrines differ in purpose and in atmosphere from Ise Jingu, for they do not so much enshrine an idea (the special origin and descent of the Japanese race) as point up the sacredness of the land that surrounds them. It is not in the shrine structures that the gods necessarily dwell, but in the hills and waterfalls of the countryside where they stand. Waterfalls are traditionally associated both with Shinto (as favourite habitations of the gods) and with Buddhism (as the haunts of hermits and ascetics who discipline their minds and bodies by standing stock still underneath them while the torrent thumps down on their heads). Nachi has one of the highest waterfalls in Japan (130 metres or 426 feet), as well as many picturesque smaller ones.

The visitor to Wakayama prefecture will find it quite hard to avoid places of religious significance, since there are so many. **Mount Koya**, most easily accessible from Osaka, has a celebrated monastery founded in 816 by the great Shingon priest Kukai, better known by his posthumous name of Kobo Daishi. Kukai was easily the busiest founder of Buddhist temples in Japan's history and many of the temples he founded are still the objects of very active pilgrimages (in particular the 88 temples of Shikoku—see page 174). The monastery on Mount Koya is vast and sprawling, not unlike the Enryakuji complex on Mount Hiei (see page 102), and among the most important focuses of interest is Kukai's own burial place.

Near the little city of **Gobo** (population 30,000) stands the small temple of **Dojoji**, founded in 701 and famous as the site of a lovers' reunion so gruesomely striking that it has been turned into one of the most popular plays in both the Noh and Kabuki repertoires. On his way to visit the Kumano Shrines, a young Buddhist monk stayed at a house where the owner's daughter fell madly in love with him. Desperate to free himself from her clutches, the monk promised her that he would visit the house again on his return from Kumano, but in fact returned by another route, whereupon the young woman set out in pursuit of him. Soon, the woman's frustrated passion changed her into a fire-breathing serpent and, in terror of his life, the monk begged the priests of Dojoji to hide him under their bronze bell. But the woman-serpent divined his hiding place and curled herself round the bell, making it glow red hot, so that, by the time she had vanished and the priests eventually raised the bell, nothing remained of her lover but his charred bones. In the Noh play, it is the serpent herself who emerges from under the bell when it is raised, while the Kabuki dance-play *Musume-Dojoji* ends with her poised triumphantly on the bell's top, a grim symbol of the unquenchable fire of female determination.

Nocturnal Tryst

enji slipped the latch open and tried the doors. They had not been bolted. A curtain had been set up just inside, and in the dim light he could make out Chinese chests and other furniture scattered in some disorder. He made his way through to her side. She lay by herself, a slight little figure. Though vaguely annoyed at being disturbed, she evidently took him for the woman Chūjō until he pulled back the covers.

"I heard you summoning a captain," he said, "and I thought my prayers over the months had been answered."

She gave a little gasp. It was muffled by the bedclothes and no one else heard.

"You are perfectly correct if you think me unable to control myself. But I wish you to know that I have been thinking of you for a very long time. And the fact that I have finally found my opportunity and am taking advantage of it should show that my feelings are by no means shallow."

His manner was so gently persuasive that devils and demons could not have gainsaid him. The lady would have liked to announce to the world that a strange man had invaded her boudoir.

"I think you have mistaken me for someone else," she said, outraged, though the remark was under her breath.

The little figure, pathetically fragile and as if on the point of expiring from the shock, seemed to him very beautiful.

"I am driven by thoughts so powerful that a mistake is completely out of the question. It is cruel of you to pretend otherwise. I promise you that I will do nothing unseemly. I must ask you to listen to a little of what is on my mind."

She was so small that he lifted her easily. As he passed through the doors to his own room, he came upon the Chūjō who had been summoned earlier. He called out in surprise. Surprised in turn,

Chūjō peered into the darkness. The perfume that came from his robes like a cloud of smoke told her who he was. She stood in confusion, unable to speak.

She followed after, but Genji was quite unmoved by her pleas.

"Come for her in the morning," he said, sliding the doors closed.

The lady was bathed in perspiration and quite beside herself at the thought of what Chūjō, and the others too, would be thinking. Genji had to feel sorry for her. Yet the sweet words poured forth, the whole gamut of pretty devices for making a woman surrender.

She was not to be placated. "Can it be true? Can I be asked to believe that you are not making fun of me? Women of low estate should have husbands of low estate."

He was sorry for her and somewhat ashamed of himself, but his answer was careful and sober. "You take me for one of the young profligates you see around? I must protest. I am very young and know nothing of the estates which concern you so. You have heard of me, surely, and you must know that I do not go in for adventures. I must ask what unhappy entanglement imposes this upon me. You are making a fool of me, and nothing should surprise me, not even the tumultuous emotions that do in fact surprise me."

But now his very splendor made her resist. He might think her obstinate and insensitive, but her unfriendliness must make him dismiss her from further consideration. Naturally soft and pliant, she was suddenly firm. It was as with the young bamboo: she bent but was not to be broken. She was weeping. He had his hands full but would not for the world have missed the experience.

"If I had met you before I came to this," she replied, and he had to admit the truth of it, "then I might have consoled myself with the thought—it might have been no more than self-deception, of course—that you would someday come to think fondly on me. But this is hopeless, worse than I can tell you. Well, it has happened. Say no to those who ask if you have seen me."

One may imagine that he found many kind promises with which to comfort her.

Murasaki Shikibu, The Tale of Genji
translated by Edward G Seidensticker

Near the tip of the Kii peninsula is the small town of **Taiji**, once the main centre of Japan's whaling industry, now driven on hard times by the international outcry against whaling and by the pressure on Japan to accept an internationally agreed moratorium—developments which have left some of the inhabitants of Taiji openly bitter.

The prefectural captial of **Hyogo** is **Kobe** (population 1.4 million), which ranks with Yokohama as one of Japan's two main 'cosmopolitan' port cities. In point of fact, Kobe accounts for the larger volume of foreign cargo (160 million tons per year), but it was opened to international commerce several years later than Yokohama, in 1867, so arguments about which is the 'senior' of the two ports rebound against each other. Kobe is certainly the pleasanter city for the casual visitor, sandwiched as it is between the sea and green hills, the summit of one of which (**Mount Rokko**) can be reached by cable car. Like Yokohama, Kobe is known for its foreign community and for the restaurants this community has established. In Yokohama the best foreign restaurants are Chinese; in Kobe they are Indian, although Kobe beef is famous among steak lovers (the beef of Matsusaka—see page 102—is more often used in *sukiyaki*). In 1981 a six-month international exposition called 'Portopia' was held on a man-made island in Kobe Bay. The island is now a residential and recreation centre. On the other side of Mount Rokko lies the overdeveloped hot-spring resort of **Arima**, popular with residents of Osaka and Kobe, two cities that share with Tokyo and Yokohama the dubious distinction of being so sprawlingly built up that it is impossible to tell from the window of a train or bus where one begins and the other ends.

Some 50 kilometres (31 miles) west of Kobe lies the city of **Himeji** (population 446,000), whose famous castle, built in 1581 by Hideyoshi and enlarged in the early 17th century, is widely regarded as the most elegant feudal fortress in Japan. It is also one of the very few not to have been destroyed and rebuilt in modern times, though it was extensively repaired in the 1950s and '60s, which is why it looks so pristine.

Between Kobe and Himeji is the city of **Akashi** (population 255,000), from where the **Akashi Kaikyo Ohashi** (Great Bridge Across the Akashi Strait) will soon transport the visitor to the island of Awajishima without his needing to take the ferry. When it is completed, the bridge will be the longest suspension bridge in the world, unless, in the meantime, some Korean construction company erects a longer one elsewhere, as happened at Penang to the chagrin of the Japanese, who had previously possessed in the Kanmon Bridge (see page 163) the longest suspension bridge in the Orient. Eventually, Japanese bureaucrats will probably draw up a hierarchical list of the 'Three Most Beautiful Suspension Bridges' and their 'Eight Most Scenic Struts'. The other end of Awajishima will soon be joined to Shikoku by a Great Bridge Across the Naruto Strait, all of this bridge-building having been spawned by former Prime Minister Tanaka's grandiose scheme to 'remodel the Japanese archipelago'.

Awajishima itself (population 170,000) is a flattish, mainly agricultural island (except for the highway built to convey motorists rushing between bridges) and is well known for a rural form of Bunraku puppet theatre. How long its comparatively unspoiled state (and its puppet theatre) will survive the remodelling of the archipelago remains to be seen since plans are already well advanced to turn more than 20 percent of the island into a holiday resort.

Hyogo is one of only three prefectures to span the entire width of Honshu and, although most of its population and chief centres of tourism are crowded along its southern coast, it offers a particularly wide variety of landscape: from the industrialized belt that hems the Inland Sea, through steep mountains and small out-of-the-way village communities in the interior, to its rugged and beautiful northern coastline, the entire length of which is a part of the **Sanin Kaigan National Park** (see also page 168).

Tohoku Region

The Tohoku Region

Homely Wilds

When, in Japanese gangster films, people flee from the vengeance of their bosses or from rival gangs, they invariably head north into the tangled safety of the Tohoku region. When Yoshitsune fled from his brother Yoritomo's attempts to have him assassinated in 1187, it was north into the Tohoku wilds that he fled. When salarymen sit in karaoke bars singing ballads about mournful, windy places to breathless Osaka bar girls, it is often of Tohoku that they sing. And when the newly urbanized Japanese find themselves pining for the old rural ways, for a simpler, uncluttered, more truly 'Japanese' style of life, it is often Tohoku that springs to their minds. In recent years the Tohoku region has become the paradigm of what the Japanese call *furusato*, a word that means literally 'old home country', and is used nowadays not only of a person's actual birthplace and the place where he feels his heart to lie, but of a Never-Never-Land where old ladies live in straw-thatched cottages with kettles singing cheerfully on sunken hearths, where their sons are charcoal burners, their daughters pale skinned and lovely as the snow, and every neighbour has a heart of gold and an impenetrably thick accent. If Yamato is the spirit-stirring womb of nationhood, Tohoku is humanity's cradle.

Throughout much of Japanese history, this great, mountainous, northeastern chunk of Honshu was an unpoliced wilderness. Originally, it was the home of the Ainu and other non-Yamato tribes, who, by the close of the ninth century, had either been wiped out or driven from Honshu into the island now called Hokkaido; the victims of a series of genocidal campaigns mounted by the forces of the Yamato, Nara and Kyoto courts. (The word *shogun* is an abbreviation of a longer title, *seiitaishogun*—Great Barbarian-Subduing General—that was first earned in 794, at the height of these campaigns.) But Tohoku's wildness survived the genocide inflicted on its earliest inhabitants. Up to the 19th century the region was not known as Tohoku (East-North), but as *Michinoku* (Beyond the End of the Road). The most famous account of a journey in Japanese literature is the poetic record by the haiku master, Matsuo Basho, of his travels through Tohoku in 1689–91. His book is called *Oku no Hosomichi*, a title that has been translated into English as 'The Narrow Road to the Deep North', but which might more accurately be rendered 'The Narrow Roads at the Back of Beyond'. Even in modern times, a sense of the wilderness persists, and in very modern times has actually intensified. With industrialization, large parts of this still mainly agricultural region have suffered a gradual decline in population as families have left the land that they have farmed, perhaps for centuries, in order to make supposedly more convenient lives for themselves in city offices and factories. Iwate prefecture, for example, has the lowest population density (93 people per square kilometre) of any part of Japan except Hokkaido. Today, the six large prefectures that make up the Tohoku region account in total for only about eight percent of Japan's population, and are among those regularly recording the lowest per capita incomes.

But, for the short-term visitor, Tohoku can be a rich and rewarding experience. It is a region where customs have generally died hard, where local arts and crafts have survived with comparative tenacity or been revived in recent decades, where good, unspoiled hot springs abound, and where the landscape of lakes, rice-plains and mountains has a stirring, rugged grandeur. In winter, the snowfall is fierce and long, especially on the high plateaus and on the Japan Sea side of the mountains. Many smaller roads are closed for the duration of the snows and, when they reopen in April or early May, they must be bulldozed out afresh between towering banks of unthawed ice. Summer is a good time to visit Tohoku, for summer is short there and the inhabitants make the most of it by mounting some of Japan's most spectacular August festivals (see page 121). If the visitor has opted to stay in Western-style hotels during his trips to Tokyo and the Kinki region, he might seize the opportunity Tohoku affords to sample the more traditional hospitality to be found at ryokans and minshukus. Tohoku consists of the six prefectures of **Fukushima, Yamagata, Miyagi, Iwate, Akita** and **Aomori**. Two broad rules of thumb when travelling in the region are: the further north you get the emptier becomes the countryside, the less urbane the people; and the Japan Sea side of the region (the side directly facing Siberia) has a much harsher climate, giving rise to a more arduous lifestyle for the inhabitants, than does the Pacific side. The Pacific side is the more easily accessible via the Tohoku Shinkansen bullet train that joins Tokyo (Ueno) with Sendai and Morioka, and will eventually reach all the way to Aomori and from there, if the newly independent railway companies can scratch together the money, beyond, through the Seikan Tunnel, to Hokkaido. The Pacific side is also the more industrialized and urbanized, the largest and most prosperous city in the Tohoku region being Sendai, the prefectural capital of Miyagi.

Just north of the border between Tochigi and **Fukushima** prefectures, stands the former castle town of **Shirakawa** (population 43,000), near where the shogun's main inland barrier gate between the Kanto and Tohoku regions stood. These gates were a principal means whereby travel could be controlled, taxes levied and road blocks effected. The main purpose of the castle at Shirakawa, one of those belonging to the lords of the region, the Matsudairas, was thus to guard the major artery of transport leading north from Edo.

But the Matsudairas' chief seat of power was **Aizu-Wakamatsu** (present population 115,000). 'Aizu' is the old name for the western part of Fukushima and Aizu-Wakamatsu is the main centre of tourism in the prefecture and a natural starting point for visits to Lake Inawashiro and

Mount Bandai. It is a city of mainly traditional industries, in particular sake-brewing and lacquerware. The castle is known as **Tsurugajo** (Castle of the Crane); the donjon was reconstructed in 1965. The Matsudairas were loyal supporters of the Tokugawa shoguns and some of the bitterest fighting in the campaigns that finally toppled the shogunate, leading to the restoration of power to the Emperor Meiji in 1868, took place in this area. As a result, Aizu-Wakamatsu is somewhat boastful of its samurai heritage, and a large samurai house (*buke-yashiki*) has been renovated in the city and provides a fascinating glimpse of domestic life among the privileged classes in the feudal age. In the nearby museum there is a gruesome display of waxwork models of the women of the clan, all dressed in white, committing gory suicide rather than fall into the hands of the imperial forces.

But the most poignant monument to Aizu's vanished samurai heritage stands on **Iimori Hill** in the western suburbs, approached either via long flights of stone steps or an absurd 'slope conveyor', a large effort-reducing escalator which testifies resoundingly to the decline of samurai vigour. On Iimori Hill stand the graves of 19 young military cadets who committed ritual suicide here after escaping from a rout on the western shore of Lake Inawashiro. They were all between 16 and 17 years old and were members of the 341-strong *Byakkotai* (White Tiger Company), a loyalist unit deployed against the revolutionary army on the rainy afternoon of 22 August 1868. 288 of the company survived the skirmish, 33 died in battle; but none of those have captured the Japanese imagination like the 19 who, seeing smoke pouring out of the Castle of the Crane and believing the battle irrecoverably lost, took their own lives in a last gesture of defiance and despair. Ironically, they were mistaken in their perception of the state of battle. The castle had not fallen, and in fact did not fall until early November. But the rashness and uselessness of their deaths have only increased the aura of glory that surrounds them.

Just outside the city to the southeast lies the hot-spring resort of **Higashiyama**, urban rather than rural, but not yet overdeveloped, so it preserves a degree of old-world charm. Further east is **Lake Inawashiro**, the fourth largest lake in Japan, on the shore of which stands a small museum dedicated to the memory of one of Japan's very few international humanists, Dr Noguchi Hideo. Dr Noguchi spent part of his life in Africa attempting to isolate the virus that causes yellow fever. He succeeded in 1928, but died of the disease two months later in Accra, where, at the University of Ghana, there is a Noguchi Memorial Institute. Dr Noguchi's example of selfless sacrifice is a favourite among publishers of inspirational children's biographies.

To the north of the lake towers **Mount Bandai** (1,819 metres, 5,968 feet), the centre of the southern sector of the **Bandai-Asahi National Park**. Mount Bandai erupted spectacularly in 1888, creating an eerie landscape of pools and lakes on its north slope. The heights offer spectacular views of the surrounding countryside and there are several popular ski resorts in the area. Mount Bandai is one of the many mountains scattered throughout Japan that arc thought in some way to resemble Mount Fuji, and it is thus sometimes called 'Aizu Fuji', though the resemblance clearly lies in the eye of the beholder. Other popular ski grounds are to be found on the slopes of **Mount Azuma** (2,024 metres, 6,640 feet) which lies west of the prefectural capital, Fukushima City.

Near the Pacific coast, the city of **Haramachi** (population 46,000), is held each 23–25 July, Fukushima's best-known festival, the **Soma Nomaoi** (Wild Horse Chase of Soma). Like other parts of the northeast, Fukushima prefecture was originally a famous centre for horse breeding, and this fame is recalled each year in the mounted procession, horse races, herding, and spectacular pitched battle fought by riders in feudal costume for the possession of banners lofted into the air by means of fireworks.

The most notable destinations for visitors to **Yamagata** prefecture are the mountains, in particular the Three Holy Mountains of Dewa (**Dewa Sanzan**), 'Dewa' being an old name for Yamagata and Akita combined. The three mountains are **Gassan** (1,980 metres, 6,496 feet), **Yudono** (1,504 metres, 4,934 feet), which is really an outcrop of Gassan, and **Haguro** (419 metres, 1,376 feet), a foothill north of the main range. Gassan especially is bathed in an aura of chilly mystery, which partly derives from the inclement, misty weather that shrouds its slopes and the snow that survives in patches throughout the year, and partly from the mystic and shamanistic practices of the Shugendo sect of esoteric Buddhism, to which the mountains are sacred. These practices included the occasional mummification of priests (their mummification began while they were still alive, the means being a diet of resinous wood) and mummified remains are still to be found in some of the area's temples, sitting in their robes of office and accepting the suppliance of pilgrims hardy and unblenching enough to pay them a visit. The alliance of early Buddhism with the older forms of shamanism and animistic spiritualism is seen very clearly at certain rural religious sites in Tohoku, particularly here and at Osorezan (see page 131). The summit of Gassan is beyond the scope of an ordinary visitor's itinerary, but Haguro is easily climbed via the two-kilometre (1.25-mile) causeway of stone steps that leads to the Haguro Shrine at the summit, which was founded in the seventh century. In the woods near the foot of the causeway stands a fine 14th-century pagoda. Originally all three of the holy mountains were inhabited by *yamabushi* (mountain-dwelling ascetics), who cultivated mystic powers (mainly that of exorcism, but they could also leap high in the air and walk barefoot over burning coals) and embraced a life of astonishing hardship. Once again, it is worth stressing that the shrines and temple buildings the visitor will see here are more like signposts to the numinous spirit of the mountains themselves than they are the actual 'houses' of gods.

South of Gassan and, like it, a part of the northern sector of the Bandai-Asahi National Park, stands the peak of **Asahi-dake** (1,870 metres, 6,135 feet), the centre of an unspoiled area of alpine woodland.

Another notable mountain religious site in Yamagata (one whose name means simply 'Mountain Temple') is the **Yamadera** complex, not far from the prefectural capital, Yamagata city. As at Haguro, a visit involves a vigorous climb up a narrow causeway, spasmodically paved with chunks of stone. The Buddhism practised at Yamadera is more orthodox than that associated with Gassan and Haguro, since the complex's parent temple is Enryakuji on Mount Hiei (see page 102). But, again, the distribution of buildings over the sides and summit of a spacious hill is partly intended to underscore the numinous nature of the entire area. The temple was founded in 860, 22 years after its Kyoto parent. The main hall on the summit was rebuilt in 1963.

Also near **Yamagata** city (population 237,000) is the small city of **Tendo** (population 53,000), famous among players of *shogi* (Japanese chess) as the principal centre for the manufacture of the wooden pieces used in the game. While the intricate and sometimes highly original design of Western chess pieces has made them popular collectors' items even among non-players, the same fate is hardly likely to overtake the pieces used in *shogi*. The pieces all have the same basic flat five-edged form, are all the same colour (natural wood—this because, unlike in Western chess, an opponent's piece removed from the board can be reused by its captor, so no distinction of colour is possible) and are distinguished from one another only by size and by the (to a novice illegible) ideograms engraved or painted on them. Still, sets of these pieces can vary enormously in price, depending on the quality of the wood and on the skill of the calligrapher. Fans of *shogi* are prone to boast that it is the only traditional board game to have defied computer programming. Computers have become proficient at Western chess and have made considerable progress with *go,* but the almost innumerable permutations that arise out of the reuse of captured *shogi* pieces have so far confined the game to merely human players.

Yamagata city itself is the site of the prefecture's largest and best-known festival, the **Hanagasa Matsuri** (see box on page 121).

In the north of the prefecture, on the coast just below **Mount Chokai** (2,230 metres, 7,316 feet) stands the industrial city of **Sakata** (population 103,000), originally well-known as a centre for rice-distribution and the manufacture of sake. Further up the **Mogami River**, on which Sakata stands, are some fine rapids which visitors can shoot safely in thin craft guided by boatmen who employ the traditional combination of tiller and long punt.

On the border between Yamagata and **Miyagi** prefectures stands **Mount Zao** (1,841 metres, 6,040 feet), a popular playground for skiers. And, toward the coast, at the southern end of the largest plain in Tohoku stands the prefectural capital, **Sendai** (population 665,000), formerly the chief seat of the powerful Date clan, whose most famous son, Masamune, built a castle here in 1602. The castle was known as **Aobajo** (Castle of Green Leaves). It was mostly destroyed during the fighting at the time of the Meiji Restoration, and the surviving structures were completely demolished in the large-scale fire bombing that Sendai suffered during World War II. In fact, much of the city required extensive rebuilding after the war, and its newness, together with its size and commercial stature, helps account for its sense of prosperity and absence of the backwoods feeling that clings to many of Tohoku's cities (it is, for example, the only city in the Tohoku region to posses a subway system). Commercial prosperity is particularly noticeable during Sendai's main annual festival, the **Tanabata Matsur**i, on 6–8 August (see page 121).

Sendai is known for its handicrafts and among the most expensive items available in the city's furniture and woodcraft shops are the heavy wooden chests called *tansu,* old specimens of which have become sought-after collectors' pieces. Far cheaper and more easily portable souvenirs are the folk dolls called *kokeshi,* traditionally made from two spartan pieces of wood, a globe for the head and a cylinder for the body, painted in designs that differ from region to region and from one dollmaker to the next. These dolls are sold throughout Tohoku and a major centre for their production is the city of **Shiroishi** (population 41,000), not far from Mount Zao, which hosts an annual kokeshi fair in early May. Japanese tourists, like foreign visitors, tend to regard kokeshi merely as quaint, curious ornaments to grace a hallstand or a television table, and if you ask a Japanese friend to explain the meaning of the word *kokeshi,* he will probably not be able to do so, nor, despite owning several examples and having bought others as gifts for relatives and friends, will he have given the matter any thought. In fact the original meaning is rendered obscure by the fact that, today, the word is always written in the phonetic *hiragana* syllabary, without the use of potentially revealing ideograms (see page 234). But it is likely that the name derives from *ko,* meaning 'child' and *kesu,* meaning 'to cut off', and that the harmless-looking dolls were originally carved as fetish substitutes for children murdered at birth, a practice that continued in impoverished rural areas into our own century. The popularity of kokeshi among Japanese tourists today is thus an eloquent testimony to the survival of a folk tradition as well as to the modern generation's ignorance of its implications.

The chief tourist attraction in Miyagi prefecture is the bay dotted with some 260 small pine-clad islands at **Matsushima**, 22 kilometres (13.5 miles) northeast of Sendai. Like Amanohashidate (see page 99) and Miyajima (see page 160), Matsushima is one of Japan's 'Three Most Beautiful Scenic

Tohoku's Four Great Summer Festivals

O-Bon is an annual nationwide observance, celebrated privately by placing food and drink on the graves of dead family members, and publicly by dancing to entertain their returned spirits. Summer is a comparatively slack time for rice farmers and O-Bon is traditionally celebrated in the seventh lunar month (giving rise to the spurious but much touted theory that Japanese people tell ghost stories in summer to induce refreshing chills). Since the adoption of the Western calendar, O-Bon has been celebrated in August, the middle of that month usually corresponding quite closely to the old lunar date. It is still the custom among many families for relatives who have moved away to return to the ancestral house for O-Bon, making it not only a festival of the dead and a pre-harvest holiday, but a celebration of *furusato*, one's birthplace and spiritual home.

Among the most spectacular of the August festivals connected with O-Bon are the 'Four Great Festivals of Tohoku': the Sendai *Tanabata*, the Yamagata *Hanagasa*, the Aomori *Nebuta* and the Akita *Kanto*. All take place during the first week of August and are staggered so that travel agents can whisk spectators round all four in as many days.

Tanabata is Chinese in origin and commemorates the yearly meeting of the two stars Altair and Vega, originally a shepherd and a weaver who fell in love and were banished to opposite ends of the Milky Way because their passion got in the way of their industry. Tanabata (formerly celebrated on the seventh night of the seventh lunar month) is observed nationwide on 7 July by decorating bamboo branches with slips of paper bearing wishes. In Sendai Tanabata culminates on 8 August, closer to the old lunar date, and features colourful lanterns and streamers hung in the city's main streets.

The Hanagasa of Yamagata city (usually 6–7 August) is a dance festival in which participants wear sedge hats (*kasa*) decorated with artificial flowers (*hana*). The dancers (up to 10,000 of them) process through the streets of the city as happens also in Tokushima (see page 175), distinguishing them from most Bon dancers whose movements are confined to concentric circles.

The Aomori Nebuta (usually 4–7 August) is a parade of huge sculpted and painted lanterns (*nebuta*) shaped like warriors, wrestlers, horses and other figures. It has been suggested that the prototypes of these lanterns were invented by a crafty Yamato general to frighten the barbaric tribes he was fighting. Lanterns of one kind or another figure large in O-Bon, where traditionally they light the way for the ghosts, arriving and departing.

Lanterns are also the chief feature of the Akita Kanto (usually 5–7 August), but here they are of normal size and hang in bunches of up to 46 from wooden poles with crossbeams (*kanto*) which are raised and balanced on the hips, hands, shoulders, foreheads and other parts of the men who handle them. As the *nebuta* display the talents of the manufacturer, so these display the skills of the bearer.

Views', and the beachfront and nearby historical sites have suffered a consequent degree of spoliation. **Zuiganji** Temple, founded in 828, has an explanatory tape loop that competes with the bullhorns of the guides who shepherd tourists round its compound. There are loudspeakers at the beach, in the corridors of the 39 hotels, and on all of the boats that ferry visitors around the bay or ply between the pier at Matsushima and the port of **Shiogama** (still a worthwhile trip because of the views of the sometimes curiously shaped islands that it affords). Many of the loudspeakers and tape loops offer the incessant gabbling commentaries without which Japanese tourists seem unable to enjoy their natural environment, and the remainder repeat at full volume the famous folk song that celebrates both bay and temple:

> *Zuiganji Temple at Matsushima—*
> *There is no temple like it!*
> *How fine! How true!*
> *And what a great catch of fish!*

Conceivably, something has been lost in translation. The poet Basho viewed Matsushima in an equally celebratory mood. 'Much praise has already been lavished upon the wonders of the islands of Matsushima,' he wrote. 'Yet if further praise is possible I would like to say that here is the most beautiful spot in the whole country of Japan.' He was similarly enthusiastic about the lovely old shrine at Shiogama, rebuilt in 1607, 80-odd years before his visit: 'I was deeply impressed by the fact that the divine power of the gods had penetrated even to the extreme north of our country, and I bowed in humble reverence before the altar.' And in 1948, three years after the catastrophic fire bombing of nearby Sendai, the English poet Edmund Blunden, in an equally reverential mood, left this poetic memento of his visit to Zuiganji Temple:

> *Here abide Tranquillity,*
> *Courtesy, Humility;*
> *The traveller pauses in deep rest,*
> *To go his way blessing and blest.*

And does so still in his hundreds of thousands, the echoes of the bullhorns tingling in his ears.

East of Matsushima lies the **Oshika Peninsula**, whose small ports were formerly busy centres of the whaling industry, now fallen on less prosperous times; and a short boat ride from the tip of the peninsula lies the picturesque little island of **Kinkazan** (Hill of Golden Flowers), so named, says Basho, because of the fecundity of the old gold mine that once stood there. In a manner more reminiscent of Chinese than of Japanese superstition, its former wealth together with the occurrence of the ideogram for 'gold' in its name have led to the island's acquiring a reputation for bestowing financial

security on anyone who visits it for three consecutive years—something the neighbouring whalers presumably omitted to do. Kinkazan is also well known for the deer and wild monkeys that inhabit it.

Iwate, the largest of the six Tohoku prefectures, has as its captial **Morioka** (population 229,-000), famous for its ironware, called *Nanbu tetsubin* ('Nanbu' being both the family name of the lords who built Morioka Castle and the old name for Iwate and eastern Aomori). Heavy knobbled kettles are the most practical form into which the iron is worked, but small lantern-shaped windbells are more popular with weight-conscious travellers. Morioka stands in the imposing shadow of **Mount Iwate** (2,041 metres, 6,696 feet) which is also called, predictably, 'Iwate-Fuji'. (The '-Fuji' designation is reserved for mountains that stand, like their archetypal namesake, in splendid isolation.) Morioka Castle was built in 1597 and its massive outer walls still stand, the steps that lead up and around them deliberately constructed in an irregular fashion to prevent their being mounted at speed—a cunning feature of Japanese castle architecture.

Iwate, like Fukushima, was an area noted for its horse-breeders, the most famous of them rearing their stock on the high pastures of **Sotoyama**, in the hills northeast of the capital, then driving them over the higher passes to fill orders from all parts of the region. The traditional farmhouses of Iwate, called *magariya,* very few of which remain standing, were built in such a way that the horse's stable and farmer's living room stood next to each other under a single roof. The horses bred in Sotoyama were solid farm stock and their robust tradition is commemorated each year on 15 June in the **Chagu-Chagu Umakko Matsuri** (*umakko* means 'young horse' or 'horse and child', *chagu-chagu* imitates the jangling sound of ornamental bridles). The festival's main event is a 15-kilometre (9.5-mile) procession of some 80 horses, gaily decked out and ridden by young children in feudal costume. They process through the streets of Morioka, beginning and ending at two shrines whose chief business is the blessing and protection of the region's horses.

Iwate is cleft into two mountainous halves by the valley that runs through it south to north, and in this valley stand not only Morioka but most of the prefecture's other cities and towns. Of particular interest to the visitor is one of the very smallest of these towns, **Hiraizumi**, situated at the southern end of the valley not far from the border with Miyagi. In the 12th century Hiraizumi was the most important independent centre of culture and power in the Tohoku region, and remained so until Yoritomo succeeded in arrogating practically all power to himself with the institution of the military government at Kamakura (see page 53). It was to Hiraizumi that his brother, Yoshitsune, fled (see page 154), in Hiraizumi that he was offered sanctuary, and in or near Hiraizumi that Yoshitsune was eventually hunted down and forced to commit suicide (though there are Arthurian-style survival legends, one of which has him escaping to Mongolia where he resurfaced as Ghenghis Khan). Hiraizumi is the site of what is regarded as the most important and magnificently endowed temple in the Tohoku region, **Chusonji**, founded here in 1105 by the powerful Fujiwara family (see page 73), whose original home Hiraizumi was. Particularly impressive is the small **Konjikido** hall, the outer walls of which were originally plated with gold. A short walk from Chusonji is the temple of **Motsuji**. Founded in the 12th century, it was rebuilt in modern times, and each 20 January is the site of a nighttime performance of ancient dances, precursors of the Noh theatre, which date from Heian times. The dances are called *Ennen no Mai*. A similarly ancient performing art, more rural in theme and aspect, is the set of Kagura and other dances preserved in the villages near **Mount Hayachine** (1,914 metres, 6,279 feet), east of Morioka.

South of Hayachine, in the rugged, sparsely populated hills to the east of the central valley, stands the small city of **Tono** (population 31,000), which enjoyed a brief spell of fame in 1910 with the publication of Yanagita Kunio's *Tono Monogatari* (Tono Stories). Yanagita was the founder of Japanese folklore studies and his Tono book was the first concerted attempt to produce an oral history of a Japanese rural area. Most of the book is devoted to legends and superstitions, but the villages and hills around Tono still preserve to a remarkable degree the progress-resisting style of rural life for which karaoke singers pretend to pine.

The coast of Iwate is justly famous for its rugged splendour, and almost the entire length of it has been turned into the **Rikuchu Kaigan National Park**, offering boat cruises, clifftop hikes and a wide choice of simple traditional accommodation.

On the high mountainous border between Iwate and **Akita** prefectures lies the **Hachimantai Plateau,** one of the central attractions of the **Towada-Hachimantai National Park**. The continuing volcanic activity here gives rise to a great many natural hot springs that issue through the brittle crust at temperatures barely below boiling point. Though several of the larger springs have been developed into resorts, these resorts retain a genuinely rural atmosphere, partly owing to their being frequented by groups of elderly local people who stay for weeks to enjoy the benefits of the springs' curative powers, and partly because some at least preserve the now often frowned-upon custom of mixed bathing. The best-known resorts are **Tamagawa, Yuze, Kuroyu, Goshogake** and **Magoroku**, all on the Akita side of the prefectural boundary. In winter, the slopes of the Hachimantai Plateau are crowded with skiers. The hot-spring and ski resorts can be reached most conveniently by bus from Morioka, or from the small Akita cities of **Kazuno** and **Odate**.

At the southern end of the Hachimantai Plateau lies **Lake Tazawa**, at 425 metres (1,400 feet) the deepest lake in Japan. It is almost perfectly circular and has one or two beaches for swimming and pleasure boating, and a fair selection of hotels, ryokan and minshuku.

Just south of the lake is the small, pleasant town of **Kakunodate** (population 17,000), a former seat of the lords of the region, the Satake family. Nothing remains of the castle, but some small samurai houses are preserved in one long street that runs between the station and the river. Much less grand than the *buke-yashiki* at Aizu-Wakamatsu, these houses have about them the plaintive feeling that inevitably arises out of a combination of seclusion and decay.

Like Iwate, Akita is a mainly rural prefecture where, in the low-lying areas, large-scale rice production is the dominant feature of the landscape. Akita was formerly a part of the province of Dewa, Iwate of Nanbu, and the men of Dewa and Nanbu have rarely, if ever, been able to agree on the relative merits of their agricultural produce. Sake is a major industry in both prefectures and competition between local brands (of which there are very many) is particularly keen. The term *jizake* (local sake) is used to distinguish the product of smaller local breweries from the blended sakes manufactured in bulk and distributed nationwide. True sake connoisseurs spend a great deal of time hunting out obscure *jizake* (much as lovers of 'real ale' hunt out obscure beers in rural England) and then usually order the second grade (*nikyu*) brew, claiming that the first-grade (*ikkyu*) and special-grade *(tokyu)* brews have been refined beyond the point where the true taste can be enjoyed. The difference in grade depends mainly on how much of the rice kernel has been used in the brewing. The more polished the kernel the less remains, the less that remains the higher the grade, the higher the grade the less fierce—in theory—the hangover. This somewhat specialized information is included here in the hope that the acquiring of a taste for *jizake* and hot springs will compensate the visitor to Akita for its comparative dearth of other forms of recreation.

The prefectural capital, **Akita** city (population 285,000), is one of the dullest cities in the region, except inside its sake shops and during its annual **Kanto Matsuri** on 5–7 August (see box on page 121).

Jutting out into the Japan Sea north of Akita city is the rugged **Oga Peninsula**, a tour of which provides a good introduction to the grimness and isolation that are inextricably associated with the whole of the Japan Sea coast. In winter, the hardships of life here are especially apparent, with the fishmongers of the peninsula having almost nothing on sale but the tiny sandfish called *hata-hata,* which, together with *kiritanpo* (baked mashed rice) are Akita staples, not out of choice but out of gloomy necessity. In the villages of the Oga Peninsula a New Year's Eve ritual called **Namahage** is enacted, one of the last genuine Japanese folk festivals to survive in an

uncommercial form (so uncommercial that the casual visitor will almost certainly not be permitted to see it). Partly this is because it takes place inside private houses, and partly because the villagers still take it seriously as a major means of strengthening community spirit. The *Namahage* are masked demons, impersonated by young men of the villages, who invade all the houses in turn (except those where a death has occurred during the year), shouting, stamping, drinking massive quantities of the sake they are offered (with no sign of worrying about what grade it is) and threatening to the point of terror the children and young wives of the families, which is the main purpose of their visit. The theory is that terrifying young children and women newly married into the village is a good way of reminding them of their comparatively low place in the social pecking order so that they do not get ideas above their station, and of their obligation to work hard for the good of the community and not be lazy and self-absorbed. From the screams, tears and barely restrained violence that accompany the demons' visits, one has to conclude that it is an immensely successful technique. It is also immensely enjoyable (if you are a demon) and a spur to adulthood for the male children who realize dimly through their screams and tears that one day they will be rollicking demons themselves. Visitors' rituals such as this were once common throughout rural Japan and have all but disappeared.

On the border between Akita and **Aomori** prefectures lies **Lake Towada**, the most popular tourist attraction in northern Tohoku, particularly in autumn when the leaves on the surrounding hillsides turn so attractively gold and red that you can't get near them for the crush. The crush tends to converge on the lakeside resort of **Yasumiya**, where there is a small beach and many restaurants, souvenir shops and places to stay; but there are quieter and more inviting places to stay at other points on the lake's shore. A good plan is to approach the lake on foot along the course of the **Oirase River**, a picturesque stream consisting of rapids and small waterfalls, along which a woodland path has been carefully laid down for strollers. The river joins the lake at **Nennokuchi** which has a bus terminal.

Due north of the lake stands **Mount Hakkoda** (1,585 metres, 5,200 feet), which provides good skiing facilities in winter, good camping in summer, and good hot springs all year round. And due east of the lake, in the village of **Shingo**, stands an even more remarkable sight: the grave of Jesus Christ. This claim may occasion a raised eyebrow among less credulous readers, but the humble grave is there for all to see, Jesus having allowed his brother to be crucified in his place (and, in case an uncrucified Jesus would not prove attractive enough to sightseers, his brother's grave is here too, Joseph of Arimathaea having presumably inherited not only the ability to walk on water, but to bear bodies across vast oceans). It is not hard to see how, one bright 17th-century morning, a bearded foreign missionary fleeing

the Tokugawa persecutions (see page 183), took the time-honoured recourse of flight into Tohoku, turned up in the village of Shingo and found the villagers so accommodating that he stayed on to attempt their conversion. His Japanese was minimal and was made even less useful a tool of faith by the villagers' gift of a fearsomely incomprehensible tongue. In the end, the villagers somehow managed to persuade themselves that the missionary himself was the Man he preached, and when he died they buried him under a cross which, crucifixion being the commonest form of execution in feudal Japan for all the lower classes, they regarded as a symbol of his own persecution. This is admittedly conjecture. But whatever the truth of the matter, the Shingo villagers scored a major triumph. The Japanese pay a fortune in licensing fees to Disneyland, but they got Jesus free.

Of the three largest cities in the prefecture, **Aomori**, the prefectural capital (population 288,000), is perhaps the least interesting, except during the first week of August when it stages the spectacular **Nebuta Matsuri** (see box on page 121). Until the ferry service was discontinued in April 1988, Aomori city was the chief rail and ferry terminus for passengers going to Hokkaido, who could transfer from train to boat without setting foot outside the station (or, if they had been in sufficient contact with the villagers of Shingo, try walking across the Tsugaru Strait).

Hachinohe (population 238,000), on the Pacific coast, is a sprawling industrial and fishing centre, which also stages an interesting festival, the **Emburi**, in February, consisting of dances at the local shrine and in the streets of the city performed by men wearing large hats trimmed with decorative horses' manes (another festive reminder of the strong tradition of horse-breeding throughout northeast Honshu).

The real urban heart of the prefecture, however, is the old castle town of **Hirosaki** (population 175,000), an attractive city, famous for its late-blooming cherries, for its apple blossom, and for the state of preservation of its small, elegant castle, built in 1610. Hirosaki also stages a **Neputa Matsuri** in the first week of August, at once less spectacular, less tourist-oriented and more imbued with the solemn, warlike spirit of the north country than its larger counterpart in the prefectural capital. The Hirosaki festival features the appearance on the streets of the *Tsugaru Joppari Daiko* (Drum to Rouse the Passions of Tsugaru, 'Tsugaru' being the old name for the western half of the prefecture), said to be the largest drum in Japan. Hirosaki is also the production centre for a colourful and not inexpensive form of lacquerware.

West of Hirosaki stands the imposing **Mount Iwaki** (1,625 metres, 5,331 feet), which is yet another 'something-or-other-Fuji' (in this case, of course, 'Tsugaru-Fuji') and can be climbed via a track which begins at the **Iwaki Shrine**, whose present buildings date from the 17th century. The orchards at the foot of the mountain and in other parts of the prefecture grow the carefully-tended, huge and expensive red apples for which Aomori is also very well known for.

The northern half of the prefecture is divided between two peninsulas, Tsugaru in the west and Shimokita in the east. **Tsugaru** is the better known, owing in part to the renaissance of its virile folk music tradition, an event which reached its peak in the 1970s and has now somewhat diminished. The folk music of Tsugaru is characterized by virtuoso performances on a long-stocked, heavy *shamisen* (see page 132), normally a humble accompanying instrument but in Tsugaru a wonderful device for the display of individual and idiosyncratic skills. The people of Tsugaru are widely thought to possess the most impenetrable of Japan's many regional dialects, and this is partly ascribed to their habit of hardly moving their mouths when they speak (the winters, it is said, are too cold to permit their mouths to open fully). The winters are also exceptionally long, so that the people of Tsugaru, because of their need to cram a whole year's work into six snowless months, have a reputation for quick action and inexhaustible energy, both of which are reflected in their music. The novelist Dazai Osamu, who drowned himself in the Tama Canal (see page 32), was a native of Tsugaru, and the house where he was born in the small town of **Kanagi** is now a ryokan. Dazai's reputation was made in Tokyo, and he is regarded by his Tsugaru countrymen much as D.H. Lawrence is among Nottinghamshire miners and Arnold Bennett among the people of the Potteries: as a man who simultaneously turned his back on his roots and exploited them for his own gratification.

The other peninsula, **Shimokita**, is shaped like an axe, and near the centre of the axe-blade is one of the most impressive and disquieting religious sites in Japan. This is **Osorezan** (The Terrible Mountain), whose temple, **Entsuji**, stands on the shore of a blue, lifeless crater lake and was founded in 845. The entire precincts of the temple are a desert of volcanic lava, grey dust and strong-smelling sulphur springs. Throughout the precincts stand small statues of **Jizo**, the Buddhist guardian of children, since this wasteland is commonly regarded as being an earthly manifestation of *Sainokawara*, the grim Limbo of the Buddhist underworld, where Jizo wages a constant battle against demons who seek to drag the souls of dead children down to Hell. Worshippers often leave straw sandals here to protect Jizo's sacred feet from the sharp, hot lava, and pile up pebbles into mounds, each pebble a prayer for the peace of a tormented soul. Within the temple compound are three dilapidated old hot-spring bathhouses open to anyone who can stand the smell and heat. And on 20–24 July each year the temple hosts the **Itakoichi** (Medium Market) during which blind or half-blind female spirit mediums from as far away as Mount Iwaki congregate in tents and offer to contact the dead relatives of festival pilgrims. The Historical Buddha is known to have inveighed against the 'low arts' of fortune telling and mediumship, but his sentiments have gone unregarded here, where, for all its Buddhist trappings, an older faith strains up through the lunar surface like the mustard-yellow and blood-red springs. Few religious centres in the world are as devoid of embellishment as Osorezan and few leave a profounder mark on the visitor's memory.

Japanese Music

The earliest extant form of Japanese music is *Gagaku*, performed by a 16–20-piece orchestra containing instruments of mainly Chinese or Southeast Asian origin, and dating, in Japan, from the eighth century. Simplified pieces, performed by much smaller ensembles, sometimes accompany ceremonies at Shinto shrines. The basic repertoire derives from T'ang China.

The *biwa*, a four-stringed lute, introduced into Japan from China at about the same time, is used in Gagaku and also to accompany long recitative-like narrative ballads, such as deal with the exploits of the Heike clan. These are not much heard nowadays.

The most familiar of the classical instruments today are the *koto*, a 13-stringed horizontal harp or zither, which is probably the most melodious-sounding Japanese instrument to the Western ear; the *shamisen*, an extremely versatile three-stringed lute or banjo, used in all forms of accompaniment, from Kabuki and Bunraku through geisha ballads to folk songs; the *shakuhachi*, a vertical bamboo flute of varying length with five finger holes, for which there is a large solo repertoire and which is also played in ensembles and accompanies folk songs; and the *fue*, or horizontal flute, which accompanies Noh performances and is sometimes heard elsewhere, though the usual non-theatrical ensemble is limited to koto, shamisen and shakuhachi. Professional recitals of Japanese classical music are rather rare, most major concert halls being used full-time for the performance of Western music.

Several types of drum exist, including the *tsuzumi*, a finger drum supported on the shoulder, and the *taiko*, which can be any kind of stick drum, such as that used in Noh accompaniments, but the most familiar forms of which are the larger drums that accompany the folk dances at summer festivals.

Folk music is alive and well in most parts of Japan, especially Okinawa and Tohoku, which have the largest repertoires of songs. Whereas many Western folk songs are about unrequited love or the exploits of courageous men, most Japanese songs celebrate places, underlining the wistful feeling for *furusato* that runs through so many avenues of Japanese life. Professional folk-song performances, especially on television, are so slick and prettified that one quite forgets to listen to the lyrics, many of which are actually about hardship and oppression. Folk songs are best heard when performed spontaneously in bars or at the long lively sessions that mark the successful conclusion of festivals.

Modern Japanese ballads (*enka*) are popular with karaoke singers and combine a folk-like feeling for place with the slushy romanticism of the soap opera. Japanese pop music is almost completely derivative, not from its Western counterparts but from itself, to the extent that many foreign visitors, even those with musical training, are hard pressed to distinguish one song from another and harder pressed to see why they should bother.

The Chubu Region

The Belly and the Back

As geographical divisions go, the **Chubu** (Middle) region is an unhandy one, comprising all the bulk of Honshu between Kanto and Kansai, and stretching across the greatest width of the island, from the Pacific to the Japan Sea coast. At its centre towers the most formidable range of mountains in Japan which, since an English mining engineer so christened them in 1881, are known as 'The Japan Alps'. The inhabitants of this mountainous inland area (particularly that part of it called **Shinshu**, nowadays Nagano prefecture) are noted for their traditional outlook, often tending in the older generation toward hidebound conservatism, particularly where such delicate matters as the marriage of their daughters are concerned. It is a region which, because of the comparative inaccessibility of much of its terrain, has resisted progress to the same extent that in the past its steep slopes resisted paddy farming. The best known traditional industry of the region was the silk industry that centred on Lake Suwa, and was notorious for its heartless exploitation of the loom girls recruited from local villages.

South of the mountains, along the narrow coastal strip of the Pacific belly, ran the main historical artery of transport between Edo and Osaka, the Tokaido highway, and consequently it is this southern part of the region that was best prepared for rapid modern development and that has suffered most from the blights as well as from the double-edged blessings of large-scale industrialization. The visitor who takes the Shinkansen bullet train from Tokyo to Kyoto and beyond will find himself travelling, for the most part, through a landscape where few horizons are not marred by smoking factory chimneys or slate-grey conurbations.

North of the mountains, by way of contrast, the entire stretch of the Japan Sea coast and its neighbouring inland areas are often referred to collectively as *Ura Nihon* (The Back of Japan), a name that NHK resists using in its radio and television broadcasts for fear the residents of the area will be offended to the point of refusing to pay their licence fees. This was a neglected area throughout most of Japan's history, partly because it was so far removed from the main channels of inter-urban communication, but more especially because of the immensely heavy snowfalls that are its chief climatic feature. Snow storms arrive in Japan from the northwest, a year-end gift from Siberia. The Japan Alps (many of whose peaks rise to between 2,000 and 3,000 metres, 6,500 and 10,000 feet, or higher) prevent most of these storms from reaching the Pacific coastal areas so that, although it can be bitingly cold in winter, Tokyo generally has little snow. But in the hills and on the plains of *Ura Nihon*, the snow falls so thick and lies so long that, in the remoter hamlets, people spend much of the winter burrowing about like moles and constructing tunnels through the snow to their neighbours' doors. In the larger towns it is common to find the pavements of shopping streets strongly roofed against snow, and the prefectures of Niigata and Toyama especially are known as *Yukiguni*,'Snow Country'. That is also the title of Nobel-prize winning author Kawabata Yasunari's 1937 novel, set in one of the hot-spring resorts that provide the few real glimmers of comfort along the otherwise gloomy Back of Japan.

The Pacific Belly

Because of the vastly different social and climatic features of the two halves of the region, it seems sensible to deal with them separately. The southern and central part of Chubu contains the prefectures of **Shizuoka, Yamanashi, Nagano, Gifu** and **Aichi**. Those with a coastline are conveniently linked to Tokyo by the Tokaido Shinkansen bullet train while landlocked Gifu is easily accessible from Nagoya, and Nagano can be reached by express either from Shinjuku (for Matsumoto) or from Ueno (for Nagano city, the prefectural capital).

    Shizuoka is close enough to Tokyo to offer several destinations suitable for one- or two-day trips from the captial, most notably Mount Fuji (which straddles the border with Yamanashi prefecture) and the Izu Peninsula, both of which are parts of the **Fuji-Hakone-Izu National Park** (see page 55).

    Its relatively mild climate has made the **Izu Peninsula** a popular leisure-time destination for residents of Tokyo. The east coast of the peninsula has consequently suffered a good deal of development, particularly in and around the hot-spring resort of **Atami** (which waggish Japanese have rechristened 'tatami' on account of its undecorous reputation and the horizontal nature of many of the pursuits to be enjoyed there). But the west coast is largely unspoiled and, in addition to the majestic views of Mount Fuji it offers across Suruga Bay, is pleasantly wooded and has some unpretentious resorts of its own, like **Toi. Shuzenji** in the north-central hills of Izu is the peninsula's best-known inland hot-spring resort, and it, in turn, is flanked by a number of smaller and more rural spas. Shuzenji affords a good introduction to hot-spring bathing for the novice; the little sloping town is interesting to stroll around and the river that runs through its centre has a small open-air communal bathing facility which is not much used. The Asaba Ryokan at Shuzenji is famous for the Noh stage in its garden, where torchlight performances are sometimes given. **Mount Amagi** (1,407 metres, 4,616 feet) in the east of Izu has romantic associations deriving from Kawabata Yasunari's haunting 1926 novella *Izu no Odoriko* (The Izu Dancer). The associations of the small city of **Shimoda** (population 31,000), at the tip of

Chubu Region

the peninsula, are historical, the first foreign consulate in Japan having been established there in 1856 by the American diplomat Townsend Harris. For a while the shogun sought to restrict foreign representation and trade to this comparative backwater, and it was largely Harris' persistence that resulted in the broadening of diplomatic and commercial relations and the opening of Yokohama and other ports to foreign trade.

Japanese people are wont to bemoan the Westerner's alleged habit of regarding **Mount Fuji** and geisha girls as the twin symbols of their nation while wilfully ignoring the cultural assets of which the Japanese themselves are most proud, such as silicon chips. Where the Western fixation with geisha is concerned, Japanese people are often right to express a degree of scorn; the newly-landed G.I.s who stood in the streets of Tokyo and Yokohama in late 1945 shouting, 'We want geisha girls!' clearly exhibited a lamentable ignorance of an old and honourable institution. But for the ongoing Western obsession with the other half of the combination the Japanese have mainly themselves to blame. Every NHK telecast during the 1964 Olympics opened with a shot of Mount Fuji accompanied by the meticulously recorded bong of a deeply resonant temple bell. Calendars and the covers of official guidebooks intended for foreigners' use almost invariably feature a coloured photograph of Mount Fuji, usually with a bullet train speeding by so that modern amenities will not go wholly unremarked. Mount Fuji is an awe-inspiring sight, so imposing that it was a major landmark for American bomber pilots on their way to reduce the capital to ash. Partly because of its splendid isolation, partly because of its almost perfectly conical shape, partly because of the divinity accorded it through the centuries, partly because (despite the formidable barrier raised by the Japan Alps) it is, at 3,776 metres (12,389 feet), the tallest mountain in Japan, and partly because though now a dormant volcano (its last eruption was in 1707) the possibility exists that it could flame again into dangerous life, Fuji does exert a very special influence on the imagination of Japanese and visitor alike.

As with certain beautiful women, it is best to maintain as distant a relationship as possible with Mount Fuji. Not to see it is a sad deprivation, but to see it too close is to court the waning of a dream. There is a climbing season (1 July to 31 August) during which tens of thousands of people make the ascent, most taking a bus either from **Kawaguchiko** in Yamanashi (to the 'Fifth Station' on the mountainside) or from **Gotenba** (to the 'New Fifth Station') and then continuing to the summit on foot. Along the track that winds up the higher slopes there are refreshment stalls (supplies dragged up by tractor) and huts to rest or sleep in. Many climbers plan to reach the summit in the early hours of the morning and watch the sun rise, though this last ambition is often frustrated by the cloud cover that Fuji attracts. Though nowadays the higher slopes are not so littered with beer cans and lunch boxes as they were 15 years ago, they are still a long way from appearing divine.

Japanese people say that not to climb Mount Fuji once in your life is foolish and to climb it more than once is foolish. They say this of other mountains too (notably Asama, see page 139), but where Fuji is concerned, I think an unanswerable case can be put forward by the first category of fool. You do not approach the Sacred Mirror at Ise because by doing so you would render it less sacred, and the same can be said of too close an acquaintance with this awesome, dream-ridden mountain.

On the **Yamanashi** side of Fuji lie its five lakes, Lakes **Yamanaka, Kawaguchi, Saiko, Shoji** and **Motosu,** which, interspersed as they are with dense, in part primeval, woodland and with spas such as those at **Shimobe** and **Oshino**, provide an alternative rural retreat to the Izu Peninsula. The chief town and springboard for a tour of the area is **Fujiyoshida** (population 54,000), while to the north lies the prefectural capital, **Kofu** (population 199,000), the old castle seat of the warlike Takeda Shingen, for years a sharp thorn in Nobunaga's and then in Ieyasu's side, and the 'Shadow Warrior' of Kurosawa Akira's 1980 film *Kagemusha.*

Easily accessible from Kofu is the spectacular **Shosenkyo Gorge**, with its falls and sharp 50-metre (160-foot) cliffs, a part of the Chichibu-Tama National Park (see also page 55); while in the southwest of the prefecture stands **Mount Minobu** (1,148 metres, 3,766 feet), yet another mountain of religious significance, this time to the more than 10 million adherents of the Nichiren sect of Buddhism, Nichiren having founded the temple complex of **Kuonji** during his residence here from 1274 until shortly before his death in 1282. Nichiren was an irascible, humourless character who found intolerable the idea that anyone should dare question the tenets he preached, and it was at Mount Minobu that he wrote the documents upon which the transmission of his doctrines are founded and which state, clearly and completely typically, that all who disregard their contents are slanderers of the Buddha's law. Nichiren's self-centred and abrasive proselytizing sets him apart from other great Buddhist teachers who, for the most part, have been men of peace and tolerance, the virtues upon which, in the dim past, Buddhism was founded.

In the decades since the war, Yamanashi prefecture (particularly the region around Kofu) has become noted for its viticulture, and the only really drinkable Japanese wines are produced here. None has yet achieved greatness, or can even honestly be called memorable, although a wine of the 'Mercian' label (manufactured by the Sanraku Ocean company) did win a medal at an international wine competition in Hungary in 1964, which is why Mercian wine labels are conspicuously adorned not only with sentences in French (*mis en bouteille au chateau*) but with medals. In general, Japanese white wines are either too acid or too syrupy (though Yamanashi wines are not as syrupy as those produced in the north of Honshu and in Hokkaido, which often taste like apple juice) while some of the reds can fur your tongue like the inside of a kettle. In any case, a lot of 'Japanese' wine turns out to be a mixture of local product and nondescript imported *vin de table*, a fact which surfaced amid some scandal in 1985, and which does not bode especially well for the future competitiveness of the Japanese wine industry.

Straddling the prefectural boundary between Yamanashi and **Nagano** are some of the region's most impressive peaks, here a part of the **Minami Arupusu** (Southern Alps) **National Park.** Favourites with climbers are Mounts **Akaishi-dake** (3,120 metres, 10,236 feet), **Shiomi-dake** (3,047 metres, 10,000 feet), **Shirane** (3,192 metres, 10,472 feet), **Senjo-ga-take** (3,033 metres, 9,950 feet), **Koma-ga-take** (2,966 metres, 9,731 feet) and **Yatsu-ga-take** (2,899 metres, 9,511 feet)—*take* or *dake* meaning 'peak'. Some of these, like the last named, have huts and lodging houses well below the summits which are accessible to ordinary hikers without the need of special equipment, but for the most part this is fully-fledged mountaineering country and the peaks should be approached with the wary respect that frequent rapid changes in weather patterns and regular annual fatalities require.

From Tokyo (Ueno), the most easily accessible part of Nagano prefecture is the high plateau that lies to the south of the active volcano, **Mount Asama** (2,542 metres, 8,340 feet), one of those mountains that fools climb twice or not at all, although in recent years even the wise have frequently been prevented from climbing by rumbles and spouts. The plateau was crossed by the old **Nakasendo** highway, like the Tokaido one of the great feudal Japanese roads and a link, though a less direct one (69 post stations as compared with 53 on the Tokaido), between Edo and Kyoto. The train journey from Ueno as far as **Yokokawa** at the foot of the steep **Usui Pass** is uneventful, but an extra locomotive must be added at Yokokawa to manage the gradient, and the short delay required to couple it provides the visitor with an opportunity to skip smartly out onto the platform along with practically every other passenger on the train to buy Yokokawa Station's famous packed lunch, a form of *kamameshi* (boiled rice topped with assorted odds and ends) which comes complete in its own take-away earthenware bowl and is said to be a particular favourite of the empress dowager, who perhaps sees a need for spare kitchenware. All major railway stations in Japan sell packed lunches and their contents and quality vary from region to region but Yokokawa is one of the last to offer its lunch in an attractive and reusable container.

The visitor emerges from the tunnels of the Usui Pass to find himself in the resort town of **Karuizawa** (resident population 14,000), 'discovered' by Archdeacon A.C. Shaw and other enterprising foreign missionaries in 1888 and used by them much as highland retreats were used by Raj society in India during the long hot summers. Nowadays, Karuizawa is popular among the energetic Japanese young who come from Tokyo in the warm weather to play

tennis and in winter to skate. The little town itself has a famous 'Ginza' shopping street, department stores and fashionable coffee shops (one of which, according to a persistent rumour, charges 10,000 yen for a cup of coffee)—all to prevent the energetic young on their day's excursion into the countryside from feeling too lost. For miles around the land has been divided up by equally energetic real estate agents into small lots which are purchased by university professors and similar countryfolk who erect weekend villas on them. Along the lanes stand bunches of neat white signposts indicating these professorial retreats.

More interesting are the old post and castle towns of the region, such as **Komoro** (population 42,000) and **Ueda** (population 112,000), which, for all their size (Ueda is the third largest city in the prefecture), preserve a sleepy old-world atmosphere, and are usefully close to such hot springs as **Bessho**. Round the skirts of Asama, at the base of its northern slope, lies the intriguing lunar landscape of **Onioshidashi** (literally, 'Shoved Out by Demons'), which was created by the massive eruption of 1783. This and the small museum there are easily reached from Karuizawa by bus.

North and west of the prefectural capital, **Nagano** city (population 324,000), which is famous for its **Zenkoji** Temple, founded in 642 and rebuilt in 1707, are other peaks, not quite so towering as those of the Southern Alps, straddling the prefectural borders with Gunma and Niigata, most of them a part of the **Joshinetsu Kogen National Park**. They include mounts **Shirane** (2,162 metres, 7,093 feet) and **Kurohime** (2,053 metres, 6,735 feet). Nagano's two most popular ski resorts—**Naeba** and **Shiga Kogen** (*kogen* means 'plateau' or 'heights')—are to be found among these peaks, as are a number of fine hot springs, including **Jigokudani** (literally 'Hell Valley'), where two colonies of wild monkeys have their own bathing facilities and frequently invade the human spa too.

The other major city in Nagano prefecture is **Matsumoto** (population 192,000), which boasts a rare black-walled castle, originally built in 1504 and known as **Karasujo** (Castle of the Crow). Matsumoto is a good base from which to launch tours of **Lake Suwa** to the southeast and the majestic peaks and spas to the west which straddle the prefectural borders with Toyama and Gifu. These Northern Alps are part of yet another National Park, this time called **Chubu-Sangaku**, and include mounts **Norikura** (3,026 metres, 9,928 feet), **Hotaka** (3,190 metres, 10,466 feet) and **Yari** (3,180 metres, 10,433 feet). Hidden among the eastern folds of the range and easily accessible by bus from Matsumoto is the picturesque **Kamikochi** valley, a favourite spot from which to appreciate the mountains' refreshing grandeur, and a starting point for several hiking trails along which the mountains' delights can be met at closer quarters. That such trails exist is due in no small part to the same hardy band of missionaries who lighted upon Karuizawa, in particular to an English missionary called Walter Weston, who pioneered the now immensely popular sport of mountain hiking in Japan. Before Rev. Weston, the more rugged countryside had been scrupulously avoided except by devout ascetics whereas, since Rev. Weston, Japanese calendar manufacturers have gone out of their way to include Alpine panoramas in calendars intended for distribution abroad in order to counter the impression, harboured by ignorant foreigners, that Japan is a backward, jungly nation like some of its unspeakable Asian neighbours.

It will be seen from this brief summary that Nagano's chief attractions are natural rather than historical or cultural. Short of a trip to Kyushu or Hokkaido (see pages 183 and 214), Nagano provides the visitor with his most convenient chance of escaping for a while from the relentless pressures of urban civilization and cultural must-sees to an area where the landscape is spectacular, the air invigorating, and the accommodation and recreation to be found in the dozens of spas, large and small, are almost entirely of the traditional kind. Nor nowadays do missionaries lurk in numbers sufficient to deny him these delights.

On the western side of the Northern Alps stands the city of **Takayama** (sometimes called Hida-Takayama, 'Hida' being the old name for this part of **Gifu** prefecture). Takayama (population 64,000) is architecturally one of the best preserved towns in Japan and, in addition to its picturesque rows of Edo- and Meiji-period houses and shops (lining streets laid out in a grid pattern like Kyoto's), it has several museums depicting local life and traditions, and a Folk Village (**Minzoku Mura**), to which a number of buildings from outlying rural areas have been brought and painstakingly reconstructed. Takayama's **Hie Shrine** also hosts (on 14 and 15 April) a spectacular annual festival, the **Sanno Matsuri**, during which large and elaborately decorated floats equipped with moving mechanical figures called *karakuri ningyo* are paraded through the streets.

Most of the population of Gifu prefecture is crowded into the flattish urbanized areas around the border with Aichi, while the northern reaches are either inaccessibly mountainous or solidly agricultural, harbouring small towns and villages that remain traditional in both appearance and outlook. The prefecture (originally the province of Mino) is famous for its Oribe ceramic ware (also called Mino ware), produced here from as early as the eighth century and gaining particular favour toward the end of the 16th century among connoisseurs of the tea ceremony. The small city of **Mino** (population 27,000) is also well known as a centre for the manufacture of hand-made paper (*washi*), the production technique for which has been designated a national treasure.

The prefectural capital is **Gifu** city (population 410,000), which stands on the **Nagara River**, whose urban reaches, together with those of the Kiso River at Inuyama in Aichi, are among the best-known places where the visitor can still view cormorant fishing (*ukai*), a tradition that goes back some 1,200 years. Though nowadays mounted purely for the sake of tourists, this event (staged nightly between mid-May and mid-October), in which trained, leashed cormorants dive by torchlight at the command of their regally aproned master, offers an impressive display of an almost vanished skill. Normally, sightseers board one of the many pleasure craft, mostly chartered by local hotels or ryokans, that follow the cormorant boats down river and which, whether the birds catch any *ayu* (sweetfish) or not, are always plentifully supplied with refreshment.

Due west of Gifu city, not far from the boundary with Shiga, lies the site of the famous barrier gate at **Sekigahara**, a name for history buffs to conjure with, since it was near here, in 1600, that one of the most decisive and significant battles of Japanese history was fought, when Ieyasu defeated the forces brought against him by Hideyoshi's son and former chief minister, and so removed the final obstacle standing between himself and the establishement of his family's two-and-a-half centuries of absolute power.

Aichi is a ferociously industralized prefecture, on a par with Kanagawa and boasting a higher gross annual value in manufactured goods than either Osaka or Tokyo. This is because some of Japan's leading export-oriented manufacturers have their principal plants here, notably Toyota, the second largest automobile maker in the world, which, not content with a mere plant, has its own city, **Toyota City**, whose population of 282,000 makes it the third largest city in the prefecture. Honda, Suzuki and Yamaha also have their chief factories nearby.

Near **Inuyama** (population 65,000), already mentioned in connection with cormorant fishing, the **Kiso River** offers the prospect of rapids-shooting. As the mountains to the northeast are called the 'Japan Alps', so the river here is called the 'Japan Rhine'. Not far away, there is **Meiji Mura** (Meiji Village), a collection of about 50 late 19th- and early 20th-century buildings and other memorabilia from around the country (including the facade and lobby of Frank Lloyd Wright's 1922 Imperial Hotel from Tokyo), so admired for having survived a century or less that they have been transported here and reassembled brick by brick. Inuyama itself has Japan's oldest existing castle, built in 1440 and not yet rechristened Neuschwanstein.

The best that can be said for the prefectural capital, **Nagoya** (population 2.1 million, the fourth largest city in Japan), is that it is comparatively easy to find one's way around it, since it was almost completely refashioned on a grid pattern following the massive destruction it suffered during the war, and that it is attempting to soften its reputation as a focal point for the prefecture's grim heavy industries by encouraging such so-called 'clean' industries as fine ceramics (for use as electronic and computer components), into which the Japan Fine Ceramics Centre, based in Nagoya, is currently

The Daibutsu (Great Buddha of Todaiji Temple), fifteen metres in height (left); stone lanterns at Kasuga Shrine (top right); ginkgo trees in the grounds of the Kyoto temple (above)

pumping a great deal of cash. To polish its forward-looking image further Nagoya staged an international design 'Expo' in 1989.

Still, Nagoya is a city that most visitors are likely to want to spend about as much time in as the bullet train does on its way from Tokyo to Kyoto (60 seconds). True, the city contains the **Atsuta Shrine**, founded in the third century, reubuilt in 1955, the repository of the Sacred Sword which forms a third of the imperial regalia (the other two-thirds, the Mirror and Jewel, are in the Ise Shrine and the Imperial Palace, respectively). And there is a feudal castle here, just as there is at Osaka (though this one was rebuilt 28 years later than Osaka's, in 1959, and is therefore less venerable, though it, too, is equipped with a convenient post-feudal elevator). If you are touring Chubu and southern Kansai, Nagoya is the perfect springboard for visits to Takayama or to Ise and the Kii Peninsula (see pages 103 and 106). Otherwise follow the example of the train.

The Japan Sea Back

Niigata city (population 458,000), the capital of **Niigata** prefecture, is the terminus of the Joetsu Shinkansen bullet train from Ueno, and thus the easiest point of access to the Japan Sea coast for the visitor from Tokyo. This Shinkansen line was inaugurated in 1982 and owes its existence almost entirely to the personal dynamism and influence of former Prime Minister Tanaka Kakuei, whose constituency was in Niigata prefecture, and whose energy in opening up this traditionally backward region to modern development ensured that his former constituents remained fiercely loyal to Tanaka through all the calamities that subsequently befell him—bribery scandal, forced resignation, court proceedings, prison sentence, stroke, and the dissolution of his political faction. Tanaka's notorious money politics and his long undisputed role of 'kingmaker' in the government are an extraordinarily clear testament to the ingrained feudalism that can flourish under a purportedly democratic system. Equally, Tanaka's own commitment to the region where his strongest support was centred is a clear example of the abiding spirit of *noblesse oblige*.

The area was a late starter, but in the last two or three decades Niigata and other cities along the coast have suffered the ravages of hectic industrialization as well as of natural disasters. In June 1964, a major submarine earthquake that triggered a five-metre-high *tsunami* destroyed between a quarter and a third of all the ferroconcrete structures in Niigata city, which is why so many of the taller buildings look conspicuously new. These urban ravages do not matter much, however, because the visitor to the region will not want to spend a lot of time in its cities, and the stretches of rugged coast between them, and the mountains of the Snow Country that tower inland, still offer the undeveloped out-of-the-wayness for which the

Back of Japan is famous.

The visitor with time and a desire to exploit this out-of-the-wayness to the full might consider a trip to **Sado** island, easily accessible by either conventional ferry or hydrofoil from Niigata. The Japanese often complain (though there is sometimes an element of boastfulness in the complaint) about their *shimaguni konjo* (islanders' complex), by which they mainly mean the insular cast of thought that comes from being entirely surrounded by ocean. The consequences of this 'complex' have been many—notably, the forced closure of the country under the Tokugawas, and at all other periods the impulse simultaneously to distrust, admire, resist and possess anything and everything that comes from abroad. Because Japan is itself an island nation, a trip to one of its many small offshore islands can provide the visitor with a remarkable insight into the preoccupations of the Japanese national character, since such islands are by their very nature microcosms of the whole.

Excepting Okinawa, which for much of its history was an independent kingdom, Sado (population 86,000) is the largest of Japan's offshore islands and thus the fifth largest island of the archipelago. It was for centuries an island of exile. The Emperor Juntoku was sent there in 1221, after a doomed attempt to overthrow the military regents, and remained there until his death. The politically ambitious priest Mongaku, for a while a protégé of Yoritomo's, was sent there in 1199 following an abortive plot against Juntoku's father. The irascible Nichiren was sent there in 1271 and spent two years on the island suffering from chronic diarrhoea. The founder of the Noh theatre, Zeami Motokiyo, was sent there in 1434 having angered the shogun for reasons no one has properly ascertained. And during the 17th and 18th centuries the island's extensive gold mine was worked by a large, grim colony of convicts whose life expectancy in the narrow choking tunnels under **Kinzan** (The Golden Mountain) was pitifully short.

Most of the island's historical sites are in some way related to these exiles. Part of the gold mine outside the town of **Aikawa** (which at the height of its 18th-century prosperity had a population of 100,000 and now has less than one-sixth of that) has been turned into a museum. Juntoku's reputedly haunted grave stands just outside **Mano**, where Nichiren's hut can also be seen in the grounds of **Myoshoji** temple. But Sado's main attractions are its rugged coast, its quiet country lifestyle, its mournful folk songs, and the neglected air of a place that has not suffered the ruination of an economic miracle. The principal town is **Ryotsu** (population 21,000), where the ferry docks. Here the visitor might take a bus to the government lodging house on **Mount Donden**, from where he can obtain a breathtaking view over the island, and next morning, if he is feeling hardy, hike down to the opposite coast through meadows, woods, and along the rough beds of old mountain streams.

In the Raw

H ad a very good dinner at the Sakamoto–ya and, though every fish served was full of spawn, it was excellent eating. I had asked the cook if he was able to carve up a carp in the way it was done in ancient days for nobles' feasts. This is known as koi–no–ikizukuri (a carp cut up alive). The cook was quite delighted, and said so, and alas, how few people ask for this ancient and honourable dish nowadays. 'Surely the Dana–san [master] was a samurai? Not twice in the year do I now prepare the dish.'

'Bring it to me then, this evening,' said I, 'after you have given me some fried ayu fish, and keep my soup so that I may be able to wash the live carp down if I don't like it.'

I told my interpreter, Egawa, that he could dine with me and help me with the dish and interpreting.

The dinner was entirely of fish and quite excellent, so far as it went, but the sight of the carp was not an enjoyable one. It was brought in on a red lacquered tray, just as in the painting. The fish opened and shut its mouth and gills, just as if swimming in water, and with the same regularity. Not a scale was missing or a drop of blood was visible. The dish was strewn with white sand and little black-brownish freshwater clams, which gave the fish the appearance of lying on the water's edge of the lake. Mountains of raw rice, which denotes luck and plenty, formed the background and there was a pine tree for old age and strength, a bamboo, also for strength and straightness, and a rice plant for prosperity. The dish was really pretty in spite of the gasping fish which, however, showed no pain and, as I said before, there was not a sign of blood or a cut.

'Now we are ready,' I said to the cook, and he proceeded to pour some soy sauce into the fish's eyes and mouth. The effect was not instantaneous: it took a full two minutes as the cook sat over him, chopsticks in hand. All of a sudden and to my unutterable astonishment, the fish gave a convulsive gasp, flicked its tail and flung the whole of its skin on one side of its body over, exposing the underneath of the stomach parts, skinned; the back was cut into pieces about an inch square and a quarter of an inch thick, ready for pulling out and eating. Never in my life have I seen a more barbarous or cruel thing—not even the scenes at Spanish bull fights. Egawa is a delicate-stomached person and as he could eat none, neither could I. It would be simply like taking bites out of a large live fish. I took the knife from my belt and immediately separated the fish's neck vertabrae, much to the cook's astonishment and perhaps disgust.

'Take it away and bring the soup,' I said, 'you have certainly operated beautifully but the sooner a law is brought in to prevent such cruelty the better.' No wonder the carp is taken as an example by all fighting classes and preached about to boys.

Richard Gordon Smith, Japan Diaries

Back on the mainland and away from the coast, the most notable spa and skiing resort in Niigata is **Yuzawa**, also called Echigo-Yuzawa, 'Echigo' being an old name for the province. It is conveniently situated on the express line from Ueno just beyond the long tunnel by means of which the train burrows under the prefectural border with Gunma.

Toyama city (population 305,000), the prefectural capital of **Toyama**, has a distinctly more prosperous air than does any part of Niigata, and this air infects the whole small prefecture. The city has been known since the 17th century for the manufacture of patent Chinese-style medicines called *kampoyaku* (Chinese concoctions) and visits can be arranged to the factory of the largest manufacturer, Kokando.

Mount Tateyama (3,015 metres or 9,892 feet) in the east of the prefecture, one of the northernmost peaks of the Northern Alps and a part of the Jo-Shinetsu-Kogen National Park, is regarded as sacred, not because of a particular sectarian affiliation as at Mount Minobu (see page 138), but, like Fuji, because of divine qualities that are perceived as inherent in the mountain itself. Below the southeastern slope of the mountain stands the massive **Kurobe Dam**, which has formed its own scenic lake, and lower down the **Kurobe River** is the lovely **Kurobe Gorge**, most easily reached via the town of **Unazuki** from **Kurobe** city. Along the private railway line that links Kurobe city with its gorge lie several small and picturesque hot springs.

Between the towns of **Tateyama** and **Omachi** in Niigata prefecture a scenic Alpine Route, not open to private vehicles, takes the visitor by means of bus, trolly bus and cable car through a series of tunnels, up slopes and over plateaus that offer breathtaking views of the surrounding mountains. The route passes the Kurobe Dam, and the journey can be broken overnight at **Murodo**. Otherwise the trip, in either direction, takes an entire day.

Toyama is a prefecture of towering peaks, lakes and gorges, ruggedly beautiful in summer and autumn and buried by deep snows throughout the long winter. Along the upper reaches of the **Shokawa River**, beyond the **Shokawa Gorge**, lies one of the many remote areas said to have been settled by the defeated Heike after their scattered flight following the battle of Dannoura in 1185 (see page 165). These areas are understandably hard of access, and this one is no exception. Its claim to settlement by the Heike is made unusually convincing by the name of the village, not far from the Gifu border, where the settlement seems to have centred. The village is called **Taira**, which was another name for the Heike clan. (*Taira* is written with a single ideogram meaning 'peace', and was the family name used by individuals of the clan, like Taira no Kiyomori. The same ideogram can also be pronounced *hei*. It is, for example, the *hei* in *Heiankyo*, 'Capital of Tranquillity', the old name for Kyoto. *Heike* consists of this ideogram plus a second that means simply 'house' or 'family'.)

The capital of **Ishikawa** prefecture is the historic city of **Kanazawa** (population 418,000), one of the major centres of tourism along this stretch of the Japan Sea Coast. The old name for Ishikawa prefecture was Kaga (see page 29), and, with an annual tax assessment of a million *koku* (one *koku* was the amount of rice needed to fee a samurai retainer for a year), it was the richest of all Japan's feudal fiefs, a fact which greatly increased the power and prestige of Kaga's most famous lord, Maeda Toshiie, whose spirit feeds off Kanazawa like a succubus. Toshiie was not a native of the region, and was appointed to the fief by his patron, Nobunaga, in 1583; so the degree of pride taken in him by Kanazawa's citizens must be counted a further testament to his outstanding abilities as a leader.

The building of **Kanazawa Castle** began with Toshiie's arrival. The donjon disappeared in the great fire of 1881, but the massive walls survive, as does a later version of the **Ishikawa-mon** gate, itself burnt down in the mid-18th century and rebuilt in 1788.

However, Kanazawa's main tourist magnet is **Kenrokuen** garden, the largest and best-known of the 'Three Most Beautiful Landscape Gardens' in Japan (the others are Mito's Kairakuen, see page 60, and Okayama's Korakuen, see page 163). Kenrokuen was laid out in its present form in 1819 by the 12th Lord Maeda, Narinaga, who also placed the much-fussed-over stone lantern called **Kotojitoro** (Lantern of the Koto Bridge) beside **Kasumigaike**, the garden's 'Pond of Mist'. The lantern is so called because its base is held to resemble in shape the bridge used for raising and separating the strings of a horizontal harp (*koto*). In fact, the entire park is much fussed over, and visitors in search of a simple stroll through attractive surroundings may well find this modest ambition frustrated by the streams of tourists and their bullhorn-wielding guides who crowd the narrow paths from morning till night.

Still, Kanazawa has other attractions, many of them to be found in its atmospheric back streets, and the city's ongoing attempts to encourage tourism have occasionally taken a happier form than the noisy exploitation at Kenrokuen; notably, the provision of maps and signboards to facilitate leisurely walking tours.

North of Kanazawa the rugged **Noto Peninsula** juts out into the Japan Sea, providing the visitor who wants to experience the rural out-of-the-wayness of this region with the same sort of opportunities presented by Sado island. The small city of **Wajima** (population 33,000) is noted for its lacquerware, and the peninsula as a whole is famous for a virile form of folk drumming in which the drummers wear colourful and hideously carved demon masks.

(Preceding page) Rice harvest in Fukushima prefecture. The smallness and inaccessibility of many paddies ensure that most farming operations continue to be performed by hand

154

South of Kanazawa, on the coast near the city of **Komatsu** (population 104,000), where Kanazawa's airport is located, stands the site of the **Ataka** barrier gate, by far the most celebrated of the old checkpoints owing to its association with the flight of Yoshitsune and his quick-witted retainer, Benkei, in 1187. The ruse by which they succeeded in getting through the barrier is the subject of the Noh play *Ataka* and of the Kabuki play, *Kanjincho* (The Subscription List), which rivals in popularity the spirit-stirring *Chushingura* (see page 37). According to legend, Yoshitsune, on Benkei's advice, disguised himself as the party's bearer and, in full view of the barrier guards, Benkei beat him for his tardiness, an action unthinkable if the ostensible bearer were really Benkei's master. As with *Chushingura,* the play depicts the death-defying loyalty of a retainer for his lord, and this loyalty and the event that epitomized it are celebrated further in the small museum that stands on the beach near the barrier's original site.

In the extreme south of Ishikawa prefecture, near the border with Gifu, stands **Mount Hakusan** (2,702 metres, 8,865 feet), the centre of the **Hakusan National Park** and, like Tateyama, a peak regarded as sacred. Ishikawa prefecture is well supplied with hot-spring resorts, most of them sprawling and well developed. Among the better known are **Yuwaka**, southeast of Kanazawa, and **Yamanaka, Yamashiro, Awazu** and **Katayamazu**, which form a group around the little city of **Kaga** (population 65,000) near the prefectural border with Fukui. Near Yamashiro lies the small village of **Kutani**, famous since the 17th century for the colourfully-glazed pottery produced in the nearby kilns; pottery which has a clear affinity with the products of Arita in Kyushu, from whose potters the Kutani men learned their skills. Kutani ware is sold in most of the prefecture's souvenir shops.

The heavily indented coast of **Fukui** prefecture is attractive enough for it to have been designed a Quasi-National Park, although one part of it has earned its reputation for a grimmer reason. The Wakasa Bay area, particularly the city of **Tsuruga** (population 62,000), long a major port, is now Japan's most rapidly developing centre for atomic power, the newest of its 12 reactors having been completed in May 1987. These reactors together produce about 9.09 million kilowatts, which is slightly more than 35 percent of all atomic-generated power in Japan. A 1985 film, independently produced, called *Ikiteru Uchi ga Hana na no yo Shindara sore made yo To Sengan* (The While You're Alive Life is Like a Flower But When You're Dead You've Had It Party Manifesto) examined in a somewhat avant-garde fashion a persistent rumour that has dogged the Tsuruga atomic facilities: that the dangerous areas around the reactor cores are cleaned and maintained by unskilled labourers press-ganged into the work by criminal organizations, and that there have been several fatalities which, since the labourers are recruited precisely because they have no families or fixed addresses, have been hidden with swift efficiency. No hard proof that this appalling rumour is true has ever come to light, but it provides a vivid illustration of one of the reasons for Japan's alleged 'nuclear allergy' (see also pages 157–60).

The capital of the prefecture is **Fukui** city (population 241,000), traditionally famous for its silk industry but now more heavily committed to the production of man- rather than worm-made fibres. A short train ride east from Fukui brings the visitor to the gates of **Eiheiji**, one of the most beautiful and beautifully situated temples in Japan. Eiheiji is a temple of the Soto Zen sect, founded in 1246 by Dogen. Soto Zen differs slightly in emphasis from Rinzai Zen (see page 94) in that, whereas Rinzai tends to stress an intellectual discipline, Soto concentrates more on a strict physical regimen and on simple silent meditation. In many ways Dogen's writings and sayings encapsulate more perfectly than any others the elusive but distinct spirit of Zen. He believed that simply by sitting still and doing nothing a man could gain a profound understanding of the world around him and his part in it. He also believed, much as the early Shinto animists did, in a tangible life-force, comparable to a divinity, that inspired all nature:

> *The landscape of the mountains,*
> *The sound of streams—*
> *All are the body and voice of Buddha.*

Eiheiji attracts a large number of tourists, not all of them inclined to be as quiet and reverent as the temple and its teachings deserve. But the temple survives them with equanimity.

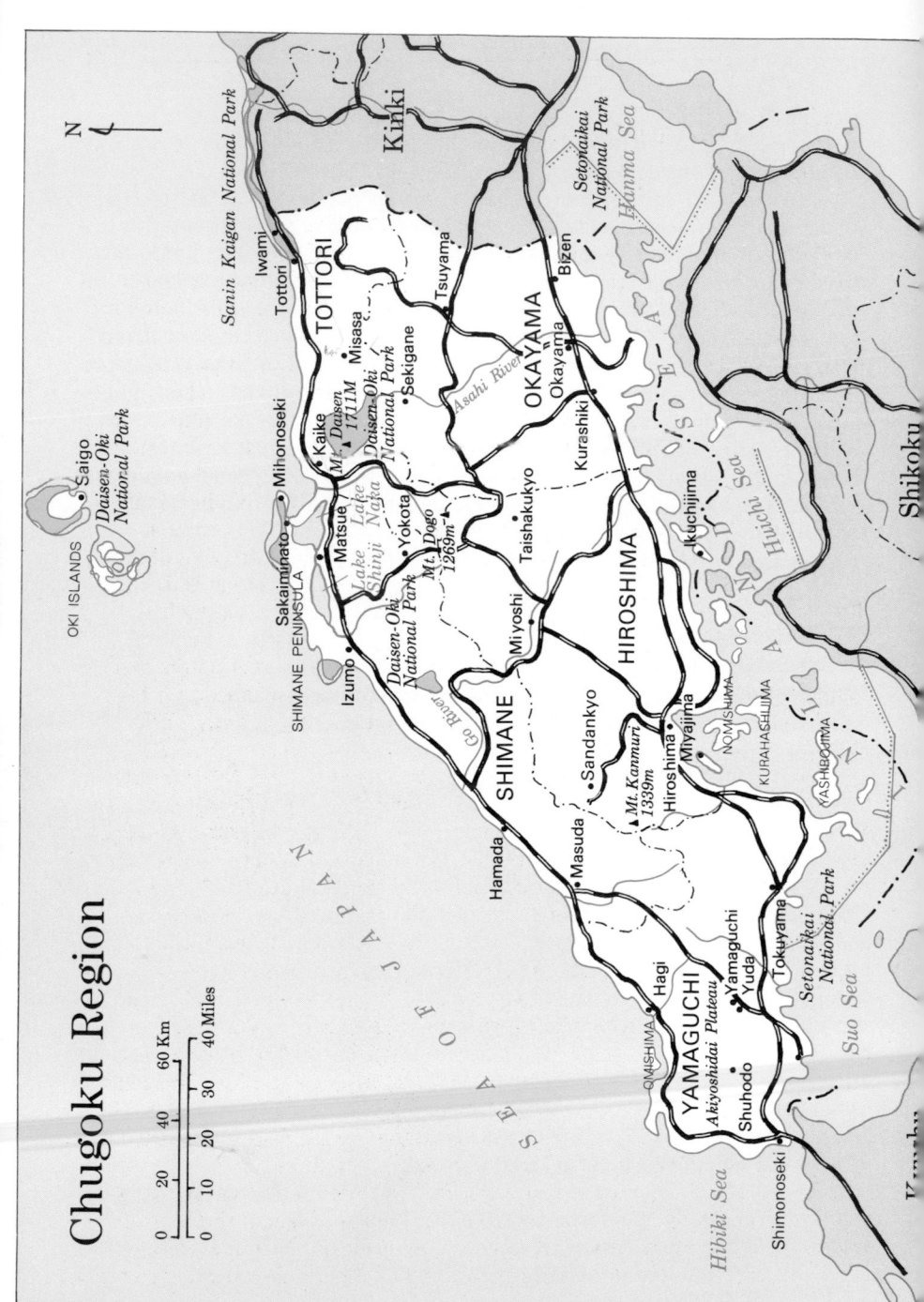

Hiroshima and The Chugoku Region

The Politics of Peace

Hiroshima (population 899,000), the commercial, administrative and
industrial centre of the Chugoku region, is a pleasant city, pulsing with
prosperity. Its roads and pavements are clean and airy, its shopping streets
roofed to make fashionable arcades. The reconstructed donjon of its feudal
castle, originally built in 1589, has been made the centre of a spacious park.
Its professional baseball club, the Hiroshima Toyo Carp, has a fanatically
devoted following not confined to the region, and is usually a strong
contender for the Central League pennant, which it has won five times.
These, however, are unlikely to be the associations uppermost in the visitor's
mind.

You can play a game of word association with the names of cities that
suffered large-scale destruction during the Second World War. Dresden:
china. Coventry: cathedral. Berlin: wall. London: fog (this at least would be
the response of very many Japanese people who are brought up to believe
that the red-eyed British must grope blindly through the streets of their
capital, alerted to the position of dangerous road junctions by the rattle of
hansom cabs). Nagasaki: well, there are the martyrs if you are Catholic and
Madame Butterfly if you are not. But Hiroshima leaves you little scope for
the exercise of imagination, and such scope as it does leave the city
authorities are particularly anxious to limit.

The authorities regard their city and its experience as a beacon lighting
the world toward peace, and they have struggled to ensure that only one
association should leap into the foreign mind, and into the malleable minds of
Japanese youngsters. They have repeatedly mounted exhibitions abroad and
invited important foreign dignitaries, such as former U.S. president Jimmy
Carter and the late Swedish prime minister Olof Palme, to visit Hiroshima
and say memorable things about the horrors of a nuclear holocaust and the
necessity of avoiding one in the future. Their most frequented tourist site
(nowadays an obligatory destination for many children on organized school
trips) is the Peace Park which lies at the point marking the hypocentre of
Hiroshima's atomic explosion. The Peace Park contains a Peace Memorial
Museum, a Statue of a Prayer for Peace, a Flame of Peace, a Children's Peace
Monument, a Peace Bell, and the road leading to it is called Peace Boulevard.
One cannot be long in Hiroshima before one starts counting the occurrences
of the word *heiwa* (peace) in its landmarks and tourist literature.

Nor can one be long in the Peace Park and its museum without noting a
number of unsettling circumstances, chief of which, perhaps, is the complete
absence of any sense of historical context. It is as though the bomb fell on
Hiroshima, figuratively as well as literally, out of the blue. Nowhere is there

any suggestion that it might have been triggered by past actions. Nowhere is there the least sign that any other nation or race might have suffered comparable wartime tragedies. This includes the Korean victims of the atomic bombing, estimated at around 20,000, who were in Hiroshima in August 1945 because they had been conscripted into the Japanese army or to work as forced labour in the munitions factories and docks. The city authorities have in fact resisted attempts by Korean lobbies in Japan to erect a monument to these victims in the Peace Park, although one now stands elsewhere. Some years ago Arnold Toynbee's granddaughter, Polly, was invited to visit Japan by the Sokagakkai, a lay Buddhist organization (see page 75) whose leader, Ikeda Daisaku, had published a series of tape-recorded 'dialogues' with Polly's famous grandfather. Polly was taken to the Hiroshima Peace Park and appears to have experienced there some of these potential discomforts. Later, she complained in a British newspaper that 'Hiroshima is the shrine to Japanese innocence', drawing attention to the fact that we are shown there, in great and disturbing detail, what terrible things the world did to Japan, but we are nowhere given any inkling of what Japan might have done to anyone else. I don't imagine Polly will be invited again.

Sympathy, even more than respect, is the attitude most required by Japan of her international partners and competitors, and one finds it solicited over and over again in the incessant reiterations of how 'small' Japan is, how 'misunderstood', how lacking in raw materials, how bent under the weight of its island complex and so on. Hiroshima, of course, provides sympathy seekers with a field day and, in a certain mood, one can stroll round the Peace Park, looking up at the Japanese flag flying from its tall pole (wondering why, if the park is dedicated to *world* peace, no other nations' flags are in evidence), itching to exclaim at the top of one's voice that feeling sorry for yourself is not the same as deploring the disasters of war, and that encouraging tourists to feel sorry for you (and foreign dignitaries to express their sorrow in public) is not the same as working for world peace.

Nonetheless, it is impossible, and no doubt immoral, to gainsay the extent and reality of the suffering visited on the people of Hiroshima, most of them civilians. Some 200,000 are thought to have died in the bombing and in the years since from related causes, chiefly radiation-induced leukemia. If, by coincidence, 200,000 is also a common estimate of the number of Chinese people, mostly civilians, who were killed by the Japanese army within one month of its entry into Nanking, let that stand recorded too, but let it not detract from the unspeakable horrors to which Hiroshima's museum, for all its want of context, provides soul-racking testimony.

When the Enola Gay, a specially equipped B29 bomber, took off from the small island of Tinian in the Marianas early on the morning of 6 August, 1945, neither pilot nor crew knew for sure their destination. The possible targets had been narrowed to four—Nagasaki, Niigata, Kokura and

Hiroshima. The final selection was made on the grounds that Hiroshima, that summer morning, was enjoying the most cloudless sky. This meant that scientific observation of the bombing could proceed with little or no impediment. In fact one reason for Hiroshima's inclusion on the short list was its topography: it is surrounded on three sides by hills, and this, it was theorized, would not only enhance the bomb's destructiveness but would allow satisfyingly accurate measurements of its destructiveness to be made.

Though it regards itself today as a beacon of peace, Hiroshima was, for much of its modern history, a city embroiled in military adventures. During the Sino-Japanese war of 1894–5, for example, the Imperial Army Headquarters was located neither in Tokyo nor in the old capital of Kyoto recently vacated by the emperor, but in Hiroshima. The Emperor Meiji, then commander-in-chief of his nation's forces, spent the duration of the war at Hiroshima Castle attending personally to its direction. The castle and practically everything within four kilometres (2.5 miles) of it were completely destroyed by the Enola Gay's four-ton payload.

Those who have sought to defend the atomic bombing have usually argued that it saved more lives than it took. If the Allies had landed in force on the beaches of mainland Japan before the signing of an article of surrender, they insist, casualties on both sides, including Japanese civilians, would have been far higher than they were at Hiroshima, and they cite the grim example of the battle for Okinawa (see page 210) to support their case. Had the Japanese succeeded in developing the atomic bomb before the United States (in fact, there was an active programme of development), the Japanese authorities would not have hesitated to sanction its use. What was wanted was an unmistakable demonstration that the war was lost for Japan in order to encourage the so-far reluctant Japanese government to steel itself for the inevitable capitulation.

These arguments have been hotly opposed. If a mere demonstration was necessary, why was it not conducted over the ocean instead of over a densely populated city where the bulk of casualties were certain to be civilian? Even assuming that the bombing of Hiroshima was unavoidable, can the same be said of Nagasaki, where, three days later, a repeat demonstration sealed the deaths of another 140,000? Besides, it has been claimed, mediation efforts were already under way and the Japanese government had itself put out peace feelers through a neutral party. All that was needed was patience and a little time.

With the benefit of hindsight, the arguments on both sides have grown more and more plausible as they have settled into the bleak realm of academic debate. Nowadays, though these historical questions remain important, they have been superseded in many minds by broader-ranging ones, such as: what constitutes a crime against humanity? If Auschwitz was such a crime, what about Dresden? If Nanking or the Bataan Death March, what about Hiroshima or the secret bombing of Cambodia? A pressing problem, for Japan at least, is the carefully selective way in which the horrors of war are taught, remembered, commemorated and deplored. Mention of 13 December 1937 (the date of the Japanese army's rapacious entry into Nanking) will elicit a look of blank incomprehension from the majority of Japanese people—indeed most will not even be able to name the year of that calamity—whereas 6 August is burned indelibly into the collective self-condoling consciousness. Perhaps that is only to be expected, but is it, therefore, less regrettable?

Personally, I think that a tour of Hiroshima's museum should be high on the itinerary of as many visitors to Japan as can be persuaded to go there. But I also think that those visitors will do well to equip themselves before they go, through a judicious amount of reading and thought, with the perspective necessary to a balanced appraisal of the things that they will see there.

Hiroshima's single most famous monument to the bombing stands just outside the Peace Park, at its northeast corner. This is the ruined **Atomic Bomb Dome**, the skeletal remains of the Industrial Promotion Hall left standing in the condition in which it was found in the aftermath. It is all the more eloquent for the prosperity and newness that gleam and bustle all around it. It has been calculated that the bomb exploded some 570 metres (1,870 feet) in the air about 160 metres (325 feet) southwest of this dome at 8.15 a.m. Similarly eloquent (much more so than the mediocre statuary) is the stone chest in the park that contains the names of all those who have died from bomb-related causes and is inscribed with these words addressed to their spirits, 'Sleep in peace: the error will not be repeated'. Most eloquent of all are the strings of tiny coloured folded paper cranes that festoon the **Children's Peace Monument**, and which are made and hung here as prayers for peace mostly by visiting school parties. Each year on 6 August a commemorative ceremony is held in the park.

In Hiroshima Prefecture

Except along its heavily industrialized coast Hiroshima is a green, rolling prefecture rising to its highest and most rugged points at its borders. Near the border with Okayama in the east lies the **Taishakukyo Gorge** and near the border with Yamaguchi in the west the **Sandankyo Gorge**, both picturesque and surrounded by attractive countryside.

But the chief tourist destination outside the prefectural capital is the small island of **Itsukushima**, also called **Miyajima** (population 3,300), which lies a short distance by ferry from the shore some 20 kilometres (12.5 miles) west of Hiroshima city, and is one of the 'Three Most Beautiful Scenic Views' in Japan (together with Amanohashidate, see page 99, and Matsushima, page 120). Miyajima means 'shrine island' and its chief attraction is the **Itsukushima Shrine**, founded at the beginning of the ninth century.

Particularly famous is the *torii* gate, erected in 1875, the largest such gate in Japan. Visitors to other shrines will have noticed how the precincts of most are entered through such a gate as this, serving to mark·an imaginary boundary between the mundane and the worshipful. Here, this line has been drawn some 160 metres (523 feet) out from the shore, emphasizing the sanctity not only of the treadable land but of the untreadable sea. The gate also serves as a thought-provoking reminder that all three of Japan's 'Most Beautiful Scenic Views'—this, the sandbar and the pine-clad islands—depend for their beauty on being surrounded, like Japan itself, by water. In fact, the main shrine buildings stand on stilted platforms over the sea so that, when the tide rises, the whole edifice appears to float. In the past no births or deaths were permitted to occur on Itsukushima, both being regarded as conditions of impurity, and there is still no graveyard or crematorium there, the dead being ferried to the mainland and the returning mourners ritually purified before disembarking again on the island. Like Nara Park, Itsukushima and the precincts of its shrine are known for the deer that wander tamely about them.

The Rest of the Chugoku Region

All of Honshu west of the Kinki region is called **Chugoku** (Middle Country), not to be confused with Chubu, the Middle Region dealt with in the last chapter, nor with China, the Japanese word for which is also 'Chugoku', written, confusingly enough, with the same two ideograms. Since Chugoku consists so clearly of the western extremity of the main island, it seems oddly named; but the explanation must lie in the fact that it spans the gap between Kyushu, where the first Yamato Japanese settlements are thought to have been located, and the Nara basin, where the first Yamato state was born. The 'middle' region between these focal points must at some time have been crossed by a considerable migration.

In addition to Hiroshima, Chugoku consists of the four prefectures of **Okayama, Yamaguchi, Shimane** and **Tottori.** In some ways it is a microcosm of the entire island of Honshu. The southern coast, washed by the once-romantic Inland Sea, is heavily industrialized and the bulk of the population of the region lives in its cities. The northern coast, like the rest of the Japan Sea side of Honshu, is relatively unspoiled and still primarily agricultural. In the centre is a spinal chain of mountains which, while not so high and forbidding as those of middle or northern Honshu, are rugged enough to have deterred much large-scale settlement, and the only inland cities of major importance in the region are Tsuyama, in Okayama prefecture, and Yamaguchi city, which has the smallest population of any prefectural capital in Japan.

So far as tourism goes, the Chugoku region is relatively underdeveloped, most sightseers tending to pass straight through it on their way to Kyushu.

But its rolling countryside is very pleasant, its climate, except on the Japan Sea coast in winter, comparatively mild, and it offers the visitor several destinations of historical and cultural significance; among them the Izumo Taisha Shrine, second only in importance to the Grand Shrine of Ise, the pottery towns of Hagi and Bizen, and the lovely old willow-lined walks and buildings in the city of Kurashiki.

Okayama city (population 546,000), the capital of **Okayama** prefecture, contains the third of the 'Three Most Beautiful Landscaped Gardens' of Japan, **Korakuen**, completed in 1700 (for the others, see Kairakuen, page 60 and Kenrokuen, page 151). Some 9 kilometres (6 miles) west of the city stands the **Kibitsu Shrine**, whose present buildings, picturesquely sited on a hill, date from 1425. And about 26 kilometres (16 miles) east of Okayama stands the small city of **Bizen** (population 33,000), which has given its name to the famous iron-pigmented pottery produced in the neighbouring kilns.

But the chief tourist centre of the prefecture is the city of **Kurashiki** (population 410,000), which contains museums of local history, archaeology, folkcraft and pottery, and an art gallery (the **Ohara Gallery**) which boasts a world-famous collection of French Impressionist paintings. The folkcraft and archaeology museums are housed in distinctive black-and-white, feudal-era buildings that were once storehouses or granaries. (The *kura* in Kurashiki means 'storehouse'; the same *kura* as in *Kamakura*.) There are other old, well-preserved buildings in Kurashiki, almost all of them located, like the museums, on or near the city's pleasant willow-lined canal, the environs of which offer an unusually restful place in which to stroll and browse, or take a sightseeing tour by rickshaw. Kurashiki is also the Honshu terminus for road and rail traffic across the 9.4-kilometre (5.5-mile) set of bridges called collectively **Seto Ohashi** (Great Bridge of Seto, 'Seto' being a name for the Inland Sea area). The other terminus is Sakaide city in Kagawa prefecture (see page 181). The bridges, opened in April 1988, form one of three land routes which will eventually connect Honshu with Shikoku, diminishing even further the romantic associations which the now crowded and smoky Inland Sea could once lay claim to.

The chief city of **Yamaguchi** prefecture is not the small prefectural capital but the heavily industrial port of **Shimonoseki** (population 269,000) at the extreme western tip of Honshu, connected to the island of Kyushu by tunnel, bridge and ferry. When the **Kanmon Bridge** first opened in 1973 it was available to pedestrians and ranked as the largest suspension bridge in the Orient. Nowadays it is neither, pedestrians having been banned from the bridge because too many of them jumped off it, and the Korean construction company, Hyundai, having since built a longer road link between the island of Penang and Butterworth in West Malaysia. However, the water that flows

August 6, 1945

"Oyamada!" I heard the upperclassman calling me. Apparently he had been calling my name for some time. Hurriedly I started to move out from under the press.

To say that I saw it at that instant is not quite accurate. The phenomenon that occurred at that instant registered on my eyeballs, but I had no way of knowing what it was. And whatever it was, it came and went with extraordinary speed. At first I thought it was something I had dreamed.

The open space in front of the factory that was visible beyond the glass window was filled with flames. But it was not that the ground was on fire and sending up flames. So I suppose I'd have to say that the flames were spewed down from the sky and were licking at the earth.

But then with astonishing speed the instant came to an end and reality returned. Only it was a kind of stunned reality, full of terrible contradictions.

Darkness was enveloping everything in front of my eyes, but at the same time I could perceive that the heavy beam that supported the roof of the workshop was lying on the ground right by my feet. The upperclassman who had been calling my name was standing in a stupor beside it. He was staring with a look of amazement at the blood spurting out of his shoulder where the arm joined it. His arm dangled limply.

As I finally began to take in the scene around me, the first words that came to my mind were, "Am I going to die in a place like this?" As yet, though, there was no sense of fear in the thought. Only a kind of astonishment. The darkness that had surrounded me probably lasted only for a moment, as did the roaring noise over my head, though I don't actually remember hearing the roar.

When the scene in front of me had brightened a little, I commenced instinctively to move around. I was crawling and searching *for some way out of the tangle of machinery, disengaged machine belts and debris of smashed-in roof that covered me. Nearby I could see a triangular window. The window had originally been square but it had been completely blown out, leaving only the twisted frame.*

I managed to make my way outside. Everything was quiet and there was no one around. But as I started to run, I saw someone's head sticking out right beside the narrow entrance. It was Dragonfly. His wings and body had been crushed under a thick beam and just his head, mixed with some kind of white substance, was poking out. Bloody vomit had come out of his mouth and he was dead.

I ran without stopping till I reached the open space in front of the factory. There everyone was running around. I noticed that the commotion was making little ripples on the stagnant gray pond where water was stored for fire fighting. The door of the air-raid shelter had been blown off and I could see smoke, apparently from burning paraffin, pouring out and ascending in a column. A hot wind was blowing from somewhere and a strange heaviness in the air seemed to envelop me. At that moment terror for the first time took violent hold of my mind. Waves of nausea swept over me as I ran toward the factory gate.

Here and there on the ground, orange flames were leaping up from pieces of shattered buildings. There were so many fires I thought someone must have set them deliberately. In the sky directly overhead, dark, low lying masses of air flowed by, but in the direction of the harbor the sky was clear blue.

Needless to say, neither I nor anyone else had the slightest idea what had brought about this sudden freakish event. What in the world kind of day was this! We hadn't heard a single bomb drop, we hadn't seen a trace of an enemy plane. The sky had been perfectly peaceful. . .

Katsuzo Oda, Human Ashes

under the Kanmon Bridge retains its deep historical significances, the chief of these being that it was here, in the Straits of **Dannoura** in 1185, that the Heike were finally defeated by the Genji, heralding the movement of real power from imperial Kyoto to the Kanto region which laid the foundation for much subsequent Japanese history. It was also here, in these narrow straits, that a pivotal event occurred in the process leading to the Meiji Restoration of 1868. Yamaguchi prefecture was the home of the warlike and xenophobic Choshu clan, who were among the prime movers in the struggle to topple the Tokugawa shogunate. Angered at what they considered to be a conciliatory attitude toward foreign powers on the part of the shogunate, the Choshu shore batteries in Shimonoseki took it upon themselves to open fire on foreign ships passing through the straits. This happened in 1863. In 1864 a combined expedition of American, Dutch, British and French warships bombarded the batteries and the Choshu forts, forcing the shogunate to intervene against the unrepentant clan, a move which was to spark an alliance between the Choshu and Satsuma fiefs that eventually brought the Tokugawas tumbling down. This small military engagement is still known in Yamaguchi as the *Bakan Senso* (Bakan War), *Bakan* (literally, 'horse barrier') being an old name for the straits and neighbouring shores.

Whether or not that name contains a clue to the migration of mounted tribes from the Korean Peninsula to Kyushu, and then eastward into Honshu, which some historians postulate must have happened in pre-Yamato times, has to remain a matter of conjecture. The city's chief shrine, too, has an equestrian reference in its name. This is the **Akama Shrine** ('Akamagaseki'—'Red-Horse Barrier'—being yet another old name for the region), and its precincts contain the small Buddhist temple of **Amidaji**, well known to readers of Lafcadio Hearn's ghost stories, or to fans of Kobayashi Masaki's 1964 film version of them, *Kwaidan,* as the temple in which the ghosts of the drowned Heike forced Hoichi, a blind lute player, to entertain them with his powerful rendition of the tale of the defeat at Dannoura. When the priest of the temple attempted to protect Hoichi from the ghosts by writing holy sutras all over his body, the ghosts wrenched his ears off, these having been left unprotected by the careless priest. In itself, Amidaji is hardly worth a visit but, for those alive to its associations, it is a sombre and moving place in which to spend an hour meditating on the tragic vision with which the Heike saga inspired subsequent generations of poets, playwrights and painters, since its tiny burial ground contains the green, crumbling graves of 14 of the drowned warriors.

There is a regular boat service between Shimonoseki and the South Korean port of Pusan.

The Japan Sea coast of Yamaguchi prefecture is mostly unspoiled and the area centering on the island of **Omishima**, which is joined by a bridge to the mainland, is especially pleasant. Just east of Omishima is the old castle town of **Hagi** (population 54,000), best known for its kilns which have been producing pottery here since the early 17th century. The castle has vanished except for its ruined foundations which, as often, have become the centrepiece of a park; but the pottery industry continues to flourish, and its delicately glazed ceremonial tea bowls are especially prized.

Inland, the principal focus of tourism in Yamaguchi is the karst plateau to the northwest of the prefectural capital, under which sprawls one of the largest stalactite caves in the world. The **Akiyoshidai** plateau is now a Quasi-National Park, and the **Shuhodo** cave features not only pools, waterfalls, streams and limestone pillars in shapes reminiscent of natural objects, but a convenient post-Palaeolithic elevator for visitors not feeling prehistoric enough to regain the surface on foot. **Yamaguchi** city (population 115,000) is a good base from which to explore the area, particularly since it contains the sleepy hot spring spa of **Yuda**. The city's most conspicuous religious edifice is the ferroconcrete Roman Catholic cathedral built in 1950 to commemorate the brief residence in 1551 of Saint Francis Xavier, the pioneering Spanish missionary who was the first to attempt the somewhat thankness task of persuading the refractory Japanese of the existence of a higher deity than those from which they claimed descent. Being themselves a chosen people, what use had they for a God who had committed the catastrophic error of fathering His son upon some other race?

Besides, Japanese people who felt themselves succumbing to Xavier's persuasions needed only to have their attention directed to the **Izumo Taisha Shrine** in neighbouring **Shimane** prefecture for sanity and refractoriness to come pouring back. Izumo is reputedly the oldest shrine in Japan; its records indicate that it was founded in mythological times, and for much of its history it was subject to the same ritual reconstruction as continues at Ise. Most of the present structures were rebuilt in the late 19th century. The Honden, or main shrine, however, dates from 1744, when it was reconstructed for the 24th time, and it is built in the oldest architectural style known in Japan, the most easily recognizable features of which are the huge crossbeams called *chigi* and the fact that the building is designed to be entered end-on rather than through one of the longer sides. The shrine is dedicated to the male deity Okuninushi no Mikoto, whose earthly palace is said to have stood on this spot, and who is credited with having instructed the Japanese in the arts of farming, fishing, medicine, and the raising of silk worms. As at Ise, the innermost and holiest part of the shrine is surrounded by a fence, and access is thereby denied. The expatriate author and journalist manqué, Lafcadio Hearn, who lived for a while in nearby Matsue city, visited the shrine and appears from what he subsequently wrote to have been under the impression that he had been permitted to enter the holy of holies at Izumo ('... I stood before the shrine of the Great Deity of Kitzuki, as the first

Occidental to whom that privilege had been accorded ...'), whereas he in fact got no further than the second storey of a gatehouse that partly overlooks the inner sanctum, and to which, in more recent times, the Soviet ambassador and the present author have also been admitted. Hearn wrote, 'This is the Shrine of the Father of a Race; this is the symbolic centre of a nation's reverence for its past.' And although, except for the sex of the progenitor, that description more properly applies to Ise, Hearn's sprinkled capitals plainly testify to the awe with which Izumo inspired him. According to local legend, thousands of gods from all over the country congregate at Izumo each October for their annual conference, which is why October is known throughout the rest of Japan as *Kannazuki* (Month Without Gods).

Matsue (population 135,000) is the prefectural capital of Shimane, and is closely associated in many Japanese minds with the aforementioned Hearn, storyteller and dreamer, half Irish, half Greek, with one good eye, who settled down to work there as a high school teacher in 1890. Hearn married a local woman in December of that year and clearly planned to live in Matsue for a long time; but the Japan Sea winter proved too much for his delicate health and, after little more than a year there, he moved to Kyushu, then to Kobe, where he took Japanese citizenship, changing his name to Koizumi Yakumo, and subsequently to Tokyo, where he died in 1904. That so few Westerners have ever heard of Lafcadio Hearn, let alone read his writings, is a real puzzle to most Japanese people, for whom his name is a household word, and among whom he is widely regarded as a pillar of English letters. Partly this reflects the incorrigible possessiveness of the Japanese, and partly their taste, where Western art is concerned, for tail-end Romantics and russet-tinted *fin-de-siècle* gloom. (The same taste stands revealed in the unshakable conviction that Millet's *Angelus* is one of the great monuments of Western painting and Sarasate's *Zigeunerweisen* one of the world's great pieces of violin music.) Hearn's house, still lived in, can be visited at the risk of some acerbic remarks from the irascible old owner, and a small museum dedicated to his life and work stands next door.

Matsue also has a well-preserved feudal castle, whose present donjon dates from 1642, and is a good base from which to explore **Lake Shinji**, Izumo Taisha, and the coastal area of the Shimane Peninsula around **Mihonoseki**, which is part of the **Daisen-Oki National Park**.

Sakaiminato in Tottori prefecture is the embarkation point for visits to the attractively distant **Oki** islands (population 30,000), the main port of which, **Saigo**, lies some 70 kilometres (43.5 miles) from the mainland, out in the Japan Sea. The islands are also a part of the Daisen-Oki National Park and, like Sado (see page 147), have historically been places of exile. Among the highest ranking exiles to Oki were the Emperors Gotoba and Godaigo, both banished for their attempts to wrest power from the military government in Kamakura. Like Sado too, the islands are a place which Japan's economic miracle has uncaringly passed by, and afford a rugged but peaceful refuge from the clang and clatter of modern urban life. A traditional form of bull-fighting, called *togyu,* is preserved there: not man against bull, but bull against bull; and the visitor fortunate enough to be present at one of the major events in the bull-fight calendar will see the animals paraded about, pampered, dressed and ranked like champion sumo wrestlers. The sport survives only in remote parts of Japan, including rural Okinawa.

The third section of the Daisen-Oki National Park stretches from **Mount Daisen** (1,711 metres or 5,613 feet) in **Tottori** prefecture south to straddle the prefectural boundary between Tottori and Okayama. Daisen is one more Something-or-Other Fuji, this time 'Hoki-Fuji', 'Hoki' being an old name for the region, and the mountain has good camping sites and ski slopes, as well as the remains of an eighth-century temple. East of Daisen lie the well-known hot spring resorts of **Sekigane** and **Misasa**. Tottori is especially well provided with hot springs, and the coastal spas of **Kaike** and **Iwami** offer more interesting and relaxing overnight stays than do any of the larger towns. East of the rather dull prefectural capital, **Tottori** city (population 131,000), lie the **Tottori Sand Dunes** *(sakyu),* which occupy some 16 kilometres (10 miles) of the shoreline and are particularly striking since the rest of this coast, especially that part of it incorporated in the Sanin Kaigan National Park (see also page 111), which begins here and stretches east across the width of Hyogo, is noted for its pine-clad shoulders and undulating cliffs and fjords— not the sort of landscape where one would expect to find a sizeable chunk of what could easily pass for the Sahara desert. No doubt its un-Japaneseness accounts for the presence of the camels, whose services have been secured by entrepreneurs of the dunes to supply visitors with rides and the material for exotic souvenir photographs.

The Inland Sea and Shikoku

This Side of Paradise

For the modern Japanese, the Inland Sea has become a paradigm of lost innocence. Kawabata Yasunari once remarked that, following the humiliation of defeat and surrender, Japanese authors of the postwar period had no choice but to write elegies; and a significant number of those elegies—in book and on film—have focussed on the islands of the Inland Sea. How much pastoral 'innocence' the area possessed in prewar times depends on the rosiness of the spectacles through which you view it. During the feudal period the Inland Sea islands were notorious as the haunts of pirates. Like most rural areas, the islands suffered from chronic poverty and crippling disease and these drawbacks to country life were magnified by the extra isolation with which the surrounding sea had burdened them. With the beginnings of industrialization the great ports along the southern coast of the Chugoku region—Tokuyama, Iwakuni, Hiroshima, Kure, Fukuyama and so on, none of which was opened to foreign trade in the way that Yokohama and Kobe were—launched themselves on a furious round of military and mercantile shipbuilding and related activities that continued ever clangier and smokier until August 1945, when they were silenced long enough for the elegies to begin.

The attractions of the Inland Sea islands to the urban Japanese imagination are complex. At one level, they simply partake in the same pastoral Never-Never-Land fiction that has shed its fairy light on Tohoku and transformed *kokeshi* into collectable souvenirs (see page 120). At a deeper level, because the sea is *inland* it belongs safely and exclusively to Japan in a way that the surrounding seas do not. All other seas are chasms, and to cross them, even from one Japanese island to another, is to be plucked up by the roots.

There are two ways of looking at islands; islands are either fortresses or dungeons. Throughout most of their history, the British took the fortress view of their country and regarded the encompassing sea both as a moat defensive and as a royal road to wealth and empire. But the Japanese have usually taken the dungeon view, hence the repeated stress on their being burdened with an island complex. Their consensus has always been that the surrounding sea weakens, not strengthens them, and it was never regarded as a royal road but as a discouraging obstacle to the full enjoyment of civilization and power. The Japanese were not great seagoers as the British were, and to them the sea was an adversary, never an ally.

The Inland Sea was the one glorious exception. By surrounding it, they tamed it and made it theirs. Thus its islands, far more than the offshore islands of exile like Sado and Oki, are protected microcosms of the whole, and the Inland Sea, contained and womblike, is the seminal fluid by which they live. It is as though the entire area were the model for a wholly imaginary universe in which Japan is perfectly self-contained, self-bounded and self-made.

The neutral observer might be forgiven for concluding that such spoliation as this paradise has suffered in modern times is due not so much to defeat and foreign occupation as to the greed of home-grown industrialists who have rarely hesitated to sacrifice fairyland on the altar of progress. One of the lessons of history, surely, is that innocence is less often lost than squandered. It is not so much the islands that have suffered as the seminal fluid that surrounds them. The red tides that wash through it—the result of the effluvia pumped into it from Osaka Bay and all points west—the massed shipping that clogs it, the bridges that span it, the smog that shrouds it, the oil spilled into it... Kawabata was right: we live in a time of elegies, and the Inland Sea provides the aptest of subjects.

But for all that, if the weather is fine and the wind is in the right direction (i.e. towards, not from, Osaka Bay) the islands of the Inland Sea can still afford a glimpse or two of what has to pass in our tarnished century for something like paradise. As an older expatriate writer on Japan once remarked to me in a tone of friendly chastisement: it is the difference between seeing that the cup is still half full and seeing only that it is half empty.

The Inland Sea *(Setonaikai)* is that body of water sandwiched between Honshu in the north and Shikoku in the south; and the 750 or so inhabited islands that dot it are variously administered by six prefectures—Hyogo, Okayama, Kagawa, Ehime, Hiroshima and Yamaguchi—but for once it seems sensible to ignore the prefectural boundaries and to treat the area of the Inland Sea as an indivisible unit. In 1934 the area was designated the **Setonaikai National Park**.

Two of the islands have already been described: Awajishima, the largest (see page 111), and Itsukushima, the most visited (see page 160). The next largest and most visited is **Shodoshima** (population 41,000), at the centre of which stand the picturesque **Kankakei** peaks and gorge, the peaks rising to 816 metres (2,677 feet). But Shodoshima's chief claim on the visitor's attention is its round of 88 pilgrim sites, associated with the prolific ninth-century temple-builder, Kobo Daishi (the posthumous name for Kukai), and revered in a minor way by the Shingon sect which he founded. Kobo Daishi may have visited Shodoshima round about 808–9, although, quite uncharacteristically, he seems not to have founded any temples there. Most of the present pilgrim sites—temples, grottoes and small monuments—were established by Shingon priests in 1686 in imitation of the 88 temples on neighbouring Shikoku, which Kobo Daishi definitely did either visit or found and which form today the best known and most devoutly followed pilgrim's

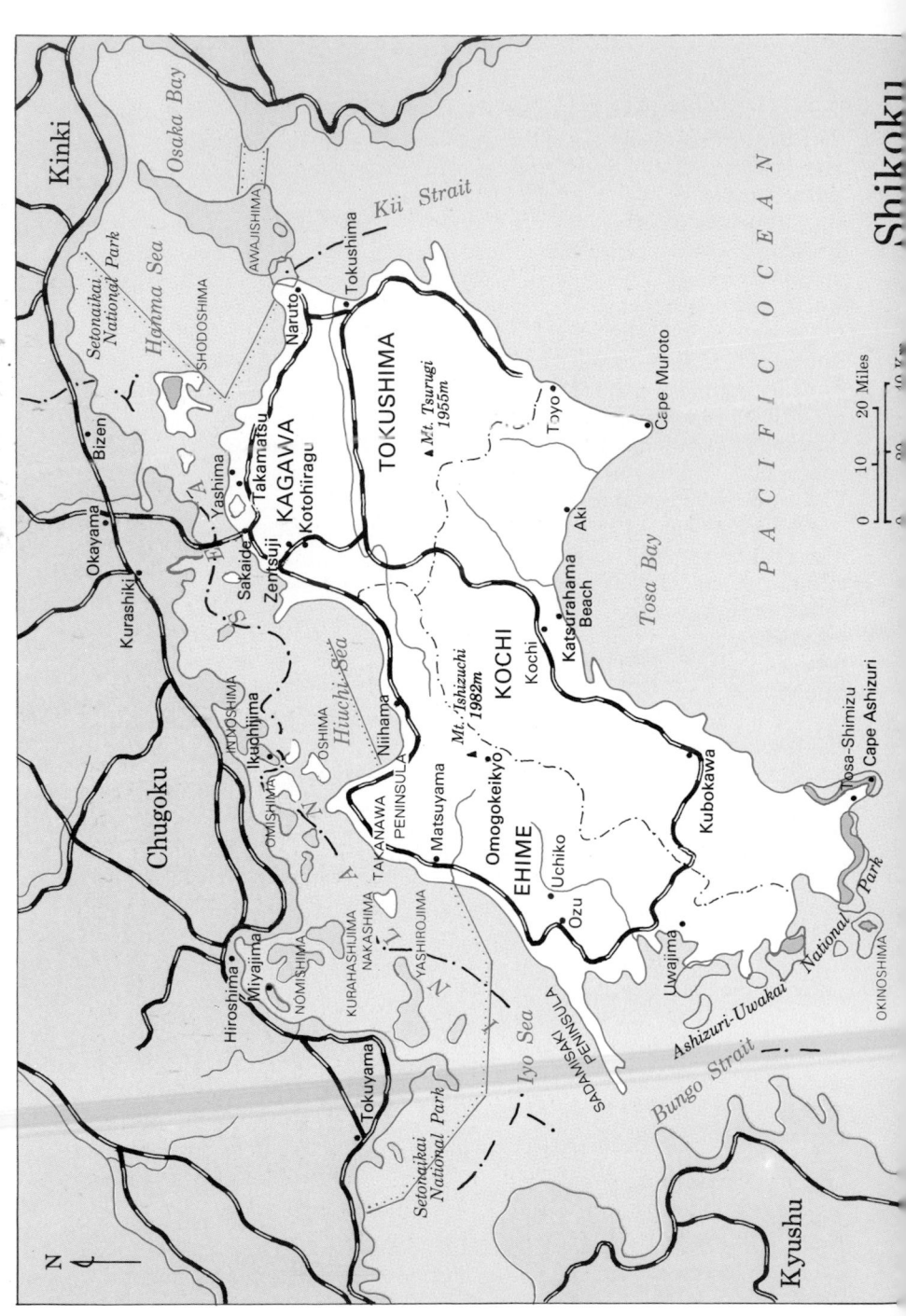

route in Japan (see page 174). Whether the Shingon priests of 1686 were motivated chiefly by piety or by an early revelation of the coming possibilities of the tourist industry is a matter for conjecture. But the unpretentious sites of Shodoshima—many in remote, out of the way corners of the island—provide the leisurely visitor with an ideal excuse for wandering off the beaten track, particularly if he can spare the four or five days needed to complete the entire circuit.

Omishima (population 12,000) is famous for its **Oyamazumi Shrine**, whose present Honden dates from 1378 and which is a repository for a collection of ancient and priceless suits of armour, comprising about 80 percent of all such suits that have been designated national treasures and which formerly belonged to, among other notables, Minamoto no Yoshitsune. On neighbouring **Ikuchijima** (population 13,000) stands a religious complex of another sort, **Kosanji** Temple, completed in 1946 by a devout island businessman-turned-Buddhist priest called Kanemoto Kozo in memory of his deceased mother. Mr Kanemoto was clearly not short of a few quid and had seen and been impressed by the Toshogu Shrine at Nikko. (In fact, his island temple is known locally as 'the Nikko of the West', and contains a full-colour replica of the Toshogu's famous gate, as well as smaller-scale replicas of about half a dozen other revered edifices from around the nation.) He can't have seen Disneyland because it didn't yet exist, although Tiger Balm Gardens, the other family monument that leaps to mind as an aesthetic progenitor, had been around since 1931. But Mr Kanemoto had been a sailor and may, therefore, have brought back to his treasured Inland Sea impressions of certain Chinese temples such as Kek Lok Si in Penang, which looks as though it has been constructed out of left-over bathroom tiles. So far as one can detect, Mr Kanemoto incorporated no left-over bathroom tiles into the construction of his deceased mother's temple, contenting himself for the most part with plywood, plaster and bright gloss paint, but one is left in no doubt that he certainly would have incorporated bathroom tiles if he had had any to spare.

There are scores of other islands in the Inland Sea less visited and worth visiting, those that lack glittery religious kitsch being generally the more rewarding. Perhaps the best way of seeing the Inland Sea and its islands is to take long ferry rides between well-separated destinations (like Osaka or Kobe in the east and Matsuyama or Beppu in the west, broken up by stops at, say, Takamatsu and Imabari to avoid too much nighttime travel). The disadvantage of this plan is that the large ferries call only at major ports and not at the smaller islands, but such a trip is leisurely enough for the visitor to take ample note of the remoter villages and harbours the ferries pass, and to ascertain from the pursers or from a travel agent how best these may be reached during the stages of an even more leisurely return.

An Unbridgeable Remoteness ?

As Nagasaki's bomb is the forgotten bomb compared with Hiroshima's, so Shikoku, the smallest of Japan's four main islands is, as far as tourism is concerned, the forgotten island. Hokkaido and Okinawa are far more distant from Honshu's urban centres and in many important ways quite unlike the rest of the country, but those are precisely the reasons why the tourist industry has been keen to open them up. Because their remoteness from Tokyo in flying time means a greater revenue for the airlines that serve them, they have been made the subjects of campaigns and package tours in a way that Shikoku never has and probably never will. Opinion is divided on the likely effect of the three sets of bridges that have just been completed, or are under construction, and which join, or will join, Shikoku to Honshu. Some argue, as they did on behalf of the Tohoku Shinkansen, that bridges will bring more tourism to the island and facilitate the siting of the new industries there. Others argue, as they did against the Tohoku Shinkansen, that the bridges will merely accelerate the already steady migration of rural people, particularly young families, to the sprawling industrial conurbations of Osaka-Kobe, Nagoya and Tokyo-Yokohama, where 46 percent of the total population of Japan now lives.

Whatever the case, most of Shikoku is likely to remain for the foreseeable future an out-of-the-way destination with an out-of-the-way destination's rewards. The main urban centres, including all four of the island's prefectural capitals, are situated on or very near the coast. The northern coast, washed by the Inland Sea, is the most industrially developed part of the island. The southern coast is mainly unspoiled and the stretch between Cape Ashizuri and Uwajima, with its coral formations and subtropical vegetation, is now a National Park. Inland, Shikoku is extremely rugged, there being no major towns or extensive highways and limited access by rail. The areas around the island's two highest peaks, Mounts Tsurugi in the east and Ishizuchi in the west, are virtual wildernesses.

The most conspicuous visitors to Shikoku are devout, wealthy or leisured members of the Shingon sect of Buddhism following the island's famous pilgrims' route round the 88 temples built by, or otherwise associated with, the sect's founder, Kobo Daishi. Dressed all in white and equipped with identical sets of rosary beads and walking staffs, they are unmistakable. In feudal times the route (which extends over some 1,200 kilometres or 740 miles, and usually occupies between three and four months if undertaken entirely on foot) was especially popular with beggars and outcasts such as those suffering from leprosy and other shunned diseases. Nowadays it is popular with pensioners who make the round of the temples in air-conditioned buses equipped with a contraption like an umbrella stand just inside the automatic door to contain their pilgrims' staffs.

These they recover solemnly when filing off the bus at the gate of each temple, since one can no more claim to be a pilgrim without a staff that one can claim to be an alpinist without a tartan shirt and a pair of herringbone knickerbockers.

It is also essential (since a part of the ritual) that the temples be visited in the correct order. Of the four prefectures in Shikoku, Tokushima contains temples 1–23, Kochi temples 24–39, Ehime temples 40–65 and Kagawa temples 66–88.

The prefectural capital of **Tokushima** is **Tokushima** city (population 249,000), nationally famous as the home of the **Awa Odori**, a form of Bon dance which, instead of being performed in circles round a central tower as most Bon dances are, is a true processional, and during the four nights of 12–15 August occupies long cordoned-off stretches of the city's main roads and some of its back alleys. 'Awa' is the old name for this part of Shikoku and the dance originated as a celebration of the completion of Tokushima castle in 1586. Nowadays it offers one more glaring example of how the nature and purpose of large-city Bon festivals have altered in postwar times from reaffirmation of local identity to floodlit, carefully orchestrated spectacle with amplified commentaries and busloads of paying spectators. Much of the dancing is performed competitively in front of grandstands erected for the purpose, to which an admission fee is charged. There are reduced rates for dead ancestors.

Little remains of the castle, but such as does remain has been transformed into an amusement park and zoological garden. Otherwise the city's chief attractions cluster round **Otaki Hill**, where there is a cable car, a prefectural museum, a **Peace Memorial Pagoda**, erected in 1958 and supposed to contain a small quantity of the Buddha's ashes, and several monuments commemorating the residence in the city of Wenceslau de Moraes, a Portuguese diplomat, for a time vice-consul in Osaka, who spent some 30 years in Japan, the last 14 of them in Tokushima. Moraes is much less celebrated than his contemporary Japanophile and expatriate, Lafcadio Hearn (see page 167), although he too wrote a great deal about his adopted country, married a local woman, and made a lot more headway with the language than Hearn did.

The little city of **Naruto** (population 63,000), some 15 kilometres (9.25 miles) north of Tokushima and the terminus for the set of bridges that will link Shikoku to Honshu via Awajishima (see page 111), has given its name to the narrow strait on which it stands and to the famous whirlpools created by the fast currents and resulting differences in water level that characterize the straits. The whirlpools can often be viewed from the ferries that ply between Awajishima and Shikoku or from the sightseeing boats that exist for the purpose of viewing them.

Mount Tsurugi (1,955 metres or 6,414 feet), in the rugged inland reaches of the prefecture, is the centre of a Quasi-National Park.

The prefectural capital of **Kochi** is **Kochi** city (population 301,000), the pleasantest, most hospitable and most relaxed of Shikoku's prefectural capitals, and the most interesting on account of certain unique traditions, among which dog fighting and the breeding of spectacularly long-tailed cocks are the best-known. Dog fighting (*token*) is still a recognized sport in the prefecture and, since most forms of gambling are officially outlawed in Japan, is a magnet for the activities of the tough *yakuza* gangs for which Kochi is a traditional haven. Demonstrations of dog fighting can be seen several times daily in the amusement area at **Katsurahama** beach, just south of the city. The city itself has an elegant castle, originally constructed in 1603 and partly rebuilt in 1748. But its traditional heart, like the heart of old Edo, was a bridge—the nowadays unprepossessing **Harimayabashi** across which trams clang, but which retains a certain romantic association through the nationwide popularity of Kochi's most famous folk song. The song tells the story of a love-struck Buddhist priest who bought his love an expensive ornamental hairpin in one of the shops near the bridge that specialized in items for the elegant and warmly hospitable women of the city (something else for which Kochi has a well-deserved and enduring reputation). The purchase caused a scandal, the lovers were arrested, arraigned on charges of public immorality, banished from the city in opposite directions, and were apparently never reunited. Today, in Kochi's souvenir shops, you can buy small wooden dolls representing the lovers: the priest looking decidedly smug as he clasps the hairpin to his bosom, standing beside his mistress who is dressed, mysteriously enough, in the habit of a Buddhist nun, so prompting the question to what possible use she could have put a hairpin.

Kochi prefecture was in feudal times the province of Tosa, whose leaders, together with those of Satsuma (nowadays Kagoshima, see page 202) and Choshu (nowadays Yamaguchi, see page 163), were prominent in the struggle that led to the downfall of the Tokugawa shogunate and the restoration of power to the Emperor Meiji. The best known Tosa hero was Sakamoto Ryoma, who was assassinated at the age of 31, one year before the restoration was carried through, and to whom thus accrues all the melancholy adulation due a man who exerted himself in a cause he was never to see succeed—a favourite qualification for heroism among the Japanese. There is a statue of Ryoma looking suitably doomed-but-determined at Katsurahama beach.

The most prominent landmarks on the Kochi coast are its two sharp capes, **Muroto** in the east and **Ashizuri** in the west. Muroto is the unhappy recipient of the brunt of frequent fierce storms and is famous for its battered lighthouse. Ashizuri is less famous for its lighthouse than for its reputation as

Silence, Exile and Cunning

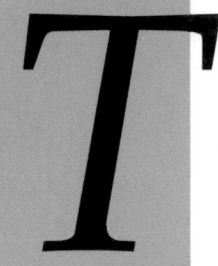

The air vibrated with the boom of temple bells as Ushimatsu neared Takajo Street; it was time for the evening services. When he was a few paces from the lodging house, an abrupt warning was shouted to passersby—outside the gate, lanterns shone, and two bearers carried a covered chair into the dark street. It must be the rich eta trying to leave without being noticed, thought Ushimatsu sadly. He knew for certain that it was the eta when he recognized the rich man's attendant following the chair. Ohinata himself he had never seen, though they had been living in the same house; but the attendant, an eta like his master, going in and out with the bottles of medicine, had become a familiar figure. There he was now, very tall and the picture of faithful service, as with the skirts of his kimono tucked up into his sash and a protective eye on his master he gave directions to the chair bearers. Of low birth and status even for an eta, by the look of it, he passed by with an oddly cringing air and a slight bow, never dreaming that Ushimatsu was in reality an outcast like himself. The landlady was standing outside the gate calling goodbye. Inside, Ushimatsu could see, there was some sort of commotion; angry voices could be heard, their owners clearly meaning them to carry.

"Thank you, sir, thank you, and please take care of yourself!" said the landlady again, running up alongside the chair.

The occupant did not reply. In silence, Ushimatsu watched the chair being borne away.

"I told you so!" the boarders were saying to each other triumphantly. When Ushimatsu, a little paler than usual, entered the house, most of them were still milling about in the long corridor that ran round the outside of the building, some fuming with self-righteous indignation, some venting their feelings by marching up and down noisily on the wooden floor, some ostentatiously tossing handfuls of salt out into the garden to purify it of the defilement caused by the eta's presence. The landlady had produced a pair of flintstones, from which she was attempting to strike a "cleansing fire."

Pity, fear, and a thousand other thoughts and feelings jostled violently in Ushimatsu. Driven from the hospital, driven from his lodging, cruelly humiliated—with what bitterness the man in the chair must have cursed his fate as he was carried out, silent, into the street. But Ohinata's destiny, inevitably, was that which all eta had to face sooner or later; and was not he himself an outcast, an eta? Miraculous, how he had managed to come safely all this way through years of study and of teaching, without fear, thinking and acting like any normal human being. . . . Out of such thoughts rose a picture of his father, who lived alone up there in the mountains, hermitlike, tending his cattle. Ushimatsu remembered the cowherd's hut at the foot of Mount Eboshi.

Muttering "Father, father," he walked to and fro across his room. Suddenly some words of his father's came back to him. When he left home for the very first time, his father, deeply concerned for his only son's future, had given him much advice. It was then that he had told him about their ancestors: how they were not descended, like the many groups of eta who lived along the Eastern Highway, from foreign immigrants or castaways from China, Korea, Russia, and the nameless islands of the Pacific, but from runaway samurai of many generations back; that however poor they might be, their family had committed no crime, done nothing dishonourable. One thing more he added: that the only way—the only hope—for any eta who wanted to raise himself in the world was to conceal the secret of his birth. "No matter who you meet, no matter what happens to you, never reveal it! Forget this commandment just once, in a moment of anger or misery, and from that moment the world will have rejected you forever." Such had been his father's teaching.

It was as simple as that. Tell no one: *that was the whole commandment. At the time, so thrilled was he to be going away to study, Ushimatsu had hardly taken in his father's words; those were the days of dreams, when it was all too easy to forget the commandment. Then suddenly he had grown up, become aware of himself; it was like leaving the agreeable novelty of a neighbour's house for the half-forgotten discomfort of one's own. Now he saw for himself the need for secrecy.*

Shimazaki Toson, The Broken Commandment
translated by Kenneth Strong

a favoured spot for romantically motivated suicides. The local chapter of the Salvation Army has placed as strategic points on top of the cliffs, notice boards bearing the simple message, *Chotto Matte Kudasai* (Please Wait a Moment). At the neck of the promontory that terminates in Cape Ashizuri is the small city of **Tosa-Shimizu** (population 24,000), which likes to pride itself on possessing a certain cosmopolitanism owing to the fact that it was the birthplace of Nakahama ('John') Manjiro who, as a result of having been shipwrecked and rescued by an American whaling ship, became, in 1842, the first Japanese person to visit the United States, where he lived for almost a decade. When the American Commodore Matthew C Perry arrived in Japan in 1853 to demand the opening of its ports to foreign vessels (an event that, quite as much as the doings of the Tosa, Satsuma and Choshu clans, significed the end of Tokugawa isolation and, eventually, of Tokugawa rule), John Manjiro was drummed into service as Perry's interpreter, a role that has ensured him a dubious—or at least ambiguous— reputation, so far as Japanese posterity is concerned.

The coast to the northwest of Tosa-Shimizu, now the **Ashizuri-Uwakai National Park** is deservedly famous for its picturesque bays and rocky cliffs that poke through the rich layer of subtropical vegetation. Scuba divers in particular favour the area, but the unusually warm climate of Kochi prefecture make the beaches and many small inlets of this coast favourite destinations for ordinary bathers too. Kochi is so warm, and its rainfall so heavy, that farmers in some parts of the prefecture are able to harvest rice twice a year.

The capital of **Ehime** prefecture is **Matsuyama** (population 402,000), the largest city on the island, whose petrochemical plants and coastal industrial zone spread a gloomy pall about it. The gloom is partly relieved by the fact that Shikoku's best-known hot-spring resort, Dogo, lies in the city's northern suburbs. Matsuyama is also famous for its very well-preserved castle, dating from 1603.

Like Mount Tsurugi in Tokushima prefecture, **Mount Ishizuchi** (1,981 metres or 6,500 feet) is the centre of a Quasi-National park, most easily reached from Matsuyama. Ishizuchi is the highest peak in Shikoku and (it comes as something of a surprise to learn since the mountains of Kyushu are far more famous) the highest in the whole of western Japan. Just south of the peak lies the **Omogokeikyo Gorge**, with its waterfalls, cliffs and unspoiled woods.

Like Kochi, Ehime has its share of odd animal-related traditions, such as cormorant fishing (*ukai*) in the city of **Ozu** (population 39,000) and bull fighting (*togyu*) in the city of **Uwajima** (population 72,000), though these practices survive more famously elsewhere (see pages 143 and 168). Both these cities have small but notable architectural monuments: Uwajima a castle dating from 1665, Ozu an elegant feudal-era cottage with garden and teahouse called **Garyusanso** (Villa of the Hill of the Prostrate Dragon), though the cities are eclipsed in this department too by the little town of **Uchiko**, some 15 kilometres (9 miles) northeast of Ozu, which has a street, **Yokaichi**, in which is preserved an entire row of fine houses and shops from the feudal and early modern periods. Uchiko is a quiet little town, completely off the tourist route. In fact, outside of Matsuyama, Ehime prefecture as a whole is not much frequented by sightseers, though its warm climate and strong agricultural base (it is one of Japan's chief fruit-growing areas, famous for its mandarin oranges) make it a pleasant enough choice for visitors in search of rural relaxations.

Kagawa is the smallest of Shikoku's four prefectures (and the second smallest in all Japan), but its location at the southern boundary of the narrowest stretch of the Inland Sea and in the corner of Shikoku closest to the great industrial sprawl of southern Kansai has given it an economic and commercial stature that belies its size. The prefectural capital, **Takamatsu** (population 317,000) was, before the bridges were constructed, the main gateway to the island and the first Shikoku port to feature a regular ferry connection with Honshu. It remains to be seen how the bridges and the faster-growing industries of Matsuyama will affect the city's commercial standing.

As were all the other prefectural capitals of Shikoku, Takamatsu was a castle town, though little remains of the castle but its site, now a city park. Though not one of the 'Three Most Beautiful Landscape Gardens' of Japan, **Ritsurin** garden is the city's chief sightseeing attraction. Like the famous trio, it was originally laid out as the grounds of a private villa belonging to the lords of the region, in this case the Matsudairas (who, like the Matsudairas of Aizu, were relatives and strong supporters of the Tokugawa shoguns). **Yashima**, on the coast just beyond the eastern suburbs of the city, was the site of several battles in the long struggle between the Genji and Heike clans, the last of which immediately preceded the final downfall of the Heike at Dannoura in 1185 (see page 165).

Outside Takamatsu, the chief magnet for visitors to Kagawa prefecture is the **Kotohiragu Shrine**, sometimes called the **Kompira Shrine**, founded in the early 11th century. Its precincts and chief buildings are laid out on the steeply sloping side of Mount Zozu and connected by long flights of stone steps. Five kilometres to the north stands **Zentsuji**, the 77th of the 88 temples on Kobo Daishi's pilgrims' route, but particularly venerated since it both marks the place where Kobo Daishi was born and acts as the headquarters of the Shingon sect which he founded. On the coast north of Zentsuji lies the city of **Sakaide** (population 66,000), the Shikoku terminus for one of the three sets of bridges that join, or will join, the island to Honshu.

Kyushu

Kyushu

Pioneers and Persecutors

Visitors with limited time to spare who are anxious to get away from Honshu at least once during their stay in Japan, but who are not especially attracted by the extreme rurality of, say, Sado or Oki or the interior of Shikoku, are probably best off making for Kyushu, the southernmost and third largest of Japan's four main islands. Kyushu is a favoured destination among Japanese travellers for pleasure, too. The air route between Tokyo and Fukuoka, the capital of the island's richest and most developed prefecture, is the second busiest in the country (after Tokyo–Osaka). In 1975 the Shinkansen bullet train, which had previously run only between Tokyo and Osaka, and then (after 1972) between Tokyo and Okayama, was extended to reach Hakata (in Fukuoka city), and now links Tokyo with Kyushu in six hours. Japan's most famous hot-spring resort, its most spectacularly active volcanoes, one of the largest caldera craters on earth, a subtropical coastline with many unspoiled stretches, four National Parks, totally empty hills and woodland, and a modern tendency to site 'clean' industries rather than pollution-prone heavy industries on the island are among Kyushu's attractions.

It is likely that the first prehistoric settlements founded by the ancestors of the Yamato tribes were situated in Kyushu. Where these ancestors came from remains a matter for conjecture. In the remote past northern Kyushu was linked with the Korean peninsula by a land bridge, facilitating the movement of flora and fauna from the continent into the archipelago, and the narrow straits that succeeded this bridge may well have been crossed in later centuries by human migrants from as far away as Mongolia. If, as is also probable, some of the tribes who eventually settled down to become Japanese made their way, via the Ryukyu islands, from the Malay archipelago and the South Seas, then Kyushu was almost certainly their first Japanese port of call. Some of the earliest creation myths and myths dealing with the mischievous behaviour of the founding gods are associated with locations in central Kyushu, and the associations are perpetuated there by the continuing performance of Kagura and other dances at shrines and local festivals.

In more recent times, Kyushu was the first port of call of Saint Francis Xavier and the Christian evangelists who followed him in the 16th and early 17th centuries, the first Westerners to reach and settle in Japan. Certain of the lords of Kyushu were happy to embrace the Christian faith because the inducements to conversion included such useful gifts as arquebuses. Eventually, the Christians were blamed, as in Nero's Rome, for stirring up troubles against the authorities, with the result that Christianity was banned and its converts and preachers cruelly persecuted throughout the Edo period, the most famous of these persecutions taking place in Kyushu.

However, Christianity survived underground and, when the persecutions ceased at the time of the Meiji Restoration, a surprising number of active Christian cells resurfaced, particularly in and around Nagasaki, where they had been most viciously suppressed. Today, Kyushu has a higher proportion of practising Christians than any other part of Japan, though still not significantly high for a country evangelized since the mid-1500s.

Throughout the period of enforced seclusion under the Tokugawas, Kyushu contained the only foreign settlement permitted in Japan, the tiny Dutch and Chinese trading post at Nagasaki, through which, seclusion notwithstanding, a surprisingly active two-way trade was carried on. With the beginning of the modern age, northern Kyushu's extensive coal fields came in for heavy exploitation. Immediately prior to and during the Second World War these areas saw a large influx of forced labour from Korea, then a Japanese possession, mainly to work the mines. Mining continued just as actively during the hectic struggle to reestablish a viable industrial base following defeat and the severe economic depression of the immediate postwar period. The worst mining disaster in Japanese history occurred at Mitsui's Miike mine, straddling the border between Fukuoka and Kumamoto, in 1963 when an explosion killed 458 people. The case for compensating the victims' families is still dragging wearily through the Japanese courts. And in the 1950s and '60s the city of Minamata on the coast of Kumamoto prefecture became a focus of attention throughout the industrialized world as an example of the terrible price to be paid in human terms for the discharge of poisonous industrial wastes into the environment.

But if, during the decades that preceded and immediately followed the last war, Kyushu provided grim examples of the things that can go badly wrong when industrialization proceeds at too frantic a pace, it has more often provided models that the rest of the country has fallen over itself to adopt. The encouragement of foreign trade and the acceptance of artefacts, ideas and residents from the West were pioneered in Kyushu. One forward-looking Kyushu lord in the mid-19th century was almost single-handedly responsible for the introduction into Japan of Morse code and the subsequent development of telegraphy, the building of Japan's first steam-powered warship, the setting up of the first gas lamps in Japan, the establishment of Japan's first Western-style textile looms, glass and munitions factories, and he still found time to design *Hinomaru*, which remains Japan's national flag. That this energetic lord's clan was at the forefront of the movement to topple the Tokugawa shogunate and the floundering feudal system of which it was the pinnacle is hardly surprising. It is a move entirely in keeping with Kyushu's pioneering tradition.

Kyushu is home to about 12 percent of the total Japanese population. The interior is ruggedly mountainous, but more accessible than that of Shikoku owing to the tourist industry's success in placing some of the island's more famous landmarks—Mounts Aso and Kirishima, for example—high on many people's lists of attractive leisure destinations. Both of those peaks are the centres of their own National Parks, while two more National Parks have been created to highlight the splendours of Kyushu's heavily indented west coast and the islands that lie offshore.

In general, the further south you go in Kyushu the more dependent life becomes on the traditional industries of agriculture and fishing. The seven prefectures that make up the island are **Fukuoka, Saga, Oita, Nagasaki, Kumamoto, Miyazaki** and **Kagoshima**. The climate of Kyushu is warm in the summer and generally mild in winter, although Fukuoka, because it faces the Japan Sea whose bleakness still clings to it in these lower latitudes, has its share of snowfall and winter gales. Southern Kyushu lies bang in the path of many of the summer and autumn typhoons that blow up through the South China Sea, making flooding and landslides frequent hazards.

The capital of **Fukuoka** prefecture is **Fukuoka** city (population 1.1 million), the chief commercial and administrative centre for the entire island. Confusion arises in the minds of some visitors over the fact that the city's railway terminus is not called Fukuoka, but **Hakata**, while the airport, a ten-minute drive away, is not called Hakata but Fukuoka. Hakata is a mere ward in the modern city, but it was the name of the ancient port out of which the modern city developed and from which envoys travelled to China as far back as the seventh century. The name Fukuoka came into existence when the castle was built in 1601 and was applied to the area around the castle which was mainly settled by the warrior class. Hakata became the merchants' and artisans' quarter, and the name of the city's famous May festival is a reminder of the association between Hakata and trade. The **Hakata Dontaku**, like Tokyo's Sanja and Osaka's Tenjin festivals, was in origin a merchants' celebration. 'Dontaku' is said to derive from the Dutch word 'Zondag', meaning Sunday and thus, by extension, 'holiday'. The main event of the festival (3–4 May, the height of Golden Week) is a long procession of groups of dancing women who accompany their dance by tapping out the rhythm with wooden rice scoops.

Nothing remains of the castle but its ruined outer walls, now incorporated as usual into a park. The city's best-known craft is the manufacture of extremely lifelike painted clay dolls called *Hakata ningyo* (*ningyo* means doll), some of which fetch astronomically high prices. The best often depict women in gorgeously painted kimonos or actors from the Kabuki theatre, but the most popular dolls among souvenir buyers represent the rotund, grim-faced figure of a samurai called Mori Tahei, standing legs astride, a huge sake bowl in one hand and an ornate spear in the other. The Lord of Hiroshima bet the Lord of Fukuoka that none of his retainers could quaff the contents of this mammoth bowl in one swallow. Mori accepted the challenge,

succeeded famously, and received the spear as a prize. The event is also commemorated in Fukuoka's best-known folk song, *Kuroda Bushi,* which has become a favourite at weddings and other occasions where the mood calls for Mori-style quaffing. Quaffing in Fukuoka tends to centre on the district called **Nakazu**, and an especially pleasant feature is the open-air stalls (*yatai*) which serve simple food and drink throughout the year. They operate only at night and are mostly to be found within sight of the bridges that link Nakazu to both banks of the river surrounding it and turning this famous pleasure spot into an island.

In the northeast corner of Fukuoka prefecture lies the sprawling city of **Kita Kyushu**, literally 'North Kyushu' (population 1.1 million), concocted by bureaucrats in 1963 out of five small neighbouring industrial cities, including **Moji**, the largest international port in Kyushu, **Kokura**, one of the proposed targets of the first atomic bomb, and **Yawata**, the home of Japan's biggest steel works. The distinction of being the largest city in Kyushu see-saws back and forth between Fukuoka and Kita Kyushu as their population figures fluctuate. Kita Kyushu is joined to Shimonoseki in Honshu by means of the Kanmon Bridge (see page 163) and the Kanmon rail and pedestrian tunnels. Largest or not, the city has little to offer the non-industrial sightseer.

In the southeast of the prefecture, near the border with Oita, stands the village of **Koishiwara**, famous as a centre for the production of folk pottery and comparable, in this regard, with Mashiko in Tochigi prefecture (see page 58). Virtually the whole village is given over to the production of pots and, although a water wheel is preserved as a tourist attraction, most of the clay is now electrically ground, the glazes chemical, and kilns oil- or gas-fired.

Saga is a mainly rice-producing prefecture and its capital, **Saga** city (population 164,000) is one of the smallest and least industrialized prefectural capitals in Japan. The two most popular destinations for visitors to the prefecture are the city of **Karatsu** (population 78,000) and the little town of **Arita** (population 15,000), both famous for their ceramics. Like the well-known street leading to Kiyomizudera in Kyoto (see page 86), Karatsu was settled by Korean potters brought back to Japan following the military campaigns in Korea during the late 16th century, and it owes its success as a pottery centre to the skills they preserved and passed on. Arita also owes its fame to a naturalized Korean potter who built a kiln there in the early 17the century. The best Karatsu ware is of an unpretentious, single-glaze type highly favoured for tea ceremony bowls. Arita ware stands at the extreme opposite end of the ceramic spectrum, being a colourful enamelled porcelain similar to Kutani ware (see page 154), which is essentially a copy of it.

The principal tourist destination in **Oita** prefecture is the coastal city of

Beppu (population 136,000), Japan's chief mecca for hot-spring enthusiasts. Beppu is the most famous hot-spring resort in the country and has suffered a consequent degree of commercial spoliation. The city boasts eight different spas, containing together more than 3,000 springs, each known for its particular curative properties. The spas vary widely in character so that, although the city as a whole has been vigorously developed, it is still possible for the connoisseur or the visitor with sufficient time and energy to locate odd corners and traditional-style inns where development has been kept within acceptable bounds. The main tourist attractions are the *jigoku* (hells), the points where thermal water issues in bubbling milky-white or muddy-brown fountains from the ground at temperatures that reach boiling point. Mud and sand baths are available in addition to the usual facilities, and the enervating pastime of wending one's way from hell to purgatory to hell again with frequent stops at the city's multitudinous bars is enjoyed by an estimated 12 million enthusiasts annually.

Some 15 kilometres (9.5 miles) east of Beppu is the prefectural capital, **Oita** city (population 360,000), a pleasant enough place but with little to detain the sightseer. In the north of the prefecture stands the small city of **Usa** (population 52,000), the site of the **Usa Hachiman Shrine**, the headquarters of a branch of Shinto to which belong the estimated 25,000 or so Hachiman shrines scattered throughout Japan. Hachiman is a protective deity variously identified as the god of war, as a bodhisattva whose special duty is the guardianship of Todaiji temple in Nara, and as the spirit of the legendary Emperor Ojin. His warlike aspect caused him to be adopted as the family deity of the Minamoto or Genji clan, but his shrines are more usually associated with such peaceful pursuits as the protection of small fishing harbours. Founded in 571, the Usa Hachiman Shrine was the first to be dedicated to this deity and is accorded only slightly less reverence than is Izumo Taisha (see page 166).

Besides Beppu, Oita prefecture is comparatively rich in hot springs. At **Yufuin** spa, in the shadow of **Mount Yufu** (at 1,584 metres or 5,197 feet, yet another Something-or-Other Fuji, this time 'Bungo-Fuji', 'Bungo' being the old name for the province), an annual week-long film festival is held each summer (the dates vary) with showings of brand new, classic and obscure pieces from the Japanese cinematic repertoire. The festival is usually attended by celebrities from the film world who, instead of preening themselves for the cameras as at better known festivals, give quasi-intelligent talks and seminars for the benefit of the conspicuously young film buffs who attend.

In much of Kyushu, particularly the southern half, the traditional tipple is not sake but *shochu*, a clear, rather bitter-tasting liquor, sometimes compared to vodka, distilled from whatever raw material is cheapest and most conveniently to hand, the commonest being sweet potatoes, barley, millet and sugarcane. The millet and sugarcane varieties, found mainly in Okinawa and

Lavatories, Baths and Other Headaches

Guidebooks to European countries tend to assume that Asian travellers possess sufficient common sense and adaptability not to be thrown into confusion by having to lift a Western-style lavatory seat or keep their shoes on in a house. Guidebooks to Asian countries for Western travellers tend to assume the opposite—that their readers are all potential oafs and dimwits—so they go out of their way to supply long lists of cultural do's and don'ts. Authors of guides to Thailand, for example, warn readers that they must not pat Thais on the head since the consequences could be unpleasant. They do not seem to have pondered the possible consequences to an Asian tourist in Great Britain of going about patting, say, Scotsmen on the head.

George Bernard Shaw refused to take his shoes off when visiting Japanese houses. The consequences, presumably, were that he made few friends, was hardly ever invited out, and was considered an insufferable boor. Shoes are removed in the entrance hall (*genkan*) of a Japanese house or inn and the host or inn staff supplies the guest with slippers for use indoors. But even slippers are not normally worn when walking on *tatami* (the straw covering of Japanese-style floors, more like large inlaid tiles than mats), nor are these indoor slippers worn in lavatories, where a different pair of slippers or clogs is customarily provided.

Western-style lavatories are nowadays very common in Japan, but they have not supplanted the traditional Japanese lavatory which is much lower, requiring the user to squat, not sit. This is healthy, since the user's behind does not touch any lavatory surface and remains inelegantly poised in the air. It is also unhealthy since the traditional lavatory has a cess pit, not a flush, so the user's nasal membranes can suffer unlooked for assaults. It is also a considerable hardship for the elderly, heavily pregnant or infirm.

The main Western complaint about the lavatories found in Japanese restaurants is that they are shared by both sexes. This has never seemed an inconvenience to me; all that is required is a knock on the door before entering. Much more inconvenient is the complete absence of hand towels. You are presumably expected to wipe your hands on your hair (unless, of course, you are Thai).

Do not wash or shampoo yourself in a Japanese bath. Wash before you get into the bath, either under a shower or by emptying small plastic buckets (supplied) of water over your body. Once in the tub, you are obliged to do nothing except sit there and enjoy the heat. Since no soap is ever brought into a tub, and since the bather is (in theory) scrubbed before he gets in, the water remains clean enough to be shared by whole families or even whole neighbourhoods—though water at public baths (*sento*) is constantly replenished from running taps. If you are bathing communally, do not force Japanese people's heads under the water since the consequences could be unpleasant. Do not do this to Scotsmen either.

the Amami islands, are called *awamori* and are far and away the most potent, some types having an alcohol content as high as 80 percent proof. The potato variety (*imo-jochu*), widely drunk in and around Kagoshima, is well known for its strong smell and long lurking presence the morning after. Both these forms are traditionally favoured by manual labourers and have never been widely popular outside their immediate localities. But in recent years the mildest form of shochu, made from barley or other grain *(mugi)*, has become fashionable with the young as a base for various mixed drinks (such as shochu and lemon or shochu and soda) and popular among office workers who drink it diluted with either hot water or water and ice, much as they drink whisky. For a while, in the early 1980s, shochu looked set to eclipse sake in nationwide popularity and to replace whisky as the bottled drink most commonly 'kept' by regular customers in the bars they frequent (the 'bottle keep' system is explained on page 231). The height of the shochu boom seems now to have passed, but the mild-tasting and almost completely odourless grain shochu produced in Oita and Miyazaki prefectures remains a favourite among the die-hards.

The city of **Nagasaki** (population 447,000), the capital of **Nagasaki** prefecture, was the target of the world's second atomic bomb attack at 11.02 a.m. on 9 August 1945, when almost the entire city was destroyed and an estimated 140,000 people killed outright or doomed to die of bomb-related causes in the decades that followed. The Nagasaki bomb was larger and slightly heavier than the bomb dropped on Hiroshima three days earlier, and packed a much greater explosive power (the equivalent of 22 kilotons of TNT as opposed to 13), though the destructive effect was not so great as at Hiroshima owing to Nagasaki's irregular and hilly topography. Like Hiroshima, Nagasaki was chosen as a target because it was a major naval base and shipbuilding centre. In fact, at the time of the bombing, the Nagasaki shipyards were the largest privately-owned shipyards in Japan. Like Hiroshima, the city has also commemorated the bombing by building a Peace Park near the hypocentre and decorating it with municipally inspired statuary. As at Hiroshima too, a single building stands as an eloquent reminder of the tragedy. At Hiroshima the building is the ruined Atomic Dome (see page 160) and at Nagasaki the **Urakami Catholic Cathedral**, with its grimly ironic symbolism: Christian target of a Christian bomb. The Atomic Dome has been left, conspicuously and accusingly, in its gutted state, while the cathedral, entirely destroyed in the bombing (before which it was the largest Christian church in the Far East), was completely rebuilt in ferroconcrete in 1959, and all trace of the holocaust expunged. In a way these two buildings seem perfectly to characterize the attitudes of their respective cities to the bombs: Hiroshima's to go on relentlessly reminding, Nagasaki's to plough under and forget.

In any case, the associations that Nagasaki has for the Western visitor are longer-standing and less one-track-minded than Hiroshima's. Christianity is, perhaps, the foremost of these. The area near the Urakami Catholic Cathedral was a centre of underground Christian activity during the Tokugawa persecutions. In **Oura**, the 19th-century foreigners' quarter, stands the city's other famous Christian church, built in 1865, a miraculous survivor of the bombing. Near Nagasaki Station lies **Nishizaka Park**, the site of the martyrdom of six foreign priests and 20 of their Japanese converts in 1597. The 26 were crucified (crucifixion being the usual method of execution for commoners during the feudal period) and, despite the official animosity toward Christianity, the place rapidly became a focus of pilgrimage owing to the miracles that were said to occur there. The 26 martyrs were canonized in 1962.

Nagasaki's other foreign associations are of a secular kind. The one Dutch and Chinese trading post that continued to operate throughout the period of national seclusion was situated on a tiny man-made island called **Dejima** in Nagasaki Bay. Little trace of this settlement remains, though there are plans to rebuild and restore it as a tourist attraction. In the meantime, tourists interested in Nagasaki's Dutch connection can visit **Oranda Mura** (Holland Village), not far outside the city, where they can see windmills, a replica of an old Dutch sailing ship, souvenir shops, museums, and specimens of real live foreigners kitted out with bonnets, clogs and pipes, bearing all the signs of having been shipped over from the Netherlands in ventilated crates. The city's other famous foreign landmark is the house of Thomas B. Glover, a Scottish engineer who came to Nagasaki in 1859 and founded an import-export business. The large and elegant **Glover Mansion**, now open to the public as a museum, stands on a prime residential site overlooking Nagasaki Bay, and credulous visitors are told that Madame Butterfly lived there (Glover, who married a Japanese woman, is sometimes said to have been the model for Puccini's Pinkerton). But, unlike Pinkerton, Glover never left Japan, and visitors to his lavish residence will have no difficulty seeing why. Another monument to Glover's enterprise stands out in the bay itself: the tiny, almost deserted island of **Takashima**, energetically developed as a coal mining centre under Glover's supervision and recently abandoned despite emotional protests from the miners and their families by its subsequent owners, Mitsubishi. The cheap ferroconcrete high-rise apartment blocks that were the miners' homes, and which crowd practically every square metre of space not occupied by slag heaps on the unhappy little island, now stand crumbling and empty.

Nagasaki's Chinese connections are evident in the **Chinatown** area with its numerous authentic restaurants, in the Chinese Ming-style Zen temple of **Sofukuji**, founded in 1629, and in the city's two main annual festivals, the **Okunchi** (8–9 October) which features a Chinese-style Dragon Dance and

the **Peiron** Dragon Boat races (the name is derived from the Chinese *P'a-lung,* meaning 'dragon') on the Sunday nearest 15 June.

Hilly and situated at the end of a long, almost landlocked bay, eminently accessible by sea (hence its foreign connections) and extremely tedious to reach by land, the city of Nagasaki is a microcosm of the heavily indented, fjorded prefecture of which it is the capital. Most of Nagasaki prefecture is made up of islands and peninsulas which are almost islands (the Japanese word for peninsula—*hanto,* literally 'half-island'—seems nowhere more explicit and appropriate than here).

The **Shimabara** Peninsula, in the centre of which stands **Mount Unzen** (1,359 metres or 4,459 feet) is famous for the rebellion that occurred there in 1637–8. The rebellion was a popular uprising inspired by chronic poverty and exorbitant taxation but, because both of the fiefs from which the rebels came had been nominally Christian before the total ban on Christianity enforced 23 years earlier, the shogunate found it convenient to blame Christian provocateurs for the uprising, a policy that enabled officialdom both to overlook the social inequities that were the actual cause and to redouble its religious persecutions. No popular rebellion in history, including that led by Spartacus, was ever suppressed more viciously. The entire rebel garrison of **Shimabara Castle** was slaughtered together with their woman and children, the dead eventually totalling some 37,000. The castle donjon was rebuilt in 1964 as a museum and monument to the unhappy early history of Christianity in a country that prides itself on its religious tolerance (by which it exclusively means the tolerance of Shinto for Buddhism and vice-versa). The area around Mount Unzen is one of four in Japan (Sakurajima in Kagoshima prefecture is another) that receive government funds to provide for possible evacuation in case of eruption and are required to carry out regular emergency and survival exercises. Unzen is very active and there are frequent earth tremors in the region, but this has not prevented its becoming the main showpiece of the **Unzen-Amakusa National Park**, which features several good hot-spring resorts, both in Shimabara and on the **Amakusa** islands (population 140,000), joined to the mainland south of the town of **Misumi** in Kumamoto prefecture via a set of bridges.

Nagasaki's other National Park is the **Saikai** (literrally 'Western Sea') **National Park**, which includes the island of **Hirado** (population 28,000), also joined to the mainland by a bridge and which was the earliest part of Japan to be settled by foreigners (Dutch, English, Portuguese and Spanish, all of whom built trading posts and warehouses there in the mid-16th century). Further offshore lie the picturesque **Goto** islands (population 97,000), less bleak and rugged than the Oki islands (see page 167) and an ideal destination for fishermen or those wanting a complete respite from urbanity and the pressures of organized tourism. The islands are comparatively low-lying which in itself is something of a relief after the mountainous terrain of most of Japan, and many of the villages still harbour small Christian churches underscoring the area's reputation as a centre for the faith.

The islands of **Iki** (population 40,000) and **Tsushima** (population 50,000), though administratively parts of Nagasaki prefecture, are best reached via Fukuoka, from where there is a regular ferry service. Lying in the narrowest straits between Japan and the continent, these islands have long served as stepping stones from mainland Asia. Iki is particularly interesting in that it is practically the last place in Japan to preserve a vigorous form of phallic worship. Phallus-shaped stones were once fairly common throughout the remoter parts of Japan, where they were set up as charms to promote fertility. In the small shrines of Iki the chief objects of worship are often small delicately-carved wood or stone phalluses, and in the island's annual festival, two huge papier-mâché constructions, one representing the female organ and the other the male, are manipulated in a manner that is explicit rather than suggestive. Tsushima is a great deal more rugged and sparsely populated than Iki, and foreign visitors disembarking from the ferry are sometimes questioned by local police who suspect that the island is one of the principal entry points for illegal immigrants from Korea. The police must know as well as everyone else that the ferry has come direct from Fukuoka, so pointing this out to them, though a natural reaction, cannot help but seem a trifle gratuitous.

The main tourist destination in **Kumamoto** prefecture is **Mount Aso** (1,592 metres or 5,223 feet), the centre of the **Aso-Kuju National Park** (**Kuju**—1,787 metres or 5,863 feet—is an extinct volcano in western Oita). Aso has five cones, one of which is still very active and last erupted in 1979. The landscape surrounding these cones is extremely arresting since the peaks of Aso stand in the centre of one of the largest caldera craters on earth, originally the mouth of a far more gigantic volcano, and the walls of this almost perfectly circular crater can be seen rearing up spectacularly from almost any point within it. The crater has a circumference of 80 kilometres (50 miles) and contains three separate townships as well as several hot-spring spas.

Due west of Aso stands the prefectural capital, **Kumamoto** city (population 526,000), famous for its very large feudal castle, built in 1607 and restored in 1960. The castle is remarkable not only for its size but in having been the last Japanese castle to undergo a medieval-style siege. This took place, incredibly enough, in 1877 (the year in which the English lawn tennis championships were first played at Wimbledon), when the castle was invested for 50 days by rebel forces from Kagoshima under the charismatic former Marshal of the Army and Counsellor of State, Saigo Takamori. Saigo had been commander of the army that had toppled the shogunate nine years

The Power of Faith

bediently we practised letting off our shots without taking aim. At first I remained completely unmoved by where my arrows went. Even occasional hits did not excite me, for I knew that so far as I was concerned they were only flukes. But in the end this shooting into the blue was too much for me. I fell back into the temptation to worry. The Master pretended not to notice my disquiet, until one day I confessed to him that I was at the end of my tether.

'You worry yourself unnecessarily,' the Master comforted me. 'Put the thought of hitting right out of your mind! You can be a Master even if every shot does not hit. The hits on the target are only the outward proof and confirmation of your purposelessness at its highest, of your egolessness, your self-abondonment, or whatever you like to call this state. There are different grades of mastery, and only when you have made the last grade will you be sure of not missing the goal.'

'That is just what I cannot get into my head,' I answered. 'I think I understand what you mean by the real, inner goal which ought to be hit. But how it happens that the outer goal, the disc of paper, is hit without the archer's taking aim, and that the hits are only outward confirmations of inner events—that correspondence is beyond me.'

'You are under an illusion', said the Master after a while, 'if you imagine that even a rough understanding of these dark connections would help you. These are processes which are beyond the reach of understanding. Do not forget that even in Nature there are correspondences which cannot be understood, and yet are so real that we have grown accustomed to them, just as if they could not be any different. I will give you an example which I have often puzzled over. The spider dances her web without knowing that there are flies who will get caught in it. The fly, dancing nonchalantly on a sunbeam, gets caught in the net without knowing what lies in store. But through both of them "It" dances, and inside and outside are united in this dance. So, too, the archer hits the target without having aimed—more I cannot say.'

Much as this comparison occupied my thoughts—though I could not of course think it to a satisfactory conclusion—something in me refused to be mollified and would not let me go on practising unworried. An objection, which in the course of weeks had taken on more definite outline, formulated itself in my mind. I therefore asked: 'Is it not at least conceivable that after all your years of practice you involuntarily raise the bow and arrow with the certainty of a sleepwalker, so that, although you do not consciously take aim when drawing it, you must hit the target—simply cannot fail to hit it?'

The Master, long accustomed to my tiresome questions, shook his head. 'I do not deny', he said after a short silence, 'that there may be something in what you say. I do stand facing the goal in such a way that I am bound to see it, even if I do not intentionally turn my gaze in that direction. On the other hand I know that this seeing is not enough, decides nothing, explains nothing, for I see the goal as though I did not see it.'

'Then you ought to be able to hit it blindfolded,' I jerked out.

The Master turned on me a glance which made me fear that I had insulted him and then said: 'Come to see me this evening.'

I seated myself opposite him on a cushion. He handed me tea, but did not speak a word. So we sat for a long while. There was no sound but the singing of the kettle on the hot coals. At last the Master rose and made me a sign to follow him. The practice hall was brightly lit. The master told me to put a taper, long and thin as a knitting needle in the sand in front of the target, but not to switch on the light in the target sand. It was so dark that I could not even see its outlines, and if the tiny flame of the taper had not been there, I might perhaps have guessed the position of the target, though I could not have made it out with any precision. The Master 'danced' the ceremony. His first arrow shot out of dazzling brightness into deep night. I knew from the sound that it had hit the target. The second arrow was a hit, too. When I switched on the light in the target-stand, I discovered to my amazement that the first arrow was lodged full in the middle of the black, while the second arrow had splintered the butt of the first and ploughed through the shaft before embedding itself beside it.

Eugen Herrigel, Zen in the Art of Archery
translated from the German by R F C Hull

earlier and his rebellion was sparked by exasperation at what he regarded as the self-serving, cowardly and pragmatic policies of the cabinet he had helped bring to power. Kumamoto was the first major battle of the six-month campaign. The castle withstood the siege (though the donjon was destroyed) and was eventually relieved by government reinforcements, whereupon Saigo withdrew and fought a famous rearguard action at **Tabaruzaka**, some 15 kilometres (9.5 miles) northwest of Kumamoto, where the battleground is preserved and a small museum commemorates the conflict. (For the final outcome of the rebellion, see page 202.)

The other great martial figure associated with Kumamoto is Miyamoto Musashi, lately famous as the author of *Gorin no Sho* (The Book of Five Rings), written in a mountain cave in the Kumamoto suburbs in 1643 and widely touted in the United States as an important key to the understanding of 20th-century Japanese business practices, a belief which vividly under-scores both the extreme desperation and the extreme gullibility of the American business community. Musashi was a famous swordsman who, after helping the government slaughter tens of thousands of peasants, women and children at Shimabara (see page 194), took to teaching, writing and ink painting as well as to lopping off losers' heads (by his own reckoning the personal head count was 60). Musashi's cave is preserved as a monument to his selfless dedication to these various arts.

Inland, south of Aso, the country is wild and sparsely inhabited, and the region spanning the border between Kumamoto and Miyazaki prefectures is so hilly and remote and its population so depleted that it is sometimes called 'the Tibet of Japan'. Survival training for the elite corps of Japan's Ground Self-Defense Forces, though conducted in secret, is rumoured to take place here. Anyone wanting a genuine taste of traditional country life and a glimpse of its attendant hardships could do worse than spend some days in the villages of these hills. On the other hand, the Kumamoto coast has suffered a large degree of industrial disruption. At the small city of **Minamata** (population 37,000), between 1953 and 1960, the Chisso Corporation's discharge of untreated methyl-mercury effluent into the sea resulted in more than 300 deaths among people who had eaten fish caught near the plant's waste disposal facility. Fishing is still prohibited in the bay.

The main attractions of **Miyazaki** prefecture are its subtropical coast, for an exploration of which the prefectural capital, Miyazaki city, is well situated, the mountainous inland region centering on the town of Takachiho, which is the site of several ancient legends concerning the founding and earliest pseudo-history of the Japanese islands, and the Kirishima-Yaku National Park, which spans the border with Kagoshima.

Miyazaki city (population 265,000) is traditionally regarded as the site of the palace of Japan's legendary first emperor, Jimmu, underscoring both

Arts, Martial and Polite

Mishima Yukio was not alone in finding in the broad field of 'Japanese culture' two opposing strains, a dark and a light. The American cultural anthropologist, Ruth Benedict, called her 1946 study of Japanese society *The Chrysanthemum and the Sword,* a title that emphasised the two strains' distinct qualities: the first natural and delicate, the second uncompromising and violent.

The West has tended to take the violent strain more seriously. Japanese martial arts have a considerable following abroad. The most popular of them, judo, became an Olympic sport in 1964, and the corridors of Tokyo's *Kodokan,* the mecca of Japanese judo, still swarm with overseas practitioners (there seems to be no convenient English word for someone who practises judo —judoist, judo-man and judo-player all seem awkward, quite apart from the tendency of the last to equate an 'art' with a mere 'sport'). The popularity of *karate* (a form of kick boxing) is more recent. *Aikido,* a purely defensive art, is the most pleasing of all the martial arts to watch, possessing qualities that are dancelike. *Kendo,* fencing with bamboo swords, is less popular abroad, but widely taught in Japanese schools and attracting more and more women (whose traditional weapon was not the sword but the short-shafted, long-bladed halberd called *naginata*). *Kyudo* (archery) was the subject of one or two books by Western authors in the 1960s, which saw it as a practical embodiment of Zen. This meant, essentially, that an archer who failed to hit the target after repeated tries could declare his interest to be spiritual, and thus above such a mundane ambition.

The West has tended to view the gentler arts—flower-arrangement (*ikebana*) and so on—as elegant indulgences for affluent wives. The Japanese regard ikebana in much the same light, though the teaching and awarding of proficiency certificates is a multi-billion-yen industry. *Shuji* or *shodo* (brush calligraphy) is still considered a serious attainment. With the advent of Japanese-language word processors it may suffer a decline; although the electronic calculator has only marginally curtailed the widespread use of the abacus (*soroban*). The writing of traditional forms of poetry (such as the 17-syllable *haiku*) is widespread and encouraged on a national scale by newspaper competitions. Perhaps the most intriguing of the gentler arts to many Western visitors is the tea ceremony (*cha-no-yu*), with its immaculately contrived rigmaroles of politeness, its snobbish conventions, and its underlying assumption that life's troubles are easily dissipated if the sufferer is subjected to a rigorous enough formality. A Western (or Japanese) guest at a tea ceremony, who finds after half an hour of sitting with his legs tucked under him that he can only get up and walk at the risk of severely torn ligaments and the complete destruction of his host's paper screens as he staggers desperately into and through them, can be forgiven for wondering whether this gentle art belongs to the dark strain or the light.

the mythological connections and the age of human settlement in the region. The **Miyazaki Shrine** stands today where the palace is imagined to have stood and is itself supposed to date from mythological times.

Takachiho (population 20,000) is accessible by rail or bus from the city of **Nobeoka**, and stands on a spectacular gorge said to have been formed by the erosion of lava from Mount Aso. The municipal authorities have spared no effort to attract visitors to this remote little town. They have erected signboards outside virtually all the shops announcing to the sightseer that he has arrived in 'the country of the gods' and commissioned a local artist to paint scenes from the sacred Kagura dances in bright gloss paint on many of the metal shop blinds. A selection of Kagura dances is performed at the **Takachiho Shrine** every evening of the year and admission tickets are available at the shrine's busy box office. Emperor Jimmu is supposed to have set out from this shrine on his journey to the Nara basin to found the nation of Japan, and at the nearby and much smaller **Kushifuru Shrine** the grandson of the Sun Goddess is supposed to have descended from heaven. But the most celebrated of Japan's god-legends is associated with the shrine at **Iwato** (often called *Ama no Iwato*, or Heavenly Iwato) some eight kilometres (five miles) away. Here the visitor can see a cave reputed to be the very one in which the Sun Goddess, Amaterasu Omikami, in a fit of pique at the riotous behaviour of her brother the Storm God, hid herself, thus plunging the earth into darkness. In an effort to encourage her reemergence, a bevy of minor gods and goddesses crowded round the entrance to the cave and one of the goddesses performed an obscene dance. Intrigued by the sounds of mirth that she could hear and wondering what caused them, the Sun Goddess poked her head out of the cave, found herself reflected in a mirror which the gods had cunningly hung on a tree, and Lo! the light of the world revived. The obscene dance of the minor goddess is considered the original of all dances connected with shrines and shrine festivals, and the mirror is the original sacred mirror that forms a part of the imperial regalia (see page 103).

Near the small city of **Saito** (population 38,000) on the coastal plain north of Miyazaki city stands a cluster of fifth- and sixth-century tombs, numbering more than 300, less than one-tenth of which have been excavated. The excavations, carried out between 1912 and 1917, uncovered large amounts of armour, weapons and tomb sculptures testifying once again to the importance of the region in early human history as well as in sacred fiction.

Mount Kirishima, the centre of the **Kirishima-Yaku National Park**, is a cluster of volcanic peaks, the highest of which rises to 1,700 metres (5,577 feet). This high point lies exactly on the border between Miyazaki and Kagoshima, but the chief focus of tourism, the **Ebino Plateau**, with its lakes, hot springs and inns, is on the Miyazaki side. The last major eruption of Kirishima occurred in 1959, making it the most dormant of the four main active Kyushu volcanoes (this, Unzen, Aso and

Sakurajima) or, looked at from a less rosy point of view, the one longest overdue. The lower slopes of the Kirishima group are especially well provided with hot springs.

Sakurajima (1,117 metres or 3,665 feet) is the opposite of overdue. Originally an island in Kagoshima Bay, it spewed out enough lava in an eruption in 1914 to join itself to the mainland, and has remained an intermittent menace. In recent years its regular emissions of ash have earned Sakurajima (once a picturesque symbol of the area's natural attractions: its name means 'Cherry Blossom Island') the unrelenting wrath of the residents of Kagoshima city on whose streets and houses the ash falls, sometimes to a depth of several inches. Local television stations advertise industrial vacuum cleaning equipment for hire but the ash has already so badly damaged the local tourist industry (before the current spate of eruptions, Kagoshima was a favourite honeymoon destination) that the advertisements seem only to perpetuate the communal gloom. That a natural symbol should turn so visibly against its promoters strikes many with the force of betrayal.

Kagoshima city (population 505,000), the capital of the prefecture, stands opposite the sour volcano in the northeastern quarter of the Satsuma Peninsula. Like Choshu (Yamaguchi) and Tosa (Kochi), Satsuma was at the head of the movement that toppled the shogunate in 1868 and ushered in Japan's modern age. This was the fief ruled by the energetic Shimazu Nariakira (see page 184) and which produced the irrepressible Saigo Takamori (see page 198), whose doomed rebellion of 1877 ended here in his native city. Saigo made his last stand on **Shiroyama Hill**, a great mound of crumbling earth that towers above the city centre. His headquarters were a cave (carefully preserved) which he quit when the government bombardment grew too fierce to withstand and descended the hill with his 200 or so remaining followers. He was hit in the groin by a government sniper and immediately decapitated by a lieutenant so loyal that he buried Saigo's head separately from his body, causing the government troops a great deal of extra effort in locating and digging it up. Many of the city's chief monuments are connected with the Great Saigo. Shiroyama is nowadays a shrine to his memory. At its base is a stone tablet marking the spot where he died, and a statue of Saigo in his Marshal's uniform stands outside the city's art gallery. His grave stands between a museum dedicated to his life and exploits and a small Shinto shrine where he is worshipped as the chief deity. That a defeated rebel should find himself posthumously heaped with official honours may strike the visitor as strange but, even in disgrace and even by his enemies, Saigo was regarded as embodying all the most admirable qualities of the rapidly vanishing samurai spirit. He was totally uncompromising, brave to the point of lunacy, intensely nationalistic, and preferred death with honour to success through opportunist machination.

As the northernmost prefecture of Honshu, Aomori, is crisply divided into two peninsulas, so is this southernmost prefecture of mainland Japan, a similarity which attests to the founding gods' taste for elegant symmetry. The two prefectures share further similarities: they are both among those regularly reporting the lowest per capita incomes in the nation and they are both famous for the impenetrability of their rural dialects, in which the inhabitants take a certain pride. The combination of extreme rurality and a reputation for martial exploits has caused some residents of Kagoshima to refer to themselves as *imozamurai* (potato samurai), a charming expression which the foreign visitor is advised to eschew in casual conversation. The natives of Kagoshima take their history seriously. In 1863 seven British warships sailed into Kagoshima Bay to demand reparations for two Englishmen killed by Satsuma samurai for crossing the path of their lord's procession. Satsuma refused, whereupon the warships opened fire destroying a large part of the city. However, the British ships were quickly dispersed by a typhoon that struck the bay, leaving some 60 of their crew dead or injured and contributing enormously to the belief that Japan is fated to be preserved from foreign aggression by a Divine Wind (*kamikaze*), the name given to the fortuitous typhoons that twice sank Mongol invasion fleets poised off the north Kyushu coast in the 13th century as well as to the special attack force mustered in the closing stages of the Pacific War to mount suicide missions against American warships. The incident of the British bombardment, which lasted all of one hot August afternoon, is still referred to in Kagoshima as the *Satsu-Ei Senso* (The Anglo-Satsuma War), and reference to it is not taken lightly.

The eastern fork of Kagoshima prefecture is the **Osumi Peninsula**, which boasts a rocket-launching facility owned by the University of Tokyo. The western fork is the more interesting **Satsuma Peninsula**, near the tip of which, in the shadow of the perfectly conical **Mount Kaimon** (922 metres or 3,025 feet), lies the hot-spring resort of **Ibusuki**, featuring thermal sand baths on the beach. The west coast of the peninsula has one of the best swimming beaches in mainland Japan in **Fukiagehama** as well as a noted centre for the production of black Satsuma pottery at the village of **Naeshirogawa**, where the first kiln was established (once again by a Korean potter) in 1604. The most easily recognizable products of the village are its elegant flat shochu-warmers.

The Satsuma lords were very keen on expanding their territory and all the long chain of islands lying between the southern tip of Kyushu and Taiwan was at one time under their control. Today the islands of Yakushima and Tanegashima, which lie comparatively close to the mainland, as well as the more distant Amami islands, still belong administratively to Kagoshima prefecture.

Despite its being the rainiest spot in the entire country (up to 10,000 millimetres or 390 inches annually in the mountains), **Yakushima** (population 15,000) remains popular with honeymoon couples, and is part of the Kirishima-Yaku National Park. **Tanegashima** (population 44,000) also has a rocket-launching facility and is remembered as the place where firearms were first introduced into Japan (by stranded Portuguese in 1543). Both islands are warm with subtropical vegetation and list sugarcane among their more important agricultural products.

Until the early 17th century the Amami islands were not a part of Japan at all but, like modern Okinawa prefecture, a part of the independent Kingdom of the Ryukyus, and are dealt with in the next chapter.

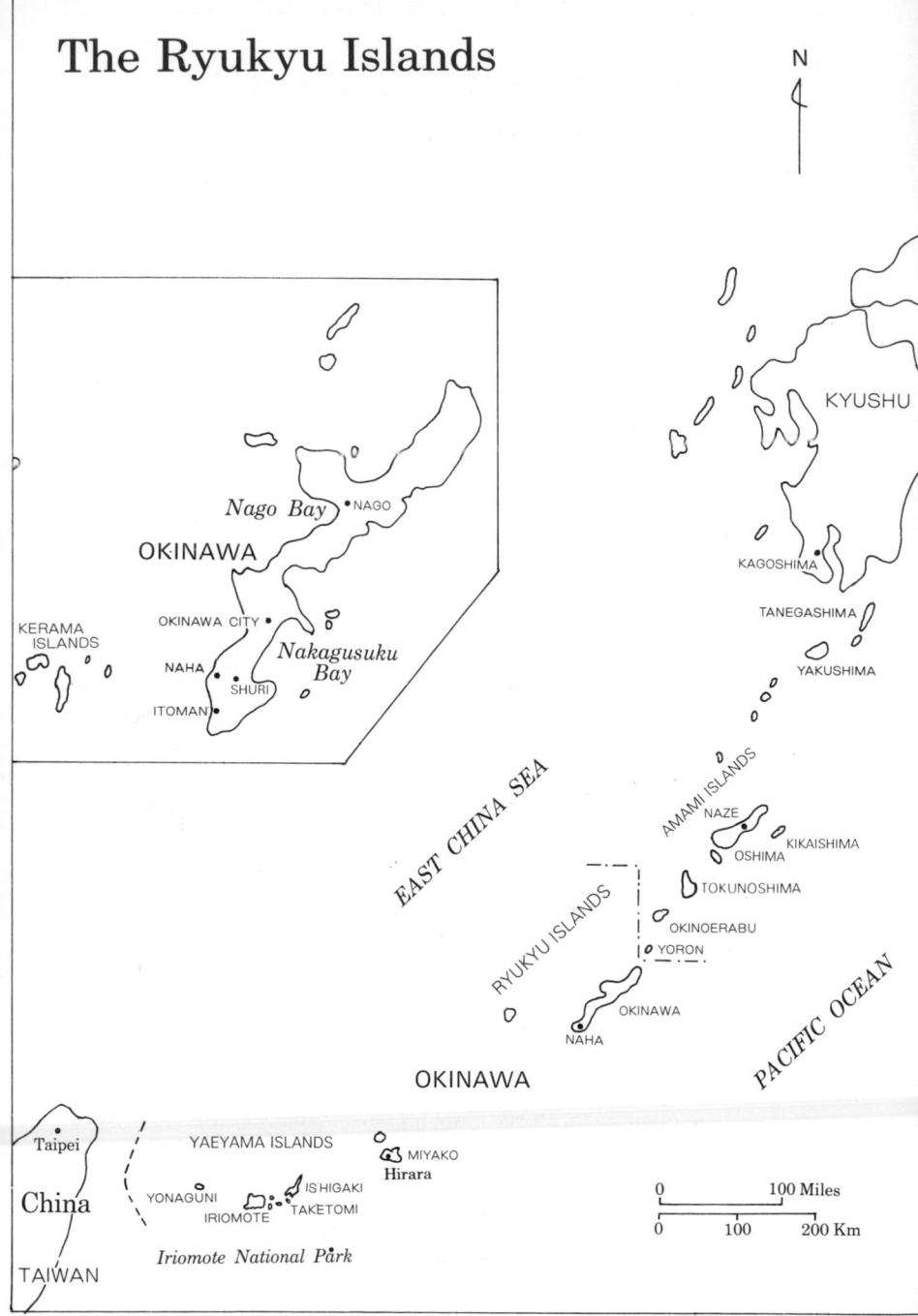

The Ryukyu Islands

N

Nago Bay •NAGO

OKINAWA

KAGOSHIMA

TANEGASHIMA

KYUSHU

KERAMA
ISLANDS

OKINAWA CITY •

NAHA

SHURI

Nakagusuku
Bay

ITOMAN•

YAKUSHIMA

EAST CHINA SEA

AMAMI ISLANDS

NAZE

OSHIMA

KIKAISHIMA

TOKUNOSHIMA

RYUKYU ISLANDS

OKINOERABU

YORON

OKINAWA

NAHA

PACIFIC OCEAN

OKINAWA

Taipei

YAEYAMA ISLANDS

MIYAKO

Hirara

China

YONAGUNI

IRIOMOTE

ISHIGAKI

TAKETOMI

0   100 Miles

0   100   200 Km

TAIWAN

Iriomote National Park

Okinawa and the Southern Islands
Invasion, Disruption, JALPAK

The history of the Ryukyu islands (comprising the four island groups of
Amami, Okinawa, Miyako and Yaeyama) is a complex and depressing one.
Until the beginning of the 17th century the islands were independent both of
China (where they were known as *Liu-ch'iu*) and of Japan, though they had
far stronger cultural and diplomatic ties with the continent. By the mid-16th
century all four of the island groups were united under the rule of a single
king whose capital was at Shuri, near today's prefectural capital of Naha on
the main Okinawan island. The court at Shuri carried on an active trade with
China, sent scholars to study there, and was so highly regarded by the
Chinese emperor that he named Okinawa 'the land of propriety'. (By
contrast, the representatives from mainland Japan were thought boorish in
that they slighted the formalities and etiquette of the Chinese court—
something the Okinawans apparently took very seriously—and were forever
urging the ceremonially inclined Chinese to get on with the down-to-earth
business of trade.)

In 1609 the Ryukyu islands were conquered by an expedition from
Satsuma (present-day Kagoshima) and the court at Shuri was forced to
declare itself a vassal state of the aggressively minded Satsuma lords. The
Amami islands were directly assimilated into the Satsuma fief, but the other
groups were permitted to maintain the fiction of autonomy together with their
king and court, which somewhat confusingly both acquiesced in this
arrangement and continued to send tribute to the emperor of China. A
complicated system of triple sovereignty thus came into force: the ruler on
the spot was the king at Shuri, but the de facto power was Satsuma while the
ritual overlord was the Chinese emperor.

In 1879 the dispute between China and the new Meiji government of
Japan over possession of the Ryukyus came to a head, and Japan settled this
dispute, to its own satisfaction, by pensioning off the king, disbanding the
court at Shuri, and declaring Okinawa a Japanese prefecture. China protested,
and at first Japan offered to cede the Miyako and Yaeyama groups. But with
Japan's victory in the Sino-Japanese war of 1894–5 all thought of
appeasement ended and China was forced to relinquish its claim. Interest-
ingly enough, though, Japan remains one of very few nations in the world
today to maintain ongoing territorial disputes with every one of its immediate
neighbours: with China and Taiwan it disputes possession of the Senkaku
islands (*Tiao-yu-t'ai* in Chinese) which lie some 160 kilometres (99 miles)
north of the Yaeyama group, with Korea it disputes possession of Takeshima
(*Tokto* in Korean) which lies beyond the Oki islands off the coast of
Shimane, and with the Soviet Union the group of islands off the northeast

Foreign Devils

When I woke up, fecund morning light was slanting through every crack in the slat walls, and it was already hot. My father was gone. So was his gun from the wall. I shook my brother awake and went out to the cobblestone road without a shirt. The road and the stone steps were awash in the morning light. Children squinting and blinking in the glare were standing vacantly or picking fleas out of the dogs or running around and shouting, but there were no adults. My brother and I ran over to the blacksmith's shed in the shade of the lush nettle tree. In the darkness inside, the charcoal fire on the dirt floor spit no tongues of red flame, the bellows did not hiss, the blacksmith lifted no red-hot steel with his lean, sun-blackened arms. Morning and the blacksmith not in his shop—we had never known this to happen. Arm in arm, my brother and I walked back along the cobblestone road in silence. The village was empty of adults. The women were probably waiting at the back of their dark houses. Only the children were drowning in the flood of sunlight. My chest tightened with anxiety.

Harelip spotted us from where he was sprawled at the stone steps that descended to the village fountain and came running over, arms waving. He was working hard at being important, spraying fine white bubbles of sticky saliva from the split in his lip.

"Hey! Have you heard?" he shouted, slamming me on the shoulder.

"Have you?"

"Heard?" I said vaguely.

"That plane yesterday crashed in the hills last night. And they're looking for the enemy soldiers that were in it, the adults have all gone hunting in the hills with their guns!"

"Will they shoot the enemy soldiers?" my brother asked shrilly.

"They won't shoot, they don't have much ammunition," Harelip explained obligingly, "They aim to catch them!"

"What do you think happened to the plane?" I said.

"It got stuck in the fir trees and came apart," Harelip said quickly, his eyes flashing. "The mailman saw it, you know those trees."

I did, fir blossoms like grass tassles would be in bloom in those woods now. And at the end of summer, fir cones shaped like wild bird eggs would replace the tassles, and we would collect them to use as weapons. At dusk then and at dawn, with a sudden rude clatter, the dark brown bullets would be fired into the walls of the storehouse.. . .

"Do you know the woods I mean?"

"Sure I do. Want to go?"

Harelip smiled slyly, countless wrinkles forming around his eyes, and peered at me in silence. I was annoyed.

"If we're going to go I'll get a shirt," I said, glaring at Harelip. "And don't try leaving ahead of me because I'll catch up with you right away!"

Harelip's whole face became a smirk and his voice was fat with satisfaction.

"Nobody's going! Kids are forbidden to go into the hills. You'd be mistaken for the foreign soldiers and shot!"

I hung my head and stared at my bare feet on the cobblestones baking in the morning sun, at the sturdy, stubby toes. Disappointment seeped through me like treesap and made my skin flush hot as the innards of a freshly killed chicken.

"What do you think the enemy looks like?" my brother said.

I left Harelip and went back along the cobblestone road, my arm around my brother's shoulders. What did the enemy soldiers look like, in what positions were they lurking in the fields and the woods? I could feel foreign soldiers hiding in all the fields and woods that surrounded the valley, the sound of their hushed breathing about to explode into an uproar. Their sweaty skin and harsh body odor covered the valley like a season.

Kenzaburō Ōe, Price Stock, translated by John Nathan

coast of Hokkaido that were occupied by the Soviets at the end of the war (see page 221).

During the early modern period, the Japanese authorities made a number of half-hearted attempts to encourage settlement on the remoter Okinawan islands, but these attempts invariably ran up against the sound historical reasons for not settling them: poverty, squalor, malaria, cholera, hepatitis, famine, drought, typhoons, snake infestation (the *habu,* Japan's most poisonous snake, still infests large parts of rural Okinawa) and such a dearth of arable land and natural resources that on islands such as Iriomote in the Yaeyama group the Stone Age continued well into the 14th century.

Then came the Second World War, and the former 'land of propriety's' geographical location placed it squarely between the jaws of a terrible and unrelenting vice. In general terms, Japan's defensive strategy was to build a network of concentric fortified rings (much like the plan of a feudal Japanese castle) with the homeland at the centre and the outermost walls consisting of the far-flung occupied islands of the South Pacific and the Malay archipelago. The innermost wall of defence—the last to stand eventually between the Japanese mainland and the forces of invasion—was the Okinawan chain, with the result that one of the most destructive land battles of the war was fought on the main Okinawan island between April and July 1945. Altogether, a total of 50,000 American and 110,000 Japanese troops died on Okinawa, as did 150,000 Okinawan civilians caught in the crossfire. That one hears so much less about these noncombatant dead than one does about the victims of the Hiroshima bomb is presumably due to the fact that many of them were killed not by Americans but by Japanese.

Okinawa was governed directly by the United States until it reverted to Japan in 1972, prior to which Okinawan citizens were required by the Japanese government to carry alien registration certificates and special travel documents when visiting or living in mainland Japan. The legacy of this period, as well as of the general burden of the history of Okinawan suppression, is that, while not strictly speaking an ethnic minority, many Okinawans feel that they have suffered the same kinds of discrimination to which such minorities are often subjected. After reversion in 1972, the Japanese government made some loudly publicized attempts to boost Okinawa's depressed economy. These included a large 'Ocean Expo' in 1975, but the principal beneficiaries of the resulting influx of tourists were the concession-owners from the Japanese mainland who, once the event was over, packed up and went home, leaving the islanders little better off than before.

The Okinawan economy remains heavily dependent on the large American military bases located on the main island and the service industries that cater to them. About 11 percent of all the land in the prefecture is owned by, or leased to, U.S. forces and in some towns such as Koza (now bureaucratically renamed 'Okinawa City'), a large percentage of the population is made up of U.S. military personnel and their families. The bus between Naha and Koza (there is no railway on the island) ferries the visitor past long, depressing stretches of barbed-wire fence behind which native Okinawans are not permitted to venture, and towns such as Koza are run essentially as garrison economies, with bars staying open till the early hours, pawn shops flanking all the gates of the base, and the menus in restaurants and coffee shops printed in English and priced in dollars. Naturally enough, these circumstances have occasionally generated friction but, by and large, they are accepted by the islanders as the latest and not the heaviest link in a seemingly unending chain of foreign suzerainty. Besides which, as thoughtful Okinawans themselves remark, without the Americans a town like Koza would simply die.

The other great pillar of the Okinawan economy in modern times is tourism, and once again it is the airlines, packagers and agents on the Japanese mainland who continue to reap the greatest profits. Since reversion in 1972, a concerted effort to 'develop' Okinawa has resulted in a long series of promotion campaigns aimed mostly at honeymoon couples leery of Guam and at unmarried female college students who respond with unthinking alacrity to slogans such as 'Cinderella Summer'. Some shards of Cinderella's transparent slipper lie scattered about Okinawa's resort areas in much the same way that fairyland flutters over Tohoku and the Inland Sea, with package-tour operators anxious to ensure that midnight, in the form of historic and economic reality, never strikes. Mainly, it is Okinawa's subtropical beaches that are touted (the southernmost island of the Yaeyama group lies a bare one degree north of the Tropic of Cancer), but there is also, for the Japanese sightseer, an unmistakable *frisson* of foreignness about the islands that adds to their attraction. The Japanese spoken in Okinawa (variously described as a dialect and as a related but separate language), the climate, the flora, the food, the landscape, the music, the festivals, the architecture, the comparatively indolent lifestyle, all make Okinawa an exotic-but-still-comfortable destination for mainland holidaymakers, and definitely not a target for the visitor from abroad in search of something 'typically Japanese'.

Despite all historic and economic hardships, some aspects of Ryukyu culture remain vibrantly alive. Television has largely ironed out the many original differences of language so that 'Okinawan' as it was spoken a generation ago teeters on the verge of extinction, and the traditional architecture of the Ryukyus is nowadays so rare that in some places it is the subject of special preservation orders. But Okinawa has far more folk songs than any other Japanese prefecture and many of the islanders, including the young, can accompany themselves very competently on the short, snake-skin-covered shamisen that is found only there. Festivals are wonderfully well preserved, particularly on the outlying islands, mainly because tourists are often resented. Old islanders have been known to snatch cameras from Japanese sightseers at rites still held by them to be sacred and expose rolls of Fujicolor to the island sun. Policemen have occasionally chided them for this out of deference to JALPAK, but the presence of outsiders at the islands' unpublicized folk festivals is more likely to be tolerated if their cameras stay in their bags.

The **Amami** islands, a part of Kagoshima prefecture, consist of **Oshima** (usually called Amami Oshima to distinguish it from the many other offshore 'Oshimas', a name that means simply 'large island') which has a population of 82,000, and the much smaller islands of **Kikaishima** (population 11,000), **Tokunoshima** (population 35,000), **Okinoerabu** (population 17,000) and **Yoron** (population 7,000). The only city in the group is **Naze** on Oshima, where more than half of the population of that island lives and which serves as the commercial and distribution centre for the sugarcane, pineapples and other exotic produce grown there. The Satsuma administration used some of the Amami islands as places of exile and imprisonment; Saigo Takamori himself (see pages 195 and 202) spent some time on Oshima, Tokunoshima and Okinoerabu during the brief period when he was out of favour with his lord, though within months of returning to Kagoshima, he was serving as the Satsuma Secretary for War. All of these islands have good swimming beaches and no shortage of simple accommodation.

Okinawa proper consists of the main island, **Okinawa** (population 1.1 million) and the 20 or so very small offshore islands that surround it. The capital is **Naha** (population 296,000) where the airport and main ferry terminals for the entire prefecture are located. Little remains on the island from the prewar period, the devastation of 1945 having been almost total. The ruined gate of the old palace of **Shuri** was reconstructed in 1958 and attracts some sightseers, but the majority of visitors head straight for the beach resorts or for the simpler and more hospitable accommodation to be found in the rural parts of the island. The southern half of Okinawa is the more heavily urbanized and densely populated, while in the north of the island, beyond **Koza** (Okinawa City, population 95,000) near which stands the huge Kadena Air Base, the landscape is emptier of both people and barbed wire. The main city in the northern half is **Nago** (population 46,000) while, south of **Itoman** (population 42,000) at the extreme southern tip of the island, the site of some of the fiercest fighting of 1945 is now the 'Okinawa Former Battlefield Quasi-National Park'. In Koza the annual Bon festival takes the interesting form of a drum dance, called *Eisaa,* in which stand clearly revealed the cultural influences of the Asian continent.

The **Miyako** group consists of the main island, **Miyako** (population 33,000), and seven other very small islands. Like the Yaeyama group, the Miyako islands were spared wartime destruction and thus preserve more elements of traditional Okinawan culture (domestic architecture, for example) than does Okinawa itself. The chief port and centre of island life is the city of **Hirara**.

The **Yaeyama** group, in many ways the most interesting, consists of **Ishigaki** (population 40,000), **Iriomote** (population 1,500), **Taketomi** (population 300), **Yonaguni** (population 2,100) and several other small islands. Ishigaki boasts the only town of any size (Ishigaki city) and, as on Okinawa, the island's population is mainly concentrated in this small urban enclave in the south. The north is rugged and sparsely populated with some wonderfully unspoiled beaches, though **Kabira Bay** in the southwest is regarded as the most picturesque spot on the island. An ongoing controversy rages about the local administration's idiotic plan to build a new airport for tourists on top of one of the island's most beautiful stretches of coral. A short boat ride from Ishigaki lies the tiny coral island of Taketomi which preserves more or less intact an entire village built in the traditional Yaeyama manner: colourful tiled roofs, sharp coral walls, and Chinese-style screens in front of the main entrances. Iriomote is the second largest of all the Ryukyu islands but it is 90 percent primeval forest, the interior being entirely uninhabited and accessible only by two mangrove-banked rivers. In 1965 a species of wildcat (*yamaneko*), long thought extinct, was discovered to have survived in the island's impenetrable forests, since when Prince Philip of Britain has visited Iriomote in his capacity as president of the World Wildlife Fund and the island has been named a National Park. Its beaches offer wonderful bathing and the best coral reefs in Japan. Yonaguni is Japan's westernmost point and, lying almost within sight of Taiwan, is obviously Japanese only by dint of the vagaries of history. Some Yaeyama islanders continue to claim a closer racial connection with the indigenous people of Taiwan than with the Japanese of the mainland.

Hokkaido

The New Frontier

Like the Ryukyu islands, the island of Hokkaido was not fully incorporated
into the Japanese homeland until towards the end of the 19th century. From
the early 17th century there had been small Japanese settlements around the
castle town of Matsumae in the extreme southwest of the island, but little
attempt was made to push further north or east except by small bands of
loggers and fishermen. Even in the 1880s the chief government office dealing
with Hokkaido affairs was called the 'Office of Colonization' and the
encouragement given by the government to settlers can be compared to the
official enthusiasm with which the western United States was being opened
up at the same time. The reasons for promoting development were similar
too. Unlike the Ryukyus, Hokkaido was rich in natural resources, particularly
timber and coal. Honshu was already perceived as being overcrowded and the
opportunity to spread the population into this vast new space (Hokkaido is
the second largest of Japan's islands) was seized with alacrity. There was also
the question of deterring the Soviet Union from mounting any claims to the
territory, the northern borders of which were still only loosely defined. The
island of Sakhalin (in Japanese, *Karafuto*) is now Russian but was previously
an object of dispute, joint settlement, and for a time split rule. It is clearly
visible from the northern tip of Hokkaido, and Russian trappers had quite
often crossed the straits from Sakhalin to Hokkaido during the late feudal
period, though they had established no permanent settlements.

Such permanent settlements as existed in the island's interior belonged to
the Ainu, Japan's indigenous people who are racially and culturally
completely different from the Yamato tribes and their descendants. It is
probable that the ancestors of the Ainu were the tribes (variously described as
Ezo, Emeshi and Mishihase, meaning 'hairy people') against whom the
Yamato, Nara and Kyoto courts mounted their genocidal campaigns aimed at
bringing the whole of Honshu under their control. These tribes originally
inhabited much of northern Honshu and, quite possibly, areas a lot further
south if place names are a reliable indication: Mount Fuji's name, for
example, is thought by some to derive from an Ainu word. By the close of the
ninth century they had been driven out of Honshu and into Hokkaido (called
Ezo until 1869), where they were left in comparative peace until fresh
Japanese encroachments began during the rule of the Tokugawas, and then in
earnest during the early modern period.

Today some 24,000 people identify themselves as Ainu, though few of
these are pure blooded. Their traditions and culture are nothing like so
spontaneously alive as those of the Ryukyu islanders, and continue to survive
mainly as quaint entertainments trotted out on the occasion of specially

concocted 'festivals'. The sight of this once dignified and solemn people dressed in their colourful appliqué robes performing dances and pretending to be 'at home' in picturesque huts doing picturesque things for the benefit of fee-paying tourists from Osaka can only sadden the thoughtful visitor conscious of the historical discrimination and suppression they have suffered. Buffalo Bill Cody's Wild West Show must have given similar pause to thoughtful Americans. Once in a while Ainu irritation flares, as it did briefly in 1986 following former Prime Minister Nakasone's much-publicized remark to the effect that Japan's intellectual standards are superior to those of the United States because Japan is a 'monoracial' society. Ainu leaders on that occasion addressed a letter to Mr Nakasone in the Ainu language, to which the prime minister responded with even greater inanity by remarking that he possessed especially bushy eyebrows and so may well have Ainu blood in his own veins, a suggestion that merely added official sanction to a resented racial stereotype.

The visitor who goes to Hokkaido in search of Ainu culture, then, is doomed to disappointment. So, to some extent, is the visitor looking for 'the real Japan', since large-scale Japanese settlement of the island is so comparatively recent. Japanese visitors favour Hokkaido because, like the Ryukyus, it strikes them as in some ways 'un-Japanese', and package-tour advertisements have capitalized on this attraction by comparing it to Switzerland and Scotland. Hokkaido has no real rainy season, very little rice cultivation, few cherry trees (elsewhere a national symbol), no marked regional dialects, and in the winter months its northern coasts are grazed by distinctly un-Japanese icefloes. The natural splendour of its mountains, lakes, pastures, wetlands and wildlife reserves makes it an ideal destination for visitors primarily interested in The Great Outdoors, but Hokkaido should not figure high on the itinerary of anyone bent on getting a feel for Japanese society and culture as a whole. Such an ambition is far better satisfied in Honshu, Kyushu or Shikoku.

Much of Hokkaido in under deep snow for up to half the year making it a mecca for winter sports enthusiasts. Most visitors, however, favour the summer, when the much lower average temperatures (18–22°C or 64–71°F) provide a refreshing break from the enervating heat of western and central Honshu. Despite Hokkaido's sparse population (less than half that of Tokyo in an island the size of Austria), July and August can find its resort areas quite as crowded as many of those on the mainland. For all its size, Hokkaido is not divided into prefectures and remains a single administrative unit, with the capital at Sapporo. Its chief attractions are its six National Parks.

The city of **Sapporo** (population 1.4 million) was laid out as the seat of Hokkaido's colonial administration in 1869 on a checkerboard pattern similar to that of Kyoto or New York. In 1972 it was the site of the 11th Winter Olympic Games, the first ever held in Asia. Sapporo is a relatively clean,

Hokkaido

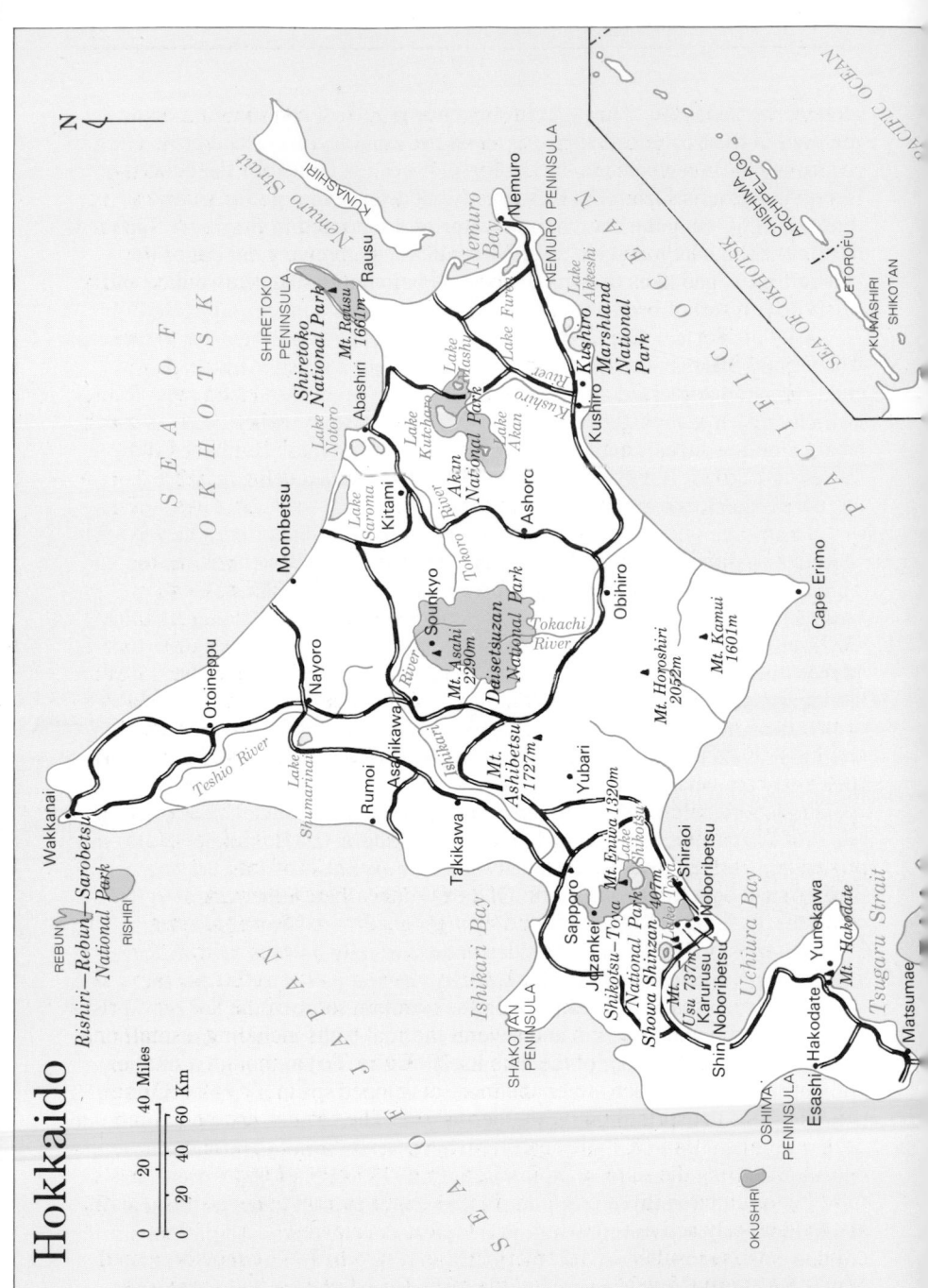

modern city, with few items of historical interest, except for the red-brick, ivy-covered buildings of the old Sapporo Brewery (built in 1876), whose attractions have been massively increased by their being converted into the largest beer hall in Japan (the **Biiru-en**, where the beverages on the menu and the notices pointing the way to the lavatories are printed in German). Sapporo lies on the same latitude (43°N) as Milwaukee, the brewing capital of the United States, and likes to think of itself as belonging, with Milwaukee and Munich, to a sort of beer-producing holy trinity.

Older residents of Sapporo treasure fond memories of an avenue called **Tanukikoji** (Badger Avenue), which in prewar days was the city's main entertainment quarter, famous throughout the island for its geisha, who found no difficulty in relieving patrons of the contents of their wallets with as much facility as the badger, an animal noted in folklore for its skill in that field. Today Tanukikoji is a tame, roofed shopping-arcade indistinguishable from a thousand others, and the chief entertainment and tippling district has shifted to **Susukino**.

The city's agricultural college, founded in the same heady year as the brewery, is chiefly remembered for its first president, Dr William Smith Clark, who, during a sabbatical from his post at Massachusetts Agricultural College, was invited to advise the Japanese government on matters of education and spent nine months doing so at the new facility in Sapporo. He is mainly remembered for the parting remark he made to his students, many of whom he had converted to Christianity, 'Boys, be ambitious!', a remark that has echoed down the corridors of Japanese academic and social life and featured prominently in television advertisements for ballpoint pens.

Twenty-six kilometres (16 miles) southwest of Sapporo is the hot-spring resort of **Jozankei**, a convenient place for visitors to spend a night before proceeding further south to the lakes and volcanic peaks of the **Shikotsu-Toya National Park**. Of the two lakes that are the park's centrepieces, **Lake Shikotsu**, standing in the shadow of **Mount Eniwa** (1,320 metres or 4,331 feet), is the less commercially developed. It is the second deepest lake in Japan, after Lake Tazawa in Akita prefecture (see page 126). The small spa at **Marukoma** on the northern shore of the lake comprises one large traditional-style inn and several thermal baths including a small one situated on the rocky shore of the lake itself. **Lake Toya**, though a smaller body of water, has a much larger and more developed spa in **Toyako Onsen** (*onsen* means hot spring) on its southern shore. The spa lies just below the peak of **Mount Usu** (737 metres or 2,418 feet) and the entire town was evacuated during the summer tourist season of 1977 following the volcano's third major eruption this century. In fact, the area surrounding this lake is still at a dangerously active stage of seismological development. In 1910 an eruption of Usu resulted in the emergence of a new hill subsequently named **Meiji Shinzan** (New Mountain of the Meiji Era). In 1943–5 a much more violent spate of eruptions and upthrusts created the larger **Showa Shinzan** (408 metres or 1,339 feet; its name means New Mountain of the Showa Era).

On the sea coast southwest of Lake Toya stands the city of **Noboribetsu** (population 57,000), which contains Hokkaido's most famous hot-spring resort. Two more spas, **Shin** (New) **Noboribetsu** and **Karurusu** lie a few kilometres inland, and some 15 kilometres (9.5 miles) further east along the coast stands the 'Ainu' village at **Shiraoi**, established here in 1965, one of several such fabrications where, on the pretext of facilitating the 'study' of Ainu life and customs, souvenir shop owners can line their pockets.

Until March 1988 visitors who did not arrive in Hokkaido by air via Sapporo were likely to do so by ferry from Aomori to the port of Hakodate. However, the ferry service was discontinued with the opening of a rail link through the new **Seikan Tunnel** across the narrowest point of the Straits of Tsugaru, at 25.4 kilometres (15.8 miles) the longest undersea rail tunnel in the world.

Hakodate (population 320,000) was the largest city in Hokkaido until the great fire of 1934 caused many of its residents to move elsewhere, and it was the first major port opened to foreign commerce toward the end of the Edo period (in 1854, five years before the opening of Yokohama). Unlike Sapporo, which was a city from the moment of its carefully planned inception, Hakodate is simply a former fishing village that has grown to fill out its natural boundaries, these being the imposing **Mount Hakodate** (335 metres or 1,100 feet), which looms like a fortress over its well-sheltered harbour, and the sea that pounds both sides of the narrow peninsula on which the city stands. It is thus a more rewarding place than Sapporo to stroll in and explore for, besides being older (it was an established fishing port in the mid-1700s), it is full of the back alleys and odd straggling lanes that add life and interest to any city and which Sapporo conspicuously lacks.

The summit of Mount Hakodate is accessible by cable car and affords a wonderful view of the city, particularly at night. Otherwise the main sights are the various religious edifices, such as the Byzantine-style Greek Orthodox church, built near the foot of Mount Hakodate in 1862 and rebuilt in 1916, and the Trappist convent near neighbouring **Yunokawa** spa, where the city's favourite edible souvenirs, 'Trappist cookies', are manufactured by the contemplative butter-fingered inmates. Another tourist destination is the star-shaped **Goryokaku**, the first Western-style fort in Japan, completed in 1864 just in time to serve as the site of the last battle in the civil war that led to the restoration of the Emperor Meiji. Some 2,000 troops loyal to the fallen shogun occupied the fort in late 1868 and proclaimed Hokkaido (then still called Ezo) a republic, but they were besieged by the imperial army and surrendered in June 1869.

The little town of **Matsumae** (population 18,000) was the only feudal castle town in Hokkaido, having served as the seat of the Matsumae family from 1606 to 1869, during which period the whole southwest corner of the island was also known as Matsumae and was the only area open to Japanese settlement. The rest of the island was nominally recognized as Ainu territory, and settlement there was restricted until considerations of convenience and profitability began to outweigh those of justice and tolerance. The castle was restored in ferroconcrete in 1961.

Of Hokkaido's five remaining National Parks, those in the deep interior have most to offer the non-scientific visitor. **Daisetsuzan National Park** (the name means Great Snowy Mountains) is the largest inland National Park in Japan and lies in the exact centre of Hokkaido, the most convenient point of access being the city of **Asahikawa** (population 353,000). The park's chief attractions are its towering forested volcanoes, the tallest of which is **Mount Asahi** (2,290 metres or 7,513 feet), the highest mountain on the island. These mountains are a principal haunt of the Hokkaido brown bear, Japan's largest wild animal and, next to the Okinawan *habu*, its most dangerous. Bears are found throughout Hokkaido and northern Honshu, but the largest seem to congregate here. East of Mount Asahi, the upper reaches of the **Ishikari River** have carved out the spectacular **Sounkyo Gorge**, and **Sounkyo Spa** at the centre of the gorge is the most popular resort for visitors planning to stay in the park overnight. There are several smaller hot-spring resorts scattered through the mountains.

The main attractions of the **Akan National Park** in eastern Hokkaido are its three lakes, which, unlike the slightly more southerly Lakes Shikotsu and Toya, are iced over in winter. The lakes are **Akan, Kutcharo** and **Mashu**, the water of this last reputedly having the greatest transparency of any lake in the world. Lake Akan is the home of a curious spherical water weed called *marimo*, which entrepreneurs have conjured into a tourist attraction. Mainly they have done this by selling small specimens of it in plastic containers so that you can take it home and watch it shrivel in the unsuitable environment of your goldfish bowl; but they have also devised an 'Ainu' ritual in which the weed is gathered, placed overnight on an altar and 'worshipped', the worship taking the convenient and lucrative form of dances and chants. This event takes place annually in October in the hot-spring resort of **Akan Kohan**, where there is an 'Ainu' village similar to that at Shiraoi (see page 218), except that, by some happy circumstance of Ainu lore, every building but one in the Akan Kohan village turns out to be a souvenir shop, the single exception being a 'house' equipped with spectators' benches and a box office, where you can watch traditionally garbed elders pretending that they live there. There is, however, nothing contrived about the beauty of the peaks and dense subarctic forests that surround the lakes, and if the real Ainu of old had little use for spherical water weeds, they at least knew the value of these.

Northeast of the lakes lies the **Shiretoko Peninsula**, nowadays the **Shiretoko National Park**. There is a hot-spring resort called **Rausu** at the

foot of **Mount Rausu** (1,661 metres or 5,450 feet), but the park's main attractions are its coastal cliffs, best seen from a sightseeing boat, and its protected wildlife, which includes the rare sea eagle.

From the east coast of the peninsula the visitor will be able to see the slender island of **Kunashiri**. Further south, visible from the **Nemuro Peninsula**, lies the small group of islands collectively called **Habomai**. And beyond these, stretching away northeast and forming the southernmost links of the Kurile chain, are the small island of **Shikotan** and the large island of **Etorofu**. All of these islands, previously Japanese territory, have been occupied by the Soviet Union since August 1945 and a campaign to demand their return is mounted spasmodically by the Japanese government. The campaign attracts little grass roots support, but the 'northern territorial issue' has complicated Japanese-Soviet affairs to the extent that, although relations were 'normalized' in 1956, no postwar peace treaty between the two nations has ever been signed. Japan continues to demand the return of 'its' islands, and the Soviet Union continues to insist that there is no outstanding 'territorial issue' to discuss.

Part of Japan's irritation with the status quo arises from the circumstances in which Russia invaded the islands. Russia did not declare war on Japan until after the bombing of Hiroshima and rushed its troops into the southern Kuriles a bare six days before Japan surrendered. Japan had previously enjoyed a treaty of neutrality with the Soviet Union and had in fact been attempting to obtain Russian mediation to end the war, so the sudden annexation of these northern islands must have seemed like the worst kind of betrayal. Alas, a sad but inescapable lesson of history is that nations which go to war for reasons that include territorial aggrandizement, and then proceed to lose the war, tend also to lose territory. Compared with the violence done to national boundaries in Europe following World War II, Japan was immensely fortunate. Had Russia been allowed to participate in the postwar occupation, there is a strong possibility that the whole of Hokkaido might have remained today under Soviet control. Once in a while, one wishes that Japan's much-touted struggle to achieve 'international-mindedness' would permit certain sections of the Japanese establishment to assess their country's status in the light of global realities.

The **Kushiro Marshland National Park** near the city of **Kushiro** on Hokkaido's southeast coast is Japan's newest National Park, opened in August 1987. It exists principally to provide a sanctuary for the sacred crane, a specially protected species. In Japan and China the crane is regarded as a symbol of felicity and often appears, together with the tortoise (symbolizing longevity) in designs intended for use at festive occasions. The **Rishiri-Rebun-Sarobetsu National Park** consists of the two offshore islands of Rishiri and Rebun and the coastal strip extending south from the windy city of **Wakkanai** (population 53,000), the northernmost city in Japan. This marshy plain, some 27 kilometres (17 miles) long, is famous in summer for its irises and rhododendrons. The two islands are topographically very different. **Rishiri** (population 12,000) is an extinct volcano rising straight out of the sea to a height of 1,719 metres (5,640 feet) and inhabited only along the coast; fishing is practically the only occupation. **Rebun** (population 5,900) is flatter, but even bleaker. It provides good hiking country in summer, particularly along the west coast where a rough hiking track is the only means of access, but there is little to see there except the grey Soya Straits and little to hear but the smack of the wind and the incessant barking of crows.

Helpful Information

Getting Around Japan

Most prefectural capitals and some other major cities are served by one or more of Japan's domestic airlines. ANA (All Nippon Airways—*Zennikku*) flies the main routes and JAS (Japan Air System) duplicates many of these as well as serving smaller, remoter destinations. The national flag carrier, JAL (Japan Air Lines—*Nihon Koku*), flies major trunk routes such as those between Tokyo, Osaka, Fukuoka, Naha and Sapporo. SWAL (Southwest Air Lines—*Nansei Koku*) serves the Amami and Ryukyu islands. Tokyo's main domestic airport is Haneda, reached by monorail from Hamamatsucho Station. Japan's mountainous terrain has meant that many local airports have been built so far from the cities they serve that one can spend as long on the shuttle bus as one does on the plane. Domestic air transport in Japan is not cheap (a return trip from Tokyo to Okinawa is more expensive than a discount return to Hong Kong).

Long-distance rail travel is not cheap either but, earthquakes permitting, it is extremely reliable. The *Tokaido Shinkansen* joins Tokyo to Fukuoka, calling at Nagoya, Kyoto, Osaka, Hiroshima, Okayama, Shimonoseki and other major cities on the way. The *Tohoku Shinkansen* joins Tokyo (Ueno) to Morioka via Sendai and other cities. The *Joetsu Shinkansen* joins Tokyo (Ueno) to Niigata. There are many other JR express services, not so rapid but equally punctual, and a fine array of local services, although unprofitable rural lines are forever being axed. Seats can be reserved on all expresses, and reservations can be made at travel agents and major JR stations. First class (Green Car) seats are available on most routes and non-smoking areas are being expanded. Timetables *(jikokuhyo)* are issued monthly and are available from book shops and station kiosks; they are in Japanese but can be worked through with a map, practice and God's benison. In addition to the JR network, there are some useful private lines, particularly in the Kinki region. Kyoto and Nara are more conveniently joined by the Kintetsu railway than by JR, and Nikko is more easily reached from Tokyo by the Tobu line, whose terminus is Asakusa.

Long-distance, air-conditioned buses are generally cheaper than express trains and overnight services can be a boon to the budget-conscious traveller. In daylight he should ensure that his bus is a regular one and not a sightseeing *(kanko)* bus, otherwise he will spend the journey being addressed non-stop through a microphone by a young lady in a stewardess's outfit who will babble to him, sing to him, and point out every passing tree to him: a delight if he is in the mood for it and a severe tribulation if it takes him unawares. Some cities, such as Tokyo, lend themselves to half-day, day or evening guided bus tours. Some cities, such as Nara, do not. The visitor who opts for a guided bus tour of Kyoto deserves the migraine it will give him.

A New Development

O utside were about fifty of the now well-known jin-ri-ki-shas, and the air was full of a buzz produced by the rapid reiteration of this uncouth word by fifty tongues. This conveyance, as you know, is a feature of Japan, growing in importance every day. It was only invented seven years ago, and already there are nearly 23,000 in one city, and men can make so much more by drawing them than by almost any kind of skilled labour, that thousands of fine young men desert agricultural pursuits and flock into the towns to make draught-animals of themselves, though it is said that the average duration of a man's life after he takes to running is only five years, and that the runners fall victims in large numbers to aggravated forms of heart and lung disease. Over tolerably level ground a good runner can trot forty miles a day, at a rate of about four miles an hour. They are registered and taxed at 8s. a year for one carrying two persons, and 4s. for one which carries one only, and there is a regular tariff for time and distance.

The kuruma or jin-ri-ki-sha consists of a light perambulator body, an adjustible hood of oiled paper, a velvet or cloth lining and cushion, a well for parcels under the seat, two high slim wheels, and a pair of shafts connected by a bar at the ends. The body is usually lacquered and decorated according to its owner's taste. Some show little except polished brass, others are altogether inlaid with shells known as Venus's ear, and others are gaudily painted with contorted dragons, or groups of peonies, hydrangeas, chrysanthemums, and

in Transportation

mythical personages. They cost from £2 upwards. The shafts rest on the ground at a steep incline as you get in—it must require much practice to enable one to mount with ease or dignity—the runner lifts them up, gets into them, gives the body a good tilt backwards, and goes off at a smart trot. They are drawn by one, two, or three men, according to the speed desired by the occupants. When rain comes on, the man puts up the hood, and ties you and it closely up in a covering of oiled paper, in which you are invisible. At night, whether running or standing still, they carry prettily painted circular paper lanterns 18 inches long. It is most comical to see stout, florid, solid-looking merchants, missionaries, male and female, fashionably dressed ladies, armed with card cases, Chinese compradores, and Japanese peasant men and women flying along Main Street, which is like the decent respectable High Street of a dozen forgotten country towns in England, in happy unconsciousness of the ludicrousness of their appearance; racing, chasing, crossing each other, their lean, polite, pleasant runners in their great hats shaped like inverted bowls, their incomprehensible blue tights, and their short blue overshirts with badges or characters in white upon them, tearing along, their yellow faces streaming with perspiration, laughing, shouting, and avoiding collisions by a mere shave.

Isabella L Bird, Unbeaten Tracks In Japan, *1880*

Getting, and Not Getting Around Tokyo

Tokyo's taxi-drivers are nowadays mostly polite and helpful. You are not expected to tip taxi-drivers anywhere in Japan and some now equip their vehicles with *karaoke* tapes so that you can croon consoling ditties to yourself as the meter reduces you to penury. The trouble is that drivers frequently require you not only to tell them where you want to go, but to furnish them, in Japanese, with a detailed set of directions. This does not apply to major hotels and tourist destinations but a problem could occur if you got into a taxi in central Tokyo and gave the driver the address of a friend who lived out in the suburbs and whom you had never previously visited. This is not to say that it can't be done; only that it requires patience, a flexible time limit, a facility with sign language, and a repertoire of some two dozen consoling ditties.

The Tokyo subway and surface-rail systems are among the most efficient in the world. Surface railway lines either belong to JR East Japan (formerly part of the Japanese National Railways, which was denationalized and split into seven private corporations in 1987) or they have been privately owned from the beginning. There are 41 different JR East Japan lines, 23 private surface lines and 10 different subway lines in the Greater Tokyo area. The JR's Yamanote Line is a useful loop line linking the downtown business districts with the middle-class residential areas, taking in all of the major city terminuses. The Chuo Line is the main east-west route through the city, beginning at Tokyo Station and providing a rapid connection with the western suburbs. Otherwise, many of the lines seem arranged in so anarchic a fashion that one glance at a map showing all of them can induce Parkinson's disease. The problem is compounded by the difficulty of buying tickets (most ticket-vending machines have destinations written in Japanese only; a ticket bought on a private-line machine will be refused by a JR ticket collector etc.) and by the fact that many of even the largest Tokyo terminuses provide few signs in Roman script. A further problem—especially for families travelling with young children or for people suffering from physical disabilities—is the extreme crowdedness of most of the 74 lines throughout the day. During rush hours it often seems impossible that any more passengers could squeeze into the already chock-full compartments, but they do; and unless you begin your journey at the terminus, a seat is rare on most lines at any hour. One bright note is the cheerful colour-coding that has been adopted in painting JR trains (Yamanote=green, Chuo=orange, etc.), which allows the newcomer to recognize his train even when the platform is so congested that he can't get within three metres of the doors.

The Tokyo bus system is wonderfully arcane, and the newcomer is advised to train himself on the mandalas of the Shingon sect before attempting to tackle it.

Accommodation in Japan

Most cities, sizeable towns and major tourist resorts boast Western-style hotels. The rooms are likely to surprise the seasoned traveller by their smallness, but service is usually prompt and polite (tipping is never necessary but a 10 percent 'service charge' is added to the bill) and Western-style food is invariably available on the premises. 'International-class' hotels in major cities can be very expensive. In some surveys, Tokyo's Hotel Okura and Imperial Hotel rank as the priciest in the world.

'Business hotels' provide a cheap no-frills alternative. There is no room service, and often not even a coffee shop, but most are located very close to major railway stations or town centres so there is usually no shortage of restaurants in the vicinity. The rooms are barely large enough to contain a bed, but there is always a cubicle with shower, bath and Western-style lavatory. Business hotels are the best bet for budget-conscious travellers who either do not like Japanese food or do not wish to tie themselves down to fixed mealtimes.

A *ryokan* is a Japanese-style inn. The guest will use a tatami-matted room, to which his meals will be brought by a maid, and in which he will sleep on bedding (*futon*) which the maid will lay out. He will generally use a communal bath, although many ryokans now have rooms with bath and toilet attached, for which a higher rate is charged. Ryokans will expect to serve breakfast and dinner, and the guest has no say in the menu; but these fixed meals are a comparatively inexpensive way of experiencing 'full-course' Japanese cuisine without the bother of ordering separate items. Dinner is usually served quite early (6–7 o'clock), so if the guest finds everything totally unpalatable he still has time to slip out for a sandwich. You can opt to stay at a ryokan without being served meals, but the cost is only marginally less than for full board. A single guest will have a room to himself. A couple arriving together will normally be alloted the same room whatever their relationship. Four or more people arriving together may also find themselves sleeping in the same room. This is a saving in cost only for the ryokan, since bills are calculated per person, not per room.

A *minshuku* is a 'lodging house', in effect a no-frills ryokan. Some differ from ryokan hardly at all, except that the guest may be expected to lay out his own bedding. At others he will take his meals communally, often with the family who own the place. Minshuku are cheaper than ryokan and are mostly found in rural areas.

A *koku-minshuku-sha* is a government-operated lodging house, often found at popular tourist destinations. They are cheap, but vary in quality and must usually be booked in advance.

A 'pension' is a Western-style minshuku, increasingly popular among the young, especially at ski resorts. Youth hostels are found at many tourist

destinations, and guests may be encouraged to take part in enervating communal activities such as parlour games.

Eating Out

It is an article of faith among Japanese people that foreigners cannot enjoy their food. They firmly believe, for example, that they are the only nation in the world to eat raw fish; and foreign guests at a sushi shop will sometimes be the objects of gasps of awe punctuated by puzzled shakes of the head.

Sushi is bite-sized slabs of vinegared rice topped with slivers of raw fish or some other delicacy, dipped in soy sauce. Sushi shops are unique in that they rarely display their prices, so the master tends to charge what he likes. For this reason, even Japanese travellers are wary of blundering into unfamiliar sushi shops. *Sashimi* is raw fish without the vinegared rice.

Unagi is grilled eel, an expensive and popular delicacy, especially in summer when its high calorie and vitamin content is regarded as a way of combating the deleterious effects of the heat. *Tempura*, said to be Portuguese in origin, is deep-fried food, usually fish, prawns and vegetables.

Sukiyaki (which, because it is a meat dish, is acknowledged to be edible by non-Japanese) is beef and vegetables cooked with soy sauce and sugar and dipped in a condiment consisting mainly of raw egg. It is a comparatively modern invention. So is *shabu-shabu*, wafer-thin strips of meat dipped briefly into boiling stock before eating. A humbler meat dish found throughout Japan is *tonkatsu*, pork cutlets.

Noodles come in a wide variety. *Soba* are thin noodles made from buckwheat, eaten in soup or fried Chinese-style (*yaki-soba*). *Udon* are thicker wheat-flour noodles and *somen* are ultra-thin noodles eaten cold in summer. Soba may also be served cold on a tray and dipped into flavoured sauce, in which case it is called *zaru-soba*. *Ramen* are thin noodles served in hot Chinese-style soup, very cheap and a staple of long-distance truck drivers.

Traditionally, restaurants specialize in one or other of these types of food, but multi-purpose restaurants also exist, where the whole gamut, or most of it, is available. Lifelike plastic replicas helpfully occupy most of the window space. A useful word is *teishoku*, meaning a complete meal. For example, *sashimi teishoku* consists of a selection of raw fish with side dishes of pickles, boiled rice and bean-curd (*miso*) soup. Many restaurants also offer cheap set-course lunches. At Japanese-style restaurants these are also called *teishoku*, while at Western-style restaurants they are called *ranchi* (lunch). In the mornings, most coffee shops offer 'morning service', generally coffee, toast, a boiled egg and a tiny salad for little more than the price of a cup of coffee.

Western-style food outside of hotels and top-class restaurants tends to be stodgy. 'Chinese' food is cheap and very widely available, though few Chinese would recognize much of it, and at Korean barbecues *(yaki-niku)* the customer cooks his order of spiced meat on a gas- or charcoal heater brought to his table.

Drinking Out

A *bar* in Japan usually denotes a place where your drink will be poured for you by a 'hostess' who will sit beside you, flatter you, accept your offer of drinks in return, and charge you five times more than you ever dreamed of paying. At a *cabaret,* in return for the entire contents of your wallet, you will be permitted to grope the hostess under the table. A *karaoke* bar, nowadays a popular form of watering hole among salaried workers, may or may not be staffed by 'hostesses', but will certainly be equipped with a microphone and tapes, or more often, laser video discs, of orchestral accompaniments (*karaoke* means 'empty orchestra') to which the customers sing. Many take this pastime very seriously and, even in you have no ear for Japanese ballads, you can gauge their talent by the loudness of the applause: the loudest applause invariably greets the most thoroughly tuneless performance. Some karaoke bars have stages with spotlights and screens on which your image can be enjoyed not only by other patrons but by unsuspecting passers-by on the street above.

A *stand bar* or *snack* or *pub* will also often feature karaoke, but there will usually be no hostess, only a 'mama-san' who, except in dire circumstances (fire, theft, love at first sight), remains behind the counter, often barely large enough to seat six customers (the counter, not the mama-san). At such places you will be charged only for what you consume plus a small dish of food (rarely more than peanuts) which accompanies your first drink whether you want it or not. Some places charge for each karaoke song, but if you are foreign-looking and not entirely tone deaf you may find yourself drinking at the other customers' expense for the rest of the evening or, if you choose to stay, your life.

Many places operate a 'bottle keep' system. This means that you buy a whole bottle of either whisky or shochu (see page 189), scrawl your name on it with a 'sign pen', preferably illegibly, and on future visits pay only a nominal charge for ice and water to mix with your drink until the bottle runs dry. If you are planning to frequent a place, this is an economical way of drinking as well as of securing the warm reception accorded a paid-up regular.

The safest, cheapest and most interesting choice of drinking spot for the curious visitor in a strange town who does not wish to exercise his vocal cords is an *akachochin* (literally, 'red lantern'), recognizable by that object's prominence above the door outside. There, you will be charged only for what you eat and drink. At some places you can eat a substantial meal of grilled fish or sticks of barbecued chicken (*yaki-tori*), an item so popular that many akachochin specialize in it. The atmosphere is often noisy and smoky and, whereas at a bar you go to flirt with a hostess and at a snack to talk to the mama-san, at a red-lantern place customers actually talk to each other; and you may find everything you have ever heard or read about Japanese reticence and politeness driven forever from your mind in the course of one heady night.

Hot Springs

Like most Asians, the Japanese have not traditionally shown a great deal of interest in the seaside as a place to go for rest and recreation; the extreme crowdedness of Japanese beaches on hot Sundays is a modern phenomenon (and still a strictly limited one since few Japanese will venture into the sea outside the month of August). Nor, before the last decades of the 19th century, did the Japanese show any interest in skiing, hiking or mountain climbing; all of those pastimes were introduced to them by energetic Europeans. Traditionally, when the Japanese (especially men) have wanted to relax, they have gone to one of the 20,000 or so thermal springs with which the earthquake- and eruption-ridden geology of the Japanese islands has blessed them, sometimes with their families and sometimes for a form of communal recreation to which their families would constitute a major hindrance.

Hot-spring spas (*onsen*) remain high on the list of favourite leisure destinations for Japanese people today, and it would be sad if the foreign visitor did not sample this hedonistic form of recreation at least once during his stay. There is no prefecture in Japan without hot springs and for many prefectures (such as Tottori, Oita and Akita), onsen are a major source of tourist revenue.

Some resorts consist almost entirely of large, garish Western-style hotels, where there are cabarets, nightclubs, theatres and 'geisha parties' (hot-spring geisha are neither as accomplished nor as hard-to-tumble as their famous Kyoto cousins and sexual adventures, discreet or otherwise, continue to be a factor in the popularity of onsen among all-male groups, though families with children can stay at the hotels in which these adventures occur and remain in complete and blissful ignorance of them).

At less ferociously developed resorts most of the inns are Japanese-style, often teetering on the banks of the river from whose bed the thermal spring erupts. Some are complete towns with numerous bars, restaurants and strip shows. Others may be little more than a cluster of traditional buildings in a glade or on a mountainside. Some consist of a single inn.

One of the great attractions is the open-air bath (*rotenburo*), which is

Balancing Acts

H e was out many nights and he saw all manner of drunks, but never once did he see a Japanese fall off the platform. It was difficult to explain why they did not, unless what was true of most skills applied equally to drinking—early training and constant practice make for mastery. The performance of drunks on platforms was miraculous. A platform ten yards across and often with as much as fifty yards to go to the next exit presented a more formidable challenge to a drunk than a tightrope did to an acrobat. Within this lethal margin Japanese drunks did everything and went everywhere but over the edge, staggering in a series of hair-raising zigzag manoeuvres from one side to the other until they reached the relative safety of the exit. Relative safety, because this was where most accidents usually happened, on the stairs leading down into the street. Just get to the exit, the drunk instinctively told himself, and so it was no further than to the exit that his residual powers of concentration and self-discipline managed to last. Here he disintegrated and gave up the ghost, entrusting his body to the wise discretion of the proverb. The fall might be painful but at least not fatal; and pain, in any case, was an account that would not have to be settled until the following day.

By no means all of Tokyo's stations were transformed into this regular nightly battlefield. One advantage of being rich was that your drunken stupor could be brought on and allowed to pass off in conditions of relative privacy, incoming on the arm of a discreet hostess at your club and outgoing in the arms of a taxi driver, who could be trusted to perform the additional services for which he had additionally been paid. It all went down on expense account anyway. The stations where these same rich men boarded the train in the morning were therefore relatively deserted at night. Boon did not even get a glimpse of this world behind closed doors until he had won his spurs in Tokyo's seedier districts by running the gauntlet of many last-train platforms very many times. . .

John David Morley, Pictures from the Water Trade

almost always available to bathers of both sexes. Not all onsen hotels have *rotenburo*, and those that lack them tend to lavish extra care and expense on their inside baths, most of which are nowadays segregated though there is often a family bath (*kazoku-buro*) to get round this awkward and untraditional prudery.

Some onsen are famous for their curative properties and many of the guests are elderly or infirm. All onsen claim some health benefits, but the sheer relaxation they afford is reason enough for paying the somewhat higher rate that an onsen ryokan charges compared with other inns. The food is usually plentiful and meals and service are often of a higher standard than an ordinary rural ryokan might provide.

Language and Names

Many Japanese people are convinced that their language is 'the most difficult in the world', and refuse to believe that Westerners can speak it. Confronted with the increasingly common sight of Westerners speaking it quite competently, they exhibit a range of emotions including incredulity, revulsion and alarm. Their belief in the language's supreme difficulty was buttressed by early foreign missionaries who called it the 'devil's tongue' and it is a notion the Japanese cling to with a grip unshaken by empirical evidence.

Spoken Japanese is actually among the easiest of East Asian languages for a Westerner because it does not depend on tones. Nor do its sounds present significant difficulties to a speaker who can pronounce consonants roughly as in English and vowels roughly as in Italian. The main difficulties of spoken Japanese are its very large vocabulary and the importance of social propriety, but these are difficulties that English and other languages plainly share.

Written Japanese is another matter. The written language consists of ideograms (*kanji*), borrowed from the Chinese at about the same time as Buddhism, and two sets of 46 phonetic symbols called *kana* which were developed from simplified ideograms during the tenth century. One set, *hiragana,* is used for the grammatical parts of sentences (such as verb endings and particles) which have no equivalent in Chinese. The other, *katakana,* is used mainly for words of foreign (other than Chinese) origin, of which modern Japanese contains thousands. The chief difficulty, apart from the huge effort of memory required to master the system, is that, unlike in Chinese, a single kanji may have up to a dozen different pronunciations (though more often two or three), depending on its context and how it is combined with other kanji (see the note on *Taira* and *Heike,* page 150). This is, of course, as much a difficulty for the Japanese as it is for foreigners, particularly where names are concerned. At present, junior high school graduates are supposed to have learnt both kana syllabaries plus 1,945 kanji.

But this is nothing like enough to enable them to read, say, a sophisticated modern novel (Mishima used upwards of 5,000 *kanji*); and one is moved to ponder the often-heard boast that the Japanese are the most literate nation on earth. The only official standard for measuring 'literacy' is school attendance, which is clearly inadequate given both the limitations of compulsory education and the fact that you can take a horse to water without its doing much more than sipping.

All Japanese personal and place names 'mean' something. Former Prime Minister Tanaka's name means 'middle of the paddy', former Prime Minister Sato's name means 'helpful wisteria'. This sounds engagingly quaint, but these meanings impinge no more on the Japanese consciousness than the name 'Smith' conjures up pictures of people hammering anvils, or 'Oxford' calls to the minds of all who hear it a vision of cows wading across a river. In this book names appear in the Japanese order: family name before given name.

The Calendar, The Years and Public Holidays

Unlike some Asian communities, the Japanese abandoned the lunar calendar in 1873, and now calculate the dates of most festivals and all other annual observances by the Gregorian calendar imported from the West. This permits them to steal a march on the Chinese when it comes to New Year, since they have retained the 12 zodiacal animals—rat, ox, tiger, rabbit, dragon, snake, horse, ram, monkey, cock, dog and boar—but each ushers in the year over which it presides on 1 January instead of in February, when the lunar year normally begins.

There are two systems of counting years in Japan, used with about equal frequency. One is the Western system based on an unreliable estimate of when Jesus was born. The other counts years from the accession of each emperor. The present emperor, Akihito, came to the throne in 1989. His reign is called the Heisei (Achievement of Peace) era, 'Heisei' being the name he will be known by after his death. Thus 1989 was the first year of Heisei, or Heisei 1. The previous year, 1988, was the last year of the Showa (1926–88) era, or Showa 63. 'Showa' is the posthumous name of Emperor Hirohito and means (somewhat ironically considering the history of his reign) Enlightened Peace. The other two reigns to which the system nowadays applies are Meiji (1868–1911) and Taisho (1912–25). Queen Victoria died in Meiji 34. The First World War broke out in Taisho 3. President Kennedy was assassinated in Showa 38. The system is rarely used for dates prior to 1868 because, aside from professional historians, few can remember the previous emperors' names, let alone their dates of accession.

There are 13 annual public holidays in Japan. As in the West, 1 January is New Year's Day *(Ganjitsu)*, the most important holiday of the year. 15 January is Adult's Day *(Seijin-no-hi)*, when ceremonies are held for people who have reached the age of 20. 11 February is National Foundation Day *(Kenkoku Kinen-no-hi)*, a day purporting to commemorate the accession of the mythological Emperor Jimmu. 21 March is the Spring Equinox *(Shunbun-no-hi)*. 29 April is Greenery Day *(Midori-no-hi)*, see page 14. 3 May is Constitution Day *(Kenpo Kinebi)*, commemorating the enforcement of the American-drafted postwar constitution. 5 May is Children's Day *(Kodomo-no-hi)*, the new name for the Boy's Festival when male children are pampered even more than usual and colourful carp streamers are flown by families blessed with them. There is a girls' equivalent (the *Hina-matsuri* or Dolls' Festival on 3 March) but it is not a public holiday. 15 September is Respect for the Aged Day *(Keiro-no-hi)*. 23 September is the Autumn Equinox *(Shubun-no-hi)*, a day for visiting and cleaning athe graves of dead family members. 10 October is Sports Day *(Taiiku-no-hi)*. 3 November is Culture Day *(Bunka-no-hi)*. 23 November is Labour Thanksgiving Day *(Kinro Kansha-no-hi)*, the only day of the year on which many Japanese people will admit to being other than middle class. 23 December is the Emperor's birthday *(Tenno Tanjobi)*.

Few offices open on these days, and all banks, post offices and similar facilities are closed, though rail and other forms of transport are unaffected. If a public holiday falls on a Sunday, the following Monday becomes a compensatory day off work.

Sources of Information

Detailed travel information can be obtained first-hand from English-speaking staff at the three Tourist Information Centre (TIC) branches, operated by the Japan National Tourist Organisation. The Tokyo branch is next to Yurakucho station at 6–6 Yurakucho 1-chome, Chiyoda-ku: tel. (03) 3502 1461. The Kyoto branch is in the Kyoto Tower Building opposite Kyoto Station: tel. (075) 371 5649. The third branch is at Narita Airport: tel. (0476) 32 8711. They are open 9–5 Monday to Friday, 9–12 noon on Saturday and closed on Sunday. In addition to answering questions, they can supply you with enough timetables, handouts, maps, newsletters and free what's-on publications (such as *Tour Companion* and *Tokyo Weekender*) to fill several suitcases.

Tokyo Journal is a monthly English-language magazine containing very detailed information on current events, eating and drinking out, festivals etc. in Tokyo and the Kanto region. It is available from foreign-language bookshops and from many hotels. *Kansai Time Out* is a similar publication covering the Osaka, Kobe, Kyoto area.

Tourist information in English is also available over the telephone. In Tokyo you can contact English-speaking tourist advisers by ringing *Travel-Phone* at 3502 1461. In Kyoto the number is 371 5649. A three-minute call costs 10 yen. Outside Tokyo and Kyoto the service is toll-free: call 0120 222800 for information about eastern Japan (Chubu to Hokkaido); 0120 444800 for information about western Japan (Kinki to Okinawa). In Tokyo you can hear recorded what's-on information by ringing 3503 2911 (English) or 3503 2926 (French).

All travel, hotel, ryokan, minshuku and other reservations can be made at any branch of JTB (Japan Travel Bureau), who also organize regional package tours. A variety of regional and period rail passes is available from JR booking offices or JTB. Most airports and major railway stations have information and reservation desks for local hotels and ryokans; ask for *ryokan annai* (ryokan information). You can, of course, walk into a ryokan or minshuku without a reservation and ask if they have a room, but at peak travel periods this is an unreliable method, besides which some innkeepers are still sufficiently thrown by the looming presence of foreigners in their entrance halls to pretend that they are full or closed, a nuisance that is usually (though not always) avoided by reserving through 'correct' channels. Still, it can be part of the delight of arriving in a strange Japanese town to wander through the streets making up your own mind about where you want to stay.

Tickets for theatres, concerts and cinemas can be obtained at *Playguide* desks, though the staff may not speak English. If you are at TIC in Yurakucho, the nearest Playguide is in the Mullion Building on the top floor of the Seibu Department Store; or you can stroll up to the Ginza 8-chome crossing, where you will find English speakers at *Ticket Pia* (tel. 3571 1003).

Further Reading

The work of many of the better-known writers on Japanese society (Nakane Chie, Doi Takeo, former U.S. Ambassador Edwin Reischauer *et al*) is marred, in part, by their too ready acquiescence in the notion that the objects of their study are 'unique' and 'different' from the rest of humankind, and their assumption that generalizations like 'The Japanese' (or that even more chimerical entity, 'The West') are sensible and useful. These attitudes have been the bane of 'Japanology' ever since its inception, but Japanese studies today seem to be moving slowly away from such dehumanizing concerns toward an acceptance of the fact that this society is as full of conflicts, contradictions, idiosyncracies, inequities and sheer mess as most other social groups, and that the Japanese people themselves are human individuals, and not some species of consensus-worshipping extraterrestrial. From this point of view, a valuable recent book on contemporary Japan is Ross Mouer and Yoshio Sugimoto's *Images of Japanese Society* (KPI), which sets out specifically to challenge the 'holistic' view, though its undisguised polemics will limit its appeal to some readers.

A more recent book still, and one which presents at least as great a challenge to recent opinion, is Karel van Wolferen's *The Enigma of Japanese Power* (Macmillan), a controversial 'revisionist' study of Japanese politics and social organization which argues that, despite appearances, Japan is neither a free-trading nation nor a constitution-governed state. Readers seeking a lighter, less critical and, in the end, less depressing account of conditions in modern Japan should turn to Peter Tasker's *Inside Japan* (Penguin), which, though less bellicose, is similarly unblinkered.

Two very good, and very different books on rural Japanese society are Brian Moeran's *Okubo Diary* (Stanford University) and Junichi Saga's *Memories of Silk and Straw* (Kodansha International). The first is a British anthropologist's memoir of his stay in a tiny Kyushu village. The second is an oral history of a town in Ibaraki prefecture in which elderly people reminisce about prewar life. Both help to dispel the cloying 'pastoral idyll' attitude toward the Japanese countryside so common among today's city dwellers.

Ian Buruma's *A Japanese Mirror* (Penguin) is an entertaining account of the preoccupations of modern Japanese popular culture. It deals with, among other things, the concept of the hero in Japanese society, a theme brilliantly expanded in Ivan Morris's *The Nobility of Failure* (Penguin), an exceptionally lucid book on those aspects of national character which 'The Japanese' most admire. For an equally lucid account of the cultural mainstream it is hard to better Sir George Sansom's *Japan: A Short Cultural History* (Tuttle), first published in 1931, revised in 1952, but not superseded. Readers seeking a brief historical introduction will benefit from Richard Storry's *A History of Modern Japan* (Penguin), which, its title notwithstanding, opens in prehistoric times. Roy Andrew Miller's *Japan's Modern Myth* (Weatherhill) is a stirringly iconoclastic book about the alleged difficulties and 'uniqueness' of the Japanese language. Several Japanese professors who specialize in detailing this uniqueness have boasted of hurling the book across the room in annoyance, so it needs no further recommendation.

My own *The Roads to Sata* (Penguin) is an account of a four-month journey I made on foot from the northernmost tip of Hokkaido to the southernmost tip of Kyushu, and of the encounters I had along the way.

General Index

Index of People Mentioned

Antoku 安徳 (1178–1185), by traditional count the 81st emperor, ascended the throne at the age of three and was drowned, aged eight, at the sea battle of Dannoura.

Asano Naganori 淺野長德 (1667–1701) was the provincial lord, immortalized as Enya Hangan Takasada in the Kabuki play *Chushingura*, who committed ritual suicide after being goaded into drawing his sword in the shogun's castle, and was famously avenged by his 47 loyal retainers.

Ashikaga Yoshimasa 足利義政 (1436–1490), the eighth Ashikaga shogun, ruled from 1449 to 1474, years marked by growing social unrest, the decline in the power of his family and the beginning of a long period of civil war. Yoshimasa had little interest in affairs of state and lavished his energies on artistic projects such as the building of the Silver Pavilion.

Ashikaga Yoshimitsu 足利義満 (1358–1408) was the third Ashikaga shogun, having succeeded his father at the age of 10. He was an energetic ruler who continued to revel in luxury and artistic refinement after retirement into the priesthood. These loves are exemplified in the Golden Pavilion, which he built.

Ashikaga Yoshinori 足利義教 (1394–1441), the sixth Ashikaga shogun, who ruled from 1429 to his death, was responsible for the downfall and exile of Zeami.

Benkei 弁慶 (?–1189) was the (perhaps legendary) retainer of Yoshitsune, whose prodigious wit, strength and fidelity to his lord are celebrated in the Kabuki play *Kanjincho*. In their last stand against the forces of Yoritomo, Benkei fought to the death in order to allow Yoshitsune time to commit suicide.

Blunden, Edmund Charles (1896–1974) was a British poet who lived and taught for long periods of his life in Japan and Hong Kong.

Clark, William Smith (1826–1886) was the American educator who advised the Japanese government on agricultural and educational matters during his tenure (1876–77) at the newly-opened agricultural college in Sapporo.

Date Masamune 伊達政宗 (1567–1636) was a warrior who, having supported Ieyasu at the Battle of Sekigahara, was rewarded with the fief of Sendai, which he developed and where he built his famous castle.

Dogen 道元 (1200–1253) was the founder of the Soto sect of Zen Buddhism and its head temple, Eiheiji. He was a prolific author whose writings stress the Buddha nature in all things and the importance of realizing this nature through insight into oneself and the world.

Ganjin 鑑眞 (688–763) was the Chinese Buddhist monk (properly called Chien

Chen) who founded Toshodaiji temple in Nara. He was blind when he reached Japan at the age of 66 and is said to have died in the full lotus position of meditation.

Gio 祇王   is the otherwise unknown lady who, according to the *Heike Monogatari* (Tale of the Heike), entered the convent now called Gioji at the age of 21 after losing the love of Kiyomori. The convent, originally called Ojoin, was renamed for her in 1895.

Glover, Thomas Blake (1838–1911), a Scotsman, established a trading firm in Nagasaki in 1859 and financially supported the anti-shogunate forces in the Meiji Restoration. In the 1860s he diversified into railways and mining, and went bankrupt in 1870.

Godaigo 後醍醐 (1287–1339), by traditional count the 96th emperor, reigned from 1318 to 1339. He was exiled to the Oki islands in 1332 for attempting to overthrow the Kamakura shogunate, but escaped the next year, when forces mustered by him defeated the shogun's army and restored Godaigo to power. The restoration was short-lived and he abdicated one day before he died, following the establishment of a new line of shoguns, the Ashikagas.

Gotoba 後鳥羽 (1180–1239), by traditional count the 82nd emperor, reigned from the age of three until 1198. In 1221 he joined Juntoku, his son, in an uprising against the Kamakura shogunate as a result of which he was exiled to Oki.

Hamada Shoji 浜田庄司   (1894–1978) was Japan's most famous modern potter, who contributed hugely to the revival of interest in folk pottery. He was named a Living National Treasure in 1955.

Harris, Townsend (1804–1878) was the first U.S. consul general in Japan. He arrived in 1856 and succeeded in concluding a commercial treaty in 1858, one of the landmarks in Japan's at first reluctant opening to the West.

Hearn, Lafcadio (1850–1904) was an author and teacher intoxicated by the romantic view of Japan which he helped introduce to the late Victorian West. He lived in Japan from 1890 to his death. A selection of his writings about Japan has been published by Penguin.

Hirohito 裕仁   (1901–1989) was the last emperor of Japan (by traditional count the 124th) and, if one excepts the early fictions, the longest reigning sovereign in Japanese history. He came to the throne in 1926 and after his death became known as *Showa*   also the name for the period in which he has reigned.

Hojo Tokimasa 北條時政   (1138–1215) was Yoritomo's father-in-law and first regent of the Kamakura shogunate, an office he held from 1203 to 1205.

Honen 法然   (1133–1212) was the Buddhist priest who founded the Jodo (Pure Land) sect, which advocates total reliance on the chanting of the *nembutsu* (the name of

Amida, the Compassionate Buddha) as the sole means of achieving grace.

Ikeda Daisaku 池田大作 (1928–) was the third president of Sokagakkai and the founder of its political party, Komeito. He retired as president in 1979 but remains the head of Sokagakkai International.

Ishida Mitsunari 石田三成 (1560–1600) was the most important of Hideyoshi's ministers and, after his master's death, led forces against Ieyasu, who defeated him in 1600 at the Battle of Sekigahara, following which he was captured and executed.

Ishikawa Jozan 石川文山 (1583–1672) was the Rinzai priest, Confucian scholar and Chinese-style poet who built the secluded Shisendo hermitage, to which he retired at the age of 58.

Jimmu 神武 (711 BC–585 BC!) was the legendary first emperor of Japan, who is supposed to have reigned from 660 BC until his death. The dates are wholly impossible and there is doubt that he even existed.

Juntoku 順徳 (1197–1242), by traditional count the 84th emperor, reigned from 1210 until his abdication in 1221 following an unsuccessful revolt against the Kamakura shogunate, as a result of which he was exiled to Sado, where he died.

Kammu 桓武 (737–806), traditionally the 50th emperor, reigned from 781 until his death. His mother was of Korean origin. He is best remembered for having established the capital at Heiankyo, later Kyoto.

Kawabata Yasunari 川端康成 (1899–1972), Japan's only Nobel laureate in literature, won the Prize in 1968. He was a lyrical and elegaic writer whose qualities are perhaps best seen in the novels *Yukiguni* (Snow Country) and *Senbazuru* (Thousand Cranes), both translated into English by Edward Seidensticker. His death in a gas-filled room of his apartment was perhaps suicide, perhaps misadventure.

Kenreimon-in 建礼門院 (1155–1213) the daughter of Kiyomori, leapt into the sea with her son, the Emperor Antoku, when defeat for the Heike was assured at the Battle of Dannoura in 1185. The boy was drowned, but the mother was rescued and retired to the Jakkoin as a nun.

Kinmei 欽明 (509–571), traditionally the 29th emperor, reigned from 540 until his death. During his reign Buddhism was introduced into Japan from Korea.

Kira Yoshinaka 吉良義央 (1641–1703) is better known to posterity as Kono Moronao, the villain of the Kabuki play *Chushingura*. Kira goaded the young lord Asano Naganori into drawing his sword in the shogun's castle, for which offence Asano was sentenced to commit ritual suicide. Asano's 47 loyal retainers bided their time before assassinating Kira at his Edo residence and laying his severed head on their lord's grave.

Kobayashi Masaki 小林正樹 (1916–) is a film director, best known for his anti war trilogy *Ningen no Joken* (The Human Condition) and for *Seppuku* (Harakiri), which calls into question Japan's vaunted warrior ethic. His 1964 *Kwaidan* is a version of four tales by Lafcadio Hearn.

Kugyo 公曉 (1201–1219) was the priestly name taken by Yoritomo's grandson, whose own father, the shogun Yoriie, had been deposed by Yoritomo's second son, Sanetomo, in revenge for which Kugyo assassinated Sanetomo at the Tsurugaoka Hachiman Shrine in Kamakura in 1219 and was himself pursued and killed.

Kukai 空海 (774–835) is more widely known by his posthumous name, Kobo Daishi. He founded the Shingon sect of Buddhism and the monastery on Mount Koya, and was an unflagging builder of temples, including the 88 in Shikoku that form Japan's most famous pilgrim circuit. He is also credited with having invented the *kana* syllabary.

Kuninaka no Muraji Kimimaro 国中連公麻呂 (?–774), the grandson of a naturalised Korean official, was according to one source, 'the most eminent Nara-period sculptor of Buddhist images' and was responsible for casting the Great Buddha of Todaiji temple in Nara, despite which, no doubt because of his parentage, his name is absent from most Japanese guides and reference books.

Kurosawa Akira 黒澤明 (1910–) is Japan's best known living film director, though his reputation has always seemed more secure abroad than at home. His most recent films are *Kagemusha* (The Shadow Warrior), about the circumstances surrounding the death of Takeda Shingen, and *Ran* (Conflict), a version of *King Lear*.

Leach, Bernard Howell (1887–1979) was an English potter who, with Hamada Shoji, introduced Japanese pottery and ceramic methods to the West. He was also instrumental in helping to revive an interest in the folk arts in Japan.

Maeda Toshiie 前田利家 (1538?–1599) was one of Nobunaga's principal vassal lords, who later fought on the side of Hideyoshi and was rewarded in 1583 with the fief of Kaga.

Matsuo Basho 松尾芭蕉 (1644–1694) was, and is, Japan's foremost haiku poet. He adopted the name Basho (Banana Tree) in 1681 after the tree that stood in his garden. His single most famous haiku is: *furuike ya/kawazu tobikomu/mizu no oto* ('An old pond/a frog jumps in/sound of water') and his best known travel book, which contains many poems, is *Oku no Hosomichi*, translated into English by Yuasa Nobuyuki as *The Narrow Road to the Deep North*.

Meiji 明治 is the posthumous name of Mutsuhito (1852–1912), by traditional count the 122nd emperor of Japan, who reigned from 1867 until his death, a period also known as Meiji. The restoration of power to him in 1868 marked the end of the shogunate and the beginning of Japan's modern era. He was the present emperor's great grandfather.

Mikimoto Kokichi 御木本幸吉　(1858–1954) was the father of Japan's cultured pearl industry. He succeeded in producing his first cultured pearl in 1893 and by 1911 had set up stores in London, the U.S.A. and China, establishing himself as the 'pearl king'.

Minamoto no Sanetomo 源実朝　(1192–1219) was Yoritomo's second son and the third Kamakura shogun, an office he assumed in 1203 at the age of 11. He was assassinated by his nephew, Kugyo, who blamed him for his father's death.

Minamoto no Yoritomo 源頼朝　(1147–1199) was the founder of the Kamakura shogunate (1192–1333), and one of the most ruthless and powerful warlords in Japanese history. Posterity's regard for him has been lessened by his jealous persecution of his charismatic younger brother, Yoshitsune.

Minamoto no Yoshitsune 源義経　(1159–1189), Yoritomo's half-brother, can claim to be Japan's chief tragic hero. He was hugely instrumental in the overthrow of the Heike, but soon after incurred the jealousy and suspicion of Yoritomo and was forced to flee from his brother's forces. He died surrounded by Yoritomo's warriors, after having first killed his wife and daughter.

Mishima Yukio 三島通庸　(1925–1970) was a prolific novelist, playwright and essayist, widely remembered for the histrionic ritual suicide he committed after leading members of his private army in occupying part of the headquarters of the Ground Self-Defence Forces and exhorting the personnel there to rise 'in defence of the emperor'. In his last years he made a cult of body-building and the martial arts and adopted extreme right-wing attitudes, but his novels are remarkable for their delicacy of observation and their rampant aestheticism. *Kinkakuji* (The Temple of the Golden Pavilion) has been translated into English by Ivan Morris.

Miyamoto Musashi 宮本武蔵　(1584–1645) was a master swordsman who developed the method of fighting with two swords, one long, one short. He was also a painter and calligrapher whose work is regarded as having been heavily influenced by Zen.

Mongaku 文覚　(dates uncertain) was a Buddhist priest and associate of Yoritomo's. He was exiled to Sado in 1199, having been implicated in a plot against the emperor.

Moraes, Wenceslau de (1854–1929) was a Portuguese naval officer, diplomat and author who spent much of his life in the East, at Macau and subsequently in Japan where he lived permanently from 1898 until his death.

Mukai Kyorai 向井去来　(1651–1704) was the poet, a disciple of Basho's, who lived in Saga, on the outskirts of Kyoto, in the rustic cottage called *Rakushisha* (Hut of Fallen Persimmons).

Nagako 良子　(1903–), the eldest daughter of Prince Kuni no Miya Kunihiko, is the mother of Akihito, the present Emperor of Japan.

Nakahama (John) Manjiro 中浜万次郎　(1827–1898) was a fisherman from Kochi who was shipwrecked in 1841, rescued by an American whaler and invited by its captain to the U.S., where he lived until 1851, studying and working as a cooper, seaman and gold prospector. On his return to Japan he became the shogunate's chief interpreter.

Nakasone Yasuhiro 中曾根康弘 (1918–) was Japan's prime minister from 1982 to 1987. During his period in office he alternately impressed foreign governments with his much vaunted 'internationalism' and horrified them with gestures and words that were widely interpreted as racist, chauvinist and ultra-nationalistic.

Nichiren 日蓮 (1222–1282) founded the sect of Buddhism that bears his name, and which teaches that salvation can be achieved by repeatedly chanting the formula *namu myoho renge kyo* (I take refuge in the Lotus Sutra).

Nogi Maresuke 乃木希典 (1849–1912) was the general who led Japan's Third Army in the Russo-Japanese War of 1904–05 and is remembered as the victor of Port Arthur, though his 'strategy' of unrelenting frontal assault cost 56,000 Japanese casualties.

Noguchi Hideo 野口英世 (1876–1928) was a bacteriologist who isolated the causative agent of syphilis and, in 1918, began work on a vaccine for yellow fever. His trip to Africa, on which he died of yellow fever, was undertaken to confirm his results.

Oda Nobunaga 織田信長 (1534–1582) was the great unifier of Japan after a hundred years of civil war. Hideyoshi and Ieyasu were both originally his vassals and could never have wielded their subsequent power without the groundwork laid by Nobunaga's blend of brutality, ruthlessness and vision.

Ojin 応神 (201–310?) was, by traditional count, the 15th emperor and is supposed to have reigned from 270 to his death. More likely he was a provincial ruler of the 5th century. A keyhole-shaped mound near Osaka is believed to be his tomb.

Perry, Matthew Calbraith (1794–1858) was the U.S. commodore who arrived off the coast of Japan with his 'black ships' in 1853 and again in 1854, and pressured the shogun into signing the Treaty of Kanagawa, under which certain ports were opened to foreign commerce.

Saga 嵯峨 (786–842), by traditional count the 52nd emperor, was both an energetic statesman and an enthusiastic poet. He ruled from 809 to 823 and, after abdicating, retired to his suburban villa, now Daikakuji temple.

Saigo Takamori 西郷隆盛 (1827–1877) was the former marshall and counsellor of state who led the last armed rebellion against the Japanese government in 1877. He is still widely regarded as a paragon of old samurai virtues. His statue stands in Ueno Park.

Sakamoto Ryoma 坂本龍馬 (1836–1867) was one of the prime movers in the Meiji

Restoration of 1868, to which he contributed by helping cement a crucial alliance between the Choshu and Satsuma clans. He was assassinated by an agent of the increasingly desperate shogunate the year before it fell.

Shimazu Nariakira 島津斉彬 (1809–1858) was the energetic lord of Satsuma who embarked on an active programme of Westernization, including the building of factories producing weapons, gunpowder, glass, ceramics and chemicals.

Shinran 親鸞 (1173–1263) was the founder of the Jodo Shin (New Pure Land) sect of Buddhism, which maintains that simple faith is the only necessary prerequisite for salvation.

Shotoku 聖徳 (574–622), usually called Shotoku Taishi or Prince Shotoku, was a great regent, administrator and supporter of the spread of Buddhism, who is credited with having promulgated the Japanese nation's first constitution.

Suinin 垂仁 (70 BC–AD 70!), traditionally the 11th emperor, is supposed to have reigned from 31 BC until his death. His tomb is in Nara. Almost nothing is known about him, but he is credited with having founded the first shrine at Ise.

Suzuki Daisetz 鈴木大拙 (1870–1966) was the Buddhist scholar largely responsible for the popularity of Zen Buddhism in the West, where some 30 volumes by him have been published.

Taira no Kiyomori 平清盛 (1118–1181) was an ambitious and powerful warrior and statesman under whose influence Taira (Heike) power at court reached its zenith. During his lifetime he retained iron control of the state, placing his grandson, Antoku, on the throne in 1180, but after his death opposition to Heike hegemony grew and the family was finally overthrown in 1185.

Takeda Shingen 武田信玄 (1521–1573) was the famous lord of Kai, nowadays Yamanashi, whose warlike ambitions brought him into confrontation with Nobunaga and Ieyasu.

Tanaka Kakuei 田中角栄 (1918–) was Japan's prime minister from 1972 to 1974, when he was forced to resign amid allegations of financial misdealing. He was arrested in 1976, accused of having received bribes from the Lockheed Corporation while in office, and was eventually sentenced to prison, though a series of appeals has kept him at liberty.

Tokugawa Iemitsu 徳川家光 (1604–1651) was the third Tokugawa shogun, who intensified the persecution of Christians, suppressed the Shimabara rebellion and instituted the policy of *sakoku* (strict national seclusion). He ruled from 1623 to 1651.

Tokugawa Iesada 徳川家定 (1824–1858), the 13th Tokugawa shogun, ruled from 1853 to his death, and reluctantly concluded the commercial treaty with Townsend Harris that spelt the end of Japan's seclusion.

Tokugawa Ieyasu 徳川家康　(1542–1616) was the founder of the Tokugawa shogunate and ruled as its first shogun from 1603 to 1605. Building on the unifying work of Nobunaga and Hideyoshi, he instituted a period (the Edo period, 1603–1867) of comparative peace and stability. The Toshogu Shrine at Nikko is his mausoleum.

Tokugawa Yoshimune 徳川吉宗　(1684–1751) was the eighth Tokugawa shogun, under whom the first nationwide census was conducted. He ruled from 1716 to 1745.

Toyotomi Hideyori 豊臣秀頼　(1593–1615) was Hideyoshi's son, on whose behalf Ishida Mitsunari fought Ieyasu at Sekigahara. Hideyori survived until 1615 when, besieged by Ieyasu at Osaka Castle, he committed suicide.

Toyotomi Hideyoshi 豊臣秀吉　(1537–1598) was the warlord who completed Nobunaga's unification of Japan. He is remembered for his humble origins (his father was a foot soldier) and for his campaigns of foreign conquest in Korea, but his chief contribution to history is the groundwork he laid for the founding of the Tokugawa shogunate.

Weston, Walter (1861–1940) was a Church of England missionary who came to Japan in 1889 and helped popularize the sport of mountaineering.

Wright, Frank Lloyd (1867–1959) was the American architect who designed Tokyo's old Imperial Hotel and other buildings.

Yamamoto Isoroku 山本五十六　(1884–1943) was commander-in-chief of the Combined Fleet during World War II and the man who first proposed a surprise attack on Pearl Harbour, even though he believed that a war with America was ultimately unwinnable.

Yanagita Kunio 柳田国男　(1875–1962) was a bureaucrat, journalist and scholar who, from 1930, concentrated his full energies on establishing the discipline of Japanese folklore studies. His classic in the field, *Tono Monogatari* was published much earlier, in 1910, and has been translated into English by Robert Morse as *Legends of Tono*.

Zeami 世阿弥　(1363–1443) was a brilliant actor and dramatist who established the Noh theatre as a respected form. He was exiled to Sado in 1434, having perhaps refused to reveal the secret teachings of his art to his nephew, a protégé of the shogun's.

A TWISTED ROOT

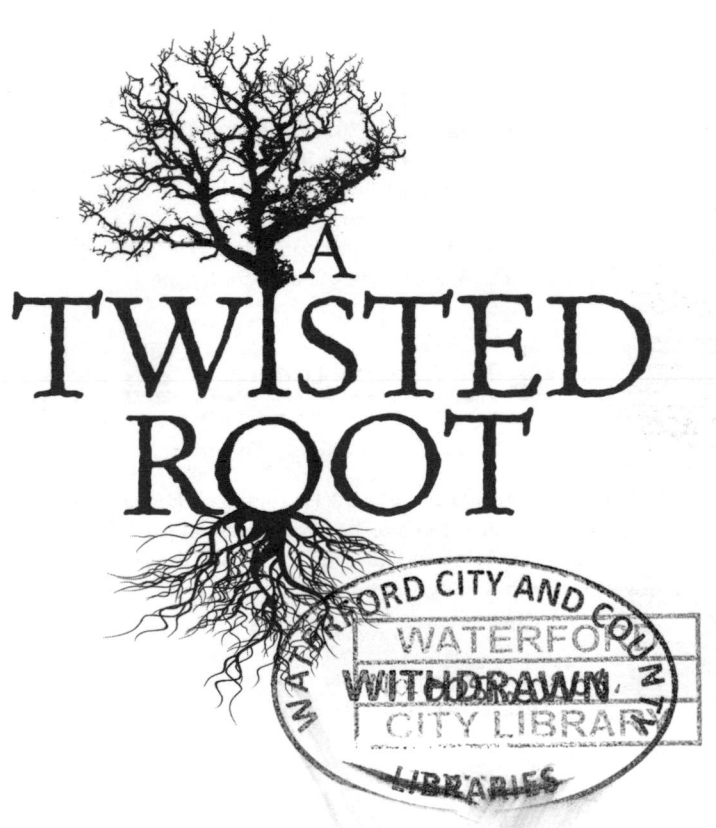

PATRICIA CRAIG

BLACKSTAFF PRESS

First published in 2012 by Blackstaff Press
4c Heron Wharf
Sydenham Business Park
Belfast BT3 9LE
with the assistance of
The Arts Council of Northern Ireland

Typeset by CJWT Solutions, St Helens, Merseyside

Printed in Great Britain by the MPG Books Group

A CIP catalogue for this book is available from the British Library

ISBN 978 0 85640 904 2

www.blackstaffpress.com

www.blackstaffpress.com/ebooks

For Harry Tipping
and in memory of my grandmothers
Sarah Brady (née Tipping), 1881–1969
Emily Craig (née Lett), 1889–1973

For history's a twisted root ...

PAUL MULDOON

CONTENTS

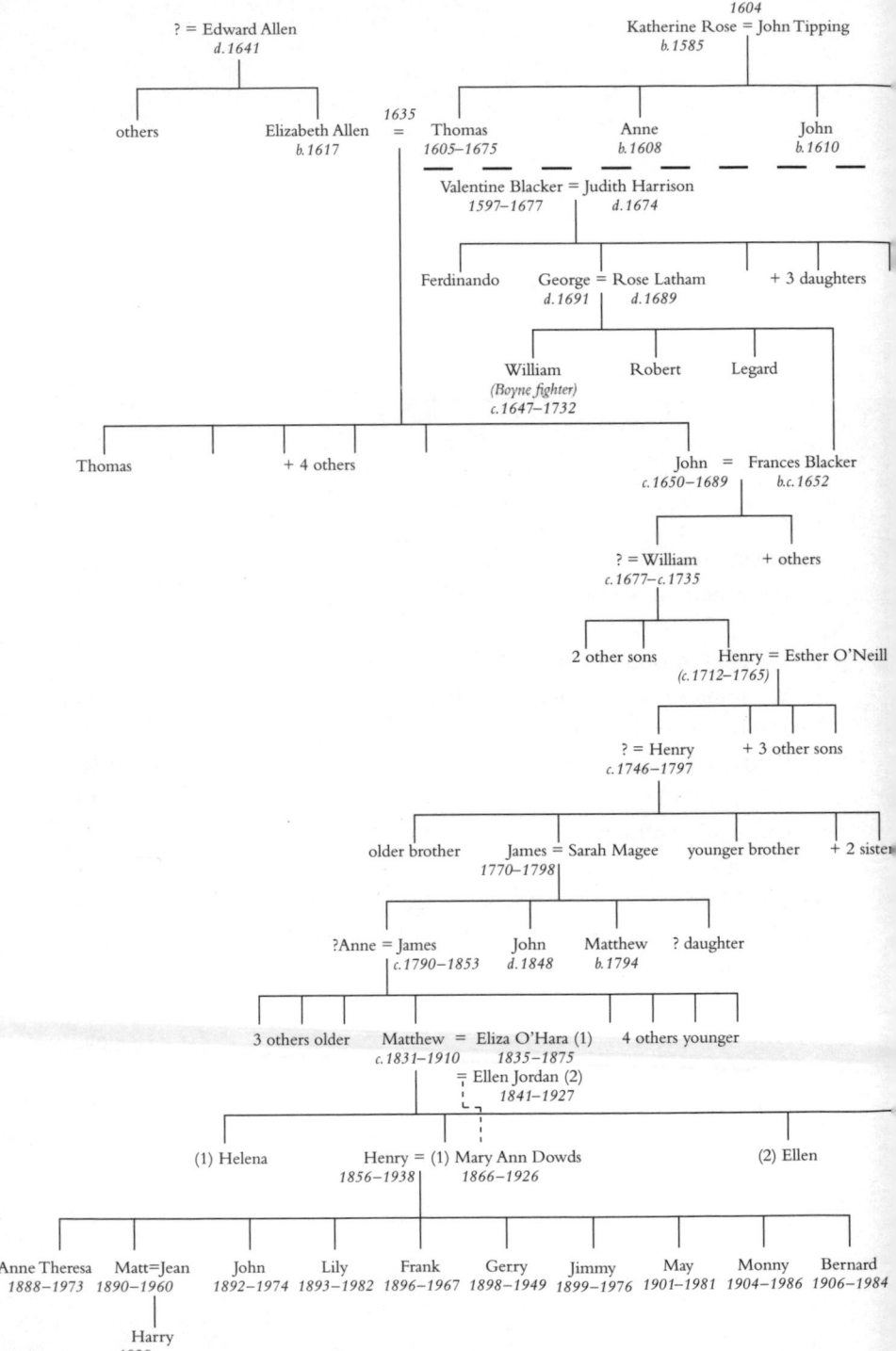

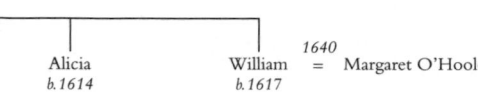

Alicia
b.1614

William
b.1617

1640
= Margaret O'Hoole

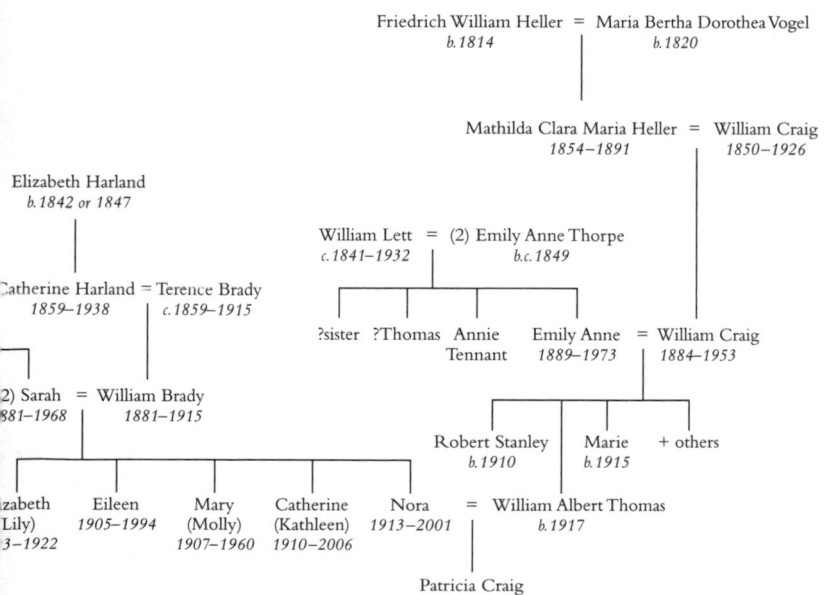

Friedrich William Heller = Maria Bertha Dorothea Vogel
b.1814   *b.1820*

Mathilda Clara Maria Heller = William Craig
1854–1891   *1850–1926*

Elizabeth Harland
b.1842 or 1847

William Lett = (2) Emily Anne Thorpe
c.1841–1932   *b.c.1849*

Catherine Harland = Terence Brady
1859–1938   *c.1859–1915*

?sister ?Thomas Annie   Emily Anne = William Craig
                  Tennant   *1889–1973*   *1884–1953*

(2) Sarah = William Brady
1881–1968   *1881–1915*

Robert Stanley   Marie   + others
b.1910   *b.1915*

Elizabeth
(Lily)
1903–1922

Eileen
1905–1994

Mary
(Molly)
1907–1960

Catherine
(Kathleen)
1910–2006

Nora
1913–2001

= William Albert Thomas
b.1917

Patricia Craig

INTRODUCTION
THE DANGEROUS EDGE OF THINGS

If there's one single unalloyed good that has come out of the overdone debates about historical 'revisionism', it's the idea of the historian as subversive. We should be seeking out the interactions, paradoxes and sub-cultures ... if only to rearrange the pieces in more surprising patterns.

R.F. Foster, *Varieties of Irishness*

Thoughts of history present themselves constantly. What version of history do we accept, though, if any?

Derek Mahon, 'Dark of the Moon'

Some years ago, I wrote a memoir called *Asking for Trouble*. *A Twisted Root* is not a sequel, but there's a sense in which it grew out of certain preoccupations of the former book. The memoir is centred on an alarming event of my early life: being expelled from a convent school in Belfast at the age of sixteen for a miniscule misdemeanour. The crucial episode of misbehaviour, with its disproportionate outcome, occurred in the Donegal Gaedhaltacht, in Rannafast, where I'd gone with some friends and fellow pupils of St Dominic's High School, in August 1959, to polish my Irish. It involved some carry-on with local boys. When word of this small carry-on reached the ears of St Dominic's nuns, they threw up their hands in horror and promptly cast out of the school the three ringleaders in the affair (as it seemed to them). I believed at the time, and still believe, their reaction was crazed and their treatment of the three of us ruthless and unjust. Others will disagree – indeed, some readers of *Asking for Trouble* did disagree, with varying degrees of vehemence. They rushed into print or went on the air to stick up for nuns, claiming that convent pupils all over Ireland and, indeed, Britain, had been summarily expelled from other schools for lesser offences. What did we expect, they snorted. Kissing boys behind turf stacks, and being caught at it, had put us beyond the pale.

Those were the sniffy brigade. Other readers, those who had suffered horrors under a convent regime, thought I hadn't gone nearly far enough in my castigation of that educational system. 'More could be told' – uttered darkly – was the verdict of the convent-afflicted. At this point, it looked as if the title, *Asking for Trouble*, might relate to the reception of the book no less than the activities evoked in it.

That title – hmmn. I was not exactly happy with it. I feared it might be a contender for a Kate Adie award for unoriginality. But I stuck with it, due to its slightly ironic bearing on the theme of the memoir, and also because I had it in mind that it referred not only to the particular events I was writing about, but to an entire society on the verge of falling apart. Given the conditions prevailing in the North in the late 1950s – economic, social, religious and political conditions – it was clear that something had got to give. And, for a brief moment in the following decade, it looked as though the inevitable upheaval might actually engender a more equitable, just and progressive reshaping of Northern Irish society – but as we know, it didn't happen. What happened instead exceeded the direst anticipations of the most pessimistic observers of Northern Ireland's sectarian ethos. James Simmons puts it succinctly in his poem entitled 'The Ballad of Gerry Kelly': 'Sixty-nine the nightmare started./Loyalist anger rose.'

Loyalist anger rose, and at the same time, republican anger rose to meet it. Things fell apart. The death toll rose too. Destruction by bomb and fire overtook not only the centre of Belfast, but the centres of many pleasant historic towns, small towns, country towns, seaside towns. 'Now with compulsive resonance they toll,' John Hewitt wrote in his bitter 'Postscript' to the celebratory 'Ulster Names' of the late 1940s:

Banbridge, Ballykelly, Darkley, Crossmaglen,
summoning pity, anger and despair,
by grief of kin, by hate of murderous men
till the whole tarnished map is stained and torn,
not to be read as pastoral again.

Living in London, and well out of it, as I thought, I watched from afar with horror and despair as my native province blew itself to pieces. I was uncertain as to where my loyalties lay – or if loyalties were even relevant in the infernal imbroglio. I had long discarded the crusading republicanism of my teenage years. Civil rights, the People's Democracy, had seemed to offer a rational alternative to out-and-out 'Irish-Ireland' affiliation; but those well-intentioned bodies had failed to withstand the warring objectives of people aligned to them. It all came down to sects and factions as conduits to chaos. And in the resulting meltdown it was sometimes hard to distinguish between ideologists and cynical exploiters of civic unrest. It was hard not to feel sympathy for the killed, bereaved, afflicted, of whatever persuasion or degree of complicity. It wasn't hard to deplore the vicious sectarian instinct that flourished like bindweed among the ignorant, depraved and psychopathic. I'm thinking of gangs like the Shankill Butchers and its leader named Murphy. Sects and factions – but with Northern Irish individuals and their ancestry, it is often hard to tell where one sect ends and another begins.

While I was writing *Asking for Trouble*, I became aware that the central story, the expulsion story, was surrounded by others endemic to the place I grew up in, and some of these had to do with family history and the way it had of throwing up oddities and ironies. Thanks to the researches of two intrepid cousins, Harry Tipping on my mother's side and George Hinds on my father's, I came into possession of a good deal of information previously unknown to me – or at best, only partially known and haphazardly assimilated. At some point it occurred to me that some of this information might be amplified to form a separate volume – not, I should say, a family history as such, but a book whose *raison d'être* is to indicate how interlocked we all are in the north of Ireland, whether we consider ourselves to be exclusively Protestant, Catholic, Presbyterian, Mormon, Shaker, Quaker or high-caste Brahmin. What I had in mind was a kind of Ulster cat's-cradle constructed from history and identity and literature, image and allusion and invention – all woven together with whatever verve I could muster. I was partly inspired by a marvellous book, *Rebellions* by Tom Dunne (2004), which has the kind of density and balance I was aiming for, with its blend of history and family history, autobiography and social comment. *My* undertaking (I repeat) is not a family history. It is illustrative rather than genealogical, even though it focuses to an extent on the lives of some of my own ancestors, those who begin to emerge with a degree of clarity from the nearly impenetrable mists of the past. I'm interested in the past and its implications for the present, in historical ironies, in revelations dismantling preconceptions about attachment to this or that tribe, or other *idées fixes*. On a personal level, I'm excited by discoveries concerning aspects of my own background, and keen to insert these into the general picture. If I've got it right, each of the following chapters should tell a good – a pertinent – story about the way things were at a particular time in the past. Extracting the personal from the historical (and vice versa) is one of my objectives, even if I'm bound to fall short in certain areas (those of characterisation and verisimilitude, for example). And I'm delighted to find my direct and indirect forebears turning out to be a wonderfully heterogeneous lot – down and up the social scale (mostly down), in and out of church and chapel, Lurgan Papes and Wexford Prods, hanged and hangmen, street-brawlers and scholars, full-blown Orangemen and republican activists. I have to say that the 'fior-Gaedhalach', true-Irish, strain in my ancestry is the most exiguous, but it does exist (I think), courtesy of an umpteen-times great-grandmother named Esther O'Neill. Well, I'm laying claim to it along with other things that can't altogether be verified.

Graham Greene was fond of quoting a couple of well-known lines from Browning, which he said could stand as an epigraph to all his novels: 'Our interest's on the dangerous edge of things, / The honest thief, the tender murderer, / The superstitious atheist.' In the context of Northern Ireland, we might adapt these lines to accommodate the Protestant Fenian, the principled rioter, the unchristian cleric, the merciless Sister of Mercy (and I'm happy to say I've uncovered none of the last among my ancestral connections). 'The dangerous edge', for me, suggests above all an edge of complexity, a subversiveness, that makes a nonsense of the monolithic certainties on which the entire structure of our centuries-old conflict is based.

An Orange procession in the early years of the twentieth century

Earlier, I quoted the Simmons line about loyalist anger. Loyalist anger is the standard response to any perceived threat to Ulster's status quo. From Thomas McKnight writing in 1896 about 'armed assemblies of Orangemen' and 'Mr Parnell' taking note of what he called 'tumultuous and riotous gatherings of Orangemen wishing to murder the Irish Catholics' to the burning of Bombay Street and Conway Street in Belfast, in August 1969, by a mob in the throes of loyalist anger, the past has always risen up, like a ghoul from a burial mound, to overwhelm any current egalitarian impulse. Whenever it showed the least sign of subsiding, atavistic outrage was easily reignited by some energetic demagogue like the Reverend Henry Cooke – described by one commentator as 'the framer of sectarianism in the politics of Ulster'[1] – whose entire being was geared to opposing what he called 'fierce democracy on the one hand and more terrible popery on the other'.

Dr Cooke in his antique clerical garb is a kind of cartoon embodiment of nineteenth-century Ulster illiberalism; but in fact, as well as contributing to the diehard Protestant ethic of the day, Cooke was also articulating sectarian doctrines to which many people subscribed, overtly or covertly. 'You know,' they might have whispered, 'there's something in what he says.' This behind-hands quotation from John Hewitt's poem 'The Coasters' takes us forward a century or so and refers to a different set of circumstances – but the author puts his finger on a continuing, low-grade, passive bigotry, a bigotry of boardrooms and suburbs, which played its part in contaminating the whole of Northern Irish society, to a point of dissolution. 'You coasted along,' the accusing poem goes:

> You even had a friend or two of the other sort,
> coasting too: your ways ran parallel.
> Your children and theirs seldom met, though,
> being at different schools.
> You visited each other, decent folk with a sense
> of humour. Introduced, even, to
> one of their clergy. And then you smiled
> in the looking-glass, admiring, a
> little moved by, your broadmindedness.
> Your father would never have known
> one of them. Come to think of it,
> when you were young, your own home was never
> visited by one of the other sort.

The 'you' addressed by Hewitt is of course a Protestant Ulsterman, but I'm not suggesting that an equal amount of bigotry, aggression, name-calling or nepotism didn't exist among 'the other sort' – the Catholics of Ulster. The novelist Brian Moore (1921–99), who grew up in Clifton Street, Belfast, recalled his doctor father's refusal to allow any member of his household to adorn the table with 'a Protestant loaf of bread' – that is, one made by the Ormeau Bakery rather than Barney Hughes's. Think of the episode in St John Ervine's novel of 1927, *The Wayward Man*, when young Robert Dunwoody strays into Catholic territory in the back streets of Belfast, and is set upon by 'a gang of rough youths' who exact a tribal betrayal from him: '"Curse King William, you Protestant *get*, you!" They crowded round him, ... pulling his hair and beating his skull with their knuckles. ... He could see the vicious face of the leader of the gang turning more vicious still.'

Or take the moment in a considerably inferior work of fiction published in 1911, *The Belfast Boy* by Agnes Boles, when a couple of Protestant girls succumb to terror on catching sight of a body of men coming towards them over Peter's Hill. ' "Look!" cried Maggie Reilly,[2] "It's the Catholics coming to wreck the Shankill." ' Confronted with all this coming from both sides, you might find yourself harbouring a degree of sympathy with the author of an even worse novel, James Douglas, when he took a look at Edwardian Belfast and its goings-on and renamed the deplorable city 'Bigotsborough'.[3] 'The clash of broken glass was a familiar sound in the streets of Bigotsborough.'

Sectarian noise was not confined to Belfast. Let us take a look at Portadown. The late George Watson, academic and literary critic, published a pointed essay in the *Yale Review* in 1986 about his experiences growing up as 'a Portadown Pape'. Each day, coming home from primary school (he says), he and his friends had to fight Protestant boys who taunted them with the epithet, 'Fenian scum'. Now – if you gave it any thought at all in this respect – you would take 'George Watson' to be a Protestant name. If you then found out that Watson's father was an RUC constable, the family's Protestantism would seem to be assured. But it wasn't so. Both his parents, in fact, were Catholics from the South, from Kilkenny and Connemara respectively, and his father (born in 1898) had got himself transferred North from the old Royal Irish Constabulary after 1922. Members of the RIC were at risk of assassination in the South, and Catholics were at risk of assault in Portadown. It seemed there was no escape from sectarian violence anywhere – well, anywhere apart from the family home, especially when the radio was on and a sonorous *English* voice, reading the shipping forecast or delivering a cricketing commentary, disseminated a tremendous sense of well-being and security.

'Cultural confusions' is George Watson's pertinent subtitle. As far as he was concerned, England was the great good place, a view compounded by his boyhood immersion in English public school stories such as *Teddy Lester's Chums* and weekly story papers like the *Champion* and the *Rover*. 'In that world,' he writes – that is, the world of honour, fair play and English uprightness – 'you would not see, with that sickening lurch of the heart, three shadowy figures detach themselves from a wall and saunter towards you, while you realised that your mental navigation had let you down ... and you had blundered into an Orange street. In Teddy Lester's world, you would not get a half brick on the head because you were a "Papish".'

The self-perpetuating momentum of sectarian misdoing was the thing that engendered the greatest despair in the hearts of liberals and social reformers of all persuasions, in the past and later. No citizens of Belfast, Benedict Kiely wrote in 1945 in his book *Counties of Contention*, 'could congratulate themselves on the uncouth, vicious thing that comes to life at intervals to burn and kill and destroy'. He wasn't singling out one faction as being more reprehensible than the other, at least at street-fighting level – but of course, as a general rule, liberal opinion in Ireland has always come down on the side of Catholicism. I don't mean the religious system, indeed, but the elements of society coming under that heading, since social oppression (roughly speaking) was a prerogative of the other side. 'Avaunt his verses be they ne'er so fine, / Who for the Catholics – REFUSED TO SIGN,' William Drennan wrote in 1811 about a clergyman-poet who'd declined to add his signature to a petition calling for Catholic Emancipation (see p. 93–4 below).

However, no one should be in any doubt that forms of Catholic bigotry exist which are just as virulent and excluding as their Protestant counterparts. If the latter seem to have more aggression about them, it's probably through being more insistently thrust in our faces. At any rate, this was true in the past. It's hard to forget incidents like the one described by James Connolly's daughter, Nora Connolly O'Brien, as she watches a terrified young shipyard worker pelting along Royal Avenue in Belfast with a gang of fifty men, all dressed in dungarees, in hot pursuit. 'Islandmen chasin' a Papish,' she is told off-handedly when she asks a passer-by what is going on.[4] Such things were still going on when Sam Thompson brought them to the attention of an audience outside Belfast with his play, *Over the Bridge* (see p. 242 below), first produced in 1960. And long before the days of political correctness you had a shoemaker in Belfast who advertised his wares with the unambiguous slogan, 'Wear Kelly's Boots to Trample the Papists'.

Well! By the time you reach this stage of bare-faced provocation, you've gone beyond bigotry and into some indigenous realm of robust street-assertion – and actually interdenominational entertainment. As a piece of unrepentant Ulster lore, the 'Kelly's Boots' injunction is fit to be cherished by all, along with 'The Oul' Orange Flute' and the story about the Orangeman on the Liverpool boat listening politely to a stranger who was singing the praises of the pope, describing the pontiff as a great statesman and a worthy gentleman personally into the bargain. 'What you say may be true,' says the cautious Orangeman eventually. 'It may be true, but I have to tell you, he has a very bad name in Portadown.' ... All right, I know I'm getting into a mode of Ulster quaintness here, but bear with me for a moment: I don't intend to overindulge in it. My aim is simply to indicate a tiny portion of the Northern Irish inheritance common to all of us, whether we kick with the right foot or the wrong foot – or whatever manufacturer's boots we wear to do it. It would, indeed, be a very po-faced Catholic and nationalist who would fail to be amused by the 'Trample the Papists' legend.

And there's another, more serious point to be made in connection with that egregious advertisement (and here, at last, I'm getting to the central theme of *A Twisted Root*). Consider for a moment the name Kelly – or Ó Ceallaigh, as it would have been in its original form. It's hard to think of anything more suggestive of Irish-Ireland, Gaelic and nationalist and Papist to the core. Somewhere in the background of your ultra-Orange bootmaker a change of allegiance must have occurred. And this, I'm convinced, would prove to be true of most of us in the north of Ireland. It's only necessary to go back a generation or two, in many cases, to find some abhorrent antecedent popping up to alarm any would-be factional purist – or delighting those of an ecumenical disposition. ... A few paragraphs back I mentioned Brian Moore's father and his aversion to Protestant bread. Dr Moore was a very prominent figure in Belfast Catholic circles in the 1920s and 30s, and utterly wrapped up in churchly activity – but, as it happens, his own father was a Catholic convert, and Dr Moore had a pair of nineteenth-century Protestant grandparents from Ballyclare to keep under his chapel-going hat.

That's just a tiny example of the pervasiveness of ancestral exogamy. Another occurs in the opening poem of Seamus Heaney's pungent sequence 'Clearances', from *The Haw Lantern* of 1987. It concerns his Protestant great-grandmother whose name was Robinson.

> A cobble thrown a hundred years ago
> Keeps coming at me, the first stone
> Aimed at a great-grandmother's turncoat brow.
> The pony jerks and the riot's on.
> She's crouched low in the trap,
> Running the gauntlet that first Sunday
> Down the brae to Mass at a panicked gallop.
> He whips on through the town to cries of 'Lundy!'

... And 'lapsed Protestant' Glenn Patterson, in his engaging book about his Lisburn grandparents, *Once Upon a Hill* (2008), doesn't have to go to any great lengths to uncover the Catholic lineage of one of them (see p. 189–90 below). And again: take the Falls Road, Catholic, Irish-speaking Carson family, and you find Liam Carson in his memoir *Call Mother a Lonely Field* (2010), and Ciaran Carson in various places, making no bones about claiming a great-grandfather – another turncoat – who started his adult life as an Orangeman in Ballymena. 'And all of us thought him a stout Orange blade.' Another memoir, the generically titled *Protestant Boy* (2004) by Geoffrey Beattie, evokes a true-blue, working-class upbringing in Ligoniel – but what the young Protestant Beattie doesn't grasp for years is the fact that his favourite uncle, his Uncle Terry, is 'one of them': a Papist. (It's true that Uncle Terence's name, O'Neill, which he shares with a prominent Ulster politician, suggests an uncertainty about his denominational origin.)

I could go on. And I will return from time to time to this melting-pot aspect of our heritage which exists as a strong undercurrent in Northern Irish life, even if many of us aren't aware of it (or would fiercely repudiate any such integrationist commonplace). As I have indicated, I intend to underscore the point by highlighting a couple of strands of my own ancestry, which for the purposes of this book may be taken as representative. I am endlessly intrigued – without, I hope, falling too easily into an 'ironies-of-history' mode of perception[5] – by the way things often work themselves out in an unexpected form; and when it comes to Northern Ireland and our sectarian divisions, it could be argued that the whole state of contention is based on a fallacy, the fallacy that every one of us is irreversibly and unequivocally attached to one tradition or the other. (I mean attached by genetics as well as political orientation.) As Irish-German Hugo Hamilton suggested in the title of his 2005 memoir, we are all 'speckled', streaked or piebald to a greater or lesser extent.[6]

So: 'Am I an Irishwoman?' This is the question Brigid Brophy put to herself in one of the wry and spirited essays which she published under the title *Don't Never Forget* (1966). Is she? Am I? Once, I'd have firmly believed I had a better right to that designation than a person born and brought up in London, but now I'm not so sure. In my case – and Brigid Brophy's, and everyone else's – Irishness, Englishness or whatever is only a part of it. If I go back far enough I find I can call myself Scandinavian (Blacar/Blacker), German (Heller, Stolzenbach) or Latvian (Lett). But if I do, I'll be in danger of disappearing up my own family tree, of taking off from its highest branches into some Never-Never Land at the top, where nationality and concomitant characteristics are watered down to nothingness. I'm really not interested in *global* interconnections; I just want to stick to one tiny spot (Northern Ireland), and try in a small way to undermine its internecine incompatibilities by emphasising all the composite undercurrents running through it.

As for those ubiquitous 'ironies of history' – sometimes something so overwhelming occurs along these lines that it can hardly be assimilated. Sometimes, too, it may get just a bit distorted to improve its impact. For example – the historian R.F. Foster has pointed out that William of Orange's victory at the Boyne 'was *not*, as so often claimed, greeted ... with a Te Deum in Rome'.[7] What a pity – however, it remains true that, due to the intricacies of seventeenth-century politics, the pope of the day made common cause with Protestant William rather than Catholic James. *Te Deum* or not, William's victory at the Boyne caused rejoicing in the Vatican. Not that it makes a whit of difference in the streets of Ballymena or Portadown. You don't see an image of Pope Alexander VIII, William's ally, borne aloft on any Orange banner.

Sixteen-ninety: let's go back a century or so from that significant date, to the 1590s and the Elizabethan Wars in Ireland. Don't worry, I'm not planning to present a potted history, either backwards or forwards: I just want to point out another staggering historical irony that's come to my attention. Everyone agrees that the outstanding enemy of Elizabethan rule in Ireland was Hugh O'Neill, Baron of Dungannon, Earl of Tyrone, last of the great Gaelic overlords of Ulster. O'Neill was a formidable strategist, well versed in 'shifts and devices', half 'civilised' by his boyhood exposure to the ways of the English court, half Irish 'savage' in the eyes of his military adversaries. For Queen Elizabeth I O'Neill was 'the fly in the ointment, the crack in the mirror, the thorn in the flesh' (I'm quoting from Elizabeth Bowen's 1943 review of Sean O'Faolain's book *The Great O'Neill*). Elizabeth's Deputy, Lord Mountjoy, saw the Irishman as 'the most ungrateful Viper to us that raised him'; and the queen herself labelled him a 'villainous Rebel'. All that – and Queen Elizabeth too (had she but known) might have echoed the cry of Macbeth when Banquo's descendants appeared before him in all their illustriousness: 'What, will the line stretch out to the crack of doom!' Elizabeth, of course, was childless and the Tudor line died out with her. O'Neill, on the other hand, was prolific in progeny and his descendants are innumerable. One of them sits on the English throne at the present time.[8] Queen Elizabeth II is not descended from Elizabeth I. She can, instead, count Hugh O'Neill, that jagged thorn in England's flesh, among her direct ancestors in the maternal line. Some kind of large dynastic wheel has come full circle here – though whether to the joy or dismay of Irish republicans I can't be sure.

Of course none of us, including the queen of England, can help our ancestors, the whole mixed bunch of them – though some in the north of Ireland, when it comes to a question of identity, may choose to believe they are indissolubly one thing or the other. They are not. One of my aims, when I started work on *A Twisted Root*, was to elevate the dark horse above the sacred cow, to argue for fusion rather than segregation, complexity instead of fixity. Here's John Hewitt, Belfastman, Irishman, native and settler, again: 'Kelt, Briton, Roman, Saxon, Dane and Scot, / time and this island tied a crazy knot.'

CHAPTER 1
WE HAD TO BUILD IN STONE FOR
EVER AFTER

Famine and pestilence, grief, greed and slaughter ...

Anthony Cronin, *Letter to an Englishman*

Not long ago I was reading, with great pleasure, Germaine Greer's book about Shakespeare's wife.[1] This attempt to rehabilitate Anne Hathaway has much to recommend it, not least the aplomb of its central admission, that every one of its conclusions in favour of its subject is 'probably neither truer nor less true than the accepted prejudice'. The accepted prejudice is that Shakespeare, as far as he could, washed his hands of his disappointing spouse. But the meagre known facts of this enigmatic marriage will bear a different interpretation, as Germaine Greer shows. Not that facts alone come into the picture. Greer has gone about the work of scrutinising every available piece of documentary evidence relating to a particular time and place – the Warwickshire market town of Stratford-on-Avon in the second half of the sixteenth century – and assessing the extent to which her findings are applicable to Mrs Shakespeare. Inspired conjecture is the method – and in the hands of an author as adept as Germaine Greer, it makes for a fascinating account. Every bit of her book is interesting and informative – but it wasn't until I'd reached page 269 that I was jolted out of the usual engaged but disinterested reader's mode. There appeared on that page a name which held significance for me personally. Katherine Rose.

Katherine Rose is listed among thirty-nine girls who were born in Stratford in 1585 and baptised at Holy Trinity Church in the town. Another is Shakespeare's daughter Judith. Of the remaining thirty-seven, Greer tells us, thirteen died young, in accordance with the usual pattern of childhood mortality. Another died unmarried in her early twenties. Most of the other Elizabethan Stratford girls in Greer's list disappear from the records, probably as a consequence of moving out of the district. They might have gone into service or married elsewhere, Greer thinks. Their subsequent history is lost to posterity, unlike that of Katherine Rose (at least in outline). She – my unimaginably-distant, multiply-great-grandmother – was married at eighteen or nineteen to a local tradesman, a cutler named John Tipping, who either came from Stratford itself, or from one of its outlying villages, Alcester, Alderminster or Leek Wootton, possibly. The marriage took place at the same Holy Trinity Church on 10 June 1604.

Was Judith Shakespeare, Katherine's contemporary and perhaps her friend, among the members of the congregation attending that summer wedding in the second year of the reign of King James I? It would please me to think so, but that's one fact among millions that can't be ascertained. Was Katherine's hair worn spread on her shoulders for the last time, before, as a married woman, she had to put it up and cover it with a kerchief? Did bridesmaids waken her that June morning by singing outside her window – her latticed window – 'The Bride's Goodmorrow'? ...And by envisaging an episode of early Jacobean revelry (with pastoral elements – in Stratford!), am I resorting to a piece of nursery-rhyme indulgence? Very likely; and I'm now about to make things worse by tying up the unreal picture I have in my head with a different set of pre-nuptial traditions and indigenous *joie de vivre*. In her wonderful book about the people, songs and traditions of Oriel[2] (*A Hidden Ulster*, 2002), Pádraigín Ní Uallacháin discusses at length a couple of spellbinding songs – among many others – '*Amhrain na Craoibhe*' ('The Garland Song') and '*Thugamar Fein an Samhradh Linn*' ('We Brought the Summer With Us'), both associated with ritual Gaelic forms of merrymaking, rejoicing in the arrival of summer, and rife with courtship and fertility implications. '*Amhrain na Craoibhe*', with its resonant chorus – '*Haigh do a bheir i 'bhaile's haigh di*' ('Hey to him who takes her home, hey to her') – is extraordinarily delicate and at the same time, racy. One heady summertime festival, at Forkhill, County Armagh, at which that particular song would have been sung, is dated precisely to 9 June; and it was probably taking place at the same time as the Rose/Tipping wedding, in another country. ... But similar jollifications held an important place in rural communities all over Europe; is there any more than a generic connection between the two different forms of celebration I've singled out here? Well, the connection is arbitrary, indeed; but perhaps not quite as arbitrary as all that. The descendants of Katherine Rose and John Tipping did reach County Armagh, but not for some time.

My mother died in September 2001. The night of the 21/22. It was an unreal time. At her funeral a few days later, at the Catholic church of Kilclief, County Down, where I absolutely did not want to be, I overreacted to the generic jabber of the young officiating priest who knew nothing at all about her, her kindness to cats, her relish for local, comic turns of phrase, the poems she could quote. 'True to her faith'; 'respected in the community': these were the clichés he spouted. Well, she was a Catholic in as much as she was anything, but for the last thirty-odd years of her life she had ceased to be a practising Catholic, in response to the pressures and influences of the modern world. Religion did not play a great part in her life. Only in the run-up to her miserable death in the Medical Assessment Unit of Downpatrick Hospital did the trappings of her Catholic girlhood begin to creep back, as something to hold on to in a disintegrating world. When a nun entered the ward and sat down by her bedside, my mother claimed to have been 'brought up' by nuns, turning herself in retrospect into an orphan and banishing her own resolute mother, and her older sisters, from a selective image of the past which she at that moment held in her head. What she should have said was 'educated by nuns', her education running in tandem with a perfectly adequate and not excessively religious home life. But her brain had softened. She was eighty-eight. She thought she was on holiday – 'This is a nice hotel, isn't it?' Then she thought she'd been stuck in some unsuitable location with a lot of drivelling pensioners. 'There's nobody my age here. They're all old people.' This was shortly before she sank into unconsciousness and ceased to think anything at all. Friends and relations came and went, stroked her hand and exchanged hopeless glances across her hospital-issue coverlet. Through it all, my father, four years her junior and in full possession of his faculties, exhibited remarkable patience and tact (he is not a patient man), going to endless lengths to tempt her with titbits and bolster her spirits. For a long time he believed that, if he got her home, he'd be able to bring her back to herself. But it was plain to everyone else the way she was going.

Her decline had come on slowly, and then accelerated towards the end. A couple of broken hips contributed to the process. It was out the window with her unique, engaging personality, her charm, resourcefulness, humour, efficiency and kindness, all the things that marked my mother off from the general run of mothers and schoolteachers, in my experience. All the things the platitudinous priest knew nothing about. His mealy-mouthed tributes could have fitted anyone, and no doubt did. When I rose up, at the funeral, to say my piece (reluctantly allowed to do so because, with my father, I was the chief mourner: the Church, it seems, doesn't really care for any form of secular speaking within its sacred precincts) – when I rose up, I began by declaring, 'One thing it's true to say about my mother –' (I stressed 'one thing') – 'is that all her life she was a Shakespeare enthusiast.' I then quoted from memory the opening verse of the funeral song for Cloten from *Cymbeline*, which begins, 'Fear no more the heat o' the sun'. In my overwrought state I could only manage one verse, but I hoped it was enough to make the point that what I said was true and pertinent and *particular*.

My mother's bible was A.C. Bradley's *Shakespearean Tragedy*, a book she'd studied closely during her golden years as a student at Queen's University, Belfast, in the 1930s. She lived at the time in a house in Sandhurst Gardens, in the middle of a dingy terrace sloping down towards the Lagan with its damp fogs immortalised by Maurice Craig (see p. 211): damp fogs were then a feature of Belfast, wrapping its workaday streets in murk and mystery, engendering a good-humoured exasperation in pedestrians bumping into one another, or stumbling for the twentieth time over the stumpy base of a green-ribbed metal lamppost with outstretched arms like an elongated scarecrow. Belfast could seem, then, like 'old, murky Edinburgh' with its Burke-and-Hare atmosphere relished by Sean O'Faolain in his *Irish Journey*. Its seasons were distinctive. At Queen's, for instance, summer was tied up with the carnival carry-on of successive rag days, 1933, '34, '35; a bench in the cloisters between lectures, flirtation, gossip with friends;[3] and the lectures

4

themselves, delivered with aplomb or eccentricity by professors with plentiful initials, R.M. Henry, H.O. White and H.O. – again – Meredith.

My mother, Nora Brady, took her studies seriously. She understood that hard work was necessary to gain her degree, and applied herself unstintingly to everything required of her – but naturally some parts of the course held more appeal than others. And at the top of her personal pantheon was Shakespeare – in particular, the tragedies; and of the tragedies the two that spoke most compellingly to her were *Hamlet* and *Macbeth*. And Bradley's sensible, character-based approach to the plays struck a chord with her, from the moment his book was brought to her attention. The full glory of every line of Shakespeare's was ingested by my mother, linguistic, dramatic and all. She didn't need to have a gloss imposed on every textual ambiguity; mystery, impenetrability, held its own appeal. She simply took it all in. Whole passages from Shakespeare came to her aid in times of anxiety or upheaval. ... And because of all this, it's a cause of chagrin to me that she died without knowledge of her own slight personal connection with the world of Shakespeare, a connection unfolding through her ancestors in the direct line who were Shakespeare's fellow-townsmen, members of the same Holy Trinity Church, and quite possibly attended the playwright's funeral there in 1616.

When I was twelve and a pupil in Form 2A at St Dominic's High School on the Falls Road in Belfast, a performance of *Macbeth* was put on at the Grand Opera House next door to the Hippodrome in Great Victoria Street. The year is 1955. One morning after assembly in the study hall comes an announcement of a treat in store for the school. Well, not the whole of the school. Pupils en masse, from Form 3 upwards, will be privileged to enjoy an evening performance of *Macbeth* (those who can afford to pay for a seat in the stalls, that is). English teachers, one per class, will shepherd the lucky theatregoers into their plush-velvet rows and block any access of overexcitement before it can get a hold. That is the unspoken agreement: the emphasis that morning is placed on the educational and recreational sides of the outing. Marks and larks. I don't know if many at the school are theatrically inclined, but a rare sense of impending festivity grips the upper forms and creates a buzz. And what of the rest of us? The excluded children of Forms 1 and 2 are left feeling resentful and flat. The edict concerning our unsuitability as playgoers especially gets up the noses of myself and my friend Fiona

Devlin, since we are actually reading *Macbeth* in English class and gaining a lot of enjoyment from it – old enough to study the play, it seems, but not to view it. So it's in an aggrieved frame of mind that I go home at lunchtime, catching a number 12 bus as usual outside the Royal Victoria Hospital and alighting at St James's Park, tearing down the Park, pigtails flying, turning right at St James's Avenue and in through our back gate, to solicit sympathy from my reliably partisan mother. 'Why can't we go as well? ... It isn't fair.'

It isn't, she agrees, and proceeds to do something about it. It is then too late to obtain a seat in any part of the Opera House except the gods. So up and up we go, on the night in question, my friend, my mother and myself, up flights and flights of stone steps to emerge at last, with a jolt of vertigo, into an unexpectedly steep area that has us hanging on to one another while we find some solid seats to sit down on. Relief! And there below us, when we nerve ourselves to peer over the edge, are the assembled upper forms of St Dominic's – there is Miss McVerry, identifiable by her turquoise hat.

I am a little disorientated; the Opera House is a pocket of opulence in the lustreless city, not what I am used to, an overwhelming extravagance of decor. But from the moment the curtain rises on the wild and incantatory witches gathered round their cauldron, I am transported. It's not aesthetic or theatrical excitement that grips me, exactly, but rather poetic – the lines, the words of Shakespeare and the way they are spoken. I am lifted out of myself and out of the downbeat ambience of Belfast. And all the way home, on the bus and on foot, a particular sinister and overpowering passage is ringing in my ears:

> Light thickens, and the crow
> Makes wing to the rooky wood.
> Good things of day begin to droop and drowse,
> Whiles night's black agents to their preys do rouse.

Night's black agents. In his poem 'The Colony', John Hewitt refers to 'a terrible year when, huddled in our towns, / My people trembled as the beacons ran / From hill to hill across the countryside, / Calling the dispossessed to lift their standards.' One town in the north of Ireland sheltering a huddle of menaced settlers was Lisburn, or Lisnagarvey as it was then: the year was 1641 and the dispossessed were on the rampage.

Among the inhabitants of Lisburn at that time we find the Stratford Tippings — two, or possibly three, generations of them — some, no doubt, taking part in the fighting which broke out at the end of November, others seeking safety wherever they could find it. To discover what brought the Tippings to this ill-omened place it's necessary to go back twenty years or so, to Sir Fulke Conway and his assembly of hardy adventurers, fifty-one families from Stratford and thereabouts, who, giving in to persuasion, had turned their backs on everything steady and familiar, every *English* blessing, and set off for unknown, remote and dangerous territory. Probably the group, in a general mood of apprehension mixed up with optimism, would have sailed from Bristol and landed at Bangor, then struck inland through the mud and murk of bedevilled Ulster — territory utterly new to them and not immediately holding out a prospect of welcome. 'One can imagine the wayside camp in the rain and mud, watched over by a weary sentinel; for that woodland on the hillside might well hold a swordsman or two; and if there were no swordsmen in it there were surely wolves ...'. You can't say historian Cyril Falls's imagination is running away with him when he envisages this scene in his 1936 account of *The Birth of Ulster*.

Sir Fulke Conway of Ragley Hall in Warwickshire was an industrious planter of the lands in South Antrim granted to him in 1609 by King James I, including the manor of Killultagh and the castle and village of Lisnagarvey. The castle had belonged to a deposed grandee of the O'Neill dynasty, but where the villagers were when Sir Fulke put in an appearance, or what state the 'village' was in, we haven't a clue. We do know that forest as impenetrable as anything out of Grimm was the first thing to be noted about the area. Well, the name tells us as much, Killultagh — *Coille Ultagh* — meaning simply the woods of Ulster. These pre-Elizabethan woods were dense. It was said that, if you'd had a mind to, you might almost have walked from MacArt's Fort[12] to Lisnagarvey across the tops of trees, oak and elm and spreading chestnut. And down below, among the gnarled trunks and the loamy undergrowth, lurked all kinds of menaces, natural and supernatural. Wolves and wild Irishmen and shadowy bogeymen. So the colonists' first task was to clear the land for ploughing and building, to fell as many trees as possible and divest the forest of most of its sinister associations. These 'modern' imperatives would have taken shape in Planter minds as a way of dealing with age-old dangers and superstitions.

Move forward to 1622 and we have to wonder if Sir Fulke Conway's new wave of settlers had the least idea of what they were coming to. What lay behind them was a place, a region of England filled with lush hedgerows and deep country lanes, catkins swaying in the breeze, plum orchards and cider vats, neat villages complete with manor house, grey Norman church and outlying farms, as placid as a child's picture book, at least on the surface, and destined to find a place in the minds of beset Irish incomers, perhaps, as a glowing Elizabethan idyll incomprehensibly relinquished. And in front of them ...? Well, recent history supplied an image of an utterly bereft and barbarous country, ruin and desolation on every side, multitudes of starved Irish strewn dead about the countryside, their mouths all green from eating shamrocks, nettles and dock leaves; violence and misery inflicted and reciprocated. '[W]e do continually hunt all their woods, spoil their corn, burn their houses, and kill as many churls as it grieveth me to think it is necessary to do so.' So wrote Lord Mountjoy before he left the country in 1604 – the year of the Tippings' wedding – bequeathing to his successors a legacy of remorselessness towards all Irish 'rebels', and an odd way of implementing the 'civilising' mission decreed by England for the benefit of outlandish Ulster.

The Tippings and their fellow-Plantees, in the throes of an absolute break with the past, probably would have understood little about the circumstances causing land in a foreign country, a remote outpost, to become available to them, just for the asking. It's unlikely they'd have heard of the Earls and their exodus, or the great defeat that preceded the 'Flight' from Lough Swilly's shores, and subsequent appropriation, by the Crown, of all the forfeit lands. Actually, the most concise and witty summing up of the situation – and its outcome – that I'm aware of, occurs in a recent poem, 'The Yaddo Letter' by Derek Mahon:

> ... I'd wander round the hills above Kinsale
> Where English forces clobbered Hugh O'Neill
> In Tudor times, wrecking the Gaelic order
> (result, plantations and the present Border) ...

Result, all those indeed. And here, unwittingly contributing to the long-drawn-out process, were some innocent Planters – I'm assuming they were innocent of any genocidal or even warlike tendencies – arriving in a desolate part of the north of Ireland with their portable belongings, prepared to the fullest extent for arduous labour, eyes firmly fixed on the long-term advantage. Having no alternative, once they'd got there, they dug in their heels and settled. The ground on which they established their exiguous settlement would evolve in time into the considerable town of Lisburn; but first it was necessary to engage in building work, land cultivation and evasion of onslaughts from the outraged Irish – all the things they'd come prepared to tackle, and a few extra besides.

Possibly the Tippings, then in their late thirties, were accustomed to manual work. They may have been employed previously as tenant farmers or servants on the Conway family's estate at Arrow, near Stratford-on-Avon, if they didn't live in the town of Stratford itself. We know they were married in it, at Holy Trinity Church, but not the location of their first home, or what persuaded them to become immigrants into the unknown.

It seems likely that invitations to proceed to Ireland would have been issued first of all to those possessing invaluable construction skills, bricklaying, plastering, carpentry and so forth, and perhaps a skill in the making and selling of knives was considered an asset too. We needn't assume, with old-style nationalist historians, that some discreditable motive underlay the Planters' willingness to uproot themselves – that Ireland, unknown and unimaginable, offered an escape route out of some sticky situation prevailing at home. It hardly seems fair to label the whole lot of them the 'scum' of two countries (England and Scotland), as some contemporary commentators did. Their aim was probably no different to that of emigrants before or since – to gain a better life. The lure of unexplored territory was strong at the time, and there was Ireland, Ulster, on their doorstep, so to speak, without the bother of going the whole way to America. These new, hopeful colonists would hardly have been aware, at least to start with, of moral ambiguities surrounding their presence in Ulster – though no doubt native hostility soon became apparent to them. We know, however, that accommodations were worked out – that it wasn't entirely a case of the native Irish being rounded up and deposited on hills and in bogs, wherever the land was scrubby and unproductive, while crowing colonists lorded it over them. The colonists hadn't exactly marched in and grabbed the good Irish lands from under the noses of their rightful owners, though there was enough truth in the perception of wholesale dispossession to fuel antagonisms for centuries to come. Scrupulous historians, from about the mid twentieth century on, have been at pains to restore complexity to what had come to be seen as a simple matter of right and wrong, with these interchangeable entities depending totally on the standpoint you viewed them from. Planter civility versus native barbarism: this was one of the accepted oppositions. Native integrity versus foreign oppression was another.

Foreign oppression. A collection of poems by Francis Carlin, published in 1918, includes a resonant contribution to the 'wronged Irish' ideology. It is called 'The Ballad of Douglas Bridge':

> On Douglas Bridge I met a man
> Who lived adjacent to Strabane,
> Before the English hung him high
> For riding with O'Hanlon.
>
> 'Before that time,' said he to me
> My fathers owned the land you see,
> But they are now among the moors,
> A-riding with O'Hanlon.'

… The ghostly speaker in the Carlin poem embodies a persisting and romantic sense of grievance about stolen lands and enforced degradation. Carlin's historical imagination embraces an idea of Ulster – we've now moved forward to the late seventeenth century – as a wilderness still populated exclusively by wronged natives and ruthless colonists, with Redmond O'Hanlon, a sturdy defender of the dispossessed, singled out as the epitome of lawlessness in a good cause. He was a man in the grip of a mission: to inflict the utmost aggravation on strangers imposed on Irish acres. Robin Hood. The Irish Rapparee. Well, 'Rapparee' is not the word, exactly. The term only became current in the 1690s, some years after O'Hanlon was shot dead. You can trace the anachronism back to the nineteenth-century novelist William Carleton who based a work of fiction on O'Hanlon and gave it the subtitle 'The Irish Rapparee', when he should have known better. He should also have known not to extend O'Hanlon's principled brigandage into the late 1690s, if he wished to stick to the historical facts. But did he? With *Redmond Count O'Hanlon: The Irish Rapparee* we're in a Sherwood Forest scenario, adapted to fit Armagh. The normally serious and impassioned Carleton has somehow slipped into a different mode, the bad-but-colourful-old-days bagatelle. This is someone who denounced the diehards of his own day in his novel of 1845, *Rody the Rover; or, The Ribbonman*. But he takes a very different attitude to the bandits of the past, whom he makes as honourable and invincible as the original *Fianna Éireann*.

Redmond O'Hanlon – with Carleton's help or without it – has bequeathed his name to a particular Planter hazard: a fear, amounting to obsession, of secretive wild men in rough garb relying on local knowledge to effect their deadly objectives. Anachronistically or not, he's the quintessential rapparee. Throughout the frantic seventeenth century an image took shape in Planter minds of marauding Irish lurking in the undergrowth intending harm to their supplanters. And after 1641 it gained a hellish and concrete crystallisation. 'There was great slaughter then, man woman, child, / With fire and pillage of our timbered houses; / We had to build in stone for ever after', John Hewitt wrote in 'The Colony', a pointed monologue in which the narrator sticks up for Planter entitlements, while admitting the justice of aboriginal affront: 'for we began the plunder'. Hewitt's apparent Roman legionary is of course meant to be taken as an Ulster incomer of the seventeenth century: a far-seeing man, and one endowed with a liberal consciousness.

Incidentally, the name O'Hanlon carries more than one connotation. Members of that clan, only a generation back from the dashing Redmond of Carleton and Carlin, were deeply implicated in the unholy activities of 1641, having a hand in the notorious shoving of Protestants off Portadown Bridge and generally contributing to the cruelty and mayhem of the age. Mary Hickson (see p. 15 below), writing at the end of the Victorian era, dissociates herself strongly from the outlaw glamour conferred by posterity on this plunderer and son of plunderers and murderers. In Ireland, there are always contradictory ways of looking at things, and always many outlets for savage indignation.

Before the anticipated eruption occurs – to return to the newly arrived Tippings where we left them, maybe digging the foundations for a house in a future high street, or helping to plot out the fortified tower house of their patron Sir Fulke Conway, with its gardens and orchards sloping down to the River Lagan – before the year of wholesale slaughter, the settler drive to wrest order from the wilderness is making headway. Hewitt again:

> We planted little towns to garrison
> the heaving country, heaping walls of earth
> and keeping all our cattle close at hand ...

The site chosen for the Conway mansion had previously been known as *Lios na gCearrbach*, Fort of the Gamblers, though who or what the eponymous gamblers were is a mystery. Were they servants or retainers attached to the stronghold nearby, so addicted to games of chance that they never stopped playing until they'd gambled the clothes off one another's backs? Or outlaws taking a break from their depredations on the earliest wave of settlers? Different accounts have different surmises to offer. But whatever the truth of the matter, the name took hold – and perhaps it wasn't too wide of the mark in settler terms as well. The whole new way of life for the ordinary colonists was a gamble, as to whether they would prosper, or go under.

We don't know, either, how 'Lisnagarvey' turned into Lisburn – Lisbourne, Lisburne in early documents – 'burn' having no obvious Irish derivation. It is surely too literal-minded to relate it to the burning of the town in 1641. But 'burn' it became, and stayed. And while I'm on the subject of obscurities and inconsistencies, I should mention that the Conway castle at Lisnagarvey was either the old O'Neill castle renovated, or a fortified manor built from scratch; that it was either Sir Fulke, who died in 1624, or his brother Sir Edward, who undertook the necessary refurbishment, or demolition and reconstruction (you can take your pick). It's certain, though, that by 1630 – when Sir Edward died in his turn – an anglified structure had taken the place of the original Gaelic castle. Its gardens, outbuildings, brewhouse, oathouse, powderhouse and office were enclosed within a wall, while the stables, stable yard, kitchen garden and slaughterhouse stood outside. With the flower gardens and orchards mentioned above, and the salmon-filled river, it was certainly an idyllic habitation.

The indigenous Irish may have watched with amazement as radical alterations to the landscape and native architecture took place around them; and we know that many of them were not too set in the ways of Gaelic feudalism to accept employment with the newcomers. The old world was giving way to the new; and no amount of Gaelic recalcitrance, or allegiance to the past, was going to halt the process. For those of a pragmatic cast of mind, the way forward was clear enough, and entailed adapting to current circumstances. At the same time, they'd have waited to see if the overthrow of the Gaelic world might not be followed by a reversal: who knew what plans for a coup or a military campaign were being fomented from above! They, the ordinary Irish, certainly had cause to resent the labels – 'barbarous', 'savage', 'churls', 'bandits' – foisted on them by colonists unfamiliar with the intricacies and sophistications of the Gaelic way of life. Settler presumptions of superiority, and contempt for an old and alien civilisation, didn't make for an easing of suspicions and hostilities.

The basic obstacle to meaningful communication between settler and native was of course the language difficulty, with the edict coming down from the new administrative class that inclusion under the heading 'civil Irish' depended on a person's command of the English language. If you couldn't speak English you were seen as nearly Neanderthal. Well, Edmund Spenser in the previous century had taken the view that the only way to deal with the entire unruly population of Ireland was to exterminate it or anglicise it, that extermination wasn't too dire a fate for those who wouldn't be anglicised. But it often happened instead that settlers became gaelicised, though it could take a few generations for the process to get truly under way.

When John and Katherine Tipping uprooted themselves from well-regulated Warwickshire and headed for the woods of Ulster, they brought with them a family of five children aged between four and seventeen. The oldest, Thomas, was born in 1605; then came Anne (1608), John (1610), Alicia (1614) and William (1617). All English-born, all attuned (we may suppose) to the enlightened civilities of the age. One would like to think these younger Tippings regarded the Irish enterprise as a great adventure. Did they exhibit a *Children of the New Forest* type of resourcefulness once they'd reached their own new forest, Killultagh? Was the strangeness of Ireland, the dark aboriginal woods sheltering mysterious ill-wishers, will o' the wisps, the beehive-shaped huts housing seeming savages, the gloomy days of winter, the fraught silences punctuated by snatches of a foreign tongue – were these things an enticement or a cause of nightmare? Did they hanker after a Warwickshire peace and quiet? Or did they soon begin to feel at home? They had their little community around them to keep the worst of the colonists' perils at bay – or so it seemed – and there in front of their eyes a whole new town was taking shape, with castle, church and street of houses.

The earliest map of Lisburn, preserved in the Dublin Rent Office and dated to 1640, lists the names of the original builders of the town. Alongside 'John Tippen' we find a George Rose who can't have been other than the Tipping children's uncle, Katherine's brother; and probably there were cousins too, in the little settler enclave. Most of the names on the builders' list are clearly English in origin (Dobbs, Bones, Butterfield), a few are Welsh (John ap Richard, Owen ap Hugh), and there's even one Irish name, Peter O'Mullred (O'Mullan, Ui Maol Riada?), to bring in a suggestion of a rudimentary democracy operating at the time (democracy, or sycophancy: again, you can take your pick). The same map shows the Tippens (Tippings) established at No. 12 the High Street (the present Castle Street), with Bridge Street on the other side of the castle descending pleasantly to the River Lagan. In 1640, this was the whole extent of the town.

Perhaps the younger children attended school in the centre of the Market Place, getting up early in the morning and, after a breakfast of porridge and buttermilk, crossing the road with their satchels and hornbooks. In winter, they might have carried lanterns to see them safely home. In the long days of summer, there were abundant fields behind the houses to play in, or to gather herbs for cooking and healing. Would the older ones have learned to read and write before they left Stratford? We have no way of telling – or of envisaging what kinds of commerce and social activity the adults engaged in. Was their aim to make a replica of an English town? More than a century later, in 1759, an English traveller called Willes compared Lisburn to Stratford-on-Avon – but by this time the town had been destroyed twice, and twice rebuilt, and descendants of the first inhabitants were long dispersed. Nevertheless, perhaps something survived, in Lisburn's layout and atmosphere, of the settler impulse to create a home-from-home; and, in the peculiar conditions of seventeenth-century Ulster, a pocket of sanity and calm amid the general disorder.

Bridge Street today (2009) is a sorry sight. Its straggle of rickety houses and shops has a dank, abandoned look about it. Redevelopment, not conservation, is horribly in the air. Well, Lisburn, now a city, is no less prone than anywhere else in the North to modern forms of crassness and philistinism. (I'm talking architecture here.) But up until a couple of years ago, there was at least one good reason for visiting Bridge Street. Right at the top, on the corner opposite the present linen museum (the old market house) stood a second-hand bookshop run by a Church of Ireland minister named William Harshaw. The Old Bookshop, Lisburn, had everything to gladden the heart of a collector. You could hardly get in for the piles of books crammed in every corner and cranny. Books spilled over from the sagging shelves and colonised large sections of floor space. Falling on them with a whoop, if your eye was caught by some desirable title wedged in the middle, might cause the whole tottery structure to topple over – but it didn't matter. The helpful, knowledgeable, laid-back proprietor was only too happy if you'd lighted on something you were looking for.

The Old Bookshop was not exactly run as a commercial concern and so it became unsustainable, in the brutal days of rising rents and rates. Its alluring abundance of bibliomaniac's *desiderata* has been transported elsewhere. Like the old Smithfield Market in Belfast, foremost resort of the bric-a-brac addict, it had about it a ramshackle headiness: you were always certain to emerge from these eccentric premises with your arms overladen. Both rarities and standard works in any subject were copiously on offer. I don't know what led me to the Old Bookshop (other than an instinct for acquisition), but shortly after I'd moved back to Northern Ireland, after long years in London, I could count myself among William Harshaw's most persistent customers. My book interests are eclectic: first editions of the twentieth century, poetry, detective fiction and what-have-you. I'm principally a children's-books accumulator, and hard-to-find titles by Mabel Esther Allan, Elinor Lyon, Winifred Darch, Evadne Price and others were apt to turn up here. Children's books – yes. But I'm also always on the look-out for material to do with Ireland, past and present, and in this respect too the Old Bookshop turned up trumps. *Ulster and Ireland*, by J. W. Good, published by Maunsel in 1919; the Talbot Press edition of Ferguson's poems; *The Truth about Ulster*, by F. Frankfort Moore; the Northern Banking Company's Centenary Volume of 1924 … all these, and more, many more, arrived on my shelves by way of Bridge Street, Lisburn. And among them was Mary Hickson's *Ireland in the Seventeenth Century* – published in 1884 – which describes in some detail 'the Irish Massacres of 1641–42'. What I didn't know, when I first read Mary Hickson's account of this atrocious episode, was that an ancestor of my own, a Tipping in-law, was conspicuous among the massacred. His name was Edward Alleyn, or Allen, and he lost his life in horrific circumstances, and as a consequence of the Irish, with their exterminatory instincts aroused, paying no heed to chivalrous rules or merciful strategies available in wartime.

Between 1622 and the autumn of 1641 the Tippings seem to have lived peaceably enough in their two-street town with the broiling countryside beyond it, the ageing parents and the growing children, who, in due course, followed the impulse to found families of their own. (The two girls, alas, as is generally the way with female siblings and the female line, disappear from the story.) By the 1630s, Stratford-on-Avon would likely have faded in the minds of all the High Street and Bridge Street immigrants, especially those of the younger generation. Ulster was the here-and-now, and a kind of social order and civic consciousness was being established in Lisburn itself and in all the little Planter towns, in small ways and according to an English pattern. The Protestant religion loomed large as an aspect of the 'civilised' life, as much for what it stood for, among a rudimentary bourgeoisie – the past, moderation, respectability – as for its value as a theological comfort.

But Irishness wasn't an insurmountable obstacle to the forming of attachments. The first Tipping to marry outside the tribe was the youngest son of John and Katherine, William, whose bride's name, Margaret O'Hoole (O'Toole, Ui Thuathail?) suggests a different type of upbringing and family background. (This is an assumption – and so is a good deal of what follows.) William, we remember, had only had four years of being a little English boy in the reign of King James, before the woods of Ulster closed in on him, bounding his horizons and perhaps endowing him with a degree of sympathy for the local underdog, the ill-treated Irish. … However it came about, the marriage of William and Margaret in the summer of 1640 is recorded in the sole surviving fragment of the earliest register of Lisnagarvey Parish Church, St Thomas's – so the bride can't have been of an unshakeably Catholic faith. No children are attributed to the couple, but that's not to say they didn't have any: we simply don't know. William went on to become an officer in the Royalist army and after the Restoration of 1662 he was granted lands in County Leitrim and County Armagh, as we shall see. But in the year of the uprising the twenty-four-year-old William was probably still in Lisburn, along with his brothers John and Thomas. All three were married by this time; John was the father of an infant daughter, and Thomas had four young children (a fifth, a girl, had died shortly after birth). ... Apart from a few brief mentions later on, the middle Stratford son, John, at this point passes out of my Tipping narrative, I am thankful to say: there are far too many Johns and Williams and Thomases making it difficult to disentangle one from t'other. One might have wished for a tad more originality in the matter of the naming of offspring; where are the Hercules and Horatios and Henriettas who might have made things easier for a future chronicler (not to mention reader)?

But now the autumn of 1641 is creeping up on us, and we have the whole lot of the Ulster Tippings – not yet multiplied immeasurably – assembled in or near the original settlement (I think). Settler fears of a native outbreak had never been entirely allayed, although – as I've suggested – life in Lisburn and other embryo towns had assumed as far as possible a flourishing character. Prophetic voices like that of Sir Thomas Phillips, governor of Coleraine, had warned against complacency: 'It is fered that they will Rise upon a Sudden and Cutt the Throts of the poore dispersed British.'

The signs were there, and eventually the time was right. It's recorded in *The Montgomery Manuscripts* that, on the afternoon of 23 October, a man, 'half-stript', dismounted from his horse and came running to the Montgomerys of the Ards bearing a missive from Bishop Leslie in Lisburn to the effect that all hell had broken loose. 'Insurrections, Murthers, and burnings' were being carried out by 'ye Irish' on all sides. The first messenger was swiftly followed by further out-of-breath runners bringing the alarming news of 'Crewell Massacres of divers persons'. Panic set in, and soon the countryside was alive with the terror-stricken settler population fleeing in droves towards reputed places of safety, towns such as Lifford, Strabane and Derry. Their houses, lands, hay, corn, farming implements, furniture, clothes ... everything they had owned was in flames behind them. 'There hath been seen great fires so near as were discerned from this place,' Lord Edward Chichester in Belfast wrote in agitation to the king on 24 October.

Two days previously, a section of the Ulster Irish under the leadership of Sir Phelim O'Neill had launched a surprise assault on major fortified positions in the North, and by now nearly the whole of Ulster, from

Newry to Donegal, was in Irish hands. The game was afoot. And some of the Irish were running amok. Most people nowadays would agree that the rising was not planned as a wholesale massacre of English and Scottish settlers – that it wasn't the 'fiendish Romish massacre' of popular Protestant mythology. But it also seems clear that the military commanders quickly lost control of headstrong recruits whose pent-up angers and resentments had finally gained an outlet – a savage outlet. The settlers, it seemed, were fair game. They could be slaughtered, robbed, stripped of their clothes and possessions, and driven naked into the wilderness with impunity. They were paying a terrible price for the depredations wrought earlier in the century on the orders of Lord Mountjoy and Sir Arthur Chichester. 'We have killed, burnt and spoiled all along the lough within four miles of Dungannon,' the latter had written in 1601. 'We spare none of what quality or sex soever, and it hath bred much terror in the people.' In Irish eyes, the long-awaited vengeance was justified in matching 'excess with excess'. I'm quoting here from the Colville Papers of 1717, in a different context but with equal relevance: 'for as we know savage customs always beget a corresponding darkness of the soul'.

As days and weeks went by, the horror stories proliferated. Lurgan was burnt to the ground, Portadown was the scene of a hellish event, when about a hundred of the settler community were flung into the River Bann and drowned, and more helpless victims were burned to death by a sept of the Maguires at Lisgoole Castle in County Fermanagh. What, we might wonder, went through the attackers' heads as they put whole communities violently to death? Did they think of themselves as avengers, heroes? The final sight to meet the eyes of many of those cut down would have been their mad malignant faces glorying in a homicidal frenzy. The imprint of these occurrences must be etched into the landscape, branded for ever on the places where the worst of human impulses erupted.

The reality was terrible enough, but it wasn't long before rumour and fabrication spewed up ever more gruesome enormities. Colonel Manus O'Cahan, a commander in the Irish army, for example, was envisaged gorging himself at the breakfast table on the heads of murdered Protestants (like a worse version of the giant in *Jack and the Beanstalk*). The bridge at Portadown soon acquired an evil reputation as cries and howlings, believed to signal a ghostly re-enactment of the drownings, made it a place to avoid after dark. (A more prosaic explanation for the

Driuinge Men women & children by hund:
reds vpon Briges & casting them into Riuers,
who drowned not were killed with poles &
shot with muskets.

A contemporary image of the massacre of settlers at Portadown

eerie nocturnal noises put them down to wolves, or to packs of dogs made homeless by the murder of their masters.)

Meanwhile, back in Lisburn. ... The townspeople, including, no doubt, the able-bodied Tippings, were rallying against the menacing Irish forces. Some among the Planters were rather disposed to stand their ground than to fly for their lives, and among them was a Captain Robert Lawson who beat a drum through the emptying streets of Belfast calling for volunteers. Having 'gathered in all about 160 horse and foot', Captain Lawson then proceeded to Lisburn, where he and his men beat off an attack on the town by Sir Conn Magennis. It was the night of 25 October. Reinforcements arrived, led by Lord Montgomery and Lord Hamilton, and by Sir George Rawdon, the current Lord Conway's agent in Ireland. In all, up until the evening of 28 November, when the ground was covered in ice and the dregs of snow, three assaults on the town took place, and all were repelled. Even stampeding a herd of cattle at the town gates didn't achieve the attackers' objective. In the aftermath of the third attack, led by Phelim O'Neill himself, Bridge Street and High Street were chock-a-block with corpses of both factions, lying where they'd been struck down. The lovely meadows behind the houses had become a killing ground too, a place of pure horror.

Soon houses, meadows and corpses were all gone, all burned to ashes, reduced to smouldering ruins. The retreating Irish set fire to the town on the night of 28 November; and the following day, for good measure, they burnt George Rawdon's house, Brookhill (built before 1611 by our old acquaintance Sir Fulke Conway, whose library went up in smoke with the rest). ... Had the women and children of Lisburn been moved to some place of safety? Were they – and I'm thinking particularly here of the female Tippings – among those residents who, with the Bishop of Down who sent the warning to the Ards, 'fled towards Belfast' with whatever they could carry? (I'm quoting from Lord Ernest Hamilton's *The Irish Rebellion of 1641*.) There are no records of non-combatant casualties in Lisburn at this time – and we know the Tippings survived, though at least one of their kinsmen by marriage didn't. This was Edward Allen, mentioned above (p. 16).

A wild and forsaken part of Ireland in the early seventeenth century was the Leitrim/Longford area, and it was decided, in 1621, to try to bring it under English control by importing strong colonists. Among them was a Humphrey Alleyn, or Allen, who was granted 810 acres in Toomonahan townland in the barony of Carrigallen on the shores of Garadice Lough, by edict of King James I. This Humphrey had a son, Edward, whose daughter Elizabeth, eighteen years old, came to Lisburn in 1635 to marry the thirty-year-old Thomas Tipping. This makes Elizabeth Allen from Garadice Lough the first Mrs Tipping to marry in Ireland; and she embarked on her wifely occupations with a will (for all we know to the contrary). Actually, of course, our ignorance concerning the private lives of Thomas and Elizabeth is illimitable. We can't tell how the marriage came about, with the two of them living, as they did, at a considerable distance from one another. How did they get acquainted in the first place, and what drew them together? Was it an arranged marriage? Did Thomas have business that took him to Longford? Was he a cutler, like his father? We have nothing to go on, to further speculation – just the stark fact contained in the St Thomas Church register. They married, and had children (the youngest, John, the most crucial to my purposes, hasn't yet put in an appearance, but he will shortly). And wherever Elizabeth and these children had taken refuge during the days of wrath, she must have been frantic with worry about her father and the rest of her family back in Longford – and with good reason.

'The Irish massacres of 1641 became part of European history, and held a place of infamy by the side of the Sicilian Vespers and the Massacre of St. Bartholomew.' This sententious sentence occurs in J.A. Froude's introduction to Mary Hickson's book, *Ireland in the Seventeenth Century* (see p. 15 above), which consists of extracts from the thirty-two volumes of depositions taken down from Protestant survivors of the bloody events. Through the centuries, doubt has been cast on the authenticity of these documents, or at least on accuracy of recollection, or concern for unvarnished veracity, on the part of some of the informants. Many people, at the time and later, had political or sectarian axes to grind, and accordingly tried to minimise or magnify the scale of the atrocities. But somewhere between the view that no massacres at all took place, and the contradictory view that entire Protestant populations were wiped out at a stroke, you might find an approximation to the truth.

The depositions, exaggerated or not, make harrowing reading; but I'm only concerned here with the murder of my umpteen-times-great-grandfather Edward Allen. The first relevant deposition has him down as Edward Allen, Gent., of Longford – so perhaps Elizabeth and his other children enjoyed a more or less urbane upbringing in a seventeenth-century house in a town, not in isolation on the sodden shores of a desolate lake, with reeds swaying in the water and curlews crying overhead. Perhaps, as time went on, the family came to believe that their lives were relatively secure and fixed in an ordained course, before disaster struck and sent them scurrying for shelter to the newly built castle of Lord Aungier in the centre of Longford, vigorously pursued by the dispossessed O'Farrell clan.

The uprising has reached the Irish midlands, and the warlike O'Farrells are out in force to repossess the lands compulsorily impounded. In their fearsome battle-garb and surrounded by Gaelic uproar, they converge on the castle where distraught Planter families are holding out – holding on for dear life until, in the first week of December, hunger and other miseries drive Longford's besieged Protestants to enter into negotiations with their hell-raising adversaries. The Irish, armed with swords, pikes, pistols, skeans and what-not, make a sight to strike terror into the hearts of their beholders. They are far from having 'Gent.' appended to their names. They are not great upholders of clemency.

A four-man delegation, including Edward Allen, is suffered to emerge from the castle and conducted under armed guard to a nearby house where terms are thrashed out and agreed in writing, signed by all parties. The lives of the English settlers will be spared, and all of them assured of 'safe convoy to Ballimowe, in the County of Westmeath ... [where] Sir James Dillon was to come ... with some English forces from Dublin.' For the starved and frightened refugees in the castle, it must have seemed as if the worst of the ordeal was over. But the worthless guarantee of safety, written down or not, is only a ruse to flush the settlers into the open. Like beaters driving game birds upwards to be shot for sport, the Irish have arranged a victory for the most unscrupulous of tactics. As the tragic procession of men, women and children staggers out from the place of refuge, they are set upon, stripped of their clothing and slaughtered on the spot – though a few get away in the ensuing melee, and live to recount the ghastly story.

My extremely distant forebear Edward Allen does not give in without a fight. Outraged and terrified, bleeding from the head where an Irish skean has struck him, he leaps into the River Camlin hoping to swim to safety. But Brian O'Cane of Longford hauls him out of the river – or maybe this person has shoved him into it in the first place; accounts become hopelessly confused at this point. O'Cane may have tried to drown an English enemy; or it's even possible he was trying to help. Still Edward Allen isn't dead. Half-drowned, bloody and exhausted, he gets himself to the house of a man named Bartholomew Nangle – the house in which the mendacious negotiations had taken place – and gains a momentary respite. It is very short. A murderous bunch of Irish avengers, scenting blood, is coming up behind. Threatened with arson and goodness knows what other acts of violence, Nangle and his brother-in-law Thomas McGeoghegan part company with the fugitive. Rather than dying with him, they send him to his death. They know what they are doing, but what else can they do? 'He forced us to take him in – here he is.' The next act in the frightful drama sees Edward Allen chained in a dungeon, two days and two nights of appalling incarceration, before his maddened enemies drag him out and hang him from a gallows in front of Longford Castle. The fate of Edward Allen's wife and younger children, who are mentioned in the depositions, is not known.

When I was young and in thrall to a nationalist imperative I'd never have wanted to hear anything bad about the Irish. This was Belfast in the 1950s, and the thing most dear to my heart was the noble conspiracy in a back room up a rickety staircase. Inspired, pipe-smoking conspirators in Donegal tweed jackets devoted to Ireland's cause. I was exhilarated by the idea of a principled lawlessness. It was as much a matter of leaning as breeding. I mean, I knew that half my ancestry was Protestant. But the other half, I believed, was Catholic Irish and Gaelic through and through, and that was the side I chose to affirm. It suited me to claim connections with Irish patriots – however far-fetched – just as it suited me to block out the Orange affiliations of my father's family, whose merits as human beings I fully acknowledged. These were my dear aunts and uncles, not oppressors or bigots or appliers of rude epithets to the pope. No member of the Craig family had the least wish to withhold from myself and my peers the package of social advantages which was increasingly coming to be known as our civil rights. Indeed, any news of our deprivation in this area would have startled and mystified my paternal relations. Aside from periodic ructions in the back streets, they'd have argued, didn't life, for all of us in the north of Ireland whatever our religious persuasion, proceed in much the same non-controversial way? At one level this was indisputable – but for those of us, historically- or crusader-minded, who craved a cause to get our teeth into, the North provided plenty of scope for indignation and right action. We were ripe for recruitment to the dissenting ideologies of the time and place.

Whenever I think of Ireland, when I am sixteen, a picture comes into my head of a country wronged, violated and mutilated (six counties lopped off), but rising above every abuse to keep its mystique intact. Its personifications are poignant and alluring. Kathleen Ni Houlihan. The Poor Old Woman. Roisin Dubh. Replete with romance and secrecy, they confer an edge of glamour on our everyday existences. The history we respond to has the fullest nationalist slant imposed on it. It's a story of unbroken rectitude on the part of the true Irish, against every kind of colonists' and oppressors' enormity and iniquity. For seven hundred years the Irish nation had suffered heroically and marshalled its resources, over and over, in a doomed but gallant revolutionary endeavour. In every generation, as it was said, Irish blood – copious and uncontaminated Irish blood – was spilt for the country's sake. Patriotic verses enshrined the ensanguined. O'Neill and O'Donnell were the names, Sarsfield, Emmet, Wolfe Tone, Mitchel, Pearse. In our iconography, the emphasis will always fall on Boulevogue not Scullabogue, on the Yellow Ford and never the Orange Boyne. We envisage a state of affairs stretching back and back to ancient times, in which freedom and Erin, or some such concept, is perpetually opposed to the Saxon and guilt.

Enlightened disaffection, edifying unrest, are modes of being we uphold and immerse ourselves in. We can't be talked to about complexity or impartiality. It's simply a case of us and them. Of course, you can choose to align yourself with the incorruptible Irish cause even without the unblemished ethnic credentials some might call for – think Mitchel, Emmett, Plunket, Tone – but those best entitled to republican kudos have names like Maguire, McMahon, O'Reilly, O'Kane. ... And where does that leave me, Irish and Gaelic, as I consider myself, to my fingertips? 'Craig' does not exactly endorse that bit of wishful thinking. In my part of the Falls district of Belfast, 'Craig' has unfortunate associations. It proclaims the very thing I am anxious to repudiate: an affinity as Orange as a Belisha beacon.

'Brady' creates a better effect: my mother is Nora Brady, and in my head is some vague genealogical commonplace, neither verified nor discredited at the time, about an Irish Brady connection to County Cavan. My grandfather Brady had married a Tipping, and the Tippings, I know – in so far as I know anything at all about them – are staunchly republican. If I think about it, though, that name too is a worry: it doesn't exactly have the Gaelic ring I'd have relished. (My cousin Harry Tipping, the family historian and a silent collaborator in this enterprise, mentions in one of his papers a desperate attempt on some family member's part to gaelicise the name by turning it into something like O Tiomhpanaigh. The version he prefers, Harry says, is O Tarbhchach – literally, bullshit.)

Around the turn of the twentieth century – I learn from my mother on an occasion in the distant past – some of our Tipping relations go in for a bit of genealogical excavation, but hastily abandon the family history project once they get back to the 1650s and uncover the shocking fact that the founding father of the family is Oliver Cromwell. It's nonsense of course, my mother says, her assumption being that an ancestral 'Cromwellian soldier' had somehow, by a process of Chinese whispers, got transformed into the old executioner and villain of Irish history himself. She's right, as it turns out – but for her, as for me, *any* Cromwellian connection is a thing to keep very dark. It would be vastly preferable to claim descent from the wonderfully named Cormac Mac Ross O'Farrell, clan chieftain and besieger of the English settlers at Longford Castle – not that any of us, at the time, know a thing about that particular episode in English/Irish relations, with expected roles of victims and aggressors reversed. My mother, like me, would choose to be as Irish as possible; although, as a teacher of history, she holds a less deluded view of historical rights and wrongs (and, indeed, many aspects of English history have a strong fascination for her, as strong as anything in her own country's past). But our lineage, as it happens, as far as pure Irishness is concerned, is worse, much worse, than she and I could ever have imagined.

I am an expert on 1641 – or so it seems to me, in my sixteenth year. I know the risen Irish have the right of it. If your lands are filched by invaders with brutal armies at their disposal, your aspirations reduced and your culture derided, you'd have to be pretty pusillanimous not to take some retaliatory action if the chance arose. Foreigners planted on stolen lands had it coming to them, in my vehement opinion. Besides, I know – everyone knows – reports of atrocities on the part of the Irish were magnified from the start for a partisan purpose. It is of course a different matter if the atrocity in question is down to the other side. An event I'm familiar with through a poem by Ethna Carbery[5] makes my hair stand on end. It concerns the slaughter of almost the entire population of Islandmagee, blameless people wiped out by soldiers of the garrison at Carrickfergus in an orgy of bloodletting. That is a true atrocity of 1641, I think (or of early 1642: the date of the Islandmagee massacre is disputed, as, indeed, is the source of the attack). I am horror-stricken by the brutality involved. The poem evoking it, 'Brian Boy Magee', is written from the point of view of the sole survivor of the Clan Magee. Coming to his senses in the aftermath of the slaughter, 'Great Christ! [he exclaims] Was the night a dream?'

> In all that Island of Gloom,
> I only had life that day.

Death covered the green hillside,
And tossed in the bay.

The terrible Phelim O'Neill of the Protestant tradition, commemorated in an Orange jingle:

Remember the steel of Sir Phelim O'Neill
Who slaughtered our fathers in Catholic zeal -

that bugbear of Protestants and unionists gets a different incarnation here. Ethna Carbery's poem goes on:

I shall go to Phelim O'Neill
With my sorrowful tale, and crave
A blue-bright blade of Spain,
In the ranks of his soldiers brave.
And God grant me the strength to wield
That shining avenger well –
When the Gael shall sweep his foe
Through the yawning gates of Hell.

The antiquated diction – 'shining avenger', 'crave', 'wield' – procures an uplifting effect; at least, it uplifted me as high as the peak of Errigal, while I wallowed in its romantic implacability. (I'm quoting the thing from memory; it has stayed with me.) I'd have been ready with my besom, myself, by those orotund infernal gates, given half a chance. In my book, the redressing of wrongs carries an especially thrilling charge. I might even have regarded the burning of Lisburn, on the orders of Phelim O'Neill, as an excusable act of war (not knowing I had any ancestral input into the business). I might have admitted, under pressure, that neither side in the interminable vicious conflicts had an absolute monopoly on honourable or on atrocious behaviour; but I'd always, in my besotted youth, have stood four-square behind the Irish troops, the Irish names.

The Cromwellian soldier preposterously conflated with Cromwell himself to loom menacingly and embarrassingly amongst the topmost branches of our family tree – this soldier can be identified as Thomas

Tipping, husband of Elizabeth Allen, son-in-law of the murdered Longford negotiator and father of John Tipping whose line of descent includes myself and the Lurgan Tippings (about whom more anon). 'Cromwellian soldier', though, doesn't seem quite right: it implies that Thomas came over to Ireland with Cromwell's army, and as we know he did nothing of the sort. He was already established in the country and committed, no doubt, to making a go of things. Did a shift in his attitude occur after Lisburn was burnt? It is possible that Thomas and his brothers lost their occupations as well as their possessions in that calamitous year. Perhaps they hadn't the heart to start all over again in the same spot; at any rate, there's no evidence to link the Tippings with the town from this point on. They, and their families, vanish from sight for a time amid the dishevelment and uproar of the age – and when the brothers next come into focus it's as soldiers caught up in the Cromwellian wars in Ireland, though on opposite sides.

I don't propose to go into the twists and turns of seventeenth-century British politics and their tangled repercussions in Ireland (I hear you breathe a sigh of relief). But it's necessary to touch on a few of the things that happened after 1641. First of all, at the time and for the future, a virtually irremovable wedge was driven between the Catholics of Ireland and the rest of the population. It left Catholic Scottish settlers in Antrim in an odd position. Some, at the start of the uprising, had joined forces with native insurgents against Protestant Planters – but, as Scottish as well as English incomers began to be listed among the massacred, significant numbers of Antrim Scots switched sides to their fellow-countrymen and deserted their co-religionists. Other Scots followed suit after April 1642, when General Munro arrived from Scotland with his army of Covenanters poised to gain redress for the murders of Presbyterians in the only available way: reciprocal massacres. A situation was taking shape whereby Planters and indigenous Irish were eternally opposed to one another; and native Irish terrain was coming to be seen as an enclave of mad brigands (an attitude persisting in some quarters right down to the present). Once the uprising was more or less quelled, the musterers of rebel forces, once again, had their lands confiscated and sold off to English investors known as Adventurers.

By this stage (the 1640s) the ongoing troubles of King Charles I with his parliament had altered the colouring of the Irish picture. As the people of England split into two factions, Royalists and Parliamentarians, so the

English in Ireland correspondingly sided with one or the other. Add the Irish Catholic rebels who came out in support of the king, the Protestants and Presbyterians who defected *to* the king, and Ulster Catholics who became Cromwellian converts, and you get the right conditions for chaos piled on top of pandemonium. Within every discernible social grouping in the country you find variation (in outlook) and vacillation (when it comes to commitment). A sense of unstoppable movement characterises the age, movement to the country and within the country, movement of troops in all directions preparing for military action, evasive movement on the part of rebels and woodkerne, restless movement of wandering poetic beggars lamenting the overthrow of the overlords, hectic movement of settlers fleeing for their lives or towards their deaths, movement of the dispossessed, westwards movement of Cromwell-created refugees, movement of irresolute recruits from army camp to camp. And against this background of disruption, you had ordinary decent Irish people, and ordinary decent settlers, doing their best to achieve a bit of stability and get on with whatever might pass for a normal life.

It's impossible for us, at a distance of more than four and a half centuries, to fully comprehend the massacres of 1641 and after. We can, of course, experience intellectual outrage on behalf of anyone caught up in annihilating events; but emotional outrage eludes us, when these events occurred so far in the past. There's only so much horror you can properly respond to before it loses its impact. After a time, the dreadful details contained in the 1641 depositions hardly seem to relate to flesh-and-blood suffering, but belong more to the realm of statistics (well, either to that or to some blood-bolter'd genre of historical sensationalism).[6] So many hacked to pieces, such-and-such a number incarcerated and burnt alive, a further lot stuck with pikes as they try, half-drowned, to scramble from the River Bann. These scenes from hell are as remote from us as Hieronymus Bosch. We can – and must, as I've said – deplore the cruelties of this incredibly historic time; but the fullest emotional involvement evades us, the recognition that these things really happened to real people.

It was all so unimaginably different, as Louis MacNeice said about the ancient Greeks, and all so long ago ... and this means I can't (for instance) realistically attribute any kind of personality or domestic circumstances to my great-grandfather-at-an-immeasurable-remove, the atrociously executed Edward Allen, or to his Carolean in-laws the Tippings, since he and they are essentially unknowable, if not entirely unimaginable (*pace* MacNeice). Something of their stories can be imagined, by building on the information we have, the bare bones, the meagre outline – and for that, the available data, enormous thanks are due to the record-keepers of old, and (personally speaking) to the ancestral detective work of my scholarly second cousin Harry Tipping.

A hanged ancestor: now there's a ghost that could haunt you, if you let it. It could come supernaturally dragging the ball and chain that secured it in a dungeon, bleeding from its head-wound – a spectral presence and nightly embodiment, or disembodiment, of accusation, re-enacting its deathly predicament by the sole surviving outer wall of Lord Aungier's castle, as avid for vengeance as Brian Boy Magee in Ethna Carbery's poem. Or, more subtly, it could insinuate itself into the brains of susceptible descendants, colouring their attitude to enormities of the past. But I don't think so. I think Edward Allen, Gent., of Longford, would wish to dissociate himself from a lurid afterlife. I think he'd like the emphasis to fall on his orderly and upright existence, not his awful death. (Sheer guesswork here, again: it's just the 'Gent., of Longford' bit that's prompting this supposition.) But the effect of his murder on those closer to him in time, his children and grandchildren – to stick with those two generations – would naturally have been vivid and extreme. (His posthumous grandson John, my particular concern, will have his say – or what can pass for it – in Chapter Two.)

For numerous succeeding generations, my own included, the knowledge that Edward Allen was hanged, not for being a law-breaker, but simply for being who and what he was (a Planter and a Protestant) – this deprives our ancestor of any of the delinquent glamour his death might have carried in other circumstances. He never lived a life of sturt and strife – or so I believe. Basically, he died for attaching credence to the binding nature of a pledge of clemency, never suspecting it to be as worthless as a wandering beggar's rags. An upsurge of hysteria and blood-thirst had O'Farrell's followers in its grip. And no supposed invader of Irish lands need expect humane treatment from them, or fair dealing. From a perspective in the present, the fate of Edward Allen can only be contemplated sombrely, the tale told with intentness and dispassion.

CHAPTER 2

VALENTINE BROWN AND VALENTINE BLACKER

...Winding-sheet and swaddling-band
Were one. Needle-flute and thimble-drum
Stitched the way to kingdom-come, to Derry,
Aughrim, Enniskillen and the Boyne:
Rat-a-ta-ta, rat-a-ta-ta, rat-a-ta-ta,
Humdrummery of history.

W.R. Rodgers, from Epilogue to *The Character of Ireland*

The great Munster poet Aodhagán Ó Rathaille (O'Rahilly) (1670–1726) has a bitter poem whose ironic adaptation of an English name – 'Bhailintín Brún' – sounds a note of increasing weariness and contempt. I first read this poem as a simple indictment of an unwelcome infiltrator into seventeenth-century Gaelic Munster; and Frank O'Connor's adept translation of three verses, under the title 'A Grey Eye Weeping', confirmed me in this view.

That my old bitter heart was pierced in this black doom,
That foreign devils have made our land a tomb,
That the sun that was Munster's glory has gone down,
Has made me a beggar before you, Valentine Brown.

O'Rahilly, says O'Connor, 'would have considered "Valentine" a ridiculous name for anyone calling himself a gentleman, and as for "Brown", he would as soon have addressed a "Jones" or a "Robinson".' Well – not quite. O'Rahilly's preferred patron would certainly have been one of the country's traditional Gaelic elite, the MacCarthy Mór – of a clan now dispossessed and dispersed. But the poet's relations with the Browns, new Lords of Kenmare, were perhaps not altogether as clear-cut as the poem called 'Valentine Brown' suggests. By one of those historical ironies I'm constantly invoking, the Catholic Browns were both supplanters and supporters of the MacCarthy sept, and adversely affected in their turn by King James's defeat at the Boyne. Sir Nicholas Brown, Sir Valentine's father, is lamented in one of O'Rahilly's poems as 'the prince who sheltered me' – but with the son it's a different matter. The son, educated in England, arrives in Kerry displaying his total ignorance of the Gaelic world and its system of patronage of the arts. O'Rahilly, an *ollamh*, a scholar and a poet, an aristocrat of the intellect if nothing else, gets short shrift when he comes within the orbit of 'Sir Val'. Sir Val, the fool, takes the great, learned poet for a beggar, in his tattered coat held together with a sugan belt. Hence O'Rahilly's litany of reciprocal insults, the 'foreign devils', the 'foreign raven' preying on the native birds, the blighted streams devoid of fish. The poet's sense of a shattered Irish world throws up abundant images of desolation: a clouded sun, a waste of scrub and heather, a drift of feathers, a palace forsaken, an *ollamh* relegated to the margins of society. The ultimate triumph, however, belongs to O'Rahilly. Valentine Brown has gone down in history – at least, in literary history – as a deplorable parvenu, an importer of new and uncongenial manners and customs into regal Kerry. O'Rahilly has set him up for perpetual ridicule, 'Sir Val' of the oafish vainglory.

Now another seventeenth-century Valentine is coming into focus, a Valentine Blacker. (I can't resist the coincidence of the forenames, even if there's little else to link the two.) Captain Valentine Blacker was a Royalist officer from the village of Poppleton, near York, who came to Ireland some time in the early seventeenth century and never went home again. He was also, to bring in a personal element once more, another of my far-back forebears. At this point I should, perhaps, make it clear that I'm not about to embark on a genealogical jamboree. My purpose is different – and besides, anyone on the trail of ancestors knows that the further back you go, the more selective you have to be (if selectivity weren't already imposed by the quantity of information available). Once you've got to some reasonably remote era of the past, the possibilities for uncovering distant progenitors are extended ad infinitum, with thousands and thousands of anonymous begetters branching off into an infinity of consanguinity. It's enough to derange one's equilibrium. In the interests of sanity, if nothing else, you have to stick to a particular familial line – with allowance for twists and meanderings and even dead-end diversions. Of course, anyone susceptible to the lure of continuity will get a tremendous kick out of placing themselves in an actual, personal historical sequence – and I'm no exception. It's great to be able to single out a few distinctive forebears among the myriads who, of necessity, must remain unidentifiable and irreclaimable. All vanished – some of them utterly, attenuated to nothingness, some bequeathing a fact or two, nothing more, to future generations, many existing as nothing more than a name on a document, or a gravestone. ... Judith Harrison, for example, daughter of Sir Michael Harrison of Ballydargan, County Down, who became the wife of Valentine Blacker and the mother of two sons and three daughters, who lived through the wars and massacres of the mid seventeenth century. ... What was her family doing in County Down? Were they part of the Old English colony in east Ulster, or new English adventurers? Did she grow up in the townland of Ballydargan? What was life like for a Jacobean Ulster girl? Did she witness terrible occurrences? Where did her loyalties lie? ... I'm lumbering myself with a lot of unanswerable questions here. One thing is certain, though, and disconcerting to a would-be Irishwoman. If I make a list of my known female ancestors of the seventeenth century – Katherine Rose, Judith Harrison, Elizabeth Allen, Rosa Young, Rose Latham, Frances Blacker (I'll get to the last two in a minute) – what strikes me about this list is the unequivocal *Englishness* of the names. Ah well.

Valentine Blacker. A little book, *For God and the King*, written by J.S. Kane and published by the Ulster Society in 1995, traces the history of the Blackers of Carrickblacker. A lot of my information about the family comes from this source, and I'm grateful for it. ... It starts with a Viking raider named Blacar, or Blacaire, a cousin of King Sitric III, sailing up the River Bann towards the future site of Portadown on a night unlike the one evoked in a heartfelt quatrain of the eighth or ninth century, translated by F.N. Robinson:

> Fierce is the wind tonight,
> It ploughs up the white hair of the sea.
> I have no fear that Viking hosts
> Will come over the water to me.

A calm night for the warrior Blacar, then, horrors for the preyed-on Irish, with a furious battle to follow; the defeat of a sept of the O'Neills, and a temporary Viking settlement in a townland called Drumlisnagrilly, which Kane translates as 'the fort of the dagger': 'broadsword' (*greillean*) would be closer. So Blackers — Blacars — were on the spot in the tenth century before making tracks for the north of England; and then, seven hundred years later, a Royalist descendant returns to Ireland 'to claim his ancient lands', as Kane has it. These ancient lands, true enough, include Drumlisnagrilly along with six other townlands. One of these, Ballynaghy (*Baile an Achaidh*, the Townland of the Plains), soon becomes the site of a manor house known as Blacker's Bawn.

'Blacker's Bawn' takes us up to the 1660s: Cromwell dead, one king executed and another restored to the English throne, and Valentine Blacker's career as a Royalist officer long in the past. He was pretty elderly by this stage — well over sixty — though energetic enough to undertake the building of his new manor house, as well as setting in motion the restoration of the Church of Ireland parish church at nearby Seagoe. The earliest church on this site — according to Kane — had been built by English settlers during the reign of Queen Elizabeth. When the alien edifice appeared in the landscape it didn't go down too well with the native Irish, who promptly made short work of it. By 1609 the church was in ruins. Settler tenacity raised it up again, and again an Irish assault destroyed it. Its second demolition occurred during the uprising of 1641, when many of Seagoe's beleaguered parishioners found themselves rounded up like a herd of cattle and driven to the bridge at Edenderry to meet their deaths in the Bann, whose level rose with the numbers of corpses crammed into it — shot, stabbed, piked, bludgeoned, whipped to death or simply drowned. (A grisly reminder of this atrocity shook the people of Portadown nearly three hundred years later, in the 1930s, when workers laying out a new bowling green near the site of the massacre turned up hundreds of bones from the Edenderry victims.)

It was due to Valentine Blacker that Seagoe Church got rebuilt yet again, and he and his wife were granted the first pew in the church when it opened for worship in 1662. In the following decade, it became their burial place. So Valentine Blacker can be judged a benefactor of his adopted Northern Irish community, and a notable presence in the locality – even if, like that other Valentine, Valentine Brown, he probably had little acquaintance with native Gaelic traditions in the area, seasonal rituals with song and dance and girls garlanded with flowers, fertility rites, mourning customs and so forth: all hidden from Protestant incomers but flourishing around them none the less. *Tugamar Fhein an Samhradh Linn.*

It is time to return to the mid seventeenth-century wars, and the brothers Tipping. The youngest, William, is listed among 'the '49 men' – that is, those who backed the king's cause in Ireland before 1649 (when the execution of Charles I took place). William's brother John was also a Royalist recruit. What caused the eldest, Thomas, to take up the cudgels for Cromwell isn't known, but probably it had more to do with expediency than ideology. Given the uncertain and insane conditions prevailing at the time, it might have seemed prudent to have at least one family member on the winning side, whatever that should turn out to be.

The outstanding Royalist in Ireland was the Protestant Earl of Ormond, James Butler, of the prominent Old English Catholic Butler family (Ormond was a Protestant convert). Lord Ormond commanded forces for the king – and with the Catholic Confederates and Puritan Parliamentarians thrown into the mix, not to mention deserters and tergiversators – the scope for mayhem and slaughter was intensified. Were the Tipping brothers in the thick of it? How much actual fighting did they do? Did they ever come face-to-face in a skirmish? Where did they settle their wives and children once they'd gone for soldiers? What happened after Cromwell came, with his assumption of a God-given licence to wipe out the perpetrators of 1641, and his terrible subduing tactics? It would be horrendous to think that Thomas Tipping had any part in the massacres at Drogheda and Wexford. One hopes (and this is likely) he was quartered elsewhere in the country; and at least we know that, Parliamentarian or not, he didn't come over with Cromwell's invasion force, which was chiefly responsible for the indiscriminate slaughter. No, I think I can absolve my ancestor of military brutality on the scale it erupted in these Irish towns. Drogheda and Wexford: the names remain conspicuous in the catalogue of horrors inflicted on the Irish. It was the number of civilian victims laid at Cromwell's door that consolidated his reputation for creed-condoned mercilessness and ethnic abhorrence, at least as far as Ireland is concerned. ... Cromwell is, of course, in one sense an anomalous figure. In England, as Elizabeth Bowen puts it in her book, *Bowen's Court*, 'he had fought for the English conception of "freedom"; in Ireland he fought against the Irish conception of it'. No Irish republican, indeed, would want to claim Cromwell as an ideological ancestor, but it's a different matter if you're an anti-monarchist in England.

The Irish conception of freedom included the freedom to be as Catholic as Mary Tudor. Even as late as the mid twentieth century, integrity in Catholic circles was measured by the way the faith had been adhered to, through thick and thin (or dungeon, fire and sword, as in the hymn we sang at school). Turncoats in one's lineage were a cause of shame. One of my great-grandmothers, Ellen Jordan, used to boast of an unfaltering Catholicism in her family, stretching back unbroken to the days of the Normans. No recusants among the Jordans! Considering what's emerged in other sections of my adulterated ancestry, though, I am not sure how far her claim to an entirely Catholic descent will stand up. (I am not sure, either, that it *won't* stand up; it's just that, given her forthright and argumentative nature, I can't help envisaging a sturdy Protestant or Presbyterian element creeping in somewhere.) Following the Jordan line, I can only get back as far as Ellen's parents, Edward Jordan of Tannaghmore West and Susan McCorry of Moyraverty, born *c*.1812 and 1815 respectively. My great-great-grandparents – and I love the pungency of those placenames, Tannaghmore West and Moyraverty, both of them well off the beaten track, in the hidden seductive depths of leafy north Armagh.

(Susan McCorry could not be more obscure but I'd like to think she might have left something commensurate with the twang of her name – a needlework sampler of the 1820s, say, painstakingly embroidered with a red plain-fronted house, three windows and a door, and perched on the chimney of its slanting roof, an exotic bird, twice the size of the door. On the right-hand side, a tree filled with smaller birds, and another, like a parrot, charmingly out of scale; and beneath the tree, a pair of storybook figures, male and female, in Georgian get-up, dwarfed by an enormous flowerpot. The whole quaint picture worked within a decorative border round the linen rectangle, with the letters of the alphabet across the top and right at the bottom, a small perky dog, and perhaps more flowers in flowerpots. And the signature of the youthful stitcher: Susan McCorry Aged 12 Years. 17 August 1827. ... I'm making this up. Still, I suppose young Susan might have attended a local interdenominational school run by some charity or other, and sat among a roomful of good little girls from Moyraverty, stitching away at a pious verse or maxim to show her needlework skills. She might have depicted a pair of angels hovering above a church, like those on a sampler in my possession, the work of a Susanna Cottrill in the relevant year, 1827. ... On the other hand, it's unlikely that a child of impeccable Catholic lineage, as her daughter Ellen Jordan asserted, would have been let near a classroom filled with potentially proselytising Protestants. No, I think I have to let her return to the chores of the day: fetching water, carrying turf, digging potatoes, gathering wild strawberries or mushrooms in the fields with a string of younger children behind her.)

Cromwell. When I was sixteen the first volume of Walter Macken's historical *Irish Trilogy* was published. I don't remember how it came to my attention, but it wasn't long before a copy of *Seek the Fair Land* came into my hands. I'd arranged to borrow it from the handsome Carnegie Library on a dusty stretch of the old Falls Road, one of my haunts. From the opening section of Macken's story, in which the life of a roaring Connaught chieftain is saved by a mild man living in Drogheda, I was enthralled. By chapter three, and the ominous date of September 1649, when the mild man stumbles on his wife lying dead in a blood-rippled street in the wake of the Ironsides' onslaught on the town, I knew I was reading a version of history – fictionalised or not – that chimed with my deepest beliefs about the suffering Irish and exterminating English. It was an old and emotional way of thinking. You couldn't but be on the side of the desperately wronged and courageous population. ... And it did no harm to Walter Macken's sales figures that his novel is an adventure story, a survival story. That mild man from the North, Dominick McMahon, leads his remaining family, a young daughter and son, out of despoiled and perilous Drogheda towards the sanctuary of the Gaelic west. It requires immense resourcefulness to evade the Cromwellian depredators along the way.

To make matters even more difficult, Dominick is burdened with a fugitive priest, Father Sebastian, who more than once endangers the little party by stopping to perform some rite of the Catholic church, administering the last sacrament or digging a grave for the dead. Gradually, however, Dominick's exasperation with Sebastian turns to admiration for the priest's continuous affirmation of a Catholic spirit, a national virtue. Dominick's children, his sparky daughter Mary Ann and mute son Peter, take the priest to their hearts unequivocally. It is clear that it's Sebastian's virtues, his goodness, selflessness and obeisance to a higher power, that will save the nation, if it's to be saved at all. Some alternatives to his priestly humility are proffered and found wanting – a fighting determination in the face of oppression, the carousing instincts and sexual license of great Connaught Gaels like the O'Flahertys. No, in Macken's book, it's the spiritual dimension that defines the true Irish. This novel, with its two sequels, adds up to an unabashed romance of the Catholic nation.

Macken is a great storyteller, and, on one level, his books remain gripping even for a reader as sceptical as myself. You accept, while you're reading it, the premise of his plot. Cromwell looms in the background furnished with every excess Irish history decreed; and not far behind him in the monstrosity stakes is Sir Charles Coote, persecutor of Catholics extraordinaire. ... What happens? After many reprieves in the course of the narrative, saintly Sebastian finally falls into the clutches of Coote and is burnt at the stake. A witness to this event, Peter McMahon, regains thereby the voice he lost as a child following a blow to the head during the massacre at Drogheda. It is, of course, a Catholic, indeed a priestly, voice that's restored to Peter. Sebastian's successor, he promptly sets off for Louvain and a clerical education to help keep the fires of the true faith burning at home (and never mind what else burns in the process). You can, if you will, equate Peter with the Irish nation, wounded, belittled, indomitable, and destined for recovery with its essence of an indigenous spirituality intact. Well!

In 1652, an Act of Parliament had decreed the removal of Catholic landowners (and some Protestant Royalists), with their families, to the wild and unproductive territory west of the Shannon. Those officially dispossessed, and also unofficial refugees like the McMahon family in Walter Macken's novel, undertook the sorry trek into poor lands, where some would rebuild their lives with a measure of confidence, and some would not. It's one of the many sorrowful set-pieces of Irish history. A contemporary poet, Fear Dorcha Ó Mealláin, has a word of advice for the harried and defeated Catholic deportees. He counsels them to take it stoically.

> If they call you 'Papishes'
> accept it gladly for a title.
> Patience, for the High King's sake.
> Deo Gratias, good the name!

When I was sixteen and my head was teeming with images of desecrated Ireland, I was happy to take credit (along with my great-grandmother) for vague ancestral stoicism and fidelity to the Catholic faith. I'm not sure, though, how far I'd have gone along with Ó Mealláin's recommended passivity, if I'd been aware of his poem at the time; what he conjures up is a line of cowed and beaten people creeping westwards on their last legs, every jot of defiance knocked out of them. It's not an inspiriting picture. These are the people among whom the popular novelist found his characters — but the way Walter Macken builds them up they're far from being a lumpen mass of misery. It's a highly sentimental ideology he's upholding, indeed, but his skill is such that you swallow it and deplore it all at once. In capitulation to the mood of the narrative, you applaud the restoration of Peter's vocal faculty and its religious implications even while your secular hackles are bristling.

Another Gaelic poem, well known to me in my youth is '*Cumhadh na Mathara fa'n Leanbh*', 'The Mother's Lament for her Child'. This was written probably in the eighteenth century, long after the events evoked, and it's been attributed to the south Armagh poet Peadar Ó Doirnín (born *c*.1684). Recent commentators have praised this poem for breaking decisively with the strict and cumbersome bardic traditions of the past, striking instead a bold new 'modern' note with its economy and immediacy. In simple plangent terms it confronts the agony of a mother witnessing the slaughter of her infant, piked to death with the blessing of Cromwell. The outpouring of grief proceeds as if issuing from the mother:

> They tied me to a tree
> To watch what was done to you,
>> Child of the branches.

You were on the end of the pike
And I heard your cry
And it tore my heart
    Child of my breast.

It's an image to set against the women with up-flung arms being pitchforked into the River Bann from the bridge at Edenderry, or the burnt remains of Planters at Lisgoole. But, prone as I was to selective outrage, I thought the second or anything like it was a figment of someone's inflamed Orange imagination, while the Peadar Ó Doirnín poem (if he was indeed the author) was consistent with the historical facts as I knew them. As everyone knew them; *everyone* abominated the actions of Cromwell. There was no denying it.

There were things I'd have liked to deny, if they'd come to challenge the nationalist certainties of my teenage years, and my own entitlement to a largely Irish identity. If someone had suggested to me then that an ancestor of my own had allied himself with Cromwell's Ironsides, I'd have growled and snorted and repudiated the nonsense. (It wouldn't actually have made much difference if Thomas Tipping had been a Royalist like his brothers; these were all English Planters, not the *fíor-Gaels* I'd have relished among my maternal forebears.) If it had then been shown beyond doubt that it wasn't nonsense, that Thomas Tipping had really existed in his seventeenth-century army uniform, with steel helmet and leather breeches, riding about on a horse quelling Royalist and native Irish alike – well, then, my next state would have been a very sheepish one, very taken aback and wishful to keep the awful information dark. I mean, this wasn't the Craig side of the family, whose ancestral non-Irishness I had long accepted. I could have turned up marauding Scots or raving Calvinist preachers among bygone Craigs without turning a hair (well, more or less). But my grandmother Brady's family I'd considered sacrosanct, as far as good Catholic genes were concerned. Never, never would I have suspected the republican Tippings of ancestral Protestantism.

The ethnically dodgy Tippings (as I'd have viewed them in my purist days) came out of the Cromwellian wars rather better than they'd gone into them. All were granted lands in Ireland in lieu of army pay. By the time the final land allocations are ratified by the restored King Charles II in 1666, Thomas has acquired portions of townlands in County Down and County Westmeath; John is also a landowner in County Down and County Cavan; while William – though his name doesn't occur in the list of recipients of royal grants – has somehow come into possession of Ballynarea in south Armagh. Harry Tipping suggests that Thomas may then have sold his County Down windfall to speculators, and leased Ballynarea from his brother William; at any rate, he and his family seem to have settled there, while William is found at nearby Creggan.

Creggan: this is a district strongly associated with the poet Art Mac Cubhthaigh, or MacCooey (*c.*1715–*c.*1773), whose life overlapped with Peadar Ó Doirnín's, both of them prominent in the nest of singing birds whose songs and verses enhanced the pungent Gaelic ethos of south Armagh. Ó Doirnín, though, was a schoolteacher and respected as such, and Art MacCooey, much lower in the social scale, led a luckless life as a jobbing gardener and agricultural labourer, while bolstering himself up with visions of reversals of fortune, both for himself and for his chosen patrons, the O'Neills of Glassdrummond. Even while trundling cartloads of dung about the countryside, MacCooey can't be stopped from composing verses in praise of the O'Neills or against his enemies, mean-spirited priests and Protestant grandees alike. ... But it was '*Ur-Chill a' Chreagain*', 'The Graveyard of Creggan Church', his eloquent exercise in the *aisling* or vision mode, that made MacCooey's name. This poem strikes every romantic chord you could ask for: the poet at his lowest ebb falling asleep in the old secluded churchyard, the fairy woman enticing him away from a life of miseries and humiliations, the classical garnish, the deep historical sense, the lament for the ruined Gaels and their emblems of an ordered world. All evoked with a lyrical grandeur and aplomb. And when '*Ur-Chill a' Chreagain*' is sung unaccompanied by a great traditional singer like Mary Harvessy or Pádraigín Ní Uallacháin, it illumines for an instant the strangeness and incomparable richness of the culture from which it emerged.

A culture, though, in no position to succour its exponents. Enrí Ó Muirgheasa, who put together a collection of Art MacCooey's works in 1916, notes the ratio of Protestant to Catholic families in the parish of Creggan during the eighteenth century. Protestant 259, Papist 718 – but, of course, with the former very much in the ascendant. MacCooey was briefly employed as a gardener by one of them, the Reverend Hugh Hill of Mounthill, rector of Creggan between 1728 and 1773. 'Mounthill', as well as being the name of a house, was also the new name of the townland previously known as Ballinaghy (it seems there was more than one Ballinaghy in County Armagh: this is not the same as the one originally acquired by Valentine Blacker in the mid seventeenth century). And in it, according to Ó Muirgheasa, lived another Protestant family, 'of such consequence' – and here my genealogical instincts perk up – of such consequence that one of them is appointed a churchwarden of Creggan parish in 1741. The name of this exalted officiary is Thomas Tipping, junior. Could he have been a great-grandson of the William who settled in Creggan around 1670 (even though we don't know whether William had any direct descendants at all)? Or of the elder Thomas who was born in Stratford-on-Avon? There's nothing to go on but the name – but it's enough to attach him, if precariously, to this branch of my family tree. Perhaps I can hook him to it by the seat of his churchwarden's trousers, like a bad boy strung up by his classmates in an old-fashioned school story. At any rate, it pleases me to visualise this Thomas Tipping, Esq., passing the time of day with the lowly farm labourer Art MacCooey – one a bit resentful of the other's airs and graces, perhaps, the other unaware of the rough fellow's learning and poetic expertise. Their paths must have crossed, in such a small community, and especially with Creggan church a place of refuge for the poet. But the ways of the Gaels remained as alien to Planters as the ways of faery hosts in their raths and souterrains. It was as if an intangible barrier divided two exclusive zones, each primed to repel any interchange.

It was never as clear-cut as that, of course, and time would make it considerably less so. Proximity, common ground, the attractions of exogamy, all worked to blur the edges of the sharp divide. But what resulted was never going to be a smoothly blended community. Well – let me modify that assertion. What resulted was never going to be *perceived*, either from the inside or the outside, as a smoothly blended community. For I would argue that the latter is precisely what we have achieved, even if we don't know it; that all of us in the north of Ireland, Protestant, Catholic or what-have-you, are a compound of the same good and bad elements from brave hearts to stiff necks.

Bloodlines got diluted, or enriched if you prefer it, almost from the moment the Planters set foot in Ireland, individuals throwing in their lot with the side they hadn't been born to. Papists en masse renouncing the Mass, and plain Presbyterians opting for Catholic ritual. If these people were looked at askance, either as traitors to the tribe or as dubious recruits – well, within a generation or two their descendants would be thoroughly assimilated into the host faction, with never a notion of any genetic or doctrinal inconsistency to agitate them. And so it has gone on right down to the present, with the wretched factions – 'accursed systems', William Carleton labelled them – flourishing side by side, and their noisiest adherents often unaware of their less than absolute entitlement to denominational integrity. It's the names, of course, that furnish an obvious pointer: a notorious butcher of Catholics from the Shankill Road in Belfast called Murphy; a president of Sinn Féin with the English name of Adams. A Protestant poet – I'm using these terms in a descriptive, not a religious sense – called Mahon, and a Catholic poet called Carson. Another poet, Paul Muldoon, has a pointed small reminder of local complexities and ambiguities:

> ...Today he remarked how a shower of rain

> Had stopped so cleanly across Golightly's lane
> It might have been a wall of glass
> That had toppled over. He stood there, for ages,
> To wonder which side, if any, he should be on.

If any. Muldoon is referring specifically to the border between North and South, but you can extend his words to apply to the immemorial border between Catholic and Protestant, Gael and Planter, Orange and Green.

The twentieth-century Lurgan Tippings knew which side they were on, but to arrive at it they'd had to accommodate a long-ago episode of recusancy. I'll get to this eventually; but, for the moment, we're still in the Protestant seventeenth century, the 1670s to be precise. Here we have Thomas Tipping, ex-soldier, nearing the end of his life in the rainy uplands of south Armagh, with his family around him. Thomas had come a long way from his beginnings in Stratford-on-Avon, with its half-timbered Englishness and Holy Trinity Church presiding over the lives of its good Protestant populace. He was born, we remember, in 1605 and enjoyed a life-span of seventy years. When he dies in 1675 his eldest son, also called Thomas, takes over the running of the Ballynarea estate. (To digress very briefly: this second Thomas engenders a further succession of Thomases who keep on stepping up and up the social ladder, until they find themselves established as minor members of the County Louth aristocracy, with family seats at Castletown, Beaulieu and Bellurgan Park. But as for the descendants of my particular ancestor among Thomas I's progeny. ...We shall see. Harry Tipping puts it succinctly in his account of the family: 'You take the high road and I'll take the low road.')

The first Thomas had six children. The youngest of these, John, was born around 1650 and called after his paternal English grandfather who may or may not have been still alive. His other grandfather wasn't, as we have seen (see p. 22). Harry Tipping again: 'As a child at his mother's knee, John Tipping, ... founder of our north Armagh branch, must often have heard the horrific and tragic tale of how his maternal grandfather, Edward Allen, was callously murdered by the native Irish in the 1641 uprising.' And doubtless young John was endowed with an antipathy towards the perpetrators of this crime. Remembering the events of that recent year was enough to send shudders down every Protestant spine. And the worst of it was, they were still around, the inimical Irish, wolfish predators in the hills and woods, ready to do murder again at the flare of a beacon.

John would likely have grown up in a detached house built of stone or brick, surrounded by a stone bawn twelve-feet high, into which the cattle were herded at night for safe keeping. The men of the house would have been armed against intruders. The evolving 'siege mentality', cited by later historians to explain atavistic Protestant loathing and aggression, was keeping every Planter nerve on full alert. At the same time, these second- or third-generation settlers were in the process of acquiring their own complicated variety of Irishness, whether they acknowledged it or not. Ireland was all they had ever known, but Ireland was like a wicked stepmother country refusing to take them to her bosom. And worse: she was only waiting for an opportunity to make away with the lot of them. ... Picture a winter evening in the mid seventeen-hundreds, a Planter house in the townland of Ballynarea; a bitter wind from the north creating an uproar outside; flickering candlelight, and a huddle of children crouched by a smoking fire, avidly taking in horror stories concerning murdered Protestants, a hanged grandfather and the ghosts of the drowned at Edenderry Bridge. Stories carrying a powerful charge of fear and outrage. A legacy of aversion persisting down the centuries. ... Move forward nearly four hundred years, and you get 'Lynn Doyle' recalling his country upbringing in *An Ulster Childhood* (1921), an upbringing infiltrated by sectarian truisms (comically evoked). 'Home Rulers', he says, 'to my childish mind were a dark, subtle and dangerous race.' They were ready to rise at a moment's notice, he continues, diabolically poised 'to murder my uncle, possess themselves of his farm, and drive out my aunt and myself to perish on the mountains.' Never mind that there weren't any mountains within easy reach of the farm, 'in my aunt's stories it was on the mountains we always died, and I felt that we were bound to get there somehow'.

Ah, but the thrill of atavistically awful anticipations was not confined to one side only. As a counterbalance to Lynn Doyle, consider an episode from the Catholic childhood of the novelist Brian Moore, in the 1930s. The Moore family home in Belfast, oddly enough, was directly opposite the headquarters of the Orange Order in Clifton Street. Each year, on the Twelfth of July, the Moore children gather at a top-floor window to watch the Orange marchers assembling for the long triumphal trek to the Field at Finaghy. They, the young Moores, are the only Catholics in Belfast to have a grandstand view! The noise, the colour, the flute bands, the dignitaries' bowler hats, the Loyal Orange Lodges each with its treasured banner proclaiming some aspect of Protestantism or enshrining King William at the Boyne, the rousing warlike reverberations from the great Lambeg drums ... all these produce a rare excitement in the little Catholic nationalists, noses pressed to the windowpane, looking down on a vibrant gala occasion which is also a threat to their own well-being. They can't take their eyes off the massing wild men, thousands strong, strutting and swirling under their window. Knowing all the while 'that you and yours [are] the very enemy they seek to destroy'.

Between the 1640s and the run-up to the Boyne forty years ahead, Planter families in towns and townlands all over the North would wake each morning gladdened by the fact that no disaster had happened overnight, no sudden uprising, onslaught or outbreak of neighbourhood savagery. A decreasing sense of loss, a measure of confidence about the security of their lives and livelihoods, would slowly have taken them over. They were here to stay – and gradually, it seemed, there were fewer fears to possess them. Even if it should prove to be something of a chimera – which it did – this growing confidence allowed them to get on more or less undisturbed with the basic business of living, birth, copulation and death, and all the embellishments in between. ... I'm now about to return to those redoubtable Poppleton Blackers, and two converging strands of my distant ancestry. Glenn Patterson, in his book about his grandparents, *Once Upon a Hill* (2008), refers amusingly to the long, long line of 'begets' to which everyone's family history boils down. Taking a cue from him, I am going to go in for a bit of 'begetting' myself. You will remember Valentine Blacker, the Royalist officer who settled in County Armagh after the Commonwealth wars and rebuilt Seagoe Church. Valentine begat George, who begat Frances, who begat William, who begat John ... and so ad infinitum – or at least, so on in a straight progression right down to the present.

Valentine Blacker, as we've seen, married Judith Harrison of a local Irish Planter family, and 'begat' two sons and three daughters. The oldest son, the surprisingly named Ferdinando, led a valiant short life before dying at a young age in some battle or other, leaving his more conventionally named brother George as the sole heir. George Blacker – according to J.S. Kane – 'served his sovereign, King Charles II, as a major in the army and was later promoted to the rank of lieutenant-colonel in an infantry regiment'. Well, good for George. You can picture this upright soldierly figure in his seventeenth-century army uniform looking down his military Blacker nose at the uncouth Irish population of Ballynaghy and thereabouts. ... Already well placed in the world, George goes on to make an advantageous marriage. His bride is a Miss Rose Latham, the daughter of William Latham and his wife Rosa Young. (J.S. Kane has George marrying Rosa Young, not her daughter, but I think he is wrong about this.) The newly-weds establish themselves with due ceremony at Blacker's Bawn, paying six shillings tax on the three fireplaces recorded at their home in 1662, and, in due course, after further begetting, raise a family of four – three sons and a daughter. George Blacker is eventually appointed High Sheriff of County Armagh to crown his undeviating career in solid citizenship. He is fortunate enough to reach this position just before the advent of King James II, and consequent shattering of what had passed for peace in the country.

I cannot tell for sure how George was affected by the Williamite wars before his death in 1691. I do have some information about his sons William and Robert, and I'll return to them, and one or two of William's descendants, later. But my attention for the moment is focused on George's daughter Frances, the youngest of his children, born *c.*1652.

... Who was Frances's mother? J.S. Kane, as I've said, claims that George married Rosa Young, not Rose Latham, and dates the marriage to the year 1658 – but this makes no sense at all, especially since Kane then refers to George's son William's marriage in 1666, when by this reckoning William would have been a boy of seven. Logically, we can attribute a birth date of 1622 to George, and 1647 to William ... but hang on, there now arises a puzzle in connection with grandfather Valentine. If Valentine Blacker only set foot in the province in 1641 or 42, how had he married an Ulster lady many years earlier and fathered five children on her? If, on the other hand, he'd been in Ulster all along, why and when did he arrive here? ... These genealogical puzzles and chronological inconsistencies are giving me a headache and I am not going to delve any further into them. I don't care if long-ago George married Rose Latham, or her mother, or her grandmother. The thing is, to keep a grip as far as possible on pungent and pertinent bits of information, and let the rest go hang. One such fact (it is a fact) concerns George Blacker's daughter Frances. In 1677 or thereabouts, Frances becomes the wife of young John Tipping and initiates a line of descent that will – eventually – be at odds in every respect with the lordly Protestant Blackers. This much I do know, and it's enough to be going on with.

For the time being, however – in the years leading up to the Boyne – the Tippings are every bit as Protestant and as strongly allied to the cause of Orange William as John's august in-laws. (Perhaps more so; the Blackers, we remember, were great Stuart supporters, at least before the advent of Catholic James.)... John and Frances, once married, set up home in a townland called Gallrock, in the parish of Tartaraghan in north Armagh. Did Frances's family object to her marriage to a Tipping? They don't seem to have bestowed much of the Blacker wealth on her, leaving her to lead a quiet farming life, which she and her husband do, undisturbed as far as we can tell, for the next twelve years or so, while they go about 'begetting' offspring. (The exact number of new young Gallrock Tippings is uncertain.) But during the years between 1685 and 1689 life starts to assume a hazardous character once again. The cause is the accession of an English Catholic king, and consequent conferring of hope for an overthrow of their disabilities on the Catholic population of Ireland. Catholic aspiration is suddenly in the ascendant, while dormant Protestant fears are about to be reawakened.

By the late 1680s, Protestants all over the North are preparing for defence, or, in the last resort, flight to some place of refuge. It's the nightmare of 1641 all over again. Had you been in a Protestant house in the last month of 1688, you'd have stood all night with a weapon in your hand, poised to repel a rebel onslaught. If neighbours had come knocking at your door, a blunderbuss thrust through a window would have greeted them, with householder nerves in tatters everywhere. ... But beyond the beleaguered houses of Gallrock and Ballynaghy, beyond the agitated towns of Derry, Armagh and Carrickfergus, great events are taking place in the constitutional and in the military sphere. By now, Prince William of Orange has appeared on the scene, with all his regalia, ready to be incorporated into Northern Irish Protestant iconography. Having landed at Torbay in the south of England in the previous month, William holds out a prospect of reinforced Protestantism, with all accompanying benefits, to the three kingdoms – and, for the most part, wins them over.

King James leaves for France in a hurry and sails from there to Ireland, landing at Kinsale in March 1689 with an army of French soldiers. Already, at the other end of the country, the gates of Derry have been slammed shut against James's Catholic troops, though the town has not yet come down decisively on the side of William. That wholehearted commitment will shortly follow. A Williamite army under the command of Frederick Duke of Schomberg arrives at Bangor in August 1689; and in the following year King William himself steps ashore at Carrickfergus and promptly sits down to take a rest on a chair which some thoughtful person has carried to the quayside. The Prince of Orange is marshalling his resources for a southwards dash, taking in Belfast along the way, towards the immemorial engagement at the Boyne.

But before this, in response to an escalating state of panic, many of the Protestants of Seagoe and thereabouts have left their homes and are hurrying northwards towards Derry, perhaps, and the safety of its enclosing walls. It's a wrong decision for many of them. The countryside is thick with roving detachments of King James's army, mostly Catholic, who take it as their mission to prey on Protestants. Terrible things can happen to those who fall into their clutches. And unlike Walter Macken's hero Dominick McMahon, in *Seek the Fair Land*, these northern refugees are not always skilled in evasive tactics. They've hurled themselves into a win-or-lose situation in which many will go under. Somehow, along the road, in the lethal year of 1689, John Tipping meets his death, and his mother-in-law and brother-in-law follow suit. (The Blacker family historian J.S. Kane includes Frances Tipping among the dead of Seagoe in the same year, but there is evidence to suggest that Frances was still alive as late as 1710 – and we know that at least one, and possibly two, of her sons survived.)

From whatever specific cause, though, John Tipping died, brought low, like his grandfather Edward Allen, by the violence and mayhem of the era. He is buried in Seagoe Church. In the meantime, his surviving brother-in-law William Blacker is undergoing adventures and misadventures of his own. Leading a party of women and children northwards towards Derry (as Kane tells the story), William comes face-to-face with some Irish army recruits. But rather than slaughtering him on the spot as a pernicious Protestant, these soldiers instead engage William's services as an emissary for King James II, positively encouraging him to press on to Derry – on condition that he carries with him the surrender terms laid down by James for the capitulation of the unruly city. ...You might wonder why these Jacobite soldiers trusted William Blacker to stick to the terms he'd agreed, once he was out of their hands. Had they required him to leave hostages behind? I think it more likely that his family's long adherence to the Stuart cause had something to do with it. We don't, of course, know what William had in mind, at the time or later – but he did reach Derry and delivered the compromising missive as instructed: whereupon he found himself imprisoned as a traitor, and one line of the Blacker dynasty nearly took an irregular turn.

But William's conspicuous survival instincts don't desert him. The next minute he's up on Derry's walls fighting off the besiegers alongside the Reverend George Walker and other luminaries of the heroic event. Did he have a change of heart? When it came to a clash between William's inherited Stuart loyalties and his Protestantism, I suppose it was never in doubt where his ultimate allegiance would lie. The next glimpse we have of William Blacker shows him fighting at the Boyne under an Orange banner, and thus, in the words of J.S. Kane, 'establishing the family's long and glorious connection with the cause of Orangeism'. He acquits himself so well in the battle that King William's 'horse furniture' from the Boyne engagement, including gloves, stirrups and an embroidered saddlecloth, is later presented to William Blacker in recognition of his military services and descends down through the family

PC's father 'Andy' Craig with his younger brother and sister outside their Dunmurry home, *c.*1928

until it finally ends up with the Grand Orange Lodge of Ireland 'for safe keeping'.

The Grand Orange Lodge of Ireland! There's a name to strike a chill into the heart of any young Falls Road republican embracing subversion in the middle part of the twentieth century. Or if not a chill exactly, a strong distaste for its alien and antiquated connotations, its diehard mentality and Sabbatarian stuffiness (when its adherents aren't draped in Union Jacks and prancing drunkenly around the Field at Finaghy reviling the pope). It's a quaint and ridiculous institution when it isn't vicious – and however you look at it, it is mired in the past; whereas we enlightened Catholics and socialists feel a breath from a more expansive future blowing on our forward-looking faces.

I haven't always been so dismissive of the Orange Order. Before I knew any better – that is, in my pre-school days – I'd been taken by my young Protestant father (now a Catholic convert) down to the city centre to watch the Orange parades pass the statue of the Reverend Henry Cooke, the Black Man on his plinth with his repudiating back for ever turned to the liberal ways of 'Inst'. Perched on my father's shoulders, I'd have waved a flag as merrily as any Shankill Billy-Boy, had one been placed in my three-year-old fist. As far as I was able, I responded to the pageantry of the occasion; and something of its dynamism must have stayed with me. Louis MacNeice's 'heart that leaps to a fife band' never leapt any more vigorously than mine did (and does).

My father's brother, and his uncle Freddie, would likely have been among the marchers glorying in their Protestant heritage and long-ago victory at the Boyne. Uncle Freddie's Orange Lodge, of which he was Chaplain with the title, 'Sir Knight F.A. Craig' (I have no idea what these terms mean), was St Nicholas LOL 782, and I am sure it was fully represented in these early post-war parades. The family's Orange affiliation was carried lightly, as far as I know, as lightly as the flutters in a summer breeze of the Union Jack flown from the roof of my grandparents' gate lodge at the end of Dunmurry Lane. It was in this gate lodge that my father grew up with his brothers and sisters in an uncontentiously loyalist atmosphere, enjoying the rough-and-tumble of crowded domestic life complete with horses, hens, whippets, cats, the doings of Captain Charley (for whom my grandfather worked as head groom) at nearby Seymour Hill, a rudimentary education at the Charley Memorial Primary school (founded in 1892), where he'd have been enrolled around 1923, with his older sister Marie (already a pupil at the school) to keep an eye on him. ... You'd have heard no talk of Taigs in my grandparents' household; no one made a thing of despising Catholics, with whom – I am sure – they were happy to share local amenities. All of them, Prod or Papist, had roots (some roots at any rate) in the same small corner of Ireland. And Ireland was important. My grandparents' Union Jack hoisted yearly around the Twelfth of July didn't signify a hankering after an English identity. It just proclaimed a simple pleasure and pride in belonging to the dominant – well, marginally dominant – culture of the place, unburdened by Papist superstition and Romish regulations. ... I'm trying to say, I think, that my Protestant relations never subscribed to any advanced form of anti-Catholic bigotry. But for all that it was definitely a Protestant, a Church of Ireland, household, that gate lodge at Dunmurry.

The fact that he, my father, had many Catholic friends even before he met his Catholic wife might suggest a refusal on his part to fit into a tribal mould. Or perhaps it was just that his sportive nature chimed in some essential way with Catholic conviviality. He took to mid-Falls life, with its pubs, betting shops, newsagents, greyhound racing, 'butterfly' nuns thronging the pavements, neighbours from all points along the social spectrum took to it like a – I was going to say, an orphan to home life;

but 'orphan' is not right for someone like my father with his strong family ties. Like a happy-go-lucky traveller to a house of hospitality, perhaps, if a simile has to be proffered here. In his middle years he became an habitué of St Malachy's Old Boys' Club, due to his enduring friendship with some St Malachy's old boys. He fitted in (helped, no doubt, by his capacity for Guinness and his fine singing voice). Nevertheless, his temperament had been shaped by Protestantism, just as my mother's was shaped by the Catholic church. As for me ... nuns got hold of me in 1947, with an eventual outcome which I've recounted elsewhere. (*Asking for Trouble*, Blackstaff, 2007.) And long before I understood their significance, Orange processions through the centre of Belfast had become for me a thing of the past. Their place was taken by May processions devoted to Our Lady, Corpus Christi processions and Holy Communion dresses. In time, I would add Easter Sunday processions to Milltown Cemetery to commemorate the dead of 1916 – giving my father something to be broad-minded about, just as my mother had been broad-minded about the early Orange parades. She was broad-minded, indeed, about that and a good deal else besides – but what neither she nor anyone else suspected at the time was her own oblique ancestral connection with the Orange Order, which outdid in piquancy that of the Craigs.

The decisive victory in the Williamite wars (or defeat, if you prefer it) was not at the Boyne but at Aughrim in County Galway.

> At the Boyne bridge we took our first beating,
> From the bridge at Slane we were soon retreating,
> And then we were beaten at Aughrim too –
> Ah, fragrant Ireland, that was goodbye to you.

Frank O'Connor's translation of the poignant '*Slan le Padraic Sairseal*' ('Farewell to Patrick Sarsfield') captures to the full the demotic, plaintive note of the Gaelic original, with its Jacobite spokesman for a sorrowful and discomposed populace. With this poem, as O'Connor suggests, we hear for perhaps the first time an unadorned contemporary Irish voice lamenting the pass the country has come to – the endless defeats, the broken Treaty of Limerick, and 'Ireland's best', including Patrick Sarsfield, dispersed among foreign armies all over the continent. ('The Mother's

Lament', mentioned above, was written, of course, long after the event it conjures up.) And the fact that it's an anonymous voice makes it all the more telling, like the Unknown Soldier's grave.

Fragrant Ireland, Catholic Ireland, is about to enter its darkest phase. With the Protestant ascendancy secured in the wake of the Jacobite disasters, measures are quickly enacted to keep the Catholic population in its place (its very constricted place). By means of the notorious Penal Laws, Catholic aspirations are obstructed in every area – property-owning, scholarship, freedom of worship, any kind of social advancement. A standard image from the era has a priest with a price on his head saying Mass on a lonely hillside with a rock for an altar, before a congregation of downtrodden peasants on their knees in the mud holding sacks across their shoulders against the terrible weather. This is what the tribe of Milesius has come down to! From 1691, and throughout the greater part of the following century, native Irish suffering and suppression make a powerful theme for historians and poets alike.

It was a different matter, of course, if you were on the winning side. William Blacker, fresh from his exertions at the Boyne, returns to Armagh to oversee the running of the family estate on the death of his father George in 1691, and begins the construction of what will become known as Carrickblacker House – described in 1909 by Robert M. Young as 'an ancient battlemented mansion bearing the date 1692 on a stone in the wall'.[1] (This architectural treasure eventually comes into the philistine ownership of Portadown Golf Club and is demolished in 1956 to make way, God save us, for a *club house*. Nearly three centuries of history eradicated at a stroke. I hope those Portadown golfers on the spot were haunted and put off their game by ghosts of the massacred settlers of 1641 spilling over from Edenderry – not to mention spectral Blackers outraged by the destruction of their family home.)

And what of William's sister Frances, Mrs John Tipping? Had she perished along with others in the ructions of 1689, as J.S. Kane invites us to suppose, Frances would surely have been buried in Seagoe churchyard alongside her husband. Instead, the Seagoe parish baptismal register for 1691 has a Mrs Frances Tippin (sic) standing godmother to an infant named Margaret Mathers. ... Move forward into the following century, and a map of 1710 shows a person of the same name, Frances Tippin, holding substantial farmlands in the townland of Collcosh just across the border with County Tyrone, seven miles north of Gallrock. Her sons, named William and George (dear God, is there no end to bloody Williams and Georges ... there are more to come) – William and George Tipping would have been in their early thirties/late twenties at this time; both were married, and probably they farmed the lands leased by their mother. Or perhaps by now they had moved to farms of their own; we simply can't tell.

These are the probable circumstances of Frances Tipping's life. Girlhood at Blacker's Bawn, with a full complement of parents, grandparents, brothers, servants and all; marriage to John Tipping (which may have represented a degree of social downgrading – he was, after all, a youngest son and had tradesmen among his immediate forebears); settling in Gallrock; motherhood; widowhood in County Tyrone; agrarian dealings and engagement in local life. Nothing out of the ordinary – well, nothing, that is, aside from the vast disruption of the pre-Boyne period, and the loss, in a single year, of husband, mother and brother.

But envisage for a moment a different scenario. Suppose that Frances does, in fact, meet her death at the hands of Jacobite soldiers in the brutal year of 1689. Say she leaves a daughter, Jane, as well as a couple of sons, and that all three children somehow scrape through, in the chaos and horror surrounding the murders of their parents. The boys then disappear from the records until they turn up as farmers in the 1700s; but two years after the fatal departure for Derry – in 1691 – the twelve-year-old orphaned Jane Tipping applies for assistance to the Seagoe Parish Church Vestry, whose members meet once a quarter to distribute alms to the poor of the parish. (Her name is there, in the church records.) And prominent among the Protestant pillars of the community charged with dispensing charity is, of course, William Blacker, Orange adventurer and poor Jane's uncle.

A plot is forming here, a standard plot beloved of authors of historical novels. It features an impoverished, even destitute, but spirited female orphan; of good pedigree though perhaps not knowing it, a victim of adversity – and the rich relation whose esteem she gains through a combination of winning ways and sturdiness of character. Certainly William Blacker, who fits one role in this story, could have afforded to find a niche for Jane Tipping in his bustling household among her boy cousins, children of his several marriages. Perhaps he did. Perhaps Jane had a room of her own in the new great house of Carrickblacker, and servants to sweeten her bed linen with sprigs of lavender. Perhaps she grew up and made a splendid marriage from her uncle's house. ... True, this story more often works itself out in a setting like rural Somerset or some picturesque region of the north of England. But what's to keep it from spawning a version in rough-hewn, factionally-beset Seagoe in seventeenth-century County Armagh? Nothing, but my own want of skill in amplifying the tale, in imposing an outline both pleasing and plausible on top of its bare bones. If I were a writer of fiction I would do it – for it is only a fiction, derived from nothing more elaborate than the final name on a list of deserving poor: Jane Tipping of Seagoe parish. That's all. I've made the rest up. To return to the facts: I think Frances Tipping did survive the wars in Ireland to resume, as far as possible, an ordinary farming life. And the likelihood is that Jane – poor Jane – was some Tipping by-blow, indigent and unwanted, nothing to do with Frances at all. She'd more likely have been twenty than twelve, and not destined to live much longer. Illness, malnourishment or unattended childbirth would have finished her off. No rich uncle would have taken her under his wing.

Frances's eldest son William Tipping (*c.*1677–*c.*1735) was himself the father of three sons, of whom the youngest, Henry (*c.*1712–1765), is the probable renegade who twitched the family line of descent into a Papist channel. This Henry is, we remember, the great-grandson of George Blacker – but by this stage, this branch of the family is diverging at high speed from Blacker aggrandisement and prosperity. (And also from the upward moving Tippings of County Louth.)

Henry at twenty-something is a Protestant farmer in the townland of Roughan in the parish of Drumcree. The whole district is part of the Brownlow estate, and Henry's farm is rented from a William Brownlow of Lurgan. Brownlow is the ground landlord, while a Bryan O'Neill is Henry's immediate landlord. By 1750, though, this particular Tipping, Henry, has become a leaseholder rather than a lowly tenant-at-will, having inherited Bryan O'Neill's rights in the Roughan property. Why? The answer would seem to be that Henry had married O'Neill's daughter Esther – making an odd case of a Protestant advancing in the world (and this in the Penal days) by means of his Catholic connections. It wasn't a very remarkable advancement, but it would do. And the price exacted? '... Turned Papish himself and forsook the auld cause ...':[2] or if he doesn't go that far, Henry at least allows the children of the union to be brought up in his wife's faith. (Nearly two hundred years later, my parents will enact a version of the same arrangement.) And after Henry's death in 1765, his Catholic widow and four Catholic sons move across the River Bann to a farm in the townland of Ballynamoney, just over a mile from Lurgan town centre. (The farm is held on a 'Popish lease' — thirty-one years in duration.) The descendants of these boys will become farmer/weavers.

The Tipping/O'Neill connection isn't absolutely watertight, though it fits the facts as far as they can be ascertained. It also fits with my purpose, and I intend to stick to it. ... 'Had I but known' of her existence in my days of hyper-Hibernianism, I'd have latched on to Esther O'Neill as a probable and desirable ancestress — a true Gael at last, among all the Planters and Blackers and Englishmen and women and Orange ditto.

The whole of County Armagh was coming down with O'Neills, some more peaceable than others;[3] and while those of Clancan and Clanbrassil (north Armagh) were distinct from the O'Neills of the Fews (south Armagh), all of them had a common ancestor in an Eoghan O'Neill who flourished in the fifteenth century. So, the Esther O'Neill whom I'm claiming as a direct forebear, would have been connected by blood to the Phelim O'Neill who instigated the uprising of 1641 and 'slaughtered our fathers in Catholic zeal'. So the patchwork of one's ancestry — anyone's ancestry — will often be found to accommodate many unlikely bedfellows.

CHAPTER 3
SCULLABOGUE

There's muskets in the thatch, and pikestaffs in the hay,
And shot in butter barrels buried in the bog,
Extrapolated powder in the tin for tay;
And everything is wrapped in blue-as-gunsmoke fog.

Ciaran Carson, 'Lord Gregory'

Among the ironies and cultural anomalies surrounding my Belfast
Catholic girlhood was my grandmother's accent. She, my father's mother,
had as strong a Southern accent as the tinkers in their gaudy caravans
parked on the old Bog Meadows near our home. She had only to open
her mouth to create a wrong impression. A rich Irish voice was not
a popular attribute in the Protestant North. It marked you down as a
rebelly Papist and contemptible alien. Whereas my grandmother, in fact,
was as Protestant as those Orange Blackers, shadowy maternal forebears
on an attenuated branch of my hybrid family tree.

She was born Emily Lett in September 1889, youngest child of a
County Wexford farmer named William Lett and his second wife Emily
Anne Thorpe. ... I'm struck again by the Englishness of these names, to
which I can add another, Eliza Stewart, my great-grandmother's mother.
Wexford, indeed, as a seaport, contained 'one of the highest densities
of Old English family names in Ireland' (I'm quoting from an essay by

W.J. Smyth in his and Kevin Whelan's *Common Ground* of 1988); and after Cromwell had finished with it, bringing its 'mediaeval era to a bloody end', the de-populated town attracted an influx of new English inhabitants. I don't know which wave of settlers my Wexford ancestors belonged to,[1] but clearly their origins were not Gaelic. I cannot attach them to ancient romantic Ireland in any of its guises. New Ross was their territory, Clonleigh in particular, and the triangle formed by it, Enniscorthy and Wexford. But the connotations of these place names worked for me in ways antagonistic to my ancestors. They, alas, were more likely to be yeomen than pikemen.[2] And rebel glamour was fodder for my adolescent view of the way things were.

'Enniscorthy's in flames', goes a line from a song that would often be running through my head (it never got outside my head since I couldn't sing):

> Enniscorthy's in flames, and old Wexford is won,
> And the Barrow tomorrow we cross;
> On a hill o'er the town we have planted a gun
> That will batter the gateways of Ross.
> And the Forth men and Bargy men march o'er the heath,
> With brave Harvey to lead on the van,
> But foremost of all in that grim gap of death
> Will be Kelly, the boy from Killane.

People who dominated my historical consciousness were those like Kelly the boy from Killane, Henry Joy McCracken hanged in Corn Market, young Roddy McCorley going to die on the bridge of Toome today, agile Father Murphy from Old Kilcormack: all the starry dead whose resistance to injustice was woven into the vast tapestry of successive Irish causes. For me, the idea of Wexford in 1798 carried all the kudos due to insurgency and idealism. It still does, in part. No one in their right mind could quarrel with the United Irishmen's principle, as articulated by Wolfe Tone: to substitute for Catholic, Protestant and Dissenter the common name of Irishman. And I've never quite divested the insurgents' emblem – the pike – of its stirring associations. Clasped in a sturdy hand, or concealed in the thatch of a radical farmhouse, the pike of 1798 is a symbol of bravery and a clandestine exhilaration. It, and other makeshift weapons, denote a magnificent foolhardiness. There's a potent early poem by Seamus Heaney, 'Requiem for the Croppies', in which the fatal confrontation on Vinegar Hill sees inadequately armed rebels 'shaking scythes at cannon' as the whole intrepid enterprise and buoyed-up resolution comes to nothing. A defeat, then, but the opposite of an inglorious defeat.

That is indisputably part of the Wexford picture, but it is not the whole picture. In 1993, in his review of R.F. Foster's *Paddy and Mr Punch* in the *London Review of Books*, Colm Tóibín has the following passage:

> The names of the towns and villages around us were in all the songs about 1798 – the places where battles had been fought, or atrocities committed. But there was one place that I did not know had a connection with 1798 until I was in my twenties. It was Scullabogue. Even now, as I write the name, it has a strange resonance. In 1798 it was where 'our side' took a large number of Protestant men, women and children, put them in a barn and burned them to death.

In that barn were people named Lett. Now, just as Armagh was awash in O'Neills, so County Wexford was home to a lot of Letts. But I'm taking it that they were all connected in some way – and therefore connected to *me*. And the place called Scullabogue – *Scoil a' Bothog*, the school at the ruined house? A wild guess[3] – Scullabogue is not many miles from the townland of Clonleigh, where my grandmother's ancestral farmhouse stands. Protestant children in the district might well have been scooped up by rogue insurgents and added to the other 'loyalist' captives in the terrible barn. A Benjamin Lett, a boy of about thirteen, was among the captives and so was his sister. (Their father was a William Lett who belonged to the Orange Order and served as a yeoman in 1798 along with his brother Charles and his son Nicholas.) Perhaps as many as two hundred terrified local people were incarcerated at Scullabogue, in the thatched barn itself and at the adjoining house (the property of a Captain Francis King), though not all of them died there. Tom Dunne, in his book *Rebellions* (2004), puts the number of those incinerated at 126; and among these victims were about eleven Catholics. The Catholics were taken solely because they worked for, or had dealings with, Protestants. The unspeakable episode invalidates the entire 'United Irish' ideology, and makes a mockery of Wolfe Tone.

The Scullabogue atrocity, depicted by George Cruikshank for W.H. Maxwell's *History of the Irish Rebellion* in 1798 (1845)

The two young Letts were lucky. There are several accounts of how they got away with their lives, but the one I prefer attributes their release from the barn to a couple of well-meaning and influential Catholics, Thomas Murphy of Park and a Mr Brien of Ballymorris. (It's cited by Charles Dickson in his book of 1955, *The Rising in Wexford in 1798*, when he quotes from a manuscript account of the atrocity written *c.*1871 by a Reverend Henry Lett, and dealing with the latter's grandfather's experience at the time.[4]) Another version of the story has Benjamin's sister Rebecca making a wild appeal to a priest and getting him to intervene to free her brother. And a disagreeable pamphlet with the lurid title *Murder Without Sin: The Rebellion of 1798*,[5] written by an Ogle Robert Gowan and first published in 1859, contains the following stark information about the Scullabogue prisoners: 'Out of the entire number, three only escaped, namely Richard Grandy, Loftus Frizzel and Benjamin Lett.' You can take your pick of the three scenarios. But whatever the truth of the matter, the Letts were safely away from the scene when the barn with its cargo of human flesh was set alight. It swiftly burned to the ground. A Quaker girl named Dinah Goff, whose home was located about two and half miles from Scullabogue, relates how 'I saw and smelled the smoke of its burning ... and cannot now forget the strong and dreadful effluvium which was wafted from it to our lawn.' The date was 5 June 1798. Four days later, on 9 June, the skeletons were cleared out of the barn and buried in a shallow hole with a covering of sods. As with other places of perdition – the Black Hole of Calcutta, or the Kenya Assemblies of God church at Kiambaa, where thirty-five Kikuyu were burnt alive on New Year's Day 2008 – Scullabogue and its horrors are etched into the landscape and into the subconsciousness of local people.

Scullabogue is burning, and at the same time, distraught Protestant families from all around Clonleigh and Carrickbyrne are piling their furniture and possessions on carts and heading for Enniscorthy, where some will find shelter in houses so crammed with their fellow citizens that no place remains for them to sleep but the bare deal boards. Others, not getting that far, spend nights on end in fields and ditches. The countryside is rife with horrors and rumours. Those refugees approaching the town are greeted with the flagrant warning noise of rebel drums beating to arms – and then they find that half the Protestant population of Enniscorthy has fled towards Wexford, many women in rags and tatters carrying children and trekking the whole fourteen miles on foot. Some, on the way, experience harassment from yeomen who take their dishevelled state to mean they are Catholics. But it was asking for death to stay at home. Dinah Goff, looking back from a distance of more than fifty years, laments the once-peaceful homes, 'abandoned in panic and destroyed in an orgy of incendiarism'.

The streets of Enniscorthy are burning too, as yeomen and Unitedmen butcher each other in droves. Genteel Protestant ladies, some never before confronted with death, step and stumble over a profusion of corpses as they head in desperation towards the Market House to put at least a solid door between themselves and the fighting in the streets. But there are no safe places. The whole town is a shambles, brimful of the noise and confusion of slaughter. Hopes for peace and prosperity, 'live-and-let-live', after gaining some ground in the course of the century, are once more dashed to pieces. A young insurgent, Thomas Cloney, looking on with horror, registers deep despair and records this emotion years later when he comes to write his *Personal Narrative of 1798* (published in 1832): 'This was my first time to behold the work of destruction performed by man against his fellow man.'

Thomas Cloney was twenty-five years old at the time, and, according to his later testimony, a reluctant rebel overtaken by the pressure of events (and by more immediate pressure from a band of his contemporaries, who turned up at his father's farmhouse 'and pressed me to proceed with them to Enniscorthy'). Of course, his *Narrative* is the work of a man in sober middle age, looking back; but Cloney makes out a good case for his youthful involvement in the insurgents' campaign, despite his many reservations. Things had fallen apart – and what could he do but make a stand against perceived abuses, with outlets for injustice proliferating in County Wexford of the 1790s? As a Catholic he lived his life in fear: fear of dispossession, fear of all the powers invested in 'a furious Orange ascendancy ... a bloodthirsty yeomanry, and a hireling magistracy', fear of going the way of his 'unoffending neighbours', whom he'd seen done to death and their property destroyed. ... Douglas Hyde, a century later, gives the picture in his 'Ballad of '98' (written under the name of *An Craoibhin Aoibhinn*):

> ...Their Captain's a fiend, from hell let loose,
> His men were the devil's crew,
> They burnt my gear; they burnt my house,
> My only son they slew.

The constant fear that gripped the Catholic population has its counterpart in stirred-up Protestant fears which come to a climax in the early months of 1798 – when everyone, it seems, Protestant and Catholic alike, is afraid to sleep at home and instead, at nightfall, makes tracks for the fields and woods where all of them will pass a troubled night. Any ditch or clump of brambles or 'friendly thorn tree' can do duty as a makeshift refuge – anywhere out of the reach of predatory neighbours intent on causing harm to neighbours. It's as if the whole of Wexford has turned into a vast open-air camp filled with cowering, frightened families trying to blend into the undergrowth, hearing any noise in the night as a portent of disaster. Most of these outdoor sleepers are women and children, men of a suitable age being occupied elsewhere – or no longer occupied. In one garden alone, it was said, thirty-two 'new-made widows' lay all night in the shelter of its rhododendron bushes. Neither faction has a monopoly on distress. And the psychological effect is ineradicable. A long way into the future, at the age of eighty-two, Mrs Barbara Lett of Killaligan, recalling the events of that dreadful year, comes out with a heartfelt imprecation: 'May we never more fall into the hands of our neighbours, who are more barbarous than any foreign enemy.'

People, neighbours, vying with one another to commit the bloodiest acts – yes, this is a part of the Wexford uprising as its purpose becomes distorted and brutality prevails. But a good many ordinary instances of humanity are on record too, some not too far away from Barbara Lett herself. At the time, she is twenty-one years old, the wife of a Mr Newton Lett – twenty-seven years her senior – and the mother of at least one infant son. She is connected in some way[6] to a Mr Joshua Lett of Ballybane House, Clonroche – who, though a man of nearly seventy, is a friend of the young rebel Thomas Cloney; and when Cloney accidentally shoots himself in the thigh and nearly bleeds to death, it's Joshua Lett who leaps on his horse and rides at high speed into Enniscorthy to fetch a surgeon, having first had the wounded Cloney 'conveyed' to Ballybane, and leaving him there in the care 'of his amiable daughters' (as Cloney describes them). (This shooting, horrifying though it must have been at the time, brings a relieving note of farce to the very fraught proceedings.)

Amid the awful spites and divisions in Wexford there were those who, like Mr Lett, refused to lead their lives in accordance with sectarian dictates. They had friends among 'the other sort', and among Mr Lett's was a Catholic schoolmaster named Walsh. At one point during the Rebellion, when it seems the insurgents have gained the upper hand, a rumour begins to circulate in the district to the effect that *all* Protestants, whether Orangemen or not, are about to be put to death. There's only one way they may save themselves – by assuming a spurious Catholic identity. So the schoolmaster Walsh, in deep anxiety about the danger facing his old Protestant friend, forces a moderately unwilling Mr Lett to sit down and undergo a crash course in Catholic theology. 'Never,' says Thomas Cloney, who is present at the scene, 'did any instructor labour more zealously for the improvement of his pupil than poor Walsh, and never did a pupil hang with more earnestness upon the dictates of his instructor than Mr Lett.' The effort of concentration required of the two old men has tears running down the faces of both. How will you feel, says the schoolteacher, if they come to pike you to death and all you have to do to save yourself is respond correctly to a question from the Catechism – and you fail to do it? But it isn't a bit of use. In the end, an exhausted Mr Lett declares roundly that even if his life were to be forfeit on account of it, he can't remember as much as a syllable of all the information so arduously imparted to him. Fortunately it doesn't come to that.

It doesn't come to that, but the danger was real. Bagenal Harvey (the rebel leader) at one point was heard lamenting to a friend that the war had become a war of religion, as certain misguided insurgents went about trying to ascertain people's denominational position – or, in the case of known Protestants, applying stringent proselytising tactics, as though an instantaneous conversion might be synonymous with a change of heart. While they thought they were carrying all before them – as in 1641 – the rank and file of Irish rebels jettisoned common sense, as well as common humanity. But sometimes they found themselves up against total defiance – and might even have been disarmed by it.

A relative of Joshua Lett's, a Richard Lett,[7] fell into rebel hands and wasn't having any of their bludgeoning and bluster. Asked if he was willing to embrace the doctrines of Rome, accompanied by a bit of jostling and threatening movement of pikes, he came back at his tormentors with the sturdy answer, 'Divil a bit'. Perhaps his candour was appreciated. At any rate, he escaped with his life; and for ever after the sobriquet, 'Divil a bit', stuck to him.

'The Letts, though belonging to the "gentry" class, were always a very broad-minded and liberal family.' This assertion comes from Katherine Lucy Lett's family history, written in 1925, and to back it up she cites the case of young James Lett, the only one of that name who fought on the rebel side in 1798. (I'll get to him in a minute.) We also have liberal Protestant Joshua, mentioned above. Other Letts, though – according to the Reverend Henry Lett, writing in 1871 – 'the descendants of men who had entered Ireland under Cromwell, who had suffered from O'Neill and Tyrconnell and James II, and who had been with Dutch William at Oldbridge, did not remain inactive during the rebellion ... [and] were found armed on the side of truth, law and order.' He means they were yeomen. Among them was Barbara Lett's husband Newton, and also Charles Lett (the Reverend Henry's grandfather), his brother William[8] and his nephew Nicholas.

When Barbara Lett succumbs to the panic-stricken mood of the day and leaves Killaligan with whatever she can carry, she gains a temporary shelter at the Enniscorthy home of a relative named Stephen. ... And here I have to attempt a bit of clarification concerning family relationships and allegiances. In the notes accompanying a recent book, *Protestant Women's Narratives of the Irish Rebellion of 1798*, edited by John D. Beatty, this particular Stephen Lett is confused with a different person of the same name: I don't know who exactly he was, but he wasn't Barbara Lett's brother-in-law Stephen. *That* Stephen, the older brother of Newton, had died in 1786, when his son James – the future rebel – was just one year old. His wife was a relative of Bagenal Harvey, and his family's sympathies were with the United Irishmen (see p. 88 below) – whereas the Stephen Lett of Duffry Gate, Enniscorthy, 'took an active part on the side of the loyalists', opening his doors to all manner of distressed Protestant refugees. And among them is Barbara, safe for the moment, though her arrival is not without its hazards, further shocks to the system. The house and its surroundings bear witness to the hellish disruption afflicting the town. In front of the house is the body of a dead rebel lying on his face beneath the parlour window. Go to the back, and, as a grisly counterpart, you find a dead yeoman lying on his face in the yard.

Further horrors are in the offing in these dark days. An elderly Protestant clergyman named Mr Hayden is piked to death by a local butcher (his trade as well as his nature), and the clergyman's body left lying 'on the steps of Mr Lett's Hall door'. Barbara Lett then adds a distressing detail: onlookers witness the corpse of poor Mr Hayden being eaten up by pigs. Couldn't someone have rescued it from this final indignity? Could it not have been dragged indoors? It seems a bit much, on top of the homicidal free-for-all and frantic debacle, to have carrion pigs roaming freely through the charnel streets.

A wounded yeoman is carried into the house of Mr Stephen Lett and tended by Barbara, who tears up a pillowcase to make a bandage for the gash in the yeoman's back. She may be thinking at the time of her own yeoman husband and hoping he will survive (he does). But this is a time when not only national, but family discords are brewing. Newton's brother Stephen, had he not been twelve years dead, would doubtless have found a different outlet for his civic consciousness; as it is, it's left to his thirteen-year-old son James to act the rebel part. James Lett makes himself conspicuous by his antics during the Battle of Ross, when he goes about waving a bannerette and egging on the pikemen. Wherever you look, you can't get away from confusion and inconsistency. Young James's cousin Benjamin Lett (the Scullabogue survivor), on the other hand, is supposed to have flaunted his Orange allegiance by festooning the bridles of the family's horses with orange and blue ribbons. I suppose these instances of juvenile bravado can be taken to represent an unthinking partisanship, a bid for top-dog status. But they take us as far as we can get from a non-sectarian blueprint, from the whole idea of an equitable society.

Reforms were needed, no one denies it, but a great divergence occurred between the Society of United Irishmen's grand revolutionary purpose, and what actually happened on the ground. Many people, historians and archivists and teachers, biographers and social commentators, have assessed the extent to which the Rising in Wexford was fuelled by United Irish principles. The inescapable conclusion is, not very much, as the green tree of liberty sprouted deplorable excrescences. In the main, the Rising broke out as a spontaneous local revolt against insupportable ills – though for some of the leaders, such as Bagenal Harvey, it was necessary action undertaken in a rightful cause.

How did the violation of the United Irishmen's anti-sectarian imperative come about? Well, perhaps Thomas Cloney has the answer – terrible social conditions, and masses of people recruited to the rebel cause who simply don't know any better. They can't differentiate between actual oppressors – i.e. the government in Dublin, the military presence, some magistrates and others in positions of authority – and their Protestant neighbours. They think they are being handed an opportunity to turn the tables on those they consider to be in the ascendant. They think they have a licence to burn and kill and maim and terrorise – and, inevitably, ferocity is matched with ferocity. A bloodbath ensues. And, when it's all over, the poor of Wexford are no better off than they were.

Barbara Lett has cause to sustain the bitterness that bedevils her even in old age. As well as Scullabogue on 5 June, another massacre of Protestants takes place on Wexford Bridge where prisoners are brought down in batches to be piked to death and thrown into the River Slaney. The date is 20 June 1798. Among the people murdered in this way is Barbara Lett's father William Daniel, who is forty-four years old at the time. (His home was a lovely eighteenth-century house, Fortview, near Wexford: now demolished by a local council to accommodate a link road.) 'Could anything be more atrocious or barbaric,' his daughter exclaims, shortly before her own death at ninety-one, 'than the cruelties inflicted at that time on innocent and inoffending persons?' To this rhetorical question we can only answer, no.

The same fate was nearly suffered by Charles Lett, also a prisoner in Wexford gaol and marked down for execution. What saved him was a band marching into the town playing 'Croppies Lie Down' at full volume, in celebration of the just-past rebel defeat at Vinegar Hill. ('At Vinegar Hill o'er the pleasant Slaney, / Our heroes vainly stood back to back ...'.) Charles manages to get out of the gaol in the ensuing confusion, and goes through Wexford broadcasting the good news – having first had the foresight to don an ill-fitting and ragged old army red coat, retrieved from a hook on a wall. Never mind how peculiar he looks, if he'd appeared in civilian garb he'd have run the risk of being shot as a rebel.

I don't know which of these Letts, if any, are among my actual forebears, so I am going to lay claim to all of them. The facts in my possession are as follows. My great-grandfather William Lett, the father of Emily Lett, was born at Clonleigh around 1841. *His* father was a Thomas Lett, to whom, logically, we can attribute a birth date at any time between 1810 and 1820. If the former, Thomas could be a son of Benjamin Lett or of the underage rebel the bold James Lett.[9] If, on the other hand, Thomas wasn't born until 1820, it's possible that his grandparents were Barbara and Newton Lett. (I'm not forgetting Charles Lett[10] and all the other Letts who crop up in connection with 1798, and their probable progeny. But, again, in the absence of documentary evidence, I've no resource but conjecture.) If the last should prove to be true – then my antecedents on both sides take on an alarming symmetry. On one side (my mother's) is an ancestor hanged by a mob outside Lord Aungier's castle in Longford for being a Protestant; and on the other side (my father's) is an ancestor done to death by a mob on Wexford Bridge for the same reason. And here's me – well, there I was, around 1960, daring to saunter down Sandy Row in Belfast with a tiny tricolour pinned to the lapel of my convent school blazer, and bringing no retribution down on my foolhardy head beyond some low-toned rumbles and growls from a gathering of elderly men outside a bookie's, whose ire is mildly aroused by the sight of the seditious emblem – what they call a 'wee fleg'.

When Thomas Cloney refers in his *Personal Narrative* to 'a furious Orange ascendancy', he, at least, unlike the rebel rank and file, holds in his mind a clear distinction between his Protestant friends and neighbours whom he cherishes, and the new Orange system which already seemed to embody all the worst excesses of bigotry, triumphalism and religious intemperance. Other accounts of the Wexford Rising single out the anti-popery brigade – the Orange Order – as a major trigger of explosive Catholic disaffection. Some would argue that rebel aggression was never meant to be directed against 'ordinary' Protestants, only against Orangemen – not, as we've seen, that this was of much benefit to the former, once all hell had broken loose.

If the Orange Order made a powerful focus for Catholic fear and detestation, it wasn't because the sentiments it purveyed were unprecedented. It was the organisation that was new, not the attitude. For at least twenty years, antagonistic factions had been active throughout the country, Protestant Peep o' Day Boys and Catholic Defenders – or whatever the equivalent local designations were, Shanavests or Caravats or Hearts of Steel, Whiteboys and Rightboys and Kick-the-Shite Boys (I've made the last one up) – all specialists in agrarian uproar. Periodic disturbances were a feature of everyday life in many rural areas, especially – and here the ubiquitous Tippings are about to re-enter the picture – in County Armagh.

It's true that some of these illegal societies didn't start by being overtly sectarian. Some, bands of tenant farmers, came into being to protest against increased tax demands and the current method of collecting tithes. Some were willing to jettison religious animosities in the interests of effective action against economic abuses. For example – the poet Art MacCooey (see p. 40 above) has among his works a ringing tribute to young Art O'Neill, last of the O'Neills of Glassdrummond, dead at twenty-six (in 1769). In his lament MacCooey refers to O'Neill's position as an elected captain in the Hearts of Oak, or Oakboys, a Protestant secret society whose members sported oak boughs in their hats and engaged in intimidatory pursuits by night. The fact that a Catholic O'Neill was selected from among scores of contenders to lead this illicit band suggests a state of *Protestant* disaffection so extreme as to render temporarily insignificant the 'natural hostility' between Planter and Gael.

But, gradually, the old sectarian bogey raised its poisonous tentacles again. By the 1790s, faction fights in County Armagh are taking place almost exclusively along denominational lines. When the Society of United Irishmen is founded in Belfast in 1791, its title has little meaning for those entrenched in their illiberalism. And Armagh in particular is getting a name for the bitterness of its conflicts.

And where in all this is the newly-Catholic Tipping family? We left the widow and sons of turncoat Henry in their new rented farmhouse at Ballynamoney in the late 1760s. Before this they were living in the mainly Protestant district of Roughan, and it may have been an increase in sectarian pressures that sent them scurrying across the Bann to the rather less riotously inclined townland of Ballynamoney. Or it may have been the latter's proximity to Lurgan, with its market for the finely-produced linen cloth in which the family specialised, that drew them in. Whatever the reason, they settled in north-east Armagh, where the widow Tipping's eldest son, another Henry (*c*.1746–1797), was chiefly responsible for running the farm and the linen-producing enterprise. Perhaps, as the Antrim weaver poet James Orr recorded, 'His thrifty wife and wise wee lasses span, / While warps and queels employed anither bairn'. Indeed, innumerable country families all over the North are employed in this way in the late eighteenth century, and Catholics, at last, are not excluded from the mild prosperity it brings.

Henry Tipping's second son James, progenitor of the direct line I'm more or less sticking to, was born at the Ballynamoney farm in 1770. Was he a sickly infant, with signs of the way his life would be curtailed apparent from the start? Or was he as robust as anyone, playing with his brothers in the fields and meadows round the farmhouse when he wasn't roped in to aid the family's finances, and loss of life only an unimaginable figment of the distant future? We can't know. But throughout his short life James must have been aware of troubles and tensions afflicting the neighbourhood – though perhaps not so aggressively as in other parts of County Armagh. One social commentator (John Byrne), writing in 1792, commends 'the peaceable inhabitants of Lurgan and its vicinity' for keeping a low profile while outbreaks of lawlessness proliferate elsewhere. Not one of them, he says, has been indicted for being a Defender or a Break o' Day man. (Can this be true?) If you headed southwards in the direction of Tandragee you'd find a very different class of carry-on. Horse-racing on narrow country roads, cock-fighting and private whiskey houses all contributing to the unruliness of the era. Coat-trailing and other provocations rampant. And underlying everything, the religious bigotry ready to flare up at the genuflection of a knee. 'Many Protestant gentlemen,' says the same John Byrne – I think he's using the word 'gentlemen' advisedly – 'lent arms to Papists' to enable them to safeguard themselves and their families against the fury of fanatics and madmen. But even so – like the people of Wexford a little later on – many Armagh

Catholics chose to abandon their homes at nightfall and sleep as best they could in little huts made of sods in the middle of a turf bog.

And so it goes on. 'Defenders' aren't backward in becoming aggressors, as in the case of the four arrested in Tandragee for smashing the windows of a constable's house in pursuit of some Peep o' Day Boys who had taken refuge there. And, as the '80s becomes the '90s and the Volunteer movement with its emphasis on *Protestant* nationalism begins to peter out – or at least to undergo certain crucial transformations – the way is open for putative unity to dissolve in a radical schism. As the historian A.T.Q. Stewart and others have pointed out, it was the Volunteer movement of Grattan and Flood that fostered the development of *both* the Society of United Irishmen and the Orange Society. Once again, we note the ways in which Irish history accommodates the strange and contradictory.

There is absolutely no evidence to link the Ballynamoney Tippings with any clandestine organisation or pursuit. It's tempting to place them in the middle of right action, as it would have appeared at the time, defensive action against bigotry and intimidation. These were things that were not to be endured or condoned. But no Tipping voice is raised in protest against abuses in County Armagh – and this does not accord with the activism of a few of their descendants when a different, but no less exorbitant, set of circumstances prevailed (as we shall see). How many of the Ballynamoney Tippings were there, who might have nurtured reasonable grievances in the 1790s? Our ancestor James had an older and a younger brother and a couple of sisters, Mary and Elizabeth; and their father Henry, still alive at the time, would have been of an age to hold forthright views and to influence his offspring. Perhaps he did influence them, to steer clear of trouble. In the absence of any information to the contrary, we have to envisage the lot of them sitting quietly at home, getting on with their hand-loom weaving and cultivation of crops, looking after their pig, cow and hens and keeping their noses clean.

Well – clean as far as factional intrigue is concerned. There are other areas, more productive perhaps, in which a spirit of waywardness or gumption may be asserted. Courtship, for example, or domestic life. By the time he is twenty – that is, in 1790 – James Tipping has married a local girl named Sarah Magee and is already the father of a son, another James. (Just to get the chronology straight in my head – that Sarah Magee was my grandmother Sarah Tipping's great-grandmother on her father's side. Whew!) There seems, as in several other instances, to have been some haste about the marriage. 'A high level of unlawful carnal knowledge' – in the sociologists' phrase – was maybe a thing to be acquired in the fields and byways of County Armagh. As with politics, sexual mores at the time could be said to hold out a prospect of liberation or repression – and we should be glad that James (if he did) subscribed to the former, since he didn't have long to enjoy any of the pleasures of the world. He was dead at twenty-eight, dead in that most significant year of the century, 1798 – though with nothing (again) to suggest his death was due to anything other than natural causes. It's just the date that makes conjecture irresistible. Perhaps James, fired by radical principles, shot up from his loom, retrieved a pike from the roof-space, and set off eastwards to join in the fighting under Henry Munro in turbulent County Down. Perhaps he died there, at Saintfield or Ballynahinch, at the hands of the York Fencibles or the Newtownards Yeomanry. But I think we'd know about it if he did. I think it's safer to blame tuberculosis, or some other common illness, for James's premature death.

Four years earlier, in 1794, James had moved his growing family (two other sons were born in 1792 and 1794, and there may have been a daughter as well) to a smallholding at Crossmacahilly in the parish of Seagoe. Going round in circles, we've now got back to Seagoe, where James's great-great-grandfather John Tipping is buried alongside his Blacker in-laws. (Keep that in mind: the Blackers are going to crop up again in a minute.) Crossmacahilly: the very name suggests an apex of uncouthness, just as the place itself proves the ultimate countrified locality. It sounds much better in the original Irish, *Crois Mhic Eachmhilidh*, McCaughley's Cross, as it was named after a prominent local sept. It's a townland of roughly two hundred and twenty acres, three miles south-west of Lurgan and about two miles from Portadown. In 1794, when James and Sarah Tipping arrived with their cartload of belongings to inhabit the smallholding, the whole area consisted of unreclaimed and worked-out bogland. The farmhouse and accompanying acreage of poor land was right on the verge of what contemporary maps call 'the Great Turf Bog', and one effect of the resulting perpetual miasma was a population particularly prone to tuberculosis – to which, as I've suggested, James Tipping may have succumbed, after four years of rigorous work to cultivate the land with constant deadly vapours circulating round his head. We can envisage him coughing and wheezing his way through the work of the farm, the children quickly learning not to aggravate him as his appearance grows gaunter and his temper worse. And then a coffin and candles and mourning dress. But not for being a pikeman.

Not a pikeman – but a republican spirit is infiltrating the family standpoint nevertheless. It is helped on by a marriage connection. In the 'trouble year', in the townland of Tamnaficarbet, three miles west of Lurgan town centre, in a two-room thatched cottage in the middle of a flood-plain, a fifteen- or sixteen-year-old boy named John Darragh is cheering on the rebels. Some years later, by now well versed himself in the ways of disaffection, John Darragh comes into the hands of the authorities. Charged with being 'an Irish rebel', he is tried at Antrim Assizes in 1809, and – after a spell in prison – transported on a convict ship to the penal colony at Port Jackson (Sydney) in Australia. A dark and horrible journey is ahead of him, but also, eventually, a new life far superior to the old one. When he sails from Cork in 1813, resentful, like Irish rebels before and since, of the convict status imposed on him, John Darragh leaves behind, in another townland of north Armagh, Tirsogue, a wife and six children. His wife, whom he'd have married around 1800 (the year of a more momentous union) was Mary, one of the Ballynamoney Tippings and the sister of dead James.

What was linen-weaver Darragh's actual offence? Alas, the records – along with many others – went up in smoke when the Four Courts was burnt. We've no resource, again, but surmise. Perhaps he was implicated in the stirring-up of trouble to coincide with Robert Emmet's planned uprising in Dublin in 1803 (see below, p. 76), and then evaded arrest for the next six years or so. 'On the run' is the stirring phrase suggesting spunk and danger and outwitting strategies. If John Darragh was on the run – or 'on his keeping' – no doubt many interconnected scions of Tipping and Darragh and Magee families all chipped in with shelter and sustenance and an eye out for danger. Like the Armagh rapparee Seamus Mac Murchaidh in the eighteenth-century song, John Darragh would have relied on his local knowledge to stay at large for as long as possible. Like Mac Murchaidh, he might have hankered after the woods of Dunreavy, or any closer woods where a fugitive might hole up. But the thing that would mostly have kept him going was the help of friends. And the shared protective mission, the sense of opposition to the way things were run in the country, would have strengthened (in particular) the Tipping commitment to Catholic Ireland. They'd only had a couple of generations to shed their Protestant colouring, and it would take another two or three generations before the republican ethic reached its fullest expression in the family. But the process was under way.

The 'Irish rebel' John Darragh, like the innocent Connerys in another popular Gaelic song, was deported to New South Wales, enduring foul conditions on the prison ship the *Archduke Charles*, and spending two years under the convict stigma, before being granted an 'Absolute Pardon' in 1815. Like many another ex-convict, Darragh then went on to prosper in his new surroundings. ... His son Felix Darragh, with wife and children, joined him in Australia in 1840. (Felix's wife was Alice Magee, a niece of the Sarah Magee who married James Tipping. ... I am sorry to cite all these convoluted connections, which are enough to make anyone's head spin; but I want to document, as far as possible, the influences impelling the stay-at-home Tippings towards full-blown republicanism, and the above information adds a detail to the picture.) ... When John died in 1858 Felix inherited the property at Figtree in the Illawarra on the south coast of New South Wales, and became a considerable landowner himself. These Darragh and Tipping descendants were thereby lost to the Irish cause. They made a new life for themselves and undoubtedly a better one, growing into their Australian identity. But John, remembering his Armagh origins and 'rebel' loyalties, called his farm at Figtree 'Tamnaficarbet'.

Tamnaficarbet, Crossmacahilly: it's a far cry from ancestral Carrickblacker House, where the teenage great-great-grandson of the William Blacker who fought at the Boyne is following manfully in his ancestor's footsteps. Once strong supporters of the House of Stuart (you remember), the Blackers turned Orange after the Siege of Derry. And in the younger William, born in 1777, the Orange affiliation reaches a kind of apex. Here he is in the mid 1790s, about to enrol at Trinity College Dublin and undergo an advantageous education – while at home in Armagh he is taking a vigorous interest in local unrest. Protestant uprightness is the bedrock of William's creed: he views the Protestants of County Armagh as an innocent people subjected to the vilest of unprovoked attacks and intimidation.

Or so the author of *For God and the King* would have it, in accord with his own opinion. In the eyes of J.S. Kane, the vicious sectarian outbreaks

A drawing of William Blacker in middle age, looking stouter of face and figure than in his rip-roaring days

infesting Armagh can be laid at the door of the Catholic population. He claims the Peep o' Day Boys came into being to defend themselves and their communities against the Defenders (most people would agree that it was the other way round).[11] He attributes a Catholic origin to almost every rampaging band provoking fear by night, oddly including the Protestant Hearts of Oak. When he gets to the famous Battle of the Diamond, he is unequivocally on the side of the victorious Protestant faction – and in all this young William Blacker of Carrickblacker takes the role of hero.

William Blacker, eighteen in 1795, is a boisterous advocate of Protestant defenderism. When Carrickblacker House gets a new roof, he commandeers the lead from the old one and sits up all night making bullets from it to aid the Protestant cause. In the early autumn of that year, after various skirmishes and outrages have made a large-scale armed confrontation inevitable, opposing forces muster at a place called the Diamond, at the junction of four highways (and only a couple of miles from Roughan, from which, we remember, James Tipping's grandmother, father and uncles had removed themselves in haste in the late 1760s). Hostilities break out on the morning of 21 September – and galloping towards the martial spot at a furious pace is young William Blacker leading 'a contingent of armed men', many of whom are workers on his father's estate. As he recalled the subsequent 'battle' later,

> The affair was of brief duration. The Defenders, completely entrapped, made off leaving a number killed and wounded on the spot ... from those whom I saw carried off on cars that day and from the bodies found afterwards by the reapers in the cornfields along the line of their flight, I am inclined to think that not less than thirty lost their lives.[12]

The jubilant Protestants, says J.S. Kane, 'had successfully driven off their oppressors [whew!] and had prevented the destruction of most of their homes and property'. William Blacker takes up the story again: immediately after the battle, he says, right on the field of action, 'measures were adopted for the formation of a defensive association of Protestants' – and thus the Orange Society came into being. Defensive: but what William Blacker fails to mention is that in the months succeeding the establishment of the first Orange Lodges, upwards of five thousand Armagh Catholics were driven from their homes.

William Blacker, whose presence adds a touch of gentry respectability to the loyalist proceedings, is right there in the thick of the hurriedly negotiated arrangements to impose a structure and an administrative system on the new society. From the start the Orange Order is composed of separate Lodges, one of which, No. 12, is quickly set up by workers on the Carrickblacker estate (the same workers who took part in the battle). 'Members of the Blacker family' – I'm quoting J.S. Kane again – 'were encouraged to join the fledgling Order and William's uncle George, recently appointed vicar of Seagoe parish ... became an enthusiastic member.'

There's a feature of the old-fashioned thriller, the 'had-I-but-known' syndrome, which provokes a sardonic response in readers of the present time. Had she, the witless Victorian heroine, but known ... that a would-be strangler or rapist lurked on the spot, she'd never have ventured into the lonely mansion, or graveyard, or oak wood at midnight, and no incident would have occurred to stimulate the plot and draw out the narrative indefinitely. I am now about to apply the 'had-I-but-known' principle to a few of those eighteenth-century Blackers and consequent implications for Orangeism in the North. Had William and his uncle George and his father the Reverend Stewart 'but known' that at nearby Crossmacahilly, in dismal circumstances, lived the stricken, industrious, Catholic James Tipping, a near-contemporary of William's and a blood relation of all of them. ... Had they but known this, would it have modified at all their Orange fervour and sense of utter moral rectitude? The dispiriting answer is, probably not. (I know I'm stretching the analogy here. One type of hidden factor has a bearing on an immediate action, the other on an attitude.)

The truth is, having got the Orange bit between his teeth and running with it at full tilt, William comes out against every egalitarian principle and aspect of enlightenment thinking that illumines the era. ... Here he is in his rooms at Trinity presiding over Orange assemblies, or holding forth to ever greater numbers of potential recruits at the Druid's Head Inn in South Great George's Street. Soon he is immersed in a full-scale 'war' against fellow students suspected of being United Irishmen. Among them is his contemporary Robert Emmet; and the rather older ex-students Wolfe Tone and Whitley Stokes (not to be confused with his grandson of the same name, the eminent Celtic philologist) can count themselves among his adversaries too. Trinity is in an uproar, between the Orange and Green contingents. The authorities find it difficult to curb the students' partisan intensity. Running battles take place along

Dame Street. Some of the 'rebel students' are described by William as 'low vulgar wretch[es] ... and probably ... Papist[s]', the ultimate slur. The University Yeomanry makes a further outlet for William's militant drive: here he is again, boldly enlisted in the 3rd Company of the College Corps. ... Back home in Armagh for the summer vacation, he throws himself into preparations for the first Orange parades to be organised since the founding of the Order (12 July, 1796); and a year later his Orange glory is consolidated when the title of Grand Master of the new Lodge at Portadown is conferred on him. He is still only twenty years old.

(Dear God, is there no end to the agitating revelations popping up like hybrid excrescences wherever I peer among the clustering branches of my chequered family tree! Where now are all my carefully cultivated liberal credentials? Not only do I have to take [ancestral] responsibility for fighting *against* Sir Phelim O'Neill in 1641, for allying myself with Cromwell in 1649, for defending Derry against the Irish troops of King James in 1689, for fighting under the standard of William at the Boyne, for ministering to wounded yeomen in 1798 ... but it seems I'm personally implicated in the founding and upholding of the Orange Order too. I'm joking.)

We haven't heard the last of the egregious William Blacker, but now it is time to consider events in the north of Ireland while Wexford went into its almighty convulsion. Those involved in fostering rebellion were frequently at cross-purposes, as we've seen. Some set out filled with oafish glee to turn the tables on their local enemies; while others, well-principled, held fast to an idea of social reform – reform much needed, with rising rents, leases unrenewed, unacceptable tithe demands, hearth money-collectors and excise officials making life difficult for everyone. Some, for these reasons and others, were driven to take up arms – but then came the news from Scullabogue, bringing despair to the hearts of Presbyterian Ulstermen and causing some of them to throw in the towel at this point. It must have seemed that the sectarian instinct in Ireland was endowed with an alarming tenacity – and for those committed to the union of Catholic, Protestant and Dissenter as a motivating principle, this was a considerable blow. Why bother, the argument might have gone, to fight for religious tolerance and an end to political abuses, when the country was coming down with sectarian diehards for whom 'patriotism' was cast in an inveterate and vicious form? The tree of liberty, that flourished in America and in France, had no chance of taking root in Ireland, it appeared, where blight had the upper hand. Where the immemorial struggle between tyranny and freedom was always adulterated by indigenous complications. Nevertheless, the Rising went ahead, more or less as the leaders – visionaries – had planned it. Two weeks after Wexford erupted, on the morning of 7 June 1798, thousands of United Irishmen assembled at Donegore Hill on the outskirts of Antrim, ready to march on the town; and two days later, battalions of insurgents from north Down joined in the action. Once more, the game was afoot.

... And it was quickly quelled. The story has been well told, by Charles Dickson and A.T.Q. Stewart among others; and I won't repeat it here. When it was all over and the leaders executed, myth, romance, all the glamour of enlightened dissent began to gather round the stark event, the United Irish defeat. 'Well, they fought for poor old Ireland, and full bitter was their fate ...': this is one expression of the popular nationalist view. But however you look at it – a resounding moment, a great endeavour, a bloody rebellion – 1798 carries the strongest possible charge of fatefulness and exhilaration.

In Presbyterian folk memory, the year – 'the trouble year' – came to be viewed as a highly consequential time when ordinary people, the opposite of hotheads, left their farms and businesses in a spirit of revolt against unutterable injustice.

> ... Us ones quet from mindin' the farms.
> Let them take what we gave wi' the weight o' our arms,
> From Saintfield to Kilkeel.

I'm quoting these lines from Florence M. Wilson's sterling ballad 'The Man From God-Knows-Where', a party-piece in the North but more than that, a reminder of the Presbyterian heritage of high-minded revolt. It was written in 1918, and its subject is Thomas Russell, librarian of the Linen Hall Library in Belfast, United Irishman and close friend of Henry Joy McCracken and his sister Mary Anne. Russell was arrested in the run-up to the Rising and seethed in a Dublin prison, unable to take part. When he got out, he returned to the North, and to his seditious ways. He was destined to go the way of his friends, McCracken and Wolfe Tone, only a few years later. A new century had arrived and with it, the Union of Great Britain and Ireland, but parts of Ireland remained unpacified, even if the end of the Rising had, for the moment, knocked the spirit out of them. Thomas Russell had hoped to stir things again towards a new revolutionary enterprise, but nothing came of it. The mood in the country was utterly changed, and revolution – rebellion – was viewed with horror, not optimism. Instead of mustering a northern contingent, Russell was arrested again and executed at Downpatrick gaol in 1803, following his forlorn attempt to rally the North in support of Robert Emmet's Dublin affray. The ballad by Florence Wilson covers the years between 1796 and 1803, and as Charles Dickson says in his book *Revolt in the North*, it expresses 'admirably the spirit of the United Irishmen in County Down'. It's a *Presbyterian* spirit it expresses, indeed, with its emphasis on everyday dealings and a slow-burning anger and bitterness.

> Well 'twas gettin' on past the heat o' the year
> When I rode to Newtown fair:
> I sold as I could (the dealers were near –
> Only three-pound-eight for the Innis steer,
> An' nothin' at all for the mare!)
> I met M'Kee in the throng o' the street,
> Says he, 'The grass has grown under our feet
> Since they hanged young Warwick here.'

Hanging is the end of the road for many of the rebels, as all the bright hopes for social amelioration come to nothing. Among those who died in this manner was Henry Munro, a linen draper from Lisburn and chief commander of the County Down insurgents at Saintfield and Ballynahinch. (Here we have another instance of things coming round full circle. Henry Munro could claim collateral descent from the Colonel Robert Munro who, with his army of Covenanters, had landed at Carrickfergus in 1642 and assumed command of all the Scottish and English forces in Ulster, whose mission was to subdue the natives.)

When Munro stepped out to meet his death on a gallows set up in Lisburn's Market Square, the person appointed to carry out the execution was so incompetent that the thing was bungled and the unfortunate insurgent left half-dead. ...And here comes William Blacker again bristling with loyalist heave-ho, rushing up to lend the hangman a hand. Whether an impulse of humanity or vengefulness dictated this action, I cannot say. It was due to Blacker's Seagoe Yeomanry that Henry Munro was captured, and William was designated 'Officer of the Day' for the execution. ('He with his loyal Orangemen united to the king/While other haughty rebels in a halter they will swing,' goes a couplet from a makeshift contemporary ballad, not one by William himself.) Years later, however, he described Henry Munro as 'shrewd, brave and active' and commended his leadership, arguing that his plan of attack might well have succeeded, had it actually been carried out. That it wasn't, he speculated, might have been because 'the Popish portion of the rebels disliked going under the command of a Presbyterian ...'. (Actually, Henry Munro was an Episcopalian, but the point remains.) So there you have the 'Popish portion' in the Blacker view: sectarian, pig-headed and inept.

Why did Armagh stay out of the Rising of 1798? For some not very creditable reasons. When the Society of United Irishmen was founded in 1791 (in Belfast, by William Drennan), its ideals and objectives were somewhat at odds with the way things were managed in County Armagh. That part of the North was saturated in ancient enmities, and a popular means of expressing hostility and resentment already existed there for young malcontents on both sides – the notorious faction fights. 'Unity' on the whole was not an option in the county while factional imperatives predominated. Though some Defenders did merge with United Irishmen, you weren't, by and large, about to see Defenders and Peep o' Day Boys sink their traditional differences in the interests of a French- or American-inspired egalitarianism. In a version of what happened in Wexford, Armagh men stuck to their sectarian guns – and without the overlying ideological gloss that gained Wexford a place in the nationalist pantheon. And when the new loyalism began to be consolidated, it was a natural progression for Peep o' Day Boys to become full-blooded Orangemen.

And now we reach a reversal of the set-piece exodus of desperate Protestants all over Ireland running for their lives (a compelling image for me, now I've discovered that so many of my ancestors were among them). In her magisterial history, *The Catholics of Ulster* (2000), Marianne Elliott quotes a set of verses written in County Armagh in the 1790s:

> The jails they are filled with your nearest relations,
> Your wives and your children are sorely oppressed,

Your houses are burned, your lands desolated,
By a band of ruffians with Orange cockades.

She goes on: 'When threatening notices signed "Oliver Cromwell" were affixed to Catholics' homes, ordering them to quit or be burnt out, most chose to leave without question.' They scattered in all directions, into County Down, southwards to Tipperary, north-west towards Donegal: any locality, however remote, in which it seemed a life free of intimidation might be a possibility. The apocryphal Cromwellian dictum, 'to hell or Connacht', took on a horrendous contemporary reality.

Some of these refugees made their way to Connemara, where they arrived in a desperate state. Help was at hand: they were taken under the wing of Richard Martin of Ballynahinch and his wife Harriet, who supplied food, accommodation, and sympathy for the Northerners' plight. Martin – 'Humanity Dick'[13] – was a substantial landowner who presided over what the author Tim Robinson calls 'a kingdom within a kingdom': a place of 'equivocal allure' due to Martin's scant regard for law, and other exorbitant qualities.[14] By providing succour for some of the people exiled from Armagh, he gained a position on the extreme edge of the Ulster story, and placed himself on the side of the angels as far as northern memories of persecution are concerned. The opposite of 'Cromwell' in every respect.

(Incidentally, Oliver Cromwell has much to answer for in Ireland, but making him a scapegoat for *every* atrocity that occurred is really going too far. I'm thinking here of Scullabogue, and how it gradually got transformed in one section of the popular mind – a mind reluctant to admit even the possibility of sectarian wrongdoing on the Catholic side. Tom Dunne, in *Rebellions*, mentions passing the site of the barn in the company of an elderly relative and being told by him in all sincerity: 'That's the place where Cromwell burned the Catholics.')

In the midst of all the alarms and instability and night frights besetting County Armagh, the Tippings stuck it out. They weren't among the thousands of Catholics forced to abandon their homes and livelihoods in the last decade of the eighteenth century. The last of the Crossmacahilly clan was still inhabiting the same ramshackle house as late as 1944. But, for many reasons, life must have lacked overwhelmingly congenial elements for struggling cottiers, subsistence farmers and hand-loom weavers, battling to scrape a living while coping, day in, day out, with neighbourly hostility. (I know that sounds like an oxymoron, but there it is.) This was a time of exorbitant sabre-rattling in County Armagh, of brawlers, fanatics, hangmen, outrages, flames from burning houses lighting up the night sky, unnerving encounters along secluded lanes. 'And neighbours on the roads at night with guns.'[15]

One's heart goes out to young Sarah Magee in the middle of it all – newly widowed, with four or five children under the age of ten, a farm to run, home-based weaving to carry on, day-to-day living with all its exertions and vexations to oversee. And no prospect before her but the fields and meadows stretching away into the distance, and beyond them the bog, and so on to infinity. How she managed in the circumstances I do not know, but manage she did. Like her great-granddaughter (my grandmother, another Sarah Tipping), who found herself similarly bereaved in 1915, James Tipping's widow showed her mettle by not falling to pieces, by acting out a dogged determination to make a go of things. Possibly, again like my grandmother, she had friends and relations at hand to ease the worst of the burdens, practical or financial or psychological as the case may have been. The rent was paid, the farm kept up, the children reared. In 1812, when the oldest son James comes of age, his mother gets him to take out a lease on the farm, which gains the family an enhanced security.

Ancestral houses. I never set eyes on the Crossmacahilly farm until it was nothing but a rickety survival fast returning to the clay. It had dwindled to a store for cattle-feed, in the middle of a morass. It was stuck at the end of a *bothairin*, or loanen, or whatever you like to call it, and approachable only by means of this swamp-like footway through which you had to struggle and squelch. The winter sky is overcast, the surrounding mud is prodigious, and the emptiness of the fields all around strikes a desolate note. You feel you might have stepped back into the early nineteenth century – only then, of course, the house and land, on the estate of the absentee Duke of Manchester, would have had a kempt appearance. I won't go as far as roses round the door, but the house and its adjunct, a smaller building at a right angle to the main dwelling, would then have been neatly thatched and the garden cultivated. Indoors, sugan chairs, settle beds, creepie stools, deal tables, a turf fire blazing in the open fireplace ... all the fixtures of a farmer-weaver's living quarters would be in place. Perhaps a dog and a cat made their home here too. A degree of order and diligence would have prevailed.

Hard to reconcile all that with the tumbledown wreck now standing – barely – on a byroad somewhere in the wilds between Lurgan and the recent town of Craigavon. Due to a quirk of temperament, I have always been enthralled by historic buildings and the associations they encompass – but Crossmacahilly is too far gone, too wretched looking, to chime with any invigorating sense of the past. It requires a tremendous act of the imagination to restore to it any form or substance whatever. Carrickblacker, on the other hand ... well, that's a handsome pile I'd have taken great delight in. I like, as I say, to savour a house with a history, and the denser the history, the more enraptured my responses. My actual claim to a share in Carrickblacker may be genetically exiguous, but it stands up well in terms of affinity (aesthetic affinity, that is, *not* fellow-feeling for its Orange ambience). Alas, the great house was wiped out of existence before I ever heard tell of it. It and I overlapped by about thirteen years, not long enough for it to impinge on my antiquarian consciousness. I know it only from photographs.

Robert M. Young, writing in 1909, describes Carrickblacker as 'an ancient battlemented mansion', standing in 250 acres, with the River Bann flowing through the grounds before it merges with the Newry canal about a mile away. Like the even more resonant Springhill at Moneymore, Carrickblacker was a rare Northern Irish architectural treasure from the seventeenth century. Unlike Springhill, it was considered dispensable. In the inter-war period, when the role of military grandees in Portadown was failing somewhat, the current Lieutenant-Colonel Blacker moved his family to Devon and sold the house to people named Atkinson, who in turn allowed it to come into the disrespectful hands of the golf club mentioned above. And that was the end of it and its vivid narrative, its venerable interior and ethical heritage attached not to Ireland and liberalism, but to Protestant conservatism and soldierly integrity. Its heavy old chimney-pieces, oak panelling, yew bannisters, Jacobean furniture, equestrian portraits lining its stately walls ... all dispersed or destroyed.

And so to Clonleigh. This was a sturdy, prosperous, two-storey Wexford farmhouse, built in the eighteenth century. Containing at least six rooms indoors, it had plentiful outbuildings and farm offices besides. It included stables, a dairy and a piggery. Five plain sash windows gleamed in sunlight at the front of the house: one on each side of the

Carrickblacker House in its heyday

door and three above, like a house on a child's embroidery sampler. In the garden were flower beds and a vegetable patch. A high, dry-stone wall surrounded it, and an iron gate was hung between a couple of those characteristic round white gateposts, which feature so prominently in the Irish countryside. Some horses lived there, and a donkey was kept to draw a small cart. There were mongrel sheepdogs everywhere. And hens. And fuchsia bushes. And the view from the front windows included a low range of blue enticing Wexford hills. And some miles to the south, beyond another hill, Carrickbyrne, lay Scullabogue.

The farmhouse survived the turbulent events of 1798, but, as we've seen, the house and its neighbourhood weren't untouched by them. Then, as far as we can tell, came years and years of obscurity and repose. More than a century and a half went by with nothing happening in this part of rural Wexford but the routines of farming and daily life. (Well, with one or two exceptions which I'll touch on later.) My great-grandfather William Lett was born at Clonleigh in 1841 and when he died in the same place in 1932 he left the farm and everything in it to his second daughter Miss Annie Tennant Lett. My grandmother, Emily Anne Craig, received a legacy of £50 from her father, and the same amount went to one of William's Wexford granddaughters. There was a son, Thomas, who was due to receive £200 according to the terms of an earlier will, but this legacy was revoked in a codicil. Having provided for Thomas during his lifetime, William announced, he was damned if he was going to go on doing so after his death. (Or words to that effect.) Let Thomas fend for himself – not before time. So we gain an impression of twice-widowed William Lett as a forthright and doughty old farmer, a person who knew his own mind and never hesitated to assert his authority as head of the household.

I went to Clonleigh once, when I was twenty-something. It would have been about 1972. My grandmother's half-sister, Aunt Annie, was on her deathbed. My father drove us – his mother, his sister Ruby, my mother and myself – all the way from Belfast to the South. Emily and Ruby Craig stayed overnight at the farm, while the rest of us had booked into a small hotel not far away – probably in New Ross. There was nothing sombre or funereal about this excursion: we were all in high spirits. It was the summer holidays, and I was home from London. The drive was exhilarating, through the different landscapes of Down and Armagh and Louth and Wicklow. Whenever I opened my mouth, the car rang with nervous laughter; I seemed to have this effect on my relatives, with the simplest statement – 'Oh look at that lovely old house over there, among the trees' – causing an outbreak of hilarity. They never quite knew what to make of me. Their incomprehension was mostly benign, though an acerbic edge to it wasn't unknown. It could go from, wonderingly, 'She's not like a Belfast girl at all', to 'Sure who's like her since Leather-arse died', pronounced with a dry intonation. It was at its peak, I suppose, when I was around twenty; thereafter my supposed eccentricities were toned down at family gatherings as I learned to fit in. Well, up to a point. A faint unease persisted on the part of some relations – not all – perhaps caused by my 1920s dresses and other London crotchets. These might have been viewed as an extension of oddities apparent almost from the word go. (The commonplace, 'Nose stuck in a book', among them.) I belonged to the family, no doubt about it, but I'd never quite conformed to family expectations. There was always something that set me apart – but if this was liable to provoke an unadmiring response, it would never have done so in my mother's presence. For all her amiability and social know-how, my mother would have made it clear that the smallest critical assessment relating to me was absolutely off-limits.

And now I was going to meet some totally unknown relations. Three women lived in Aunt Annie's farmhouse: herself, and the two

PC's great-aunt Miss Annie Tennant Lett, *c.*1920

elderly nieces whose role was to minister to her needs. (Aunt Annie would have been well over ninety at this time.) Bessie and Dolly. These were a pair of stout Wexford women, probably in their late sixties. Their mother, long dead as far as I know, was Annie's older sister. They, just to clarify these family relationships, were my father's cousins. I don't think my mother and I would have made the slightest impression on them. We were visitors, no more, to be offered hospitality in the kitchen-cum-dining-room with its autumn-leaf wallpaper and old-fashioned accoutrements. I don't know if we ever got upstairs in the house – though I know about the four-poster beds in every bedroom, so perhaps we did. They, the nieces, in my brief view of them, showed a surface jocularity which overlay their countrywoman's toughness and tenacity. They had handsome battered faces surrounded by wiry grey-brown hair, and their clothes were protected by patterned overalls. They looked well able to transact all the business of the farm, with only a hired hand named Danny for the rougher jobs. A capacity for hard work was all the nieces had in common with their aunt, my grandmother, as far as I could judge. She did not have a strong personality or any instinct for intrigue. She liked things to be blithe and uncontentious. She left opinions to others. I believe she was a dab hand at a pigeon pie, but if any such carnivorous cooking had taken place in my presence, no doubt I'd have run out of the room screaming.

The point about Bessie and Dolly is that their name was Hornick. The Hornicks were of German Palatine descent, having originally arrived with other refugees from the Rhine Palatinate to settle near Old Ross in the early part of the eighteenth century. These Continental immigrants were, of course, Protestant, and what they were fleeing from in many instances was 'Popish' persecution. Like the Huguenots before them, they threw in their lot with the Irish Protestant community – which made them doubly vulnerable, as outsiders with odd names and conspicuous non-Catholics to boot, when the 1798 Rebellion went awry. A Philip Hornick was burned with the other victims at Scullabogue and his bones shovelled into the shallow grave by the side of the barn.

So – the ancestral web I'm constructing reaches a point of thickening and darkening, with more of my family connections (if only by marriage) leading back and back to Scullabogue. And it doesn't end with the Hornicks. It recently emerged that Bessie Hornick had been married at some time, though – whatever went wrong – this was a circumstance she kept very quiet. Many of the Craigs and other cousins were unaware of it, taking both sisters to be spinsters. But married she was, and her married name was Parslow. It's a name, like Hornick, with a devastating resonance. Two among the dead of Scullabogue were also named Parslow.

I didn't have Scullabogue in mind at all when I went to Wexford in the summer of 1972, and I'm certain no one else did either. These particular relations, to the best of my knowledge, were not history-minded. I'm sure our 'Catholic' orientation, my mother's and mine, wasn't held against us. We wouldn't have been blamed for Scullabogue, if Scullabogue had had any currency at the time. But I doubt that it did. It was just – if, indeed, it was known at all – a fragment of a desolate past, a shadowy horror and indisputable wrong. Nearly two centuries after it happened, Scullabogue had no place in the validating of local renown. It was best obliterated. Catholics weren't about to assume ancestral guilt and go about beating their breasts, and Protestants had no wish to dwell on their victimhood, even long-ago victimhood. The years of peace, relative peace, counted for more than ancient and hellish pandemoniums. The heartfelt cry of Barbara Lett against 'barbarous' neighbours held not the slightest relevance for farming families in the middle of the twentieth century, when neighbourly cooperation and civility cut across religious barriers.

And yet. A little Protestant enclave survived in Catholic Wexford, composed of people with names like Lett, Parslow and Hornick. Belonging to the Church of Ireland was the thing that bound them together. They had their rituals: church, Sunday best, high tea, evensong, excursions to nearby coastal resorts such as Fethard-on-Sea, business and social dealings with one another. It all seems very distant and decorous, and unequipped to persist into the present. Modern life eventually caught up with it. What happened – well, what happened to Clonleigh in particular? Aunt Annie died, the nieces inherited, the old house was abandoned, a new dwelling appeared – one of those bungalows of horrid aspect that erupted like boils all over the countryside as Ireland got into the grip of a rage for modernisation. ... In due course, the bicentenary of 1798 occurred and gave rise to a lot of commemorative edifices and activities, including a good many specially built Heritage Centres and a Vinegar Hill Day. And Scullabogue? If it couldn't be entirely ignored, it wasn't highlighted. The atrocity is commemorated as a 'tragic departure' from United Irish ideals, in a rather uninformative inscription on a stone positioned in a corner of the little Church of Ireland churchyard at Old Ross. No mention of Protestants or pogroms. There, in the graveyard, the Scullabogue stone stands – a blip in the middle of all the nationalist brouhaha.

At this time too, a rash of plaques went up on walls connected with

1798 and its legends, and one of these of particular interest to me is situated at Newcastle House, Cleariestown, where the children of Stephen Lett (brother-in-law of Barbara) grew up and devoted themselves to the thrilling rebel cause. Yes, here comes that valiant boy James Lett again:

> When Erin gives due honour
> To those who fought and fell
> Beneath her flashing banner,
> 'Mid roundshot, grape and shell,
> Upon the scroll of glory,
> Historian, don't forget
> To write the name and story
> Of brave young Master Lett.

James is commemorated at Newcastle House along with his equally valiant sisters, on whom the sobriquet 'the Rebel Angels' was conferred, as a consequence of their skill in embroidering banners proclaiming a subversive allegiance. The inscription on the children's plaque reads: 'In memory of young James Moore Lett and his sisters Mary, Dora, Frances and Sarah, who courageously played their part in the cause of Irish freedom in 1798.' Then comes a line in Irish: '*Go ndeanfaidh Dia trocaire orthu go leir.*'[16]

Well! I now have to backtrack, to say that – via those distant Letts – I can after all claim an ancestral connection to the 1798 Rebellion on the romantic-Irish side – and to Scullabogue, and to the loyalists of Enniscorthy, and to Cromwell's massacres, and to centuries of high and low deeds, all rolled into one. If adolescent James Lett's[17] behaviour on the field of battle – as I now learn – secured for his family name 'an immortality in the annals of Irish patriotism' (I'm quoting from an old newspaper article about a hundred years after the event), where does that leave his Aunt Barbara (to whom his mother and sisters weren't very nice, at the height of the turmoil), his Uncle Newton and all the other 'loyalist' relatives? In a blurred or blended, murky, complex and inconsistent genetic mould along with all the rest of us, that's where.

Scullabogue. When all those patriotic poems were surging into my highly receptive head, when my green-white-and-orange immersion was absolute, it might have surprised me to learn that another perspective was available, that a whole different set of circumstances existed, to which

I might have had access if I'd taken the trouble. (Had I but known ...). I chose not to envisage more than one kind of trigger for retrospective outrage. I ignored the possibility of putting the complex into the simple – as William Empson has it, in a different context – but simple-mindedly cried up every bit of family lore confirming an Irish identity, and blotted out the rest. I mean, I knew my attachment-by-breeding to Irish-Ireland was never going to be as secure as I'd have liked, but I was happily ignorant of just how much of a nonsense it was.

CHAPTER 4
BARDS OF ARMAGH

... I hear an old sombre tide awash in the headboard:
Unpathetic och ochs and och hohs, the long bedtime
Anthems of Ulster, unwilling, unbeaten,

Protestant, Catholic, the Bible, the beads,
Long talks at gables by moonlight, boots on the hearth,
The small hours chimed sweetly away ...

Seamus Heaney, from 'The Settle Bed'

My mother's well-stocked mind contained a lot of songs and recitations. Sometimes she had to laugh at the things that swept into her head: comically sad verses, absurd-Irish doggerel. She didn't choose to repeat these things, either silently or out loud, but they simply wouldn't leave her alone: 'Poor Pinch and Caoch O'Leary'; 'The woman was old and feeble and grey'; 'The Garden where the Praties Grow'. Her repertoire was prodigious. 'The Old Bog Road' was a feature of her mental landscape, along with 'The Deserted Village'. 'Barbara Fretchie' was in it, rubbing shoulders with 'Wee Hughie'. These and many other items of bromide were a permanent acquisition of her brain. Some party pieces, and other more serious lyrics and stanzas, were a legacy of her Catholic primary school in Lurgan, where a class of seven-, eight- and nine-year-olds sat undergoing a programme of rote-learning, with a variable outcome. It was the 1920s, a doleful decade. Some pupils – 'scholars', as they were called – were hopeless from the start, big ungainly girls with vacant expressions, or sharp-featured little oddities undone by poverty. But not my mother. My mother is destined for better things, including an education unimaginable to the bulk of her early classmates. She is singled out on account of her quick responses and her retentive memory. This is a girl, a little half-orphan from a poor background, who is clearly *not* mill-fodder. Before she's thirteen, my mother is enrolled at a swanky new fee-paying convent school on top of a hill called Mount St Michael's, to which she hastens every morning, bursting with pride in her second-hand navy school uniform, carrying a leather satchel filled with books and a hockey stick as a symbol of her new status. She is walking on air.

She's got to Mount St Michael's on a scholarship, of course, and a succession of scholarships will see her through to her eventual BA degree from Queen's University in Belfast. It's an exhilarating time for her: she loves everything about the school, the nuns, the lessons, the atmosphere, new friendships formed and consolidated, her own prime position in the class, the sense of possibilities opening for the future. And, although her attributes (like mine) don't include a good singing voice, she has, as ever, no bother with the words of songs and poems (and passages from Shakespeare). A high proportion of the songs she learns are Irish-orientated – though a long way from *sean-nos*: a local anthem is more likely to begin, 'By Lough Neagh's shores where the fisherman strays ...' than '*Ag Ur-Chill a' Chreggan 'se codhail me 'reir faoi bhron ...*'. The great revival of interest in traditional Irish singing hasn't yet happened, and when it does happen it's too late for my mother to be affected by it. For her, the store of national, and nationalist, songs is confined to ballads and folk songs in the English language of varying degrees of authenticity. Some have authentic airs and new words – 'She Moved Through the Fair', 'Boulevogue', 'Down by the Salley Gardens' – and some are entirely new: 'The Kerry Dancers', 'The Rose of Tralee'. Most are pleasant and soporific and supposedly enshrine a devotion to Ireland even if they lack the genuine, austere or plangent note of a complex Gaelic folk tradition. One of them, 'Bold Phelim Brady, the Bard of Armagh', is a particular favourite of my mother's despite its shillelagh and brogues-bound-with-straw motif.

Well, it's understandable: was she not herself a Brady of Armagh

(County Armagh, at any rate)? I am sure she envisaged a kinship with this bold Phelim, whoever he was (actually I think the original of the song was an eighteenth-century Gaelic poet, though the English lyrics cast 'the poor Irish harper' in an unduly sweet-and-bland patriotic mode). That song — never mind its trite emblematic overload ('the shamrock', 'the Saxon lion's paw', etc.) — its heart was in the right place. It was embedded in its ancient harpist's dear native land. And that Phelim Brady was the goods, in my mother's view. He had exclusive rights to the designation 'the Bard of Armagh'.

The original Brady sept belonged to Cavan, but some of its members, like the bold Phelim, must have migrated north-eastwards through Monaghan and into Armagh and Down. At any rate, the first of my known, or unknown, Brady forebears turns up in nineteenth-century Newry. What he was doing there, or what his occupation was, I have no idea. His name was Bernard, and I think he had married a Miss McManus. (I'm basing this supposition on the fact that three maiden aunts named McManus turn up at the Lurgan home of Bernard's son Terence in the census of 1901.) Did he keep moving backwards and forwards? According to the 1911 census, the birthplace of Terence (1859–1915) was County Cavan. But Terence and his brother Michael grew up in Lurgan town. Terence became a tailor and married a local dressmaker named Catherine Harland. Their oldest son, William Brady (1881–1915), in due course married a girl from nearby John Street, Sarah Tipping. (William's cousin David Brady, a son of Michael, had already married Sarah's sister Ellen ... but that's another story.) Hence my mother Nora Brady, and then me. So I suppose I can claim a miniscule line of descent from the 'illustrious' Mac Bradaigh sept of Cavan mentioned in the seventeenth-century *Annals of the Four Masters* (so can nearly every Irish person called Brady, for that matter ...).

My mother was proud of her Irish name and its nationalist associations. She was happy to share a surname with the Bard of Armagh. ... Would it also have pleased her to learn of a rival 'Bard of Armagh' to whom she really was obliquely related? Not likely, since the second so-called bard was the redoubtable William Blacker (also known as 'the Orange Minstrel'). He'd acquired the title on account of his Orange songs, in one of which occurs the alarming line, 'But put your trust in God, my boys, and keep your powder dry.' In full flow, with Williamite triumphalism firing his imagination, this scion of the Blacker dynasty goes on to compose the definitive Orange anthem, 'No Surrender':

> And Derry's sons alike defy
> Pope, traitor or pretender,
> And peal to heaven their 'prentice cry,
> Their patriot, 'No Surrender'.

This is partisan history with a vengeance (but note that it's Derry throughout, never Londonderry). We can picture William Blacker in the early years of the nineteenth century, stouter of face and figure than in his uproarious Trinity days, sitting at home in his study at Carrickblacker and cheerfully giving vent to an impassioned illiberalism. He is Protestant through and through – and Protestant unity, he holds, is the best defence against a bugbear of the times, a creeping Catholicism:

> Let the Presbyter strike by the Prelatist's side,
> And stem, in strong union, fell Popery's tide.

We have to wonder what made him so implacably anti-Catholic – and wonder even more what he means by statements like the following: 'But Popish power, in evil hour, / Has o'er us flung its galling chain.' Popish power has done nothing of the sort. Popish power is non-existent in Ireland, especially in the years before Catholic Emancipation.

Protestantism didn't have to be so venomous and melodramatic. Many upholders of the Protestant faith were also subscribers to the liberal ethic. A supreme example here, I suppose, is Dr William Drennan (the actual founder of the Society of United Irishmen, back in 1791). Drennan is responsible for inventing the phrase 'the Emerald Isle' – but his verse in general provokes a lot more admiration than William Blacker's, and not only because it's written from a different standpoint. While Blacker urges, 'On, on, gallant hearts, for the Bible and Crown', Drennan is more concerned to 'drive the demon of Bigotry home to his den'. As with many reasonable people before and since, the demon of bigotry is, for him, a cause of the utmost despair. ... At one point, reviewing in verse for the Belfast Monthly Magazine a long topographical poem called 'The Giant's Causeway' by the Reverend Hamilton Drummond, Dr Drennan delivers to his readers an unabashed injunction: 'Avaunt his verses be they ne'er so fine, / Who for the Catholics – REFUSED TO

SIGN!' The immediate cause of his ire (the year is 1811) is a past refusal by Drummond to add his name to a petition in support of Catholic Emancipation. But reading the Reverend Drummond's lines about the recent Act of Union – 'No more fell faction hurls her flaming brand, / But smiling concord waves her olive wand', and so on, and on, florally and obsequiously – you can see why the whole drift of the poem would get up the nose of an old Irish separatist like Dr Drennan.

It was not a good time for principled dissent. The Reverend Drummond is at one with William Blacker in his adulation of the English connection, and consequently his historical references fall within a tradition of unionist orthodoxy: 'Boyne foams with blood – a coward monarch flies, / War sheathes his gory blade – Rebellion dies' (the coward monarch, of course, being the unfortunate James II). It's likely that Drummond had a more recent rebellion in mind when he wrote these lines; and indeed, at this reactionary moment (the early years of the nineteenth century) 'rebellion' was discredited as a means of effecting social change, and not only among those of a conservative bent. The weaver poet James Orr, for example – author of the wry and disabused poem 'Donegore Hill' – never relinquished his hopes for a true democracy in Ireland. But after 1798, when he'd witnessed the inadequacy of republicanism in action, he attached these hopes to a different system: reformist rather than revolutionary.

Orr, as an ex-rebel, one-time contributor to the radical newspaper the *Northern Star*, and ultimate pragmatist, exemplifies the attitudes prevailing one after the other among the Presbyterians of the North. At one moment, it seemed, the republicanism of Wolfe Tone, Henry Joy McCracken and others was an impeccable doctrine, and the next moment it wasn't. It was impeccable while it grew apace in opposition to misgovernment; but lost repute when it began to be viewed solely as a disruptive force. Events were taking some complicated turns, and among them arrived a hesitancy, even among liberals, in relation to the kind of anti-Catholicism purveyed by Blacker and others. This was still to be deplored – but deplored, perhaps, with reservations. The anti-sectarian instinct had a strong foundation in the North, and the thing that chiefly got it up in arms was the treatment of Catholics. But at times it looked as if any such benevolent instinct might not weather an absence of democratic principles among Catholics themselves, whenever this absence became apparent – as it did, for example, in Wexford during the Rebellion, and again at the height of the Emancipation struggle. Catholic smugness or xenophobia is as much to be regretted as any other sort.

Those Protestant 'United Irish' advocates of tolerance, though, who lived on into the nineteenth century, continued to speak out on behalf of Catholic Emancipation – even though it's unlikely that Daniel O'Connell, with all his magniloquence and southern showmanship, would have held much personal appeal for them. It's true that both James Orr and William Drennan had died (in 1816 and 1820 respectively) before O'Connell's Catholic campaign reached its zenith in the 1820s, and thereby evaded a possible erosion of their sympathies. They retained their liberal values to the end. Drennan's famous directive with regard to his funeral arrangements shows a wit and a kind of enshrinement of his lifelong concerns. He left instructions that his coffin should be carried to its final resting place in Clifton Cemetery, Belfast, by an equal number of Protestants and Catholics – six of one and half a dozen of the other.

Daniel O'Connell's 'Catholic Rent' – the scheme by which a penny a month was subscribed by individual Catholics to a pro-Emancipation fund – this scheme was embraced less vigorously in Ulster than in other parts of the country. Poverty was the reason: many poor northern Catholics lacked even so small a surplus income as the Catholic Rent required. They found themselves 'overwhelmingly confined to the lowest rungs of the social ladder', the historian Jonathan Bardon says. The most prosperous members of the Catholic population, and it was only a very limited prosperity, were 'the farmer-weavers of the Linen Triangle'. Among them, I think, we may place the Crossmacahilly Tippings, who probably would have contributed their penny-a-month as the idea of a Catholic nation took hold among the disaffected. Was 'Popish power', at last, actually becoming a possibility? If so, it was a glorious prospect for the downtrodden and something to be encouraged at all costs.

At this time, the 1820s, the Tipping farm is home to the brothers James, John and Matthew, and possibly their mother Sarah (née Magee) is still alive and living there as well – though by 1833 it seems she isn't, since her name has disappeared from the records. Within the next ten years the youngest son Matthew has vanished too, maybe dead of whatever it was that had killed his father, when he (Matthew) was only four. That leaves James and John. By the mid 1820s both were married and occupied adjoining farmhouses, the smaller forming a right angle with the larger.

At this time, it is possible that Matthew was employed by his brothers as a labourer. And, if the Catholic Rent was paid by anyone in the family it was undoubtedly James who paid it, as the oldest and steadiest of the brothers and the one most strongly endowed with Tipping gumption.

James might have relished the sense of a growing Catholic solidarity not tied up with what he already knew only too well, the deadly and ruinous faction fights still bedevilling the Armagh countryside. The old Defenders and their Peep o' Day antagonists hadn't died out, they hadn't gone away, and neither of them had absorbed a jot of United Irish idealism. Under the new names of Ribbonmen and Orangemen they went on implementing their complementary programmes of cruelty, blackguardism and intimidation. ... I don't know if any of the Catholic Tippings were caught up in Ribbon activity, but I think it unlikely: at least, I hope I needn't add arson and attacks on innocent Protestant *cattle* to the list of ancestral (or quasi-ancestral) enormities I'm contemplating with alarm.

A Ribbon/Orange confrontation which later gained a magnified status had taken place in County Derry in 1813. It became known as 'The Battle of Garvagh', after the title of an anonymous ballad which began to circulate shortly after the event:

> The day before the July fair
> The Ribbonmen they did prepare
> For three miles round to wreck and tear
> And burn the town of Garvagh.

Needless to say, their terrible plan of action was foiled by the Orange Boys of Garvagh, who shot dead one Ribbonman and wounded others. This, along with many other similar incidents, didn't have a calming effect on denominational excitability. Finally, local and national authorities could stand no more of it, and by 1823 both Ribbon and Orange societies were proscribed organisations under an Unlawful Oaths Act passed in that year. This piece of 'anti-Orange legislation' – I'm quoting the useful J.S. Kane again, in his Blacker family history – was followed by the Unlawful Associations Act of 1825, which to Kane's indignation clamped down on the Orange Order, and even (God save us) on the Freemasons, 'neither of which was in any way unlawful'. Well! As a consequence, he adds, 'the Grand Orange Lodge of Ireland dissolved itself in March 1825'.

But unholy passions continue to be exacerbated. Picture a scene in Lurgan town, in May 1828, when hundreds of anti-Emancipationists take to the streets armed with sticks and cudgels in an episode of organised violence against Catholics. ... There they run, in an access of roaring hostility. Papist doors and windows succumb to their blows, driving them on in a triumph of rage to further acts of destruction. And here comes John Hancock, Protestant magistrate and agent to Charles Brownlow, riding up on his chestnut horse to read out the Riot Act, confident in his position as law-enforcer. Well, he can read it out till he's blue in the face but no one takes a bit of notice. Restraint is not imposed on the Lurgan berserkers, whose number includes members of a local yeomanry corps. Far from helping to round up the rioters, these yeomen are running pell-mell with the worst of them, yelling and bawling and wrecking all before them. At the same time, their overexcited sergeant heaps abuse on the head of John Hancock for his 'Papist' pusillanimity.

In the end, only nine of the rioters are arrested and dispatched to Portadown gaol. The others get off scot-free, dispersing themselves among alleyways and back streets known only to local residents. On the way to the gaol, passing along Edward Street in Lurgan – location of the magistrate's substantial home – the caught miscreants are accompanied by an Orange band blaring out 'The Boyne Water', 'No Surrender', 'Croppies Lie Down' and anything else guaranteed to cause offence to any Papist ears in the vicinity. A hastily composed ballad attacking the Protestant magistrate Hancock hits the streets a few days later:

> Oh, Lurgan town's an altered town,
> Since Papish Hancock he came to it.
> If ye walk out upon the Twelfth,
> You may depend he'll make you rue it.
> And if you sing an Orange song,
> You'll be jailed for eight and forty hours;
> Fresh orders he gave the police,
> To make prisoners of none but ours.

That's Lurgan for you: a town of bitter enmities, where 'the residents of Ballyblough and the Pound River are for ever stoning and fighting'. At this date, the late 1820s, the Orange Order is still an illegal body, and rumbles among disbanded Orangemen deprived of their July shenanigans finally come to a head in 1835, when, from all over County Armagh, they converge on Carrickblacker House and assemble on the lawn (an awesome twenty thousand of them, according to a contemporary newspaper report, 'of all ages and sexes'), thereby involving the upright Colonel Blacker in an inadvertent act of law-breaking. He rises to the occasion, however, addressing the crowd like a Dutch uncle and prevailing upon the lot of them to go home in a peaceable spirit (as reported, again, in the *Evening Packet*), never deigning to notice any Ribbon provocation they might encounter along the way. (The leaders of this demonstration were, nevertheless, brought to justice by the aforementioned John Hancock, an action creating strong ill-feeling between him and William Blacker.) The colonel's lady, Mrs Blacker, makes a rare appearance on the same crowded lawn, causing questions to arise: how did she fit in among that vast assembly? Wasn't she intimidated by the masses of Orange hoi polloi? It would seem not – for here she is, wearing an orange dress to proclaim her enthusiasm for the Protestant cause. And, for good measure, in festive exuberance, Carrickblacker servants are milling about the place with orange lilies entwined in their hair.

(I think of my grandmother Tipping's pronunciation of the word 'orange' which she reduces to a single syllable, articulated with a growl: ornge. 'Them oul ornge bigots'. And again, I think of the field at Edenderry in the twentieth century, with daft middle-aged women draped in Union Jacks weaving drunkenly through the thickets of Orange celebrants.)

Crossmacahilly, 1830s. The place is coming down with children, the offspring of James (eight born between 1826 and 1839) and John (father to at least four). We can visualise them tumbling about the stone-floored kitchen, boys and girls alike wearing woollen petticoats, and applaud the adults' unremitting efforts to maintain a certain standard of comfort and hygiene. (I'm taking this to be true, because it was a ferocious preoccupation with all of their descendants. Woe betide the speck of dirt that would show its face in any Tipping or Tipping-related household.) If it's summer, we might see homespun blankets spread over hedges drying in the sun; or the same lumps of children foraging for wild strawberries and mushrooms in the fields (and maybe exchanging insults with infantile Protestant neighbours: 'Proddy gets'; 'Papist pigs'). Cold damp winters might bring running noses and chilblains (a common Tipping affliction).

And always, there are chores to perform: water to be fetched for cooking and washing, floors to be swept, the kitchen 'redd'. By this stage it's likely that the linen-weaving enterprise is merely a sideline, as the growing number of flax mills and factories signals an end to home production. Farming would be the main source of income for households like the Tippings', with all its drawbacks of incessant labour and uncertainty of outcome.

Crossmacahilly. I'd like to think the place provided scope for seasonal pleasures too, with ancient customs like the Cutting of the Calliagh still going strong. 'The calliagh' was the last sheaf of corn left standing after the rest had been harvested. Separated into three strands where it grew, and plaited by one of the women working in the fields, it was then cut down by having a sickle thrown at it. 'Cut her down, cut her down,' the reapers would cry, and afterwards raise a cheer when the deed was done. A celebratory meal – the calliagh feast – would then take place in a farm kitchen, with perhaps dancing and singing until well into the night. Though the purpose of this ritual would largely have been forgotten, even in the nineteenth century, it had something to do with an idea that 'the spirit of the corn' resided in the last sheaf, and that the actions connected with the calliagh would ensure a good future harvest.

There were other rituals, to be enacted at due seasons. 'Above my door the rushy cross', John Hewitt wrote,

> The turf upon my hearth,
> For I am of the Irishry,
> By nurture and by birth.

The 'rushy cross', St Brigid's cross, placed above the door to protect the home, was traditionally fashioned from rushes gathered on the last day of January – they had to be plucked, not cut, and carried indoors after sunset, whereupon the work of shaping them into crosses would begin, accompanied by a meal of pancakes or apple potato bread. Rushes grew in abundance around the Crossmacahilly bogs, and no doubt generations of Tipping children were sent out to collect them, with instructions not to get their feet wet or their clothes destroyed. Like other country families the Tippings would have been dutiful towards immemorial customs, I think, and wishful not to neglect any time-honoured means of drawing good fortune to themselves.

But even in towns and cities the custom of making Brigid's crosses persisted until well into the twentieth century. I was shown how to do it myself, instructed by the nuns of my primary school Aquinas Hall in Windsor Park, Belfast, in the 1950s. It made a welcome respite from the usual classroom ennui (geography or elocution lessons – ugh!), and it was satisfying to view the finished article you'd knocked together with your own hands, once you'd grasped the technique of folding the rushes one on top of the other into a swastika-like shape. The crosses we turned out each year on 1 February made a pretext for a lecture on our religious heritage. We sat at our desks wearing royal blue gym-slips over grey winter blouses, hair neatly plaited or cropped and curled, and learned that Brigid was one of Ireland's holy trinity of ancient saints, along with Patrick and Columcille – but not that the abbey over which she presided at Kildare was a 'mixed house' (i.e. one in which monks and nuns were at liberty to marry, if they chose); or that Brigid herself was ordained a bishop, in a society that placed few restrictions on women's advancement. These facts would not have been considered suitable for our infant ears. Neither was the fusion of pagan and Christian customs dwelt on. This was the 1950s: Irish Roman Catholicism reigned supreme and nuns' power over their charges was absolute.

At Crossmacahilly there are good years and bad years, and through it all it's James who shoulders the heaviest burdens of both families, his own and his brother's; James the good manager, the cautious risk-taker, the one blessed with foresight; James my grandmother's grandfather. James pays the whole of the Crossmacahilly rent to the Duke of Manchester's agent Henry John Porter (John repaying his share whenever he can). James borrows money from the Tandragee Castle Loan Fund – set up by the same agent – to buy lime, rye grass, turnip and parsnip seeds, making regular repayments to the fund. John borrows too, for clothes as well as seeds and crops, but, unlike his brother, he gets into difficulties and has to appeal to James to settle his debts (which he does). James takes advantage of a drainage scheme which improves the land and increases the yield of farm produce. It is all carefully thought out – and when he dies in 1853, James leaves no debts for his heirs to grapple with. All his borrowing is repaid to the last farthing. It's a lesson in good husbandry, confounding the implications of indolence and fecklessness attached to the letter 'R' – 'R' for Romanist – which appears beside the names of the Tipping brothers in the estate rentals. In the townland of Crossmacahilly there are only eight Catholic families, alongside forty Protestant.

'Romanist' or not, throughout his industrious life, James would have had more pressing worries than the state of his soul. The Tippings and their neighbours lived with constant fears, fear of sectarian harassment, fear of bad weather, fear of hard times. Praying is a resource though, especially when it seems apocalyptic anticipations are about to be realised. There comes a night in January 1839 when, through sheer expedience, the entire townland would likely have been down on its knees asking God for deliverance from a raging storm: the Night of the Big Wind, as it's gone down in folk memory. This was the night when roofs were lifted clean off houses and hurled through the air, when trees toppled like a deck of cards, when the 184-foot chimney of Mulholland's flax mill in Belfast crashed to the ground. To those of a religious turn of mind, it looked as though the end of the world had come. One consternated cleric, the Reverend William Boyce of High Street, Belfast, could hardly take in the extent of the destruction being wrought around him, and later recorded his impressions of that wild night in an awestruck outburst.[1]

> How dreadful raged that storm o'er Erin's face!
> And who may tell t'effect on Land, in part?
> Chimneys, tiles, and slates, gas lamps, and spinning mills,
> Demolished windows, houses, roofs, huge funnels tall,
> Factories, walls, mill-chimnies, prostrate laid;
> A watchman killed by Falls-road mill's descent! ...
> The wings of Windmills, canvas, rails, and nails,
> Completely torn asunder! ...

So it goes on, page after page of heartfelt unrestrained verse commentary: 'Then yelled the tempest furious through Portrush'; 'It rushed through Aghalee, by Finaghy, / By Lurgan, Markethill, the Middleton, Pointzpass.' 'It broke huge elms, / and oaks,' so it did, while going about the fearsome work of 'smashing ships, trees, towers, and men'. No portion of the North escaped its fury. Even at supposedly unassailable Carrickblacker, alarmed inhabitants felt the great house shake to its foundations, they heard hundreds of tiles erupting from the roof, and then the tremendous noise of trees uprooted in the demesne. The following day, the damage was contemplated with awe and disbelief. Hundreds of Carrickblacker elms lay strewn about the estate like fallen participants in some mythical battle.

But it wasn't all despair and ruin. A future prosperity was in store for local carpenters who rushed to buy up the sudden glut of wood. (Just as the income of glaziers was substantially increased during the Troubles of the late twentieth century.) One uprooted elm, however, carefully selected by William Blacker himself, was set aside and earmarked for his coffin. Duly constructed and stored in an outhouse, the coffin sat awaiting its future occupant who wandered out every now and then to take a look at it – not a morbid procedure at all, he said, just a practical acknowledgement of his ultimate end.

I believe I have a slight understanding of what the population of Ireland went through on that January night in 1839, having experienced the great English storm of 1987, when my husband and I lay huddled together on the top floor of a tall house in Blackheath waiting for the roof to blow off or the chimney to crash down on top of us. ('Terrific howled the hurricane around,' as Boyce might have put it.) Earlier, we had listened to the wind increasing in volume and were shocked by the sudden extinguishing of all the lights of south London as the power supply went kaput. Plunged into total blackness, we twentieth-century sceptics were braced for a moment to undergo an apocalyptic outcome. And indeed the morning's devastation didn't seem to fall far short of it. Though it wasn't on the scale of *Oidhche na Gaoithe Moire,* the Night of the Big Wind, enough havoc was caused by the 1987 storm to etch it into the remembrance of everyone who endured it. As for me – I'm exhilarated by most extremes of weather, cold, rain, snow: but not wind. My anxiety level rises with every blast of rising wind.

So I can all too easily enter into the state of mind of the Crossmacahilly family hunkered round the fire – to borrow an image from Richard Rowley's *Tales of Mourne* – 'waitin' every minute for the walls to blow in on top o' them'. Did one of them, again like Rowley's narrator, see himself in desperation 'houldin' on the thatch wi' my finger-nails ... afore mornin'? However the thatch was held on – perhaps weighted down with ropes and stones before the worst of the weather struck – it seems to have stayed in place; at least, there are no reports of the farm or outbuildings being whirled away into oblivion. But appalling sights met the eyes of people creeping out at daybreak to begin the work of salvage. Dead birds and animals, fields churned up, hedges flattened. A yellow, overladen sky and an ominous atmosphere. And in the battered towns of Lurgan and Portadown, where people gathered in the streets to view the wreckage left by the storm, the dishevelled houses and shops, the broken-down factory chimneys, the fallen spires of different churches, all crushed alike by a force of nature.

Tenant farmers gritted their teeth, in the wake of the storm, and got on with the next thing. But the nineteenth century has further catastrophes up its sleeve for the Irish nation. Some years after the Big Wind comes the first potato-crop failure. The ensuing Famine provides a standard against which all subsequent calamities may be measured. Nothing – the reaction to some later scourge might go – nothing has bred so much consternation in the townland since the wee boy came running into the farm kitchen bearing news of a terrible smell in the potato fields.

He might have been my great-grandfather Matthew Tipping, that archetypal small boy, Matthew the third son of diligent James and one of a clatter of weans – that's the word they'd have used, weans or the equally expressive 'childer' – growing up on the edge of a bog, all imbued with a strong sense of kinship and thoroughly schooled in argument and assertion. (Remember those forty Protestant families occupying the same small area.) All of us there. What kind of people were they? Even if the world they inhabited is essentially unknowable, faded away to nothing like a badly preserved sampler, there are clues to be picked up about the way they viewed it and each other, and how particular traits were evolving within the family, distinguishing each individual member from all the rest. I think I'm right, for example, in attributing a certain headstrong quality to Matthew, a kicking-over-the-traces predilection. I'll come back to this – but in the meantime the overwhelming consideration is the rotting potato crop of 1845 and subsequent years.

No one died of starvation on the Tipping farm and this was probably due to James and his turnip- and parsnip-sowing, his continuing production of flax and whatever oats could be salvaged from a lesser but not insignificant blight, concurrent with the potato blight. None of the family died of actual hunger, but the Famine claimed its Tipping victim nevertheless. In December 1848, James Tipping's younger brother John, the one continually in need of propping up, is admitted to the Lurgan Union Workhouse suffering from typhoid fever. It kills him within a couple of weeks. Fifty-seven years old and long a widower, John Tipping already had the disease – the dreaded famine fever – before he went in, but conditions in the workhouse made it a place to die, not a centre of proper medical treatment. ... There John lies among the destitute poor, perhaps on a damp and insanitary cot, bedlam around him, until he simply gives up the ghost. He is hastily buried on the following day, taken from this place of doom and wretchedness in a makeshift coffin, over which not a single funeral offering is made (according to the Seagoe Catholic parish church records). The previous horrendous year, Black '47, had depleted all the meagre Tipping resources. James at least must have suffered bitterness and mortification at the failure to do things properly, to arrange a respectable exit for his brother John, but circumstances were against him. For all his frugality and astuteness, he was overtaken by events. And he could point with some pride to what he *had* achieved: a tribe of children pulled through the crisis. All of them, on their shaky smallholding, were lucky indeed not to go the way of John.

The Lurgan Union Workhouse – hmn. Who is chairman of its board of guardians at this fraught time? Stiff-necked, high-principled William Blacker, that's who. While John Tipping lies approaching his appalling end, we might find Colonel Blacker journeying abroad on one of his holiday trips to Frankfurt, Paris, Brussels or London, avoiding the chills of an Armagh winter and the countryside heaving with disease and distress. Driving in a carriage around Belgian boulevards might be on the cards for the Blacker party, or elaborate dinners attended by glittering guests. At Cheltenham, another favourite holiday destination, Ulster grandees away from home, including Charlotte Lennox-Conyngham of Springhill, play host to one another or gather to applaud Colonel Blacker's speechifying at a Conservative dinner. A lavish, assured and highly organised life – and with all these divertissements to absorb his attention, a dying Catholic workhouse inmate, one among hundreds, would be the least of William Blacker's concerns.

Don't worry, I'm not making a facile point here about heartless gentry and suffering peasantry (though there's scope enough for it). I don't mean to do down William Blacker and his lord-of-the-manor hauteur (well, not really). His views on social responsibility are in line with the mores of the day. He is deputy vice-treasurer of Ireland. He's a great committee-man, militiaman and occasional host at Carrickblacker to the 'cream' of the Protestant ruling elite. And if it's a world away from the scrabbling, swarming underclass of tenant farmers and tramps and artisans – well, no one can blame Colonel Blacker for making the most of his fortunate position in the world. Nothing happens in his life to topple his landowner's certainties. But – here comes another instance of 'had-he-but-known' – there were reasons why this particular stricken subsistence farmer John Tipping might have impinged on the aloof Blacker consciousness. Though neither was aware of it, both the gentleman and the famine victim had a common ancestor, in the direct line, in the Royalist officer Valentine Blacker who built the manor house known as Blacker's Bawn and restored the seventeenth-century Seagoe parish church. It's the genealogical irony that snares my attention here.

But let us consider young Matthew growing up in the wilds of Crossmacahilly, living through the years of Famine with all the frantic expedients to stay alive, and perhaps already fixing his sights on better things. Matthew is the fourth child and third son of farmer/weaver James, and himself an eventual father of twelve – whose lives, bar two, I don't propose to examine in detail (Whew! I hear you go). The exceptions are Matthew's youngest child, my grandmother Sarah, and to a lesser extent her half-brother Henry, twenty-five years her senior, who frightened her under the kitchen table with his impassioned rendering of the patriotic ballad 'Fontenoy' when she was two years old; but as yet, these are only figments of a shadowy future.

Matthew gets round to begetting early on. Like his grandfather James (perhaps), he doesn't curb, indeed I imagine he flaunts, his erotic drive; and it's possible that more than one local girl is warned to consider him a danger and affront to good Catholic chastity. One girl at least pays no heed to the voices of prudence, however: Eliza O'Hara from nearby Legahorry, who bears Matthew a daughter long before the pair of them are out of their teens. Is agitation engendered by this event? Or is a shrug and a grimace more in keeping with contemporary country attitudes? You can't stop nature taking its course, any more than the effects of the potato-crop failure can be reversed, or the howling wind be stopped in its tracks. And here's Helena Tipping to prove it, a babe in arms when her parents finally stand before the parish priest of Seagoe to take their marriage vows. What took them so long? Was it reluctance on the part of one or the other? Perhaps Eliza O'Hara was gifted with foresight and jibbed at the state of almost continuous pregnancy looming in front of her like a wrecking ball. It would finish her off before her time, she might have feared – and it did. Or maybe it's simply a question of space, the marriage-delaying factor, with the Crossmacahilly farmhouse so crammed with inhabitants that absolutely no further bodies can be squeezed in.

Be that as it may, Matthew the married man installs his wife and daughter in his parents' home, and swiftly increases the congestion on the spot by begetting another six young Tippings. (Inadequate accommodation, caused by too much procreation, is just one of the scourges the nineteenth-century poor have to put up with.) Before the first new infant arrives, however, Matthew's father James has bowed out of the proceedings, creating a bit of space by dying in 1853 at the age of sixty-odd years. ... No doubt James Tipping's funeral is an altogether more seemly affair than his poor brother John's. But for a real showpiece Armagh interment we need to look higher up the social scale. And here it comes. Two years after the death of James, in November 1855, his distant kinsman William Blacker's long and punctilious existence reaches an end. The elmwood coffin from the Night of the Big Wind gets its rightful occupant at last. At twelve noon on the last day of November Colonel Blacker's funeral cortège leaves Carrickblacker House for old Seagoe Church, 'headed by the children of the schools which William Blacker had done so much to encourage over the years'. A long line of respectable gentry follows, J.S. Kane goes on; and next come high-up representatives of all denominations: Church of Ireland, Presbyterian, Roman Catholic,[2] Quaker. Also present are 'William's most trusted Orange colleagues' (well, they would be there, wouldn't they), his nephew and heir Stewart Blacker, members of parliament and peers of the realm. (Kane is careful to specify the peers of the realm.) And lining the funeral route along the Gilford Road are rows of tenant farmers and weavers come to pay their last respects and suitably chastened, no doubt, by the solemn appearance of the six black horses festooned with black ostrich feather plumes, the hearse with its black-clad coachman, the mourning coaches, the slow procession of dignitaries following after. I don't think you'd have found any deferential Tippings, though, standing with bowed bared heads along the roadway, even though the stately cortège was making its way towards the very spot where an ancestor of theirs, the seventeenth-century John Tipping, lay buried with his in-laws in the Blacker family mausoleum.

Eighteen-forty-eight, the year of the later John Tipping's death from famine fever, was also the year in which the planned 'Young Ireland' uprising failed to come to fruition. In March, Charles Gavin Duffy of *The Nation* had announced that 'Ireland's opportunity, thank God and France, has come at last'; but his rhetorical gratitude turned out to be without foundation. Neither he nor his colleague the Banbridge Presbyterian solicitor John Mitchel was able to drum up sufficient fervour in the North to get any kind of revolutionary enterprise going. The reason isn't hard to find: 'a starving people,' comments Jonathan Bardon drily in his *History of Ulster*, '... had no interest in insurrection.'

No interest, but in households like the Tippings', nevertheless, there'd be talk of misgovernment, and of ways to engage in nationalist dissent. In the parishes of Shankill, Seagoe, Tartaraghan, people were dying of hunger and disease until it seemed the whole of society was collapsing in on itself, its day-to-day enactments driven by fear and distress. A world was being unravelled, and then, at some point, it would have to be put back together again, as survivors like the Tippings were left to pick up the pieces. It was a defining moment. Protestants had died – indeed, in north Armagh, more Protestants than Catholics were counted among the famine victims – but for Catholics and nationalists, the potato famine was tied up with cruelty and exploitation of the whole population of Ireland. Starving people standing on a quayside, silently watching as tons of provisions are shipped elsewhere, 'relief work' consisting of roads going nowhere, soup kitchens, derelict townlands, mass graves, coffin ships: these images are entering into the nationalist mythology, as a powerful opposition to all representatives of a ruling elite takes hold. Being '"agin" the government' is coming to constitute a way of life.

Another image from those years comes to mind. It was relayed to me by my mother, who got it from her grandmother, who figures in it. Ellen Jordan was a young child when the Famine struck north Armagh, and among her sharpest memories was one of herself, wrapped in a shawl, being carried by *her* mother, Susan McCorry from Moyraverty, to a soup kitchen hastily set up to aid the starving poor. She recalled the sense of desperation felt by many in the blighted countryside as their livelihood, and indeed their lives, were put in jeopardy. There is utter subjugation in the air. ... And here's another anomaly of my up-and-down ancestry. These Jordans may have been poor (how poor I don't know), but some of their relations were, on the other hand, well placed to savour the benefits of a provincial affluence.

Ellen's father is Edward Jordan, and Edward's cousin Thomas is the founder and managing director of the Lurgan linen-handkerchief-manufacturing firm of T. Jordan & Sons. They are business people with a steady income and highly developed sense of their own importance. Thomas has arranged matters so that his wife and children will rise to their feet when he enters the breakfast room of their Lurgan home, and has them call him 'Sir'. 'Good morning, Sir'; 'More toast, Sir?' And this in plebeian Lurgan with its adept deflating tactics! (Actually, of course, this kind of paterfamilias formality was a commonplace of the era, and I shouldn't make too much of it – it's just hard to resist a soupçon of mockery at mercantile Thomas Jordan and his pretensions. ...)

The prospering Thomas Jordans will eventually take over the former home of Lord Brownlow's agent John Hancock in the centre of the town, the manor house at the bottom of Edward Street. By this time, though – the late Victorian era – the Jordan sons have probably succeeded the autocratic father. They may have been equally full of themselves, for all I know. I only mention this pompous branch of the Jordan family, my great-grandmother's relations, to show an unprecedented type of life evolving in post-Famine County Armagh. These factory owners and large-scale employers may be taken to represent a new rising class, the Catholic middle class despised by W.B. Yeats for its go-getting drive and philistine orientation. It had gained a foothold once Emancipation was secured, and now nothing was going to stop its progress. (It pleases me to think of these uppish Jordans in their grand town house being disgraced by the presence of huckster relations just round the corner in lowly John Street. ... and how the latter came to be there I'll relate in a minute.)

The Lurgan of those days in the nineteenth century has a reputation for discord. Rioting in its streets is a feature of the times. Fury and resentment are in the air it breathes. And anyone may get caught up in its shindigs.

Take the elderly John Hancock – still the owner of the Manor House – who, driving home in his carriage one day along Edward Street, is attacked by a stone-throwing mob assembled at the corner of Shankill Street (though it seems their main targets are members of the police force and I don't think Hancock is hit, though no doubt he is shaken and his horses frightened). One of the attackers caught and arrested on a charge of riotous behaviour is a young James Tipping, a son – one of many – of Matthew and his wife Eliza O'Hara. James, unable to pay a fine of 16s 6d, is sentenced to fourteen days in gaol.

A twisted pattern begins to take shape around this incident. Hancock, in fact, is at one with the young stone-throwers in being a major opponent of the Orange Order – a circumstance which, in the past, has got him into very bad odour with Colonel Blacker in particular. Blacker, as a matter of principle, opposes every suggestion put forward by Hancock when both are serving on the Lurgan Union Workhouse board of guardians. The aversion felt by this pair towards one another goes back to the Orange demonstration in the grounds of Carrickblacker House in 1835 and subsequent arrest of some of the demonstrators by the then young magistrate Hancock. ... Had the 1870s rioters been apprised of this fact, would they have held their fire while Hancock and his son drove by? Or, for the young male Lurgan poor and derided with stones in their hands, is *any* carriage-owning person fair game? The spirited thing is to be for ever trying to get your own back for the miserable circumstances fate has dumped you in, to achieve social or tribal recompense in any way available.

So here is Matthew's son James, the first and most heedless of the tearaway Tippings, perhaps, immersed to the full in games of defiance and 'Fenian' assertion and ignorant to the same degree of his own oblique family connection with the topmost Orange dynasty of them all, the bigwig Blackers. And here's John Hancock, whose effigy was once burned by Orangemen, now a target for the other lot and similarly unaware that one of his would-be assailants possesses a modicum of the dread Blacker blood – or indeed that his own well-appointed home will be taken over in due course by people related to the same young stone-thrower through his stepmother Ellen Jordan. Ah, hindsight.

James Tipping was ten years old when his father Matthew uprooted his family from Crossmacahilly and its bogs and trundled them into nearby

Lurgan town on a cart; wife, seven children, belongings and all. We can picture the weariness, the squabbling youngsters, the put-upon wife and exasperated father, as they finally reached their destination, a recently constructed terrace house in James Street, and set about obtaining a bit of order. The year is 1869, and along with its meagre possessions the family comes carrying its strong convictions to a town already vehemently divided along sectarian lines. Two years previously, in the wider world of Irish politics, the Fenian uprising was quelled by the Irish constabulary, aided by 'a great fall of snow' which scattered the insurgents. Jubilation among Orange Lurganites, and concomitant nationalist bitterness, ensued.

The Irish Republican Brotherhood, better known as the Fenian movement, was founded in 1858 by the veteran revolutionary James Stephens; and although it never really took hold in the North, its progress would have been carefully monitored by Catholics and proto-nationalists such as the Tippings. Major events of the time such as the attempted rescue of Fenian prisoners in Manchester and subsequent execution of three of those involved (the Manchester Martyrs), and the explosion at Clerkenwell in London which killed twelve people in the same year, 1867 – these would have had a tremendous impact on ordinary families all over Ireland primed to come down with ferocity on one side or the other. I don't know what degree of literacy prevailed among the nineteenth-century Tippings, but I believe at least some of them would have had sufficient reading skills to get to grips with a newspaper. And certainly, after about 1850, you had local and provincial papers circulating even among the poorest of the population. Even the illiterate had a resource. In every townland there were special houses where groups could gather to hear one person read out the burning news of the day, after which a heated discussion would be set going. (The Tipping farm at Crossmacahilly was one such gathering place in its later days; see p. 116 below.)

'... a deep fall of snow'. This phrase, which I misquoted above, comes from Alice Milligan's best-known and most beguiling poem, 'When I Was a Little Girl'. When she was a little middle-class girl in Omagh, County Tyrone, in the 1870s, the Fenians had acquired an extraneous role. The name was uttered with fear and drama as a topical bugbear, like Bonaparte earlier in the century, to scare small Protestants into instantaneous obedience: 'Come in! or when it's dark / The Fenians will get ye.' The old nurse's nightly threat has an immediate effect on all the little Milligans who scuttle indoors squealing – all bar one.

> But one little rebel there,
> Watching all with laughter,
> Thought 'When the Fenians come
> I'll rise and go after.'

> Wished she had been a boy
> And a good deal older –
> Able to walk for miles
> With a gun on her shoulder ...

Thus was the family rebel shaping up to be an Irish nationalist of the future. Even when the Milligans had moved to Belfast, where Alice found herself 'submerged amid an Orange population' (going to school at the Methodist College), the convictions she'd acquired at an early stage didn't undergo the smallest modification.

It was a cause of annoyance to Alice Milligan that anyone should be considered less of an Irishwoman through being born a Protestant. A strong tradition of Protestant nationalism, from Grattan onwards, reinforced her own particular attachment to Ireland's cause. Among her antecedents, she could point to a great-grandfather who, with his sons, had marched on Antrim with the insurgents of 1798. ... Her attitude in this respect, perhaps inevitably, provoked a degree of estrangement from at least one sibling, her sister Edith who was married to a unionist; but on the credit side it brought Alice many dazzling friendships. She conducted Yeats on an excursion up the Cave Hill when he visited Belfast, and accompanied Roger Casement to a feis at Toomebridge. And among her neighbours on the Antrim Road she found a kindred spirit and fellow poet in Anna Johnston ('Ethna Carbery'). The two young women, one Protestant and one Catholic, joined forces in Belfast, in the late 1890s, to edit a nationalist newspaper, the *Shan Van Vocht*.

James Connolly, who believed the working classes were 'the incorruptible inheritors of the fight for freedom' in Ireland, was a regular contributor; and the name of Miss Maud Gunne (sic) occurs in more than one issue. (But not Constance Markievicz, whose peculiar gardening notes were reserved for the slightly later *Bean na hÉireann*. She advised her readers to look on the English in Ireland in exactly the same light as slugs in a lettuce bed – a view which would have found favour with the *Shan Van Vocht* clientele.) Poets in droves came up with verse for the magazine whose dominant motifs – the heathery hill, the spinning wheel, the milk churn, the holy well, the misty glen, the little green linnet, the black, black wind from northern hills – are full of potent associations for the romantic nationalist. I know, because I lapped them up at an appropriate age, while I was undergoing a sentimental education.

Some of them I encountered for the first time in a small thick notebook, four inches by six and a half, carefully covered in brown paper, into which my mother, as a sixth-former at Mount St Michael's, Lurgan, and later as a student at Queen's University, had transcribed her favourite poems. Yeats was there, and Wilfred Owen, and Hardy and James Stephens and Padraig Pearse and Helen Lanyon. Ethna Carbery and Alice Milligan were well represented in this personal anthology. Their verses struck a chord with me too, when I was sixteen and believed the essence of Irishness resided in some mystical locality of the unadulterated West. Mary O'Hara, Donal of the Rosses, mirth and song, windswept heather ... all these denoted an indigenous exquisiteness far removed from the cinema-going, coffee-drinking, fashion-conscious populations of towns and cities that was our milieu. And by extolling the West, we thought we might aspire to a touch of that aboriginal integrity.

When Alice Milligan's *Hero Lays* was about to be published in 1908, she didn't want the poem 'When I Was a Little Girl' included in the collection. She thought its spirited pro-Fenian stance might offend the Catholic clergy (who had proscribed the movement), or aggravate readers averse to infant militarism. Fortunately George Russell, AE, who edited *Hero Lays* for the publishers Maunsel & Co. in Dublin, told her to catch herself on (or words to that effect). 'The story of your little night-dressed Fenian has put fire in me and in the name of that child I confront you and defy you.' The appeal was irresistible. The poem went in.

Though he regarded himself as a Dubliner, George Russell was actually born in Lurgan (in 1867) and spent his first ten years in the town, attending the non-denominational Lurgan Model School along with his brother and sister. The Russells lived in William Street at the time of his birth, before taking up residence in a gate lodge inside the North Street entrance to Lord Lurgan's demesne. Their circumstances were undoubtedly a lot more comfortable than those available to the incoming Tippings; but, since the town was not large in the 1870s, the younger members of both families must at least have passed one another in the street. Were catcalls exchanged? The insults-and fisticuffs atmosphere of the Lurgan streets was anathema to the future poet and mystic – and once the Russells had bettered their prospects by moving to Dublin, George never ceased to give thanks 'to Providence for the mercy shown to me in removing me from Ulster'. '[T]hough I like the people,' he goes on, 'I cannot breathe the political and religious atmosphere of the North-East Corner of Ireland.' However, he continued to spend long childhood holidays with his maternal grandparents in County Armagh, staunch Church of Ireland people whose parish church was the one at Seagoe originally restored by Valentine Blacker in the seventeenth century.

The James Street lodging was only a temporary resting place for Valentine Blacker's disreputable descendants, Matthew Tipping and his brood. Before long we find the family installed in another terrace house, this time at 3 John Street,[3] which becomes a permanent residence for some of them. Matthew has his trade as a cambric weaver, whether he engages in it at home, or in one of the numerous factories and spinning mills springing up all over Lurgan in response to the increased demand for linen cloth. (It was probably at home; my grandmother remembered an enormous loom taking up half the meagre ground-floor space in the house during her childhood in the 1880s.) To supplement the family income he also sells foodstuffs such as buttermilk and vegetables, obtained from his relations left behind in Crossmacahilly. His outlet for this produce is either an improvised huckster's shop set up in another tiny portion of the John Street house (a common expedient at the time, and later), or a barrow in the market, I am not sure which.

Six years after the move to Lurgan, in 1875, Matthew Tipping's wife Eliza dies in childbirth and is buried in Dougher Cemetery. She is forty years old. She bequeaths to her husband a houseful of children, ranging from Helena (aged twenty-four) down to newly born Peter. Both of these, too, will be dead within a few years, one a victim of tuberculosis and the other uncared for in the immediate aftermath of his mother's death.

As well as sickly Helena, the disrupted household contains two girls

PC's great-grandmother Ellen Tipping – née Jordan – in her Victorian finery

aged eight and five, but the others are all boys and probably not attuned to domestic management. Something needs to be done – and it's up to Matthew to do it. Within six months of Eliza's death, her widower has entered into a new arrangement to restore a measure of order and felicity to the bereft, throughother and overcrowded house. In St Peter's Church in North Street, on 15 May 1876, he is married for the second time, this time round to a tough-minded widow and mother-of-three named Ellen Dowds (née Jordan). This step, indeed, doesn't ease the problem of household congestion; but in other respects, we may suppose, it engenders an improvement. The mystery is how Matthew Tipping persuaded Ellen Dowds to take on the hefty domestic burden he was offering her.

Her own children were then aged ten (Mary Ann), eight (Susan) and five (John), and when the newly-wed couple emerged from the chapel in North Street, instead of confetti they were showered with stones by Ellen's infuriated five-year-old in a bid to drive away the bearded old man who was stealing his mother. It wasn't an auspicious beginning – however, the newly configured family had no option but to settle down and make the best of things. Matthew, the champion 'begetter', promptly sets about founding an extra Tipping dynasty. Fortunately this time he stops at two. I think this final pair of girls may not have been entirely welcome in a house already bursting at the seams, but they quickly learned to stand up for themselves (and for each other). Their names were Ellen and Sarah, and they grew up mettlesome and attractive, with their leg-o'-mutton sleeves and tennis rackets and ability to gad about on bicycles in their spare time. Like all their half-siblings, they were put to work in a local factory at the earliest possible age (maybe the factory owned by their mother's relations), as veiners or stitchers or winders or smoothers. But a new century was dawning, and with it came an opening out of possibilities, hardly discernible at first but increasing as time went on. The last two Tipping daughters were among the brightest of the family – a family sufficiently extensive to form itself into cliques and groups, at one minute antagonistic, the next conciliatory. A saying of Matthew's, in this respect, has gone down to posterity. Ructions were going on upstairs in the tiny house, and Matthew was dispatched by his formidable wife to put a stop to the uproar. When he came back down, having quelled the noise, his wife Ellen demanded to be told what was going on. He shrugged. 'Ach, just the usual. Your childer and my childer fightin' wi' our childer.'

There must have been occasions when Matthew took his youngest daughters to visit the farm at Crossmacahilly where he grew up. I see these Lurgan girls, wearing black laced boots and pinafores, running through the fields, making daisy chains, searching for new-laid eggs, 'supping' buttermilk with oatcakes baked on the griddle. ... All right, a tinge of rose-coloured spectacles is entering into these images of alluring country pursuits, but for all that I don't believe they're unduly fanciful. What else would they have done? ... It's unlikely that Matthew's girls would have had any memory of their Uncle James (another James!), their father's older brother, since he died in 1884 when they were only five and three. But James's remaining offspring stayed on ... and on. The few that were left, that is: out of a family of eleven, it seems, only three survived beyond the age of twenty-five. One of these was a daughter, Bridget, who married a blacksmith from nearby Lylo. The other two turned gradually into a pair of those old bachelor brothers who feature strongly in the literature of the Irish countryside. 'Only Pad is married,' writes Polly Devlin in her enchanting memoir of County Tyrone, *All of Us There*; 'the other brothers, like so many of that generation, have continued to live where they were born.' And Benedict Kiely's story, 'Homes on the Mountain', has 'John and Thady ... still alive in the old house on Loughfresha. Like pigs in a sty ...'.

We needn't, I hope, attribute a comparable degree of slovenliness to Mattha (an archaic form of Matthew) and Barney Tipping, as their seniors and siblings one by one died or moved away from Crossmacahilly until only the two remained. The farm, by this stage, was known in the district as 'a ceilidhe house', where, as I've indicated, neighbours would gather on Saturday nights to hear Mattha read aloud the entire contents of the *Irish Weekly* (a weekend supplement of the nationalist paper the *Irish News and Belfast Morning News*) and debate the urgent events of the day. Mattha enjoyed a reputation as the leading Catholic intellectual of the neighbourhood, and his opinions carried a good deal of weight. When he died in 1922, his brother Barney took over his role. After all the years of overcrowding, the house has now come down to a single occupant. Barney lived on for a further twenty-two years, until 1944, after which time the farm fell into a state of dereliction. Returning to the clay, in William Trevor's potent phrase. Returning to the clay.

I don't think old men like Barney exist any more, living on in the houses in which they were born, eking out a diminished existence in deteriorating circumstances. They'd be whipped off to sheltered accommodation at the first sign of a memory lapse, or tea spilled down an ancient jacket unaccustomed to dry cleaning. But the past, in actuality and in fiction, is full of them. Michael McLaverty's short story, 'Stone', has one, Jamesey Heaney, 'sitting with his hands on his knees, his shoulders drooped forward, [waiting] for the fire to light. At his feet lay his black and white collie, her forepaws in the ashes, a wet nose on the flags. The closed door was slitted with light, and through the nests of cobwebs on the deep windows came a blue wintry brightness. It was cold.' It could be Barney Tipping he's describing.

The two unmarried Tipping brothers (my grandmother's cousins) had a good deal of local and national news, at various times, to air with their friends and neighbours. The fall of Parnell, the presentation and defeat of successive Home Rule Bills, the Boer War, the formation of the Ulster Volunteer Force and then the Irish Volunteers, gun-running at Larne, the signing of the Covenant, the outbreak of war with Germany, the 1916 uprising, Michael Collins visiting Armagh, Partition. ... And always and incessantly, trouble in the streets: the streets of Belfast, Lurgan, Armagh, Portadown. ... Trouble sparked off by deadly and ineradicable religious affiliations. As the novelist and satirist John Morrow has it, the problem with Ireland has always been sects (and you have to be very careful how you say it).

CHAPTER 5

ALL THE DEAD DEARS

Processionals of lives go by
On delicate, crisp treads;
Blurred fragrances, gently percussive,
Stir among leaves.
Top-hatted heads of firms and kitchen-maids
Visit the instincts of the eye.

Douglas Dunn, from 'The People Before'

Like everyone else in the world, I have four great-grandmothers. Unlike many people, though, I know their names: and there isn't an Irish name among them. Ellen Jordan, Catherine Harland, Emily Anne Thorpe, Mathilda Clara Maria Heller. The closest is Ellen Jordan's, though that name is likely of Anglo-Norman provenance; still, if your ancestors have been in the country since the twelfth century, I think you can call yourself Irish. She certainly did – and claimed an unbroken Catholic lineage to boot. She was my mother's feisty maternal grandmother. Nora's other grandmother, her father's mother, was Catherine Harland. At least, Harland was the name she went by. It was her mother's name. Young Catherine began life in post-Famine Lurgan under a serious social disadvantage. She was illegitimate. And unlike Helena Tipping, who was also born out of wedlock in the same decade, she didn't have parents who belatedly gave in to church and family pressures (if that was what Matthew and Eliza did). She didn't have parents, plural. As far as we know, her father's identity was never disclosed.

There's a story here, if only one could get to the bottom of it. Catherine was born in 1859 – and for succeeding generations, right down to the mid twentieth century and beyond, illegitimacy in the family betokened the ultimate loss of face. A sense of sin and degradation was tied up with failures of chastity, and it pervaded every religious group and every social class. A generation later, for example, we find even the worldly (and wealthy) Maud Gonne passing off her daughter Isolde as her niece. People were very prone to be sexually censorious, and if you knew of any irregularity in this respect among your immediate forebears, you'd simply have edited it out of the family narrative. I think it entirely possible that my mother never heard a word about her grandmother's dubious origin. I'm sure she believed Catherine Brady's family background to be as sound as anyone's. It was Catholic, that was the main thing. But was it? 'Harland' is not an Irish or a Catholic name. Harlands first set foot in Ulster in the mid seventeenth century, arriving as immigrants from County Durham. A lot of them then proceeded on to America and a prosperous life, but some stayed put, sinking roots into County Down and County Armagh. They belonged to the Society of Friends. They were very plentiful around Lurgan and Seagoe. They married wives with striking non-Irish names like Duck and Bullock. They called their daughters Elizabeth, Abigail, Rebecca and Catherine. And they remained committed to the Quaker faith – or most of them did. According to the 1911 census, Catherine Harland's mother Elizabeth Harland is the solitary Catholic of that name in the whole of County Armagh.

We can take it, then, that a switch of allegiance occurred at some point in some irresolute branch of the Harland family (which then died out); and as with the Tipping line, conversion to Catholicism goes hand-in-hand with a drop in social status. In 1861, when Catherine is two years old, a hotel called the Greyhound stands in Lurgan's High Street, and round the corner from it is a dodgy cobbled lane or court known as Greyhound Hotel Lane. In that lane lives a family called Harlan. (The Harlan and Harland spellings of the name are interchangeable.) Is this where Catherine grew up? Nothing is known about these obscure and lowly Harlans; but Catherine's mother Elizabeth worked as a servant for the well-to-do Johnston family of brewers at 19 High Street, close by, which suggests a connection in terms of propinquity, if nothing else. We don't know whether Elizabeth at the time was a live-in servant (and later cook) – but it wouldn't have been unusual to find her illegitimate child being brought up by its grandparents and fed an assuaging fiction: that its biological mother was just an older sister in the family.

The ascertainable facts (if they are facts) would have backed up this assertion, in Catherine's case. According to the 1911 census, again, Elizabeth Harland was twelve years old when she gave birth to her only child. (Not that she discloses anything of the sort to the census-takers: the spaces under 'children born' and 'children living' are blank.) We can work this out from her own stated date of birth, 1847. But is it a true date? I don't think so. Many people falsified their ages for the census returns, whether to prolong their working lives, because they'd simply got it wrong, being born before the era of record-keeping, or through forgivable vanity. And in the previous census (1901) Elizabeth had claimed to be fifty-nine years old, which pushes the year of her birth back to 1842. Whatever her true age, though, twelve or seventeen or something in between, Elizabeth was certainly young enough at the time of her daughter's birth to require looking after or shoring up. And maybe she got it at her place of employment. Maybe she kept the child with her in a back room of 19 High Street. Maybe the Church of Ireland Johnstons were sufficiently conscientious to try to do right by their 'wronged' Catholic maidservant – short of incorporating her into the family, of course. For what we have here – well, possibly – is a kind of *December Bride* situation.

In Sam Hanna Bell's novel, set on the Ards peninsula of County Down around the turn of the twentieth century, the eponymous bride Sarah Gomartin works as a servant of the Echlin family, Presbyterian farmers in a desolate spot, and in due course gives birth to a child whose father's identity she either doesn't know, or refuses to specify. Which of the younger Echlins is responsible for the girl's predicament, diminishing her standing in the eyes of the primitive, church-going, bible-clutching community? Either of the Echlin brothers would be glad to marry Sarah, but she holds out, biding her time, driven by an austere integrity, until circumstances bring about a change of heart. This occurs a long time after the initial transgression: hence the title. You read this novel for the pleasures of its Ulster rock-hardness, its spare but somehow picturesque Presbyterianism, the ancestral clock ticking away in the parlour, the scrubbed stone floor, the patchwork quilts. But I don't know if women like Sarah Gomartin ever existed, sufficiently grounded in their own self-reliance to go against community regulations. A nineteenth-century, pregnant, unmarried girl, you feel, wouldn't have hesitated to accept *any* offer of marriage, to get back her squandered reputation. Otherwise, it's all up with her: 'The neighbours will know of my black disgrace.' Propriety matters. 'The Girl's Lament', by William Allingham, gets at the essence of seduction and betrayal, Ulster-country style:

> In our wee garden the rose unfolds,
> With bachelors' buttons and marigolds;
> I'll tie no posies for dance or fair,
> A willow twig is for me to wear.
>
> For a maid again I can never be,
> Till the red rose blooms on the willow tree.
> Of such a trouble I've heard them tell,
> And now I know what it means full well.

The telling phrase, 'My apron-string now it's wearing short', encapsulates the sorry story, the whole grotesque (grotesque to our minds) atmosphere of shame and blame. It's important to stress how deep-rooted was the dread of community censure; no point in applying free-thinking attitudes of the present to past sexual misdemeanours (if that's what they were). I've uncovered quite a few lapses from strict pre-marital chastity among my forebears on both sides; but in most of these instances, *someone* intervened to put things right, before the social damage became irreversible. A hasty marriage was one thing; no marriage at all, another.

Certainly the most dramatic case is that of my great-great-grandmother, Elizabeth Harland. Picture an attractive young child-servant employed in a household containing three lusty boys, all around her own age: James (born 1839); William (born 1844); and Courtney (born 1846). It's not hard to envisage the kind of carry-on that might have taken place – or the inevitable outcome. I can't be certain about this, of course; I may be barking up the wrong family tree entirely. Everyone can point to missing forebears, broken lines of descent – and I've no reason to jam these brewing Johnstons into an ancestral gap of my own. Well, no reason except the obvious one. And suggestive silences and inactions. Where, for example, was the local priest with his holy water and domestic-regulatory impulse? If a young, available, Lurgan Catholic had fathered Elizabeth's child, you'd expect the pair of sinners to be dragged, protesting or not, before the altar. If the girl's condition had nothing to do with the Johnstons, you'd think they would wash their hands of their erring housemaid. But they didn't. We don't know what arrangements were entered into, but they kept her on. Time passed. In the natural course of things the Johnston parents died and the sons entered the professions (as managing director of the family business, tobacco manufacturer and practising solicitor respectively). Their Catholic housemaid Elizabeth Harland was promoted to cook. She never married, and neither did they. The three bachelor brothers and the spinster servant lived on and on in the same High Street house. One wonders what terms the unequal quartet were on: did Elizabeth turn into a stately elderly housekeeper, a known and respected figure in the neighbourhood, or did gossip and scandal plague her all her life? Did her juvenile disgrace stay with her, like a tin can tied to the tail of an inoffensive dog? Why did no one ever teach her to read and write? (The census return has her down as illiterate.) Was she brave or defeated? Did she acknowledge her daughter, or try to pretend she was some other relation? And where *was* baby Catherine during her early years?

Maybe her mother brought her up, as a single parent, and maybe Catherine knew who her father was, but was cautioned never to mention his name. 'If anyone asks – just say he's dead.' On second thoughts – this seems a bit too enlightened a course of action for close-knit, nineteenth-century, stuck-in-the-mud Lurgan. As for Catherine's father – he could have been a passing tramp, for all I actually know to the contrary, with Elizabeth too young or naive to understand what was happening to her when the child was conceived. Maybe the Johnstons were totally disinterested Christians. All one can be sure of is that Catherine was not abandoned, however her presence in the world was explained, and that mother and daughter were, and remained, on good terms. In later life, during the First World War, they lived together for a time in Glasgow. Elizabeth died in 1920, aged seventy-three (or perhaps a bit more). I don't know when the Johnston brothers died, or who inherited the brewing fortune. It was considerably depleted anyway, due to the large sums donated by James, the head of the family, to help fund the building of a Temperance Hall. Was this to atone for some form of intemperance in his past, one wonders? (Ah, irony.)

Family lore has Catherine, in her later years, inhabiting a house in Lurgan crammed with antiques – which suggests that some residue of the Johnston estate may, just may, have ended up with her. Alas, by this stage she'd taken to drink, and as the house was – conveniently – located next door to a pub, these valuable objects one by one found their way over the back wall dividing the two properties in exchange for bottles of gin. (Some of Catherine's grandchildren knew not to call in on her on their way to school if the curtains were drawn: this meant she'd had a rough night.) ... When she died in 1938, Catherine had sufficient resources to leave £5 (£185 in today's money) to each of her grandchildren, of whom there were many (my mother among them).

However and wherever she was reared, Catherine acquired sufficient sewing skills to get employment as a seamstress. It was the lower of the two standard occupations assigned to women in nineteenth-century fiction (the other was the governess, which I'll get to in a minute). Think of Little Dorrit, in the Dickens novel, going out daily from the Marshalsea Prison to sew for survival. Or Mrs Gaskell's heroine Mary Barton, who earns a meagre living as a needlewoman in congested, soot-stained Manchester of the 1840s; or the same author's Ruth, in the novel of that title published in 1853, who exemplifies the wronged-but-virtuous young dressmaker. Indeed, there's a whole 'seamstress' genre featuring long-suffering stitchers whose fate is either to rise in the world, via marriage, or to descend even further into prostitution and a lurid death. Bastard infants accompany them along the latter route. And even for those who will make something of their lives in the future, the present drudgery is unremitting.

> Work – work – work!
> From weary chime to chime,
> Work – work – work
> As prisoners work for crime!
> Band, and gusset, and seam,
> Seam, and gusset, and band,
> Till the heart is sick, and the brain benumbed,
> As well as the weary hand.

'Seamstress' indicates more than a job: it signifies an entire condition of female lowliness and ill-paid labour. I don't know to what extent the conditions evoked by Thomas Hood in his famous 'Song of the Shirt' were replicated in 1870s Lurgan, but certainly the town offered scope for hardship and exploitation, along with its sectarian delinquencies. Sore eyes and malnutrition. Perpetual exhaustion. Closer to home, too, and some way in the future, you have the poet 'Richard Rowley' (pen name of the businessman Richard Valentine Williams, who died in 1947) impersonating one of his own Belfast factory workers – 'The needles go leppin' along the hem,/And my eyes is dizzy wi' watchin' them' – in a tone akin to the resentment and fatalism of the Hood poem:

> Monday morning till Saturday,
> I sit an' stitch my life away ...
> An' what have I ever done or been,
> But just a hand at a sewing machine?

Catherine Harland, though, as the bastard child of an illiterate servant, might have counted herself lucky to gain a foothold in the sewing profession, whether she worked from home (wherever 'home' was), sewing shirts for a pittance, or, more likely, as a stitcher in a local handkerchief factory (maybe even the factory owned by the prospering Catholic Jordans). Later on, she describes herself as a dressmaker, which indicates a slight progression upwards. But she's married by then. Through her work, Catherine has met a young Lurgan tailor named Terence Brady, and the two of them get married in 1880 when they're both just twenty-one. (Unusually for my family, I don't think Catherine is pregnant at the time. But she'd have had the best incentive in the world to practise abstinence: her own situation, and her mother's.) To become a tailor, Terence would have had to serve an apprenticeship and gain necessary expertise, and as the wife of a respectable tradesman, Catherine could hold her head high and cast off the scandal of her origins. It was a triumph of a kind. Her mother's ill luck, or ill judgement, was not revisited on Catherine. (But Elizabeth, the Johnstons' servant, may have enjoyed a luxury unavailable to the vast majority of her contemporaries: a room of her own.)

Young Mr and Mrs Brady set up home at 37 Edward Street, where their first son William was born in 1881. He was my grandfather. He was followed swiftly by ten brothers and sisters, of whom only half survived into adulthood. Losses and gains. I'm happy that Catherine overcame her social handicap to fit into normal Lurgan Catholic plebeian life. But in some ways her mother Elizabeth had the better part – room to breathe and congenial surroundings. Yes, I know her work as a servant and cook was hard, but independence and security of a kind must have counted for something. And she'd have had time off, perhaps to lend a hand with her proliferating grandchildren, whether these were acknowledged as such, or not. Or perhaps I'm talking through my hat. What do I know about it? The details of Elizabeth's life, like those of innumerable other lives, are simply and utterly irretrievable. I've decided, though, that my great-great-grandmother was seventeen, not twelve, when her daughter was born. I'm basing this conclusion on the fact that many census respondents are overtaken by vagueness when it comes to the question of age. They make a wildly inaccurate estimate of the number of years they've been alive. The old rogue Matthew Tipping, for instance, claims a date of birth in 1841, which would make him ten years old when he first became a father. Sexually precocious he may have been, but we needn't cast him as a biological phenomenon.

Yes, Elizabeth was seventeen; and this makes the eldest Johnston son the most likely candidate for illegitimate fatherhood. But everything surrounding this time of drama – the shame and horror and remorse and agitation – is now lost for ever. The facts can never be recovered; and so, for the moment, I think, I've indulged in sufficient speculation about the matter. To stick with an unadorned sequence of events within a hundred-year span: Elizabeth gave birth to Catherine, who gave birth to William, who 'begat' Nora, who gave birth to me. While William lay in his cradle in a house in Edward Street, his future bride – already three months old when he came into the world – lay gurgling and kicking her heels in another cradle by the side of a hand-loom, in a house only a couple of streets away. She lay in her cradle, taking everything in, while her stern half-brother Henry Tipping prowled beside her with his hands clasped behind him, back and forth, back and forth, in the tiny room.

Henry is twenty-five, and may already have his eye on fifteen-year-old Mary Anne Dowds, his stepmother's daughter. But it will take another six years to get these two to the altar, though they've lived in the same house, along with all the rest of the mixed-up family, since 1876. When the Tipping/Dowds wedding takes place, it is – again – under duress.

Henry Tipping's greengrocer's shop in Edward Street, with Henry himself standing in the doorway

Mary Anne, twenty-one, is three months pregnant. No, says her grandson, my cousin Harry Tipping, it's not incest: though complications on the domestic front may suggest otherwise. Henry and Mary Anne are not related by blood; it's just that his father's wife is her mother (or as my grandmother and her full sister Ellen might have put it, testing their contemporaries with a conundrum, their mother's daughter married their father's son). ... And considering the conditions under which they all mucked in together, all the Tippings and Dowds and overlapping generations, it's surprising that more in the way of coital shenanigans didn't take place (as far as we know). ... At any rate, in September 1887, whether in a furtive or a festive spirit, Henry Tipping and Mary Anne Dowds (the gentle Mary Anne, she was known in the family) are pronounced man and wife and detach themselves from the whole jing-bang of John Street, from parents and siblings and half-siblings and step-siblings and all. Henry, showing a bit of enterprise, has already set himself up as a greengrocer, renting a small shop in Edward Street and the flat above it; twenty-odd years later, well into the new century, Henry transfers his business to rather better premises, still in Edward Street (76). Here his and Mary Anne's ten children grow up conscious of Orange hegemony and Catholic 'underdog' status, and in due course align themselves with the republican movement in the North, up to and beyond the signing of the Treaty. (I'll consider their activities at this time in the following chapter.)

Henry never came before a magistrate on a charge of riotous behaviour, and in this he failed to uphold the family reputation. They were great belligerents, all highly active on the nationalist side. I've already mentioned the young James Tipping (b. 1859) who was caught 'clodding' stones at poor John Hancock (who wasn't his enemy) and gaoled as a consequence (see p. 108–9). Henry's and James's brother Matthew,[1] born at Crossmacahilly in 1861 and likewise a dab hand with a cobblestone, was arrested in 1881 and charged with assault on the say-so of a Protestant youth named Thompson, who claimed he was innocently passing the Convent of Mercy in Edward Street when a stone flung by Matthew struck him in the face. It split his lip wide open, he complained, and broke a couple of his teeth. The incident took place in the early part of the summer, with the marching season imminent and sectarian passions running sky-high. Matthew's offence was beyond dispute, and the presiding magistrate, fed up with rowdyism and hotheads and endless faction fights disfiguring the streets, sentenced him to a month's imprisonment. (Matthew could have stayed at large if he'd had the resources to fork out twenty shillings and costs, but I doubt if this was an option for a poor factory hand.)

It wasn't the last of Matthew's court appearances. Four years later he's up again before the same JP, Colonel Waring, after supposedly running with a crowd in North Street pelting the police with stones and bottles, shouting and rampaging and barging their way through to a Protestant quarter. A St Patrick's Day parade was the occasion for this particular fracas. The nationalist faction was asserting its right to march along a stretch of ground at Church Place – between North Street and Edward Street – which the Protestants held to be Orange territory. It was the usual recipe for a flare-up of violence, with the usual police injuries suffered as a consequence – for which, in this instance, Matthew Tipping was held responsible. He denied the charge but several witnesses put him at the scene, making a guilty verdict inevitable. This time, it was a forty-shilling fine or two months' imprisonment. I don't know which of the two Matthew opted for. But by proclaiming his innocence, he added fuel to the nationalists' burning conviction of being unfairly targeted, penalised and kept down, in a hostile state. It was always and ever, 'us and them'. 'There was then,' William Carleton had asserted earlier in the century, 'no law *against* an Orangeman, and no law *for* a Papist.' The nineteenth-century Tippings would have gone along with that, and no doubt could have cited experiences of their own to back it up. But it was only from the 1880s on, in the bitter, grimy, insubordinate streets of Lurgan, that their Papist orientation blossomed into a full-blown commitment to all things Irish. Playing Gaelic football, joining *Cumann na nGaedhal*, attending every local ceilidhe and Irish concert, marching with *Na Fianna Éireann* and *Óghlaigh na hÉireann* ... these activities brought a charge of glamour and purposefulness to workaday Catholic existences, and Tippings were there in the thick of them, along with other prominent local families, Thornberrys and Bradys and O'Hagans and Haugheys and others. (I'll go into this more fully in Chapter Six.)

Another of that unruly generation, the first Matthew's oldest son and Henry Tipping's brother John, fulfilled family expectations by getting himself arrested in his turn for disrupting the peace. Twenty-eight years old, John faced a charge of being drunk and disorderly and assaulting a sheriff's officer in the street. The date of this particular shindy was September 1882, and the magistrate, wearied, no doubt, by all the unrepentant Tipping faces popping up before him, one after the other in a grim succession, delivered a typical verdict: ten shillings or fourteen days. I'm sure Colonel Waring hoped he'd seen the last of them. But then, only a month later, up comes yet another of the hooligan crew. Bernard Tipping, born in 1862, the youngest of Henry's brothers. This time, though, proceedings are the other way round. Bernard is the plaintiff here, charging a youth named James Mulholland with having stabbed him in the left side during an encounter in Market Street on the night of 9 October. 'Some blows were struck between him and me before I was stabbed,' Bernard declared; and, in a burst of candour, 'I believe I struck the first blow when we "squared" out to fight.' Mulholland, an employee of Bullick, Hamilton & Co.'s linen factory and a Protestant, said he happened to be carrying an opened knife when Tipping hit him in the eye, implying that the subsequent stabbing occurred more or less by accident. Confronted with exhibit A − Bernard's bloody shirt − Mulholland insisted he was so frightened and damaged that he couldn't help striking out with the knife. Matthew, Bernard's father, then weighed in with a statement to the effect that a Dr Gribben, summoned by him to patch up his bleeding son, had pronounced Bernard 'dangerously ill'. This drew from the exasperated Colonel Waring a surprising retort. 'I would not take Dr Gribben's evidence as to the health of a cat,' he snapped. The case was adjourned – and as the press failed to follow it up, the outcome remains unknown. I suspect that Bernard won a small amount of compensation, but I can't be sure about this.

One does not envy Colonel Waring his job as presiding magistrate at Lurgan Petty Sessions Court in the 1880s, inundated as he was with batch after batch of cases involving sectarian delinquency. The old courthouse on the corner of William Street and Charles Street might have been purpose built to discourage Protestant-versus-Catholic street-ferocity. Not that *any* deterrent was sufficient to restrain ancestral, or quasi-ancestral, convictions, during encounters between immemorial opponents. But local JPs did their best. And irony, albeit unrecognised irony, was not excluded from the courthouse precincts. I'm thinking not only of the Tipping/Blacker connection, with its implications for neutralisation, but of slighter anomalies which inevitably crept in. For example, in the case of Tipping versus Mulholland, a member of the bench was John Johnston, Esq., JP – original employer of the child Elizabeth Harland and father of her three contemporaries, James, William and Courtney. If my suppositions regarding the Johnston family have any substance, the JP is involved at this moment in passing judgement on his infant great-grandson's future wife's half-brother. Ah, Lurgan interdenominational, cross-community complexities.

This was the world into which my grandmother arrived at the tail-end of a boisterous family, in a house filled with firebrand half-brothers and flouncing half-sisters, a world of grievances, street brawls, arrests, consternation and uncertain tempers in the home. Born on 10 July, she'd have woken, at two days old, to the sound of Orange menace, drum-beaters and Taig-baiters marching in a show of domination and pageantry. It was a day for Papists to stay behind firmly closed doors (though many didn't). My grandmother is getting a foretaste of the life of contention in front of her, with which certain well-honed survival skills, including self-reliance, humour and assertion, will enable her to cope. I don't see her as suffering from the character defect she later attributed to me, when she'd inform all and sundry that I was 'very backward in coming forward'. She meant it kindly, but it bewildered her. Shyness was not an option in the household to which fate had consigned her. The quality she most admired was gumption, and in this, at the time, I was sadly deficient.

When Sarah is just eight years old, her father Matthew has his turn before the magistrates – not in the guise of an elderly brawler backing up his street-fighting sons, as you might think, but standing accused of selling ale from his front-parlour shop without a licence to deal in liquor. Some 'begrudger' has tipped off the police, who raid the John Street premises and confiscate a half-barrel of ale. Matthew claims the ale was brought in for his own use, to appease a weak digestive system which baulks at milk and tea. (Was there laughter in court? And did the aforementioned Dr Gribben testify on Matthew's behalf? One wonders.) He pulls it off. The case is dismissed. Counsel for the defence, a Mr Menary, is eloquent about the state of affairs that leaves 'a rich man's cellar' free from intrusion, while a poor man's solitary half-keg of ale makes an occasion for a criminal prosecution. His remarks raise a cheer in the courtroom, where it is felt that some kind of democratic principle has been asserted. Matthew's ale is returned to him. His wife Ellen Jordan, herself a tremendous 'argufier' by all accounts, would have relished the verdict but found it mortifying to be so publicly designated 'poor'. Ellen has many obstacles to surmount in her bid for respectability, with the antics of her immediate family high among them.

It's 1889, and Lurgan resounds to the blare of factory hooters, the din of rappers-up rousing people out of their beds to hasten to their work, the clip-clop of horses' hooves, the raucous voices of bulky Belfast women, just off the train and trundling handcarts towards the Thursday market. Dealers in second-hand clothes and poor people's delph. The raggedy, heavy, crow-black clothes of these market women would have rendered them slightly sinister in the eyes of local children, including eight-year-old Sarah Tipping on her way to and from her girls' elementary school in an outbuilding attached to the convent in Edward Street. Baba Yaga. The Hansel-and-Gretel woman. Not that Sarah isn't venturesome and alert, for ever on the go, dodging in and out of the crowds, maybe licking a toffee apple or buying a penny bun from a countrywoman come to town with her huge wicker basket full of wares. Is the eight-year-old dressed in a pinafore over a woollen dress and black laced boots? (I don't want to superimpose an E. Nesbit garnish over nineteenth-century Lurgan realities, but some images stick in your head and won't be eradicated.) Is her sister Ellen larking about with her, or her best friend Minnie Cochrane? If they step incautiously into alien territory, are their ears assaulted with sectarian taunts (while they give as good as they get: 'Fenian scum'; 'Proddy pigs' – accompanied by giggles and scurrying down the nearest alleyway)? ...Well, I know you can't conjure up a truthful picture of ancient unrecorded activities; but perhaps if you make an effort you may just catch sight of some ghostly ancestral figure vanishing round a corner – the corner of Wellington Street and Black's Court, say – with a swish or a flash of an antique garment, corduroys or britches or a ground-length woollen skirt, intent on some pursuit of the far distant past.

Grandmothers, great-grandmothers. In my particular line of descent, the counterpart to Catholic Lurgan is Protestant Wexford. However, the great-grandmother I know least about is the Wexford one, Emily Anne Thorpe. My paternal grandmother's mother. Born in Enniscorthy (I think), c.1849. She was farmer William Lett's second wife, and that date of birth would put her at forty when her only child, my father's mother, was born. (As with the Lurgan Tippings, there were Lett half-siblings about the place.) Am I right in attributing to Emily Anne a background filled with Enniscorthy shopkeepers? Perhaps. Some 'modest gentlemen's houses' in the neighbourhood were inhabited by people with the name of Thorpe – Castle View, New Ross, for example, Knockroe House, New Ross, and Shanballyroe House, also in New Ross – but again, I can't pin down a connection to any of them. I wish I could, for these are elegant, evocative, stone-built, eighteenth- or early nineteenth-century houses, not unlike the house in Antrim in which I've lived for the past decade or more. ... As a passionate conservationist and architectural aficionado, I offer thanks to God, or whatever means the good (and to the Irish Georgian Society), that so many ancient Wexford houses have survived into the twenty-first century. I don't care if these houses carry associations with yeomen or Orange magistrates or Protestant supremacy or any other historical embodiment of devilishness. Even those disfigured by oppression or bloodshed have long transcended the darkness imposed on them. Their aesthetic impact today is the thing that counts. They are vivid conduits to an earlier life. They are part of the Irish heritage common to all of us, high or low or at whatever point in between.

Having a Wexford grandmother and further-back relations from the tail-end of the country, was for me a way of boosting my Irishness in the eyes of my contemporaries – as long as I didn't mention the awkward Protestant bit. Wexford, Loch Garman, was all to do with heroic pikemen, 1798, 'The Croppy Boy', the thatched houses of the Irish poor, extreme devotion to the Catholic church. It's hard to fit Letts and Thorpes and Hornicks into that cultural dynamic, but I was happy if the implied indigenousness passed unchallenged. I suppose I was hoping to transmit an impression of my grandmother as a barefoot *cailín* in a red cloak on a wild mountainside surrounded by gorse and heather and the fumes of turf.

The turf may be authentic, but the rest was not. It derives from a picture postcard, *c.*1910. (I shouldn't forget the Connemara donkey-and-cart along with the rest of the 'autochthonous' baggage.) My grandmother's father belonged to the 'strong farmer' class; he kept indoor and outdoor servants and slept in a four-poster bed. He attended the local Church of Ireland church. He had four daughters and a son – the son he disinherited in a fit of pique in 1928. Everything he owned was willed to his second (unmarried) daughter, Annie Tennant Lett. Well, aside from two bequests of fifty pounds each, one to his daughter Emily Craig. Father and daughter must have been reconciled by this stage – if reconciliation was required. I'm guessing again, but there is evidence to suggest they fell out earlier, and it's possible that Emily came very close to being disowned altogether: she was a wayward girl! (I see the hand of Aunt Annie as a peacemaker in any subsequent mending of relations.)

I was thirty or thereabouts when my grandmother Emily died, but I never got to know her well, or felt that she and I had a great deal in common. True, until I was twelve or so, I was taken at least every other Sunday to visit her Dunmurry home, travelling with my parents from Belfast on the Hillhall bus; and after that time I'd still see her at regular intervals. But I never spent time alone with her. The gate lodge was always coming down with grown-up relations and other visitors, and I'd escape into an outhouse to leaf through mildewed copies of *Woman's Home Journal*, or a pile of my Auntie Hazel's old *Girls' Crystals*. Or I'd borrow an old rusty bike and keep on wobbling round and round the house until I'd actually succeeded in staying on the rickety thing, sailing past the kitchen window before the amazed eyes of assembled grown-ups. (Perhaps.) That was how I learned to ride a bicycle, in my tenth year. Some relations I was pleased to see (and the spaniel Sha), but my grandmother's presence I just took for granted. She was part of a world filled with fixed points of reference and changeless circumstances, changeless as the whitewashed gateposts and Belleek china tea set laid out on the damask tablecloth. Besides, old people really were old in those days – nowadays they're Claire Tomalin or Joanna Lumley. My grandmother would only have been sixty-something when I knew her best, but she seemed ancient to me, slippered, toothless, shapeless, clad in a patterned overall, a hairnet enfolding her thin grey hair.

So it came as quite a surprise when I first saw a photo of the young Emily Lett – or Emily Craig as she'd have been at the time (you can see her wedding ring). It's a formal photograph of a well-dressed couple seated side by side on elaborately carved chairs in some photographer's studio, my grandparents in their glossy youth. They gaze impassively at the camera, seated bolt upright, he with folded arms across a well-cut jacket and waistcoat, she in a pale cotton, high-necked blouse, thick dark hair arranged on top of her head in accordance with the style of the day. The very image of a handsome, well-omened Protestant Irish pair. They seem to be asserting their presence in the world, and their commitment to one another. There's an innocence about her, however, a guilelessness, while he wears a challenging look. And what you don't see in the picture is the drama and agitation surrounding their wedding, the tears and recriminations and delays. Neither do you see their infant son Stanley, born in October 1910. The Craig/Lett marriage was solemnised just a month earlier, on 7 September. A significant date: it was also my grandmother's twenty-first birthday, the day she came of age. You'd have to infer from this that Emily's engagement to William Craig did not go down well with the Clonleigh household. I don't know if Emily's mother was still alive (she wasn't a year later, I learn from the 1911 census). She is missing from the domestic fracas. But the girl's father was there, a man of strong opinions, and something impelled him to keep his fecund daughter from 'regularising' her situation until the last possible moment. Had he had other plans for her? It made no odds. The instant she was free to do so – and just in the nick of time – Emily Lett married William Craig. Had she already run away from home and moved in with the villain of the piece at his New Ross lodgings? Or did she remain at Clonleigh and brazen it out before the neighbours, all the while enduring paternal anger and disapproval? It can't have been an easy time – and I'd never have thought of my grandmother as bold or strong-willed or enterprising; a pliable girlhood, I'd have attributed to

Patricia Craig's grandparents, *c.*1911

her, a docile, amiable disposition. Perhaps I was wrong. Or perhaps none of the above scenarios existed. But you can't get away from the facts, the dates of the marriage and of Stanley's birth.

Stanley – or Robert Stanley, as he was christened – was born in Ayr, far from Clonleigh and its contretemps. The previous month, as we've seen, his parents were married in the parish church of Templeudigan, County Wexford (St Peter's), where the officiating vicar no doubt averted his gaze from the bride's protuberance. The witnesses were an Annesley Kavanagh and an Annie McClintock (about whom I know nothing whatever). The bridegroom's place of residence is down as 'New Ross'. His occupation is 'coachman'. The fathers of bride and groom are both described as farmers. (Why do I think my great-grandfather Craig was at one point in his career a policeman on the Lisburn Road in Belfast? Either it's a genealogical fallacy – and a few of those will creep in from time to time – or there's an explanation for the change of occupation which I may find later.) Once married, the errant couple hasten to Scotland, where as far as anyone knows they've been man and wife for years. In a short time Robert Stanley comes into the world (was the 'Robert' in honour of Burns? Again, I have no way of knowing). Did my grandfather obtain employment as a coachman? It would have been something to do with horses anyway, he worked with horses all his life.

With a name like Craig, you would think the small family would fit like Cinderella's foot in the slipper into lowland Scottish life. But less than four years later we find them domiciled in Dublin where a second child is born. The abundantly named Emily Charlotte Annie Marie Heller Craig – fortunately soon abbreviated to plain Marie – is the first of four daughters. The original delinquent pair are now well settled and forging ahead as unimpeachable procreators. And if it wasn't for nosy descendants prying into their private history, the initial sexual transgression would never have surfaced to slightly undermine their church-going respectability. As with my mother and Catherine Harland, I don't believe any of their children knew a thing about it.

But who exactly was this William Craig whom farmer Lett declined to take to his bosom? (As far as I know.) A wild boy who'd run away from home in 1898 at the age of fourteen and got himself taken on as a stable hand at Finnebrogue, near Downpatrick – in defiance of his parents' project to secure for him a start in life as a railway clerk. They thought it would make a good career for him, but he wasn't having any of it. He knew what he wanted, and it didn't include dispensing tickets to the travelling public, or sitting on a high stool poring over a ledger. So he fled to Finnebrogue. How he subsequently arrived in County Wexford, or when he first encountered the comely but vulnerable Miss Lett, I have no idea. He seemed to get around, my grandfather, before he brought his family to settle in Dunmurry where he took up a post as head groom to the Charley family, sinking roots into the district and adapting to its ways. Here, at the end of 1917, a third child, christened William Albert Thomas – my father – was born. As for my grandfather's father, the coachman/farmer/policeman who may or may not have been born in Dublin, but who definitely had connections with Leitrim, Donegal, the Ards peninsula and Belfast ... I know only a little about him. I know his political persuasion was as Orange as William Johnston's of Ballykillbeg. And I have his death notice from the *Belfast Telegraph* of 28 April 1925. '... Suddenly, at his residence, Drumawhey, Newtownards, County Down ... late of Kinlough, Bundoran.' Seventy-five years old, so he'd have been born in 1850. His grave is in Belfast's City Cemetery – ten minutes' walk from my birthplace. Between himself and his peripatetic second son, my grandfather, a good deal of Irish ground gets traversed. If they'd had a more distinctive name than Craig – Tipping, Topping, Twyble, Trimble, Turkington – their antecedents might be discoverable. As it is, researchers are stymied by the nearly generic patronymic. (When I was eighteen and determined to be as Gaelic as possible, I was known as Pádraigín de Creag: of the rock.)

Well, I could claim the family originated in Ayrshire, Aberdeen or Orkney, and that one of them – the Reverend John Craig – was a colleague of John Knox, and therefore implicated in the start of the Covenanting movement and the whole exodus to Ulster. But hypothesis and probability can only take us so far. My Craig great-grandfather remains essentially unknown, along with all his forebears. With his wife, however – his first wife, my great-grandmother – it's a different matter. And here my religious ancestry takes an unforeseen turn. To the whole admixture of Catholicism, Protestantism, Quakerism and probably Scottish Presbyterianism, I have to add a German Lutheran dash. In 1881, the three-generations-back William Craig, definitely a coachman at this stage, had married a young German governess named Mathilda Clara Maria Heller (she was known as Marie).

Both of them were employed by the May family, one-time sovereigns of Belfast. We've now gone back to the 1870s and the Dublin residence of the Rt Hon. George Augustus Chichester May, Lord Chief Justice of Ireland between 1877 and 1887.[2] George Augustus and his wife Olivia (née Barrington) had a lot of children, including Charlotte Olivia, Edward, George, Stella and Josephine (who died in 1873, aged four) – ten in all. During the months of winter and spring, the May family lived at 13 Fitzwilliam Square, in the lofty and punctilious manner appropriate to their standing, and to the era. The handsome square with its enclosed central garden was home to a lot of doctors and lawyers, soldiers and academics, and many of the families occupying its elegant, five-storey Georgian houses were related to one another. For instance, the younger Mays had hordes of cousins – Barrington, Jellett and le Fanu cousins – living close by, creating a juvenile network of gaiety and seasonal pursuits. A treat for the children might consist of a walk to College Green, in the charge of a nursemaid, to view the illuminations celebrating the Prince of Wales's marriage; or a visit to the pantomime at the Theatre Royal, going through dark winter streets festooned with stalls attended by women selling apples and oranges by the light of lanterns made out of paper bags. On Sundays, they were all marched to church at St Stephen's, Mount Street, with their parents walking arm-in-arm behind them, 'after the fashion of the day'.

PC's great-grandmother Marie Heller, *c.*1878

A pattern for the children's upbringing went something like this. A nurse or nursemaid for the infants, followed by a governess once the age of reason was attained. Then, at ten or so, the boys would be enrolled at a Dublin day school, before going on to Rugby in Warwickshire (or some similar establishment). By this stage they'd have had manliness instilled into them by being encouraged to kill every bird, fish or non-domestic animal that came within their orbit. It was called sport. It was a preparation for killing Boers, Asiatic wild animals and Irish insurgents, when 1916 came around.

I learn all this, and more, from a very stilted book of reminiscences by an old soldier, Major-General Sir Edward Sinclair May.[3] When Major-General Sir Edward S. May was a boy in Fitzwilliam Square, he listened to a lot of servants' gossip about the Fenian Brotherhood and its hopes for Ireland, and among the things that stayed in his mind was a recollection of daily walks with his governess past Mountjoy Prison, while Fenian trials were taking place inside it. He doesn't say what his attitude to the Fenian uprising was, but I think we can take it that it wasn't approving. The governess in question can't have been my great-grandmother as she was only thirteen at this time, and still living with her family in Bremen. (Edward May was two years younger.) But she may have come next in the succession of May family governesses. She was with the family in Howth on her twentieth birthday in July 1874, and the cards she received on that date from her employers – and kept for ever after in her personal photograph album – suggest she was held in high regard by the lot of them.

This wasn't the usual situation of the nineteenth-century governess. Numerous novels, journals and autobiographies tell a different story, one of taunts, privations and humiliations. Between *Jane Eyre* and *The Turn of the Screw* – between the force of destruction emanating from the attic, and exposure to extreme psychological or psychic peril – the young woman teacher sent out to make her way in the world requires constant vigilance to keep her from harm.

She also needs to be endowed with fortitude. At a time when most women never moved far from the place where they started, the idea of uprooting oneself and living among strangers must have loomed like a nightmare before the faint-hearted. But my great-grandmother, not a whit daunted, left her home in Bremen with her Saratoga trunk, waved goodbye to her parents and siblings, and crossed the North Sea and then the Irish Sea to reach her destination in Dublin. It was a great adventure. The Mays, for their part, would have got what they paid for: a young woman well equipped to instruct and win over their daughters and younger sons, and keep order in the schoolroom. They were well enough placed to pick and choose among the applicants for the post of governess, and something about Marie Heller must have commended itself strongly.

A lot has been written about the socially ambiguous status of the governess in a grand family. Is she a servant or isn't she? What degree of hobnobbing is permitted between her and her employers? How does she deal with resentment in underservants obliged to wait on her? Each case was different, of course, and I get a sense that Marie Heller was something of a pet with the Mays and their social circle, perhaps because of the novelty of her origins. (She was also a good deal better educated than most of them: I know of her immersion in the world of literature, and I'd like to attribute to her a certain moral and intellectual refinement as well.)

She was born in Berlin, a city of tall houses, balconies and linden trees, in 1854. The previous year, her father, Friedrich Wilhelm Heller – how German that is! – had received an honourable discharge from the Prussian army, and was free to resume his original, ancestral occupation. He was a potter, the third son of a master potter, born in a place called Zellin, in 1814 – Zellin being located in Prussia then, though I think it was ceded to Poland after the Second World War. At any rate, it was somewhere close to what is now the border between Germany and Poland. His wife, Maria Bertha Dorothea Vogel (b. 1820), had a different upbringing as a Berliner and the daughter of a piper in the king of Prussia's army. The names of Maria Bertha Dorothea's parents were Johann Gottlieb Vogel and Julianne Stolzenbach – and that's as far back as I'm going along the German line. These are only names to me, and foreign names at that. I can hardly comprehend that people called Vogel, Heller and Stolzenbach are among my direct ancestors: but there they are. Their northern European faces – those born in the age of photography, that is – gaze out inscrutably from the pages of Marie Heller's family album. There they stand, in their studied poses, frock coats and nineteenth-century silhouettes, transfixed in a faraway realm of the past and utterly unapproachable. An image has survived of my Berlin great-great-grandmother Bertha Vogel, but it's as enigmatic as the apparition of Miss Jessell in the Henry James story, and as wispy as woodsmoke. Indeed, I have very little grip on my German forebears; though – when I think of historic European cities with mediaeval courts and cobbled streets and four- or five-storey, half-timbered houses, I could wish it was otherwise. '*Je regrette l'Europe aux anciens parapets.*'[4]

When Marie was five, the family upped sticks for the Free Hanseatic city of Bremen (with a population of about sixty thousand, as opposed to Berlin's nearly half a million). To move home at the time was quite a business, requiring all kinds of certificates including one which stated that the Hellers 'had given no cause for complaint' while they lived in

Berlin. An unimpeachable family then, to which were added several offspring during the 1860s (though Bertha was well into her forties by this date). Marie, the fourth daughter, would have been a bright little girl who shone in the schoolroom (just like her future granddaughter-in-law, my Lurgan mother), with a good grasp of languages and a love of German literature. Heinrich Heine, Ludwig Uhland, Joseph von Eichendorff and Karl Simrock were among the poets whose works she wrote out meticulously – page after page – in a special poetry notebook: a resource for difficult times, a talisman she kept by her for the rest of her life. Marie's future as some kind of teacher was already marked out, perhaps, at an early stage; though no one could have envisaged her eventual resting place in a desolate Leitrim graveyard with incessant Irish rain coming down in sheets against the headstones, and the wind soughing among the yew trees.

Interspersed with the German family photos in Marie's album are sepia pictures of the beau monde Mays and their acquaintances, and of the young governess's Dublin friends. Among the latter is Miss Maria Merrin who seems also to be a resident of 13 Fitzwilliam Square – was she perhaps another May employee? Marie has inscribed a photograph of herself, a present for this Miss Merrin, with the words: 'Remember in later years always your old friend in pleasure and pain, Marie Heller. 19 November 1876.' The photographic studio is that of Geo. Mansfield, 90 Grafton Street, Dublin. You also find a Cissy Dempsey in the album, and Louise Helms who writes to Marie, 'Forget me not', in the standard sentimental fashion. One of the governess's twentieth birthday greetings comes from her employer Mrs Olivia May, 'with affectionate love'. It is dated Locksley, 16 July 1874. There was a country house called Locksley, of recent construction (1860s), one of a pair, the other being Rosedale, built at Howth for the Guinness family – is it the same Locksley? Possibly the Mays had rented the house for the summer. Other summers saw them ensconced at Violet Hill, near the seaside resort of Bray, at Killarney Wood or Bray Head House (the property of the Putland family). No doubt there were picnics, with hide-and-seek and the younger contingent dodging in and out of the trees, croquet on the lawn and excursions by carriage to local beauty spots.

And there in the midst of all these decorous goings-on is my youthful ancestress, revelling in her popularity, speaking German or French to her charges, contributing to the gaiety of every innocuous occasion. I like to think that Marie Heller crammed a lot of enjoyment into the thirty-six years vouchsafed to her. I see her as a small girl with a watering-can attending to geraniums, nasturtiums or climbing roses on a balcony in Berlin; or − wrapped in rugs − being drawn on a sleigh through the snow-laden streets. Christmas, the great festival of the German year, was a time of magic and wonder to her. 'O Christmas, Christmas! Highest feast!/We cannot comprehend its joy ...'. These lines, in German, by the poet Nikolaus Lenau, have a place in Marie's hand-written anthology. Her relish for the Christmas season may have been transmitted to me, genetically − I can't otherwise explain my delight in the changed atmosphere obtained by the glittering fir tree and other trappings of the time of year. I'm not and never was a crackers-and-paper-hat person; but each December, and more so as I get older and older, I insist on bringing into the house a Christmas tree to be festooned with antique baubles. This frivolity certainly isn't an inheritance from the other side of my family, for reasons I'll touch on later. Even my mother, who made something utterly enchanting of *my* childhood Christmases, was apt, on her own account, to disparage the whole annual fuss-about-nothing and tinselly tomfoolery (as she saw it). There was a defensive element to this, supposedly common-sense rejection of festive indulgence, as we shall see.

I don't know if Marie Heller ever made the return journey to Germany once she'd left home to be a governess, but I am sure the pull of the homeland remained. ... However, her position with the Mays is consolidated; and, in the great houses of her employers, she is sheltered from the fraught events of the day − Land Wars, evictions, boycotts, assassinations. The legacy of the Fenian movement. Time passes − 1876, (bringing the death of Mrs Olivia May, with what repercussions on the governess's position, I don't know) ... 1877, '78 − and, on the home front, trouble occurs. Does the twenty-two-year-old son of the family cast a seigneurial eye on the twenty-four-year-old governess, or is it someone else who has designs on her? The truth can never be known now, but an established fact is that, in the early summer of 1880, the young German woman finds herself in an age-old predicament. Like Eliza O'Hara, like Elizabeth Harland, like her future daughter-in-law Emily Lett, she is pregnant out of wedlock. I am sorry to harp on all this amatory irregularity raging through my background like wildfire on a heath − and perhaps the source of the 'bad blood' attributed to me by the nuns of St Dominic's High School in Belfast – but I can't seem to get away from it.

Bad enough for this to happen within a familiar, more or less supportive community, like Catholic, rural Crossmacahilly, or a family primed to take the matter in hand and act for the best; but for a lone German girl away from home, a 'respectable', God-fearing, Lutheran German girl committed to rectitude in holy Victorian Ireland, the shame and stress must have been excruciating. Talk there would have been, salacious gossip and avid speculation (such as I'm about to go in for). Was Marie shunned by her erstwhile friends Maria Merrin and the Helms sisters? Did Cissy Dempsey turn up her nose, once she'd enjoyed being properly shocked and enthralled? Above all, what was Marie's view of her situation? Was she defiant or demoralised? Even if she lacked the adamantine integrity of Jane Eyre, she'd never have cast herself as a Hetty Sorrel figure. How deluded was she, and by whom? Were her employers sympathetic, or not? Was the future Major-General Sir Edward Sinclair May, who married at forty and sired five daughters and a son – was this individual, at this dramatic juncture, in a study or billiard room shaking in his shoes; or holding himself aloof and a bit contemptuous from a family emergency that really and truly had nothing to do with him?

The unanswerability of these questions doesn't make them any less pertinent. The elder Mays, at the very least, bore some responsibility for Marie's welfare, being in a sense *in loco parentis*. They'd hardly have put her out on the street, but what did they do? Was she sent away to some distant place of refuge or private nursing home? Was the whole thing just a botheration and annoyance to them, or did they know themselves to be more deeply implicated in Marie's disgrace? How were the young May daughters shielded from the evidence of immorality? What urgent negotiations were carried on? All impossible to determine. Documentary evidence gives a little, just a little, to go on; and it discloses Marie, still single, in February 1881, with a baby in one hand – and no doubt her book of poems in the other.

Enter the demon-king coachman William Craig. (I'm joking; it's just that his copious moustaches, in the one photograph I have of him, make him the perfect model of a pantomime villain.) On the other hand, perhaps this person has been in the picture all along, a known seducer with an aversion to matrimony – at least, when the prospective wife is not an Irish girl (he married again, after Marie's death). Perhaps he really

The 'demon-king coachman': PC's great-grandfather William Craig

is the father of the child, the baby Bertha, called after Marie's mother back in Bremen. Certainly I never received the smallest intimation that all was not as it should be with the parentage of 'Aunt Bertha', as the 1880s baby became known to my father and his siblings. Of course I didn't; it was the 1950s, when respectability reigned and no one in their right mind would have brought up an ancient scandal in the family. No one would have given any credence to it, either. All right, you can't get round the date on the marriage certificate, April 1881, proclaiming extraordinary tardiness on the part of bride and groom — but no need to go further and make it a marriage of convenience into the bargain.

I can't quite accept this version of events. The marriage was certainly a come-down for Marie Heller. Coachmen were very numerous in the carriage-owning era, and for all their sumptuous livery they were classed as servants; whereas she was on the next thing to an equal footing with the employing family. I can't believe that this accomplished young woman, speaking several languages fluently, and possessed of a certain European urbanity, would choose to throw in her lot with a rough Irish coachman, had any reasonable alternative been available to her. The alternative she faced was, of course, social ostracism and probably penury, as an unmarried mother at an especially censorious time.

The scenario I envisage is this. Some unknown person beguiled and bamboozled Marie, conscripting her for the sorrier role in the standard, not to say trite, seduction-and-humiliation plot. The Mays,[5] whether interested or disinterested parties, were then faced with the task of finding a husband for matrimonially downgraded Marie, and the best they could do in the circumstances was the coachman. And that only after protracted to-ing and fro-ing. Perhaps a financial inducement was proffered, or an undertaking given, *de haut en bas*, that a well-disposed eye would be trained on any future children born to Marie and William Craig. (And so it proved. At any rate, my grandfather William Henry experienced no trouble in finding employment as a coachman, a stable hand or groom with local grandees at Finnebrogue, in Wexford, in Scotland or, eventually, in the Lagan Valley.)

Marie's life was in shreds, however, and she opted out of it, ten years and five children later, by turning her face to the wall. I doubt if she'd ever have become acclimatised to the moods of the Irish countryside, or a day-to-day existence decidedly at odds with the future she might have mapped out for herself. Perhaps sex was a consolation – or a punishment accepted in a penitent spirit for the mess she'd made of things, her social wrongdoing and foolish gullibility. At any rate, the children of the marriage came quickly, following on from John in 1882 (my grandfather was next, in 1884), and from the first son on were indubitably Craigs. But over Bertha, I think, a question mark remains.

All this may be wrong. But there *is* that fact of the back-to-front sequence of birth and marriage. Another fact is that her Germanness and his Leinster identity (if that's what it was) combined to breed a family of Ulster unionists and Orangemen. They signed the Covenant in 1912, at the height of the stupendous outcry against Home Rule. They paraded on the Twelfth with their sashes and banners. In her well-tended, hedged-in garden at Dunmurry – her special domain – my grandma Craig grew clumps of Orange lilies.

George Augustus May outlived his children's German governess by a year. He died, for some reason at a house called Lisnavagh in County Carlow, in 1892, aged eighty-seven. He died as he had lived, a toff, unknown to the ceilidhe house, the agitators' meeting place or the soup kitchen. The household over which he presided during his heyday would have been a conservative one, committed to 'ascendancy' values. The glamour of the Fenian movement, 'cultural' Irishness or an affinity with the aspirations of Charles Stuart Parnell would have passed it by. Irish disaffection would have been anathema to it. Particularly, at one end of the century, George Augustus might have remarked the fate of a predecessor in the role of Lord Chief Justice, Lord Kilwarden, murdered by a mob in Dublin during the uncoordinated rebellion of Robert Emmet; and at the other end, in 1882, he had the Phoenix Park assassinations of Lord Frederick Cavendish and T.H. Burke by a reprehensible offshoot of the Irish Republican Brotherhood called the Invincibles, to underscore in his eyes the fiendish nature of Fenianism.

None of this would have meant a thing to the girl from Bremen. But, worldly or workaday, it was Protestant Ireland, not Catholic Ireland, that reeled her in. Her Lutheran sensibility chimed with a Church of Ireland decorum (leaving aside the lapse of chastity rebarbative to both). She wasn't to know that, a long way in the future, a renegade grandson would throw in his lot with the other camp and help to build barricades in Belfast against a 'Protestant' onslaught, during the troubles of the early 1970s. (At the time I'm writing, that grandson, my father, is a healthful and cheerful ninety-three-year-old, loosely attached to the Catholic church at Kilclief, near Strangford, County Down, and strongly attached to his local Catholic community.)

Take a year at random in the nineteenth century – say, 1859. In the north of Ireland the great religious revival is gathering a head of steam, as Presbyterian staidness flies out of the window and unbridled hysteria enters in. Susceptible people all over the place are 'saved' or 'converted' with maximum melodrama. A situation prevails in previously inexcitable Ulster communities which is curiously akin to Lewis Carroll's 'reeling and writhing and fainting in coils'. The social commentator James Winder Good, writing in 1918, describes what happened:

> From the North of Antrim, where the first manifestations were displayed, the fire spread rapidly south, until ... practically the whole of Presbyterian Ulster was ablaze. The enthusiasm was even more vehement in towns than in the rural districts ... [with] 'screams of the most unearthly description proceeding from places of professedly Christian worship at all hours

of the day and night, girls with dishevelled hair and pallid faces ... supported in the arms of young men and young women, to their homes from the churches where they had been struck ...'.

(The quotation comes from an embarrassed observer of these unprecedented antics, the Reverend William McIlwaine.) Trances, seizures, visions and 'miracles' are the order of the day – and one can envisage the bemusement of Catholic onlookers as *their* church's reputation for 'superstition' and emotionalism is suddenly and exorbitantly overtaken.

Among the latter, possibly, are Matthew Tipping and his wife Eliza, a young couple still occupying part of the Crossmacahilly farmhouse with its linen-weaving accoutrements and its apple orchard in full fruition, and with a new arrival – their son James, the future Lurgan stone-thrower – added to the rest of the inhabitants jostling for a bit of space. ... In another part of County Armagh, eighteen-year-old Ellen Jordan (Matthew's next wife) may also be witnessing unexpected religious excitements among the overwrought of the area, and thanking her lucky stars for her own ancestral, sensible and dignified, Catholic creed. She may also, in the usual way of spirited adolescents, be exhibiting impatience with her parents' harping on the awful old Famine (safely in the past), and on the failed, and farcical, uprising of 1848 – though she is probably herself a supporter of the embryo Fenian movement. There is plentiful news of evictions and other evils in the Irish countryside to keep Ellen's nationalist instincts working at full throttle.

In the town of Lurgan itself the young domestic servant Elizabeth Harland is giving birth to her daughter Catherine, an occasion not calling for rejoicing on anyone's part – though, as we've seen, Catherine does not allow herself to be disabled by her origins. Catherine's route to respectability, her future husband Terence Brady, is at this moment taking into his infant lungs the purer air of County Cavan – 'lakeside orchards in first bloom' – though before long he too will be transplanted with his family to dusty, sect-ridden, throughother Lurgan.

I haven't the smallest peg on which to hang speculations about the setting or the circumstances of my great-grandfather William Craig's upbringing (he who ended up buried in the City Cemetery in Belfast). Nine years old in 1859, and Protestant to the core (that much at least

I can infer), the future coachman may already be working with horses, somewhere in the south of the country – though not as far south as County Wexford, where another forebear, young William Lett, is getting the hang of the farming business in the face of a severe agricultural depression afflicting the country (and becoming entrenched in his Church of Ireland identity). In the nearby town of Enniscorthy, ten-year-old Emily Anne Thorpe. ... But here I really do come up against a brick wall of total ignorance. Whatever she's doing, I have to leave her to get on with it.

It's easier to conjure up a picture of Mathilda Clara Maria Heller, a solemn little girl of five, saying goodbye to Berlin and the balconies and cobbles and flower shops, the Kranzler-Ecke, the fish market, the smell of coffee and confectionery, the carts laden with branches of young birch trees in the spring and streets thronged with officers in military uniform. Utterly unaware of remote, bleak Ireland and everything to do with it, she is on the way to Bremen, where her father will set up his pottery business. I hope there is space among the family's possessions for her cherished children's books and books of poems (I'm sure she owned some of these). All right, I know I'm attributing some of my own proclivities to this unknown great-grandmother, but it's not entirely without foundation.

John Hewitt has recorded in verse his mild antipathy towards his Methodist grandmother, describing her as 'stiff and hard'. But, he adds, she had a mitigating feature: she carried a cache of poems clipped from newspapers in a pouch on her garter. Tennyson, Whittier, Longfellow, George MacDonald. And, 'remembering that satin pouch of poems / I clasp her bony hand'. Yes, keeping poems by you seems to be a measure of integrity – one I'd go along with anyway. And to bolster that conviction in my mind I have those skilled amateur anthologists, my mother and my father's grandmother, bequeathing to me an intense susceptibility to the power of poetry. And it was probably that dual genetic inheritance that predisposed me to become an anthologist – if not entirely a poetry anthologist – myself.

At school in Belfast in the 1950s I never won prizes for anything – with one exception. When we were twelve or thirteen, and in Form 2A at St Dominic's, our English teacher, Miss McVerry, announced one morning a competition for the class. 'Now, children, I want each of you to take an unused exercise book. And in it, in your best handwriting, between now and the end of term, I want you to copy out any poems or pieces of prose that you particularly admire. It must be your own choice, remember, and it can be absolutely anything you like, from a nursery rhyme to a passage from Shakespeare. If any of you have a clean exercise book in your desk, you can start now by writing "My Anthology" on the first page. [She then proceeded to chalk up these words in large letters on the blackboard.] And at the end of term, there will be a prize of a book-token for whichever of your efforts I judge to be the best. Now – any questions, or does anyone have any idea about the sort of thing you might start with? Yes, Mary?'

It was the first time I'd heard the word 'anthology', but I knew at once that this project was right up my street. I couldn't wait to get it under way. In fact I produced two 'anthologies' (the first exercise book was filled pretty quickly), spending most of my evenings over the next couple of months seated at the kitchen table surrounded by papers, books, paint-boxes and jars of dirty water. I went one better than everyone else by illustrating my choices, mostly with pictures copied from books I owned ('Where is Persephone, you naughty sea children?'; 'He tied Lucy and Henry to the kitchen table'). I was nothing if not an eclectic compiler. I had Chaucer (surprisingly, in the Middle English versions) and Spenser alongside Louisa May Alcott and 'Roddy the Rover'. Kipling's poem about not 'giving your heart to a dog to tear' (I was very fond of dogs) is followed by 'Charlotte Bronte's Creed'. Poetry and prose are intermingled throughout. Thus was the pattern set – minus the illustrations – for my Blackstaff *Belfast* and *Ulster* anthologies, and *Oxford Book of Ireland*.

I won the prize. It was a book-token for seven shillings and sixpence. I'd like to say I bore it off to Mullan's or Erskine Mayne's and exchanged it for something like *The Faber Book of Contemporary Poetry* or Sean O'Faolain's translations from the Irish, *The Silver Branch*. But I know it was expended joyfully on the *School Friend Annual for 1956*, or *The Secret of Grey Walls* by Malcolm Saville. I needed poetry to amplify my life, but I also needed – and still need – a large element of frivolity in my bedtime reading. (Nowadays it's supplied by wonderful contemporary thriller writers like Andrew Taylor, Sue Grafton, Michael Connolly, Alafair Burke and the incomparable Reginald Hill.) I was – and still am, as a collector – a children's books addict.

As for the poetry business – some of my ancestors on both sides,

I am sure, never gained pleasure from a line of verse in their lives. But it's not fair of me to single out the two who did, and elevate them, for that reason alone, above all the rest. And, if you make assumptions about people's relations to literature, you may be setting yourself up for a salutary comeuppance. My utterly unpoetic and ill-educated father could, for example, in his prime, recite from start to finish not only 'The Shooting of Dan McGrew', but Portia's central speech from *The Merchant of Venice*. And my two-times-over half-great-uncle Henry Tipping – but hang on a minute, I'm getting entangled here in the skein of my own ancestral complications. Two-times-nothing; that only applies to his and Mary Anne Dowds's children. His mother Eliza O'Hara was not related to me. My half-great-uncle Henry Tipping, then, an uncouth and grumpy old sod by all accounts, nevertheless revered Thomas Davis's 'Fontenoy, 1745' – to the point of not restraining his rendering of it in the presence of his terrified infant half-sister Sarah.

> ...The treasured wrongs of fifty years are in their hearts today –
> The Treaty broken 'ere the ink wherewith 'twas writ could
>   dry,
> Their plundered homes, their ruined shrines, their women's
>   parting cry,
> Their priesthood hunted down like wolves, their altars
>   overthrown –
> Each looks as if revenge for all were staked on him alone.
> On Fontenoy, on Fontenoy, nor ever yet elsewhere
> Rushed on to fight a nobler band than these proud exiles were.

Fontenoy was the site of the battle in which the Irish troops of King Louis XV inflicted an overwhelming defeat on the English forces under the command of the Duke of Cumberland – 'the Bloody Duke of Cumberland'; and, of course, you could say it's not so much poetry as patriotism that animates great-uncle Henry as he roars out the list of 'treasured' enormities. The wrongs done to the Irish were entwined in his heart and head – and never mind if the blood of those on the side of Thomas Davis's plunderers and desecrators has sneaked to an extent into his own bulging nationalist veins. There's no one to say, 'But hold on a minute,' to disturb his conviction of possessing an unblemished Irish ancestry.

CHAPTER 6

CULTURAL CONFUSIONS

The roll call in the side chapel of the Royal Irish Fusiliers might have taught us something: O's and Macs mingled in death with good Proddy names, Hamilton, Hewitt, Taylor, Acheson.

John Montague, from 'History Walk'

Throughout the nineteenth century, savage street-fighting occurred periodically in key towns in the North, including Belfast, Derry, Portadown and Lurgan. Belfast's bad reputation in this respect goes all the way back to 1813, when two men were shot dead in North Street – victims, as George Benn has it, of 'party collision'.[1] The affably sardonic F. Frankfort Moore, in *The Truth about Ulster* (1914), records an experience of his early life, when a careless nursemaid led him into a turbulent quarter of the town while a riot was in progress. Too young to understand what was going on, but quite old enough to relish the excitement of the occasion, he stood with his nose pressed against an upstairs window of a local house into which his nurse had hastily bundled him, watching Belfast go about its usual stormy business. 'I saw a flying crowd of men and women, boys and girls of the mill-working order, and behind them were riding at the trot three dragoons with their sabres drawn and at the "carry".' It was 1857, Twelfth-of-July parades had just taken place, and rumours of 'Papist' threats to cherished Orange clergymen such as Dr Cooke and Dr Drew had inflamed the situation. Protestants and Catholics were once again at one another's throats.

Paving stones, porter bottles and iron nuts all came into play and inflicted considerable damage on sectionally undifferentiated heads and limbs. The most vicious and violent years of the century were 1857, '64, '72 and '86, the last tied up with the Liberal government's first Home Rule bill (and Protestant jubilation over its defeat). Major sectarian outbreaks were a feature of Belfast, where street-fighting had swiftly assumed a strategic character, but provincial towns like Lurgan weren't behindhand in taking up the cudgels in support of one side or the other. Most of the combatants fuelled by factional fury would have had nothing in their heads but enlarged folk-memories of atrocities perpetrated against their co-religionists – or perhaps not even that. For some it was just a matter of a distorted birthright: if you're born a Protestant the onus is on you to fight the Taigs, and vice versa. You don't need to know what it's all about.

Hence the missiles propelled into Protestant faces by Tipping hard men of the 1880s. The first Lurgan generation – sons of weaver/shopkeeper Matthew – had nothing to lose, and something to gain in the way of community prestige, by standing up for their Catholic entitlements. I don't think their actions at street level – assault and rampage – were motivated by any idea of political reform. It was more instinctive than that. It was bred in the bone and expressed with the fists. As for their Protestant counterparts – well, from the year of Emancipation on, 'the theory of insatiable Catholics extorting privilege after privilege at the expense of harassed Protestants colours all Orange thought', wrote the social commentator and historian James Winder Good in his study of 1919, *Ulster and Ireland*. True – but again at street level, thought didn't come into it. Nothing more elaborate than blows struck at foes was the rationale.

But things are about to change. The succeeding Tipping generation is rather more perspicacious and better informed, and its militant instincts become attached to an ideology. This is true at least of the family it suits my purpose to concentrate on – for you needn't worry that I'm about to delve into the procreative histories of all the Tipping offspring of Matthew and his wives. For the moment at least, I'm sticking to the progeny of one son, Henry and *his* wife Mary Anne Dowds – quite enough to be going on with. Four daughters and six sons were born to this pair between 1888 and 1906. All of them grew up devoted to Ireland and their mother, but at odds with their father – except perhaps the youngest, Bertie, the sole beneficiary, in 1938, of Henry's will. Henry was not likeable. Even if he failed to manifest the backstreet truculence attributable to his brothers, Henry possessed a nasty feral streak of his own (according to his grandson Harry Tipping), and would sometimes incite his sons to bash one another in the face, this being his idea of fun. The sons were great pals, as it happened, and if they went along with this, it really was only a game as far as they were concerned. Family solidarity was strongly developed in this branch of the Tippings – with father in his brown grocer's overall, maybe, excluded from its benefits. (Though Henry did stick up for his sons when they got into trouble, as we shall see.) The girls in particular had no cause to love their father, whose position on women's rights was not advanced. Despite this, I think, Mary Anne Dowds kept her husband more or less in order, and exerted as much of a civilising influence in the home as she could manage.

Outside the home, other, enlightening, nationalist and cultural influences were mustering. In 1892, in a lecture delivered to the Irish Literary Society in Dublin, you had the Protestant *Gaelegoir* Douglas Hyde calling for the total 'de-anglicisation' of Ireland, and, in furtherance of this object, going on to found the Gaelic League (with a little help from Glenarm man Eoin MacNeill, and others). It was a crucial moment in the history of Ireland: 'I have said again and again,' wrote Padraig Pearse, 'that when the Gaelic League was founded the Irish revolution began.' The existing Henry Tippings were only babies at the time, too young to sit up and take note of what was happening in the sphere of nationalist politics; but for reasons of birthright, location and so on, they were predestined to be responsive to all the exhilarating forces coming at them from various directions.

The first of the family, Anne Theresa, was born in 1888. Once she'd come of age, the eldest Tipping daughter washed her hands of Lurgan and its turmoil by emigrating to Rhodesia and passing out of this story. (She kept in touch with her family, though.) A batch of brothers followed the birth of Anne Theresa, starting with Matt in 1890 and interspersed with Lily, May and Monica (Monny). By the time the oldest were into their teens and twenties, an Irish cultural revival was dominating the social climate of the day. Just after the turn of the century, people like the young Quaker nationalist Bulmer Hobson were flocking to join the junior branch of the burgeoning Gaelic League which met in a hall in Albert Street in Belfast, poring over Irish-language primers to the detriment of their nerves and eyesight, and flinging themselves with abandon into violent games of hurling at the back of the old Falls Park. The *caman* – hurling stick – became a symbol of a new and exuberant nationalist *aithbheodhchaint*.[2]

Some time during 1902, and in collaboration with Constance Markievicz, Bulmer Hobson conceived a brainchild, Na Fianna Éireann – an organisation geared to train up boys, North and South, in the ways of patriotic thought and activism. (It only got going in the North after 1910.) The young Lurgan Tippings got themselves enrolled in the local Fianna branch as soon as they were of an age to do so, and joined with a will in its marches, merrymaking, and Gaelic games. I don't know if any of them ever became adept Irish-speakers, but they were great at Gaelic football. They were energetic goalkeepers, players and administrators of the team known as the Lurgan Davitts. All were deeply attuned to the Fianna's *raison d'être*, which – here comes an irony – was devised by a Protestant Irishman as a strenuous riposte to the Catholic Boys' Brigades which functioned at the time as a kind of recruiting centre for the British Army.[43]

Hobson's biographer, Marnie Hay, tells a story about the young Quaker taking over a class of boys in a building attached to St Paul's Church on the Falls Road in Belfast, and proceeding to dun into their more or less attentive heads the Lord's Prayer in Irish. He had them chanting away in unison, '*Ar nAthair ata i Neamh ...*', while people passing by in Cavendish Street outside wearing shawls and caps might have wondered what the hell was going on. Marnie Hay records the surprise of the St Paul's curate on entering the classroom and finding a *Protestant* engaged in this activity.

He needn't have been surprised, really. It was Protestants who saved the language when native Catholic Irish-speakers were desperate to gain a bit of fluency in English and rise in the world. It was Protestants, by and large, who had the leisure and resources to go about the work of collecting and preservation. They were rectors' sons like Douglas Hyde, businessmen like Robert MacAdam, or ex-Trinity students like Samuel Ferguson, whose commitment to Gaelic culture *and* unionist politics has often been remarked. Ferguson acknowledged absolutely no incompatibility between the two. The term that quickly came into being was 'cultural nationalism', with the unspoken exclusion from it of any political follow-up.

If you'd been around, say, in the fifty years between 1870 and 1920, you might have found it a bit of a strain to grapple with all the overlapping, contradictory, competing, evolving and ingrained versions of Irishness floating around in the public sphere. First of all you had the fundamental divisions, Protestant and Catholic. ('Not men and women in an Irish street,' William Allingham lamented, 'but Protestants and Catholics you meet.') But being Protestant, in many people's eyes, needn't debar you from proclaiming an Irish identity, being a Gaelic-speaking aficionado or embracing separatism (to whatever degree). There were liberal Protestants and diehard Protestants (I'll get to the latter shortly). Among Catholic nationalists were many who welcomed the enlistment of non-Catholics to the national cause, holding fast to Wolfe Tone's idea of an inclusive nation. They thought it didn't matter what faith, or non-faith, you subscribed or didn't subscribe to, as long as you had the good of the country at heart. But then there were others for whom the concept of being Irish was absolutely entwined with Catholicism, who believed you couldn't be one without professing the other. And it mattered that you were a 'cradle Catholic' of impeccable lineage like my great-grandmother Ellen Jordan, rather than simply adopting the faith like the renegade Leslie of Castle Leslie in County Monaghan (say) who changed his name from John to Shane and went about clad in a saffron kilt.

The Church had for some time been increasing its hold over its adherents, and by the turn of the century it had many of them in its vulturine grip. In 1902, an actual 'Catholic Association' came into being to oppose Protestant influences and impose a priestly formulation on cultural activities (let alone daily activities). Clear the way for D.P. Moran and his 'Irish-Ireland' movement. 'The Irish nation is de facto a Catholic nation,' the author of *The Philosophy of Irish-Ireland* unequivocally declared. Short shrift was given in this philosophy to Yeats's and Lady Gregory's campaign to add dignity to Ireland in the face of ongoing 'Paddy-and-shillelagh' slurs. A different brand of dignity, decidedly church-based if not positively awash in holy water, was postulated by Moran's Irish-Irelanders. It might be embodied in pious peasants or dressed-up ecclesiarchs. But it didn't reside in emblems extracted from sagas and folk-tales – perish the pagan thought – or in a cornucopia of crepuscular allurements. The literary achievement of the Revivalists was beside the point when the spirit of the nation eluded their best efforts. The Catholic spirit of the nation.

It isn't too hard to understand the resistance of Orange Ulster to all this, or even to accord a little, just a little, credence to the slogan of the day: Home Rule is Rome Rule. But alas, the Orange version of ethnic identity carried an obduracy and intolerance all its own. Clear the way, again, for Sir Edward Carson and his Ulster Volunteers recruited from Orange Lodges and geared to the fullest extent to withstand any impulse in Ireland towards democracy. You can see the shade of the 'No Surrender' bard William Blacker presiding over Protestant preparations for defiance, when it seemed the spectre of Home Rule was about to become a reality.

What form did these preparations take? First you had 'Ulster Day', 1912, when a 'Solemn League and Covenant' against Home Rule was signed by nearly half a million Ulster men and women, all afire with loyalist indignation. Ulster Volunteers take over local fields, set up rifle ranges in them, and practise shooting in anticipation of a civil war. They wear badges proclaiming 'No Surrender'. The future poet George Buchanan, eight years old at the time, observes these activities going on in the vicinity of Larne where his father is a Protestant rector. 'Ping-ping! The shots strike the targets. The Volunteers are learning how to kill.'[4] A short time later comes the famous gun-running episode of April 1914, when arms and ammunition from Germany are brought ashore at various seaports along the northern coast. George Buchanan continues his lively account:

> ... all through the night, on the road beside the rectory, we can hear the cars and we can see the trees constantly illumined by their headlamps. In the morning it is understood that an extraordinary event has occurred. A ship from Germany landed a cargo of arms at Larne Harbour. The police barracks were surrounded and the telephone wires cut. Already the arms have been distributed to points through the province, some being concealed under chancel floors in Protestant churches.

But the wind is taken out of anti-Home Rule sails by overwhelming events occurring elsewhere. It's 1914, and an entire world war is about to engulf the nations. The Protestant sons of Ulster, jettisoning their Orange outrage for the moment, rush to enlist in the British Army – which only a month or so earlier they'd planned to engage in battle – and distinguish themselves at the Somme and other major theatres of conflict. So do thousands of Irish Catholics, among them my grandfather Brady – though in deference to a nationalist imperative he enlists with the Dublin Fusiliers rather than any of the Ulster regiments. He does so in the company of Lurgan friends and connections-by-marriage, including his wife's half-nephew two times over, Henry and Mary Anne's son Frank Tipping. I believe these innocent recruits would all have regarded the prospect of training and fighting as something of a lark, before hell set in around them. I think of the Heaney poem about Francis Ledwidge, the 'Tommy's uniform', the 'haunted Catholic face, pallid and brave'. Some of the Lurgan army boys with their Catholic faces came home to tell the ghastly story, and some, like my grandfather, didn't.

A few months earlier, in the autumn of 1913, the Irish Volunteers had come into being as a counterblast to Carson's Ulster Volunteers. While the latter were motivated by the most implacable determination 'to resist Home Rule to the very death, [and] keep "the Covenant of God"',[5] the former held fast to the primary purpose of fighting for Ireland. Some among the Irish Volunteers achieved this purpose, when 1916 came around; while others, like their Ulster Protestant counterparts, though from an entirely different standpoint, were undergoing bombardment elsewhere. I don't want to go into the reasons why, after 1914, some Irish Volunteers joined the British Army without relinquishing their nationalist principles, while others stuck to their republican guns. Most of us know the reasons, and the outcome, the uneasy resolution imposed on the country by the Government of Ireland Act of 1920. As many historians have pointed out – with more or less glee – what unionists acquired after 1922 was a version of the Home Rule against which, with so much hullabaloo, they had previously set their faces.

On the scale of ironies, though, that's only about halfway up. It was the *nationalist* version they'd resisted, and that had been warded off, even if the terms of the eventual compromise were thoroughly satisfactory to no one. On the subject of ironies – here's another which I can't resist noting, having come across it while reading Jonathan Bardon's *History of Ulster*.

It concerns Sir Edward Carson and *his* muddled family. It was a cousin of Carson's, I learn, called Maire Butler, a member of the Gaelic League, who coined the imperishable term 'Sinn Féin'. And, '...we in Ulster will tolerate no Sinn Féin,' thunders Carson in 1920, addressing an assembly of twenty-five thousand Orangemen, 'no Sinn Féin organisation, no Sinn Féin methods ...'. The comforting solidarity of 'Ourselves', it seems, can accommodate or repudiate whomever it pleases. ... But we needn't be surprised by anomalies of consanguinity, which pop up to intrigue us all over the place, once we start to look for them. Take another pair of unlikely cousins, Charles Stewart Parnell and Sir Basil Brooke[6] – and then imagine yourself located somewhere above the whole cat's cradle of Irish affairs, looking down in bemusement.

As for the subject of my immediate interest, my own family connections: half of them were signing the Covenant at the appropriate moment, while the other half were shaping up to be republican activists. (All right, I'm simplifying things to underscore the point.) My Craig grandfather certainly celebrated 'Ulster Day', at least in spirit,[7] along with his father and brothers. But the outbreak of war with Germany placed him in a double bind. He didn't volunteer to join the British Army – well, how could he? He was half-German himself and disinclined, I am sure, to take up arms against his close relations. I don't even know if he was eligible for army service, given his background. But I do know that no hint of 'Hun' affiliations would have passed his lips, or those of his children.

One of the most cogent and entertaining discussions of confusion and complexity in Ulster politics was published in 1919, and has long been out of print. It is James Winder Good's *Ulster and Ireland*. I've already alluded to this study here and there, and I applaud it again for its adept engagement with contemporary – and perennial – issues, and for its liberal stance. It employs the kind of logic that undermines ideological idiocies. I recommend it to any student of Ulster inconsistencies. The mode in which it is written is that of satirical common sense. For example, when Good points out that 'during the progress of the Home Rule controversy the unionist case has been twisted right round', you want to stand up and cheer. First, in his speeches, Sir Edward Carson expressed vehement sentiments culled from Fitzgibbon and Castlereagh, but before the thing was over, Good says, 'his denial of the right of British statesmen to intervene in Ulster was uncompromising and passionate enough to have satisfied Wolfe Tone himself'. Sinn Féin Abu.

And here is my own fundamental contention in a nutshell. Compiling a list of speakers on a Protestant platform, all of them immersed to the hilt in the business of preserving Ulster's Orange integrity, Good is surprised – or perhaps not surprised – to find names like Maguire, Murphy, Quinn, Moriarty, MacNeill, O'Neill and O'Donnell occurring over and over among the denouncers of 'Romanism' and Fenianism. The names themselves, he says, 'are the best refutation of the doctrines their bearers preached'. Quite so.[8] And just occasionally, against the grain of Ulster fixity, you find the bearer of such a name endowed with sufficient aplomb to revel in the contradictions thereby adumbrated. I'm thinking of someone like the nineteenth-century anti-Papist firebrand cleric Dr Kane, Grand Master of an Orange lodge and pioneering member of the Gaelic League. 'My Orangeism,' Kane said (quoted by Good), 'does not make me any less proud to be an O'Cahan.' And an even more thoroughgoing proponent of the eccentricities-of-allegiance school of behaviour was the lawyer John Rea (c.1822–1881), whose Belfast house sported Orange and Green flags flying side by side, no doubt to the bewilderment of his neighbours. At one moment, Rea appears at the head of a procession of Orangemen asserting their right to public assembly and free speech, and at the next moment, mounted on a horse and waving a green flag, he's leading nationalists engaged in a similar demonstration. John Rea's label for himself, 'her Orthodox Presbyterian Britannic Majesty's Orange-Fenian Attorney-General for Ulster', might put us in mind of Walt Whitman's 'Do I contradict myself? Very well then, I contradict myself, / I am large, I contain multitudes'.[9] Alas, the general run of Ulster's larger-than-life figures were all on the side of their own preferred faction.

The exceptions like John Rea are heartening, but they're only exceptions. They do, however, recur from time to time to bolster the sense of limitless possibilities in Ulster affairs. Alongside the sticklers for sects are those who refuse to be constrained by factional requirements of any kind. Like Dr Kane before him, Frank McCollum of County Antrim was Grand Master of an Orange Lodge in the 1960s, and at the same time chairman of the Irish Musicians' Association, Comhaltas Ceoltóiri Éireann, when a branch of the latter was established in his home town of Ballycastle. Well, traditional music, as the fiddle-player Alex Kerr was fond of pointing out, 'knows no border, nor no creed'.[10] This is true, or ought to be true, but immediately a contradiction arises when you consider the effect of certain 'traditional' party tunes on the tempers and dispositions of clashing partisans. Anything, *anything* native to Ulster can be turned to an integrating or a disintegrating purpose.

As the stuff of fiction, the Home Rule crisis of the early twentieth century engendered one outstanding work, a narrative equivalent of an aspect of *Ulster and Ireland*. It is George A. Birmingham's *The Red Hand of Ulster*, published in 1912. Birmingham's central character is an astute and genial Irish peer of the realm who observes with a certain playful detachment the complete volte-face overtaking rival camps whose standpoints vis-à-vis Great Britain have somehow got interchanged. For example, a character in the novel is an ardent Sinn Féiner who, having sought out the most potent source of rebellion against Britain and locating it amongst the unionists of the North, cheerfully accepts the editorship of a 'loyalist' newspaper. And all around him, loyalists are tying themselves in knots in the effort to assert their loyalty to Britain at the same time as disembarrassing themselves of it. And, once the refusal of Home Rule is backed by a demand for a complete British withdrawal from Ireland, a state of semantic deadlock is brought about, and the author has tremendous fun with this and all the other egregious anomalies which make up his theme.

It's not the first time the sectarian instinct in Northern Ireland has had salutary fun poked at it. You will find, for example, a wonderful set-piece in William Carleton's novel of 1843, *Valentine McClutchy*. It exploits to the full the farcical element in sectarian inflexibility. What Carleton presents to his readers is a pair of complementary converts, an ex-Catholic Protestant and his ex-Protestant counterpart. Both men are bursting with new-found zeal and quickly square up to one another as the author brings them face-to-face. However, in the course of the ensuing argument, each man involuntarily reverts to his original theological position. The one-time Orangeman atavistically curses the pope, while the supposed ex-Catholic comes out as a Papist partisan. By this stage a crowd of supporters has gathered, an equal number of Prods and Taigs, and, Carleton tells us, 'the Catholics, ignorant of the turn which the controversy had taken, supported Bob and Protestantism; while the Protestants, owing to a similar mistake, fought like devils for

Darby and the Pope.' It is hard to think of a more telling indictment of the whole incorrigible business, or one more drily expressed.

But these are works of fiction, you may say, whose impact would not amount to much among hardliners in the streets of Lurgan or Belfast. Well, yes, but such things work, or should work, both in cumulative and subliminal ways, and at the very least suggest a structure for thoughtful, rather than instinctive, action. There are truths to be found in books which may filter down even to the non-reading public – even to the illiterate.

It's likely that my grandmother's parents, and her older half-siblings, could read but not write (unlike her father's country cousins, who were adept at both); but she herself was fully literate, as I can testify: a skill she owed to a short and piecemeal education with the Mercy nuns of Edward Street.[11] According to the census of 1901, the previously jam-packed house in John Street had dwindled by that date to three occupants: Matthew and Ellen Tipping, and their daughter Sarah. Sarah's age is given as nineteen, and her occupation as 'veiner' (that is, a person sewing veins in flowers decorating pieces of muslin, probably a factory job). ... Move around the corner to 37 Edward Street, and here you find a whole family of reading-and-writing Bradys, plus three old aunts named McManus who seem to have lived with them. I assume these were Terence Brady's maiden aunts on his mother's side,[12] since his wife Catherine's relations, as we've seen, were not conspicuous about the place, or at least not acknowledged as such. ... Here is the oldest Brady son William, also aged nineteen and a plasterer by trade. (His nearest brother James – Jim – is a draper's assistant, though at some point, I think, 'Uncle Jim' gains experience as a soldier with the British Army.)

Like the Tippings, the Bradys are ardently Catholic, and this means the courtship of William and Sarah is conducted at church-hall dances and ceilidhes, fund-raising concerts, outings organised by St Peter's Church and in the company of co-religionists. Do they ever duck out of priestly and family supervision and get away by themselves? Probably, for I don't doubt the pair of them were properly spirited young people, despite the pinched and seedy circumstances surrounding them. My grandmother was always one for a good laugh. And she's already been complicit in the elopement of her friend Minnie Cochrane (with a boy called Thornberry), whose luggage she helped deposit on the Belfast train.

Other escapades I have no knowledge of, but I'm sure they took place. My grandmother was voluble and filled with strong opinions. When I was fifteen or sixteen, she advised me to go about only with good-looking friends, lest those of unattractive appearance should drive boys away. (Or maybe she meant I needed a counterbalance to my unglamorous looks.) She wasn't a gadabout, I think, being always conscious of life's serious aspects. But she enjoyed gossip, as well as taking an interest in events of the wider world (and reading detective novels). She followed the Suez crisis and understood the implications of the death of Stalin. She wore smart coats and hats with veils.

Young Sarah Tipping and William Brady have the whole of Lurgan Park to go wrong in – not that I think they did – not to mention the shores of Lough Neagh, or the fields and country byways surrounding their grim home town. I can't say what drew them together, never having known my grandfather, but he'd have needed a certain robust self-assurance to go after the redoubtable Miss Tipping (she was still redoubtable in my day, though life had knocked a good deal of the undauntedness out of her). They were married in April 1902. She remembered washing her hair on the morning of her wedding day, and drying it in front of the kitchen fire. If she wasn't pregnant at the time – and I don't think she was – she quickly became so. The newly-weds had moved in with her parents at John Street, and there their first daughter Elizabeth – Lily – was born in January 1903 (nine months almost to the day).

She was followed by Ellen, or Elly – later Eileen – ('It was a cynical babe'[13]) two years later; then came Mary Joseph (Molly, or 'Ructions'), sweet-natured Catherine (Kathleen), and finally my mother Nora Theresa in June 1913. At some point – probably after 1910 when Sarah's father Matthew Tipping dropped dead in the street, causing consternation ('Dear God this holy day and hour') – the younger Bradys had installed themselves in a house in Edward Street: a better house, still opening on to the pavement, but with stairs leading up to an attic (as my mother recalled it). A few doors away lived Sarah's sister Ellen, also called Brady, and *her* expanding family (nine in all). To the David Brady household was added the widowed Ellen Tipping, who lived on until 1927. So: in Lurgan's Edward Street were domiciled two cousins – David Brady and William Brady – married to two sisters – Ellen Tipping and Sarah Tipping; also resident in the same significant street was a whole different bunch of double-kin: the Henry Tipping tribe (I hope you have all this clear in your head). All were in the grip of ideological grievances, coupled with a bit of blissful ignorance. As we've seen, all of them exemplified some undisclosed dilution of the Catholic, 'true-Gaelic' line.

Times were hard. There was no way round incessant scrimping and saving. A plasterer's wage wasn't adequate to keep body and soul together, not in a household consisting of seven anyway. And work for the breadwinner was not always available. So the call for British Army volunteers, when it came, fell on receptive ears. It was suddenly permissible for Irish nationalists to align themselves with Britain in the worldwide 'fight for freedom'. The expectation was that Home Rule would come out of it ('For England may keep faith ...'[14]). And never mind that a contradictory expectation sustained huge numbers of Ulster unionist volunteers.

Frank Tipping[15] was eighteen years old when he joined the 6th Dublin Fusiliers along with his Aunt Sarah's husband William Brady. Frank's son Brian Tipping later recalled his father's support for John Redmond, and his belief in the rightness of the Irish Parliamentary Party's pledge to join in the conflict on the side of England. The Redmondite 'National Volunteers', twenty-seven thousand of them, had come round to the new way of thinking. But the change of heart was not universal. Irish Volunteers held fast to the old, anti-British, separatist ideal. Their flag was hoisted under the slogan, 'England's difficulty is Ireland's opportunity'. Their path was set towards 1916 and the Easter Rising.

When it came to the bit, a fair number of Irish recruits may have been uncertain about what exactly it was they were fighting for, and how it chimed with nationalist aspirations. What had Salonika and the Dardanelles to do with Ireland and conditions at home ...? For this heat-scorched, utterly alien territory was the place the 6th Dublin Fusiliers found themselves in 1915, and where Frank Tipping sustained a leg wound in the fighting around Suvla Bay.

I don't know if my grandfather ever had a chance to go at an actual enemy, after all the months of training. He may have evaded involvement in combat activity by dying too soon. It wasn't only on the battlefields that casualties by the hundreds and thousands occurred. *The War Diary of an Irish Soldier*,[16] by Captain David Campbell, tells a shocking story of non-existent hygiene among the troops in the Dardanelles, plagues of insects, ants and flies unavoidably swallowed in droves along with bread and bully beef. Dysentery, Captain Campbell says, played havoc with the Irish battalions, and William Brady – perhaps lacking a strong constitution to begin with – fell a victim to it. There's a grave bearing his name and the date, 14 September 1915, in the Military and War Memorial Cemetery in Alexandria, though among some of his descendants a belief exists that he died and was buried at sea. I have his wedding ring on my finger. It was returned to his widow, who gave it to her youngest daughter; and when she died, it came to me.

Nineteen fifteen has been described as the year of the telegrams, as postmen burdened with appalling news knocked at door after door. To Edward Street in Lurgan in due course comes one of these ominous messengers, and life thereafter for the William Brady family assumes a stricken and savourless character. But my grandmother Sarah Tipping – like *her* great-grandmother Sarah Magee – has reserves of stoicism which she summons up to help her adjust to her new and unwelcome identity: war widow. Instead of a husband, a partner and helpmeet in the upbringing of five young daughters aged between twelve and two, she has a solid bronze medal, four and three-quarter inches in diameter, inscribed with her husband's name and the legend, 'He Died for Freedom and Honour'. Freedom and honour, *mar 'eadh*. 'Dead Men's Pennies' was the name the irreverent gave these medals. And in Catholic Lurgan, the thing was an ambiguous token.

My Catholic, Irish-nationalist grandfather gave his life for England. That much is indisputable – but no uplifting rhetoric of the 'Tell England' variety was available to mitigate the bereavement of his and all the other Irish war widows. 'Know that we fools, now with the foolish dead,' Tom Kettle wrote,

> Died not for flag, nor crown, nor emperor,
> But for a dream, born in a herdsman's shed,
> And for the secret scripture of the poor.

Dying for England was one thing, and an equivocal thing, dying for Ireland another. Easter 1916 came with all its confusion, upheaval and glory, and when the Rising was quelled and its leaders executed, there were those in the Irish battalions fighting in the First World War who wondered if they'd made the right decision. Popular songs like 'The Foggy Dew' took up the theme of bravely but mistakenly transferred loyalties:

'Twas England bade our Wild Geese go,
That small nations might be free;
But their lonely graves are by Suvla's waves,
Or the fringe of the great North Sea.
Oh, had they died by Pearse's side,
Or fought with Cathal Brugha,
Their names we'd keep, where the Fenians sleep,
'Neath the hills in the foggy dew.

When I was fifteen or thereabouts I had an old 78 record of this and other rebel songs which I played over and over on a second-hand record-player in the front room of our red-brick, semi-detached house at 551 Donegall Road, Belfast. These songs made my hair stand on end. 'All Around my Hat I Wear the Tri-Coloured Ribbon-O' – I did indeed, at least in a metaphorical sense. Like John Hewitt's grandmother with her cache of poems, I had images, clipped from newspapers, of Padraig Pearse and other 1916 leaders which I carried around in my purse, until they eventually fell to pieces.

My single-minded admiration for every proponent of an Ireland free and Gaelic and unique and righteous eventually fell to pieces too, but not before it had bitten pretty deep into my psyche. Revisionism made sense when I became aware of it in later life, but during the romantic-Irish years I vastly preferred the crepuscular view, the clandestine affiliation, the unimpeachable cause. I remember a ferocious argument with some would-be cynical schoolboys over the integrity or otherwise of the hanged republican Kevin Barry. 'He was eighteen years old,' I hear myself shouting, 'he died, actually died, for his beliefs, and you can stand there making excuses for his executioners ...'. Call yourselves Irish, I probably went on, before stomping off in a temper, utterly unaware of the extent to which I myself was, or was not, entitled to call myself Irish.

Like mine, like George Watson's (see p. xix above), my mother's cultural confusions were among the greatest blessings of her life. The literature of England, high and low, was for all of us a refuge, a source of pleasure and enlightenment, an inestimable resource. A bibliophile propensity overtook us early. 'Delight in books' was our unspoken motto. Without books, we'd have languished unconsolably. An unimaginable deprivation would have eaten away at us. Books were a necessity, not a luxury as our forebears might have regarded them.

We had our different areas of enthralment, of course, along with a good deal of overlap. My poetry-enthusiast mother really appreciated very little poetry after Yeats. With some exceptions, 'moderns' such as Eliot and Auden left her cold. She was more attuned to Keats and Shelley than the Byron of 'Don Juan'. And Tennyson: 'glamour', for her, meant 'The Lady of Shalott,' 'embowered' within her 'four grey walls and four grey towers'. Certain lines by James Ellroy Flecker, from 'The Old Ships' and 'The Golden Journey to Samarkand', made her hair stand on end. The exotic-narcotic cadences perfected by this poet easily overwhelmed me too, whenever I gave myself up to them: '...for Famagusta and the hidden sun, / That rings black Cyprus with a lake of fire ...'. Famagusta: it's a far cry from Lurgan jeers and brawls and backyards and chilblains and the waterlogged Head of the Plain. ...Then, my range of children's reading was considerably wider than my mother's had been (more was available in the 1950s), but both of us, at different times, were addicts of Greyfriars School and the incomparable doings of Harry Wharton and Co. She rather liked historical fiction of the Margaret Irwin–Jane Lane variety, about which I took a slightly snooty tone (it was different if it was *Irish* historical fiction, when the subject would win out over any perceived stylistic infelicity). She revered Graham Greene rather more than I did, while my detective novels – Christie, Sayers, Nicholas Blake – didn't hold much appeal for her. We both liked humorous verse, and local verse, and Scottish ballads, and poets of the First World War. With the last, though, I opted for Owen and Sassoon, and she for Rupert Brooke.

There was a personal reason for that. Her father had died a death as inglorious as Rupert Brooke's, in the same year and in the same part of the world, committed to the same cause. Frances Cornford's tribute to Brooke, beginning, 'A young Apollo, golden-haired ...' caught my mother's imagination. That the poetry of Brooke was saturated in Englishness didn't matter a jot: it was lyrical and elegiac and accessible, and composed in a spirit she found it easy to respond to. 'Just now the lilac is in bloom, / All outside my little room.' *It rhymed.* Also, and it probably wasn't even a conscious transference, I imagine a tinge of the glamour attaching to the person, and the poetry, of Rupert Brooke became associated, in my mother's mind, with her own dead father. Since she'd never known him, she was free to attribute to her missing father whatever traits she chose.

Not that she ever talked about him; no one talked about him, to me at least. I used to think my grandmother's silence on the subject of her husband's death betokened indifference: now I think the opposite was true. It was simply too painful to make a topic for casual comment. And the pain didn't go away as time passed: other pain got added to it. When I was growing up, I'd have found it hard to envisage my grandmother *with* a husband: she seemed essentially to stand alone, a bit aloof, not liking to be touched, slightly detached from the routines of our small household, of which she was a part. (My child's-eye view was faulty, of course; my grandmother's domestic and financial acumen contributed greatly to all our well-being.) As for my lost grandfather ... as far as I am concerned, he disappeared into a void, leaving virtually no tangible mementoes of his existence: no photos, possessions, autographs, marks of identification. Only the ring on my finger and the Dead Man's Penny in the drawer upstairs. No repeated anecdotes illumined his character or passed into family lore. As far as I know, only a solitary saying of his has survived, preserved in the memory of his second daughter. It relates to the children. 'Make them do as they're bid,' he would say, as infantile chaos threatened to overwhelm the house, 'make them do as they're bid.' It isn't much of a pointer to the texture of a life.

Nineteen hundred and fifteen. Within the close-knit, extended Lurgan family circle, my grandmother isn't the only person to suffer an annihilating blow. Catherine Harland had already lost her husband Terence Brady earlier in the year, and now comes the terrible news of the death of her oldest son. It may have been the double affliction that drove her to drink (as we've seen, above). But, at the time, like everyone else connected to the Edward Street William Brady family, she rallied and suppressed her emotions for the sake of the children. The newly fatherless children were the focus of everyone's attention. Catherine, the dressmaker, sewed clothes for them and sometimes had them for breakfast on their way to school. She made them porridge, which they hated, but were too polite to refuse. On one occasion at least, the porridge went into a pocket, to the detriment of the new, exquisitely worked clothes. ... Perhaps a resolve was entered into to ensure that all the young Bradys should thrive, in spite of everything. It didn't work entirely, but considerable goodwill was there. And the baby Nora in particular came in for a lot of cosseting and indulgence.

But my grandmother was defeated by Christmas. Between poverty and bereavement, she had no cause to love its overcharged atmosphere. I doubt if much of a festive spirit prevailed at 26 Edward Street, in the first year following William Brady's death, or later. A packet of sweets, a couple of oranges or tangerines in a stocking, was all each child could hope for. But again, an exception was made for Nora. The year she was five or six (she remembered), the entire family left the house on Christmas Eve and walked up the town to a toy shop to buy her a doll. I see them proceeding in single file, in their dark winter coats, like an illustration from an annual – *Blackie's Children's Annual*, say – the mother striding ahead and the straggle of daughters following, all for a stupendous purpose. The Christmas tree lit up with fairy lights in the town centre, the carol singers in the streets, would have added to the pungency of the occasion. In later life, I think, all of them to some extent made a thing of despising Christmas. But in that one year at least, a little of the magic of the season was vouchsafed to them.

My mother related another childhood incident, a grimmer one. She is still around five or six, and she has a bosom friend, a little girl of her own age: let's call her Bridie. Bridie lives nearby. Some streets away – Black's Court, perhaps? – in an unkempt kitchen house, lives a friend these two have in common, a motherless girl whose father and older sisters neglect her shockingly. We'll call this one Sheila. My grandmother does not approve of Nora's friendship with Sheila, due to the family's bad reputation. There is even a suggestion that Sheila's older sisters may supplement the family income by engaging in a bit of amateur whoring, bringing into play a dark and slatternly side of Lurgan life. But Nora sticks up for her friend, and she and Bridie are often at Sheila's house. It's a great venue for childish carry-on: no grown-ups to put a damper on things.

One day, a group of four or five small girls, including Nora and Bridie, has gathered for the purpose of play in Sheila's kitchen. At one point they take a notion to wash dolls' clothes. They are being serious and aping the domesticity of grown-ups. The clothes are duly washed in the sink with everyone lending a hand, and then hung up around the open fire to dry. Nora, wiping her hands on a dirty old kitchen towel, suddenly remembers she's promised to be home by a certain time, and needs to leave at once. The others try to persuade her to stay on. But she knows she'll be in trouble if she doesn't get back when she said she would. She lets herself out by the front door and runs through the streets, arriving out of breath in time for her tea. Some hours later comes the news that Sheila's house has burnt to the ground and everyone in it. Sheila, Bridie and the others – all burnt to a cinder. I don't know if Nora drew from this horrendous event a moral lesson about obedience, if she felt later that she, the survivor, had been singled out for some celestial purpose, if the Catholic faith made a way of assimilating and assuaging the tragedy. *I* don't want to take a moral tone about it. But it must have alerted her, at a frighteningly early age, to the unutterable fragility of existence.

No doubt my grandmother went down on her knees and thanked Providence for steering her youngest child away from an inferno. But Providence has yet a diabolical trick up its sleeve. Some time during the autumn of 1922, nineteen-year-old Lily Brady complains of abdominal pains. She becomes feverish. The pains escalate. A frenzy of anxiety engulfs the house. It's no small matter, in those pre-National Health days, to summon a doctor: but a doctor is sent for. He comes with his Gladstone bag and diagnoses a stomach ache. Has Lily eaten something that's disagreed with her? He prescribes some powders or pills and goes on his way. Some time later, before the horrified eyes of her mother and sisters, Lily dies of a burst appendix. Black days follow: the coffin, the priest, the rosary beads, the weeping relatives. And the terrible image in everyone's head: the back bedroom, the screaming girl, the fruitless efforts of those around her.

The date is 2 October 1922. Two days later, Lily is buried in Dougher Cemetery with the full rites of the Catholic Church. How was this death allowed to happen? I envisage my grandmother at this moment, aged forty-one and dressed in black, as a kind of '*bean caointe*' – keening woman – as in the *sean-nos* song which is rendered with such feeling by the great traditional singer Pádraigín Ní Uallacháin. The woman in the song is burying the last of her children – '*Suilfaidh me an rod seo gan lui na leapa, / Faoi mo Neilli beag mingheal 'ta sinte faoi thalamh*' ('I'll walk the roads without sleep or bed, / Since my sweet gentle Nelly is lying dead'). It's an Omeath song, but, Pádraigín Ní Uallacháin says, a version was current in south Armagh, and no doubt it would have migrated northwards. Not that my grandmother or any of her family would have known it. They weren't Irish-speakers; and, at the time, there wasn't much general interest in the heritage of Irish-language song. But there would have been an empathy with the strong emotion contained in the searing lines of 'The Keening Woman'.

Tragic Lily Brady went under the sod, and for ever after a steely silence was preserved on the topic of her life and death. It was almost as if she had never existed. Only the photo that came into her sister Eileen's possession testifies to Lily's presence in the world of factory work, huxters' shops, sectarian onslaughts, Sinn Féin activities, sisterly companionship and friction, St Peter's Church, flirtations with boys from round about, Sunday best. All the elements of intense, unexalted life. Lily's story, which can barely be imagined now, has to be fitted into what's known of early twentieth-century Lurgan, and also into a poor, or poorish, Catholic household, but one very conscious of occupying a notable position in the neighbourhood. Once the shock of sudden bereavement was over, the 'keening woman' image was not a thing my grandmother Sarah would have clung on to. She'd have hated people to associate her, or those belonging to her, with a stricken or ill-fated course in life. A needy comportment was not her métier. Within the limits of her environment, she went all out to create a sense of auspiciousness, an up-and-coming atmosphere. Perhaps it was the Blacker blood coming out in her, but what she repudiated utterly was the poor mouth. You wouldn't have caught her creeping off to the pawnshop with a shawl flung over her head, or borrowing anything from anyone. She stood on her own two feet. 'A great manager' was what her children said about her, looking back, and paying tribute to her resourcefulness in making a meagre income go a long way. No one in her care went hungry or barefoot, even if a lot of mending and making do went on.

I'm not sure if the two events are connected, but it's around the time of Lily's death, I think, that Sarah's youngest, Nora, is briefly sent to sleep across the road, in some supportive arrangement with a neighbour. Nora crosses the road to go to bed, and then returns home in the morning to eat her breakfast and set off for school. ...Am I right to read into this an instance of the impulse to protect this child from the worst of the anguish afflicting the disrupted household? I suspect a benign conspiracy, initiated by her mother, to spare the nine-year-old a too-close acquaintance with the devastating effects of death and despair. Nora is favoured, in this and other respects, in ways her sisters might have come to resent – as, indeed, at least one of them did. Between Nora and Eileen, now thrust into the position of oldest daughter, deep resentments combined with mutual

Eileen and Lily Brady (seated), *c.*1919

admiration and affection to create a complicated relationship. (When Eileen died in 1994, well into her eighties, my mother said it was the worst day of her life.) Nora's *friend* in the family was Kathleen, the closest to her in age; but for the whole of her life, her sister Eileen was among the people who meant most to her.

Once I'd gained an inkling of the circumstances surrounding this second tragedy in my mother's family[17] (information acquired not all that long ago), I held the doctor's incompetence to blame for the destruction of a promising life. I say 'promising', because that single existing image of Lily Brady shows an attractive, composed, intelligent girl, seated on a chair in some photographer's studio, while her considerably less well-adjusted sister Eileen stands grimly by her side. Eileen's expression suggests she's about to burst into tears, that she's having her photo taken very much against her will. It's clear that she would rather be anywhere else in the world than standing mutinously there beside her self-possessed sister. And in a way, this discontent with her lot was a marker for the rest of her life. Like my mother – and not, perhaps, like the two middle sisters – Eileen would have benefited from an education, but, after primary level, one was not available to her. Every step she tried to take to further her own interests was thwarted in some way. From an early age, she developed a sense that the world was against her. She developed, too, a good line in glares, some of which were directed half-humorously at those around her. Eileen had a formidable presence – and being aggrieved, pragmatic and good-natured all at once endowed her, at the very least, with an interesting personality.

I blamed the doctor for Lily's death: but it seems, at the time, it was fatally easy to confuse the symptoms of appendicitis with those of a lesser ailment. It was a matter of carrying out a cursory examination and hoping for the best. But you can't get away from the fact that a more conscientious or enlightened doctor would have got the sick girl to a hospital in time to save her life. She didn't have to die, but she did die, leaving a ruptured and grieving household behind her. That year, 1922, saw a deeper than ever repudiation of the follies of Christmas among the North Street[18] Bradys. The house was wrapped in darkness and lamentation. But gradually, very gradually, a slight degree of optimism about the future revived. It was tied up with Catholic neighbourhood solidarity, with continuing support from concerned relations, especially the large contingent of Brady cousins nearby (Sarah's sister's lot), and with the emerging scholarly abilities of the youngest child of the family, for whom the nuns of her primary school had high hopes.

The background to all the home-front adversity was a town awash in dissension and bigotry. The children going to Mass on St Patrick's Day were preyed upon by gangs of jeering Protestant contemporaries who tore the shamrock from their lapels. Reciprocal aggravations: I think of my great-uncle Jim Brady drilling Irish Volunteers up and down Edward Street under the noses of old-established enemies (how did he get away with it?). Irish Volunteers – but, as it happened, Great-Uncle Jim was a British Army veteran. His sister-in-law, my grandmother, was a Dardanelles widow. Poppy Day in the future put her in a quandary. Confusions concerning questions of loyalty and allegiance proliferated. When the Treaty was signed in December 1921 my grandmother thought something momentous had been achieved – only to be put right by her Tipping relations who were holding out for a united Ireland. She'd hung out a tricolour in celebration: but some of her half-brothers and their sons came to her home in a rage and told her to take it in to hell's gates out of that. There was no cause for jubilation: nationalists in the North had been sold down the river. The War of Independence – total independence – would continue.

Thinking about a particular period – the years between 1910 and 1920, say – and trying to place myself within a web of family and extended family connections, I'm brought up against so many diametric opposites that it seems a wonder I wasn't cancelled out before I got started. Pro-Home Rulers and anti-Home Rulers, Carsonites and Redmondites and revolutionaries, those for and against British Army enlistment, subversives and conservatives and (mostly female) minders-of-their-own-business, unequivocal and ambivalent supporters of the war effort.[19] ... The war effort. Here an extra anomaly of a personal character enters into the family history narrative. While my Brady grandfather was, with however many reservations, committed to fight on the side of the British, direct descendants of my Heller great-great-grandparents were fighting on the other, the German side. There's scope here for a stranger meeting than Wilfred Owen's.

However, if the end product of chance and interfusion (myself) adds up to a bundle of genetic and ideological inconsistencies, it's an admixture – in my case and everyone else's – for which there is a good deal to be said. It should (though it doesn't always happen) exclude the possibility of fanaticism and discredit the chimera of a 'pure' bloodline, of any coloration whatever. As I've said before – and I make no apology for saying it again – all of our bloodlines in the north of Ireland are very likely to be tempered by a bit of the other strain – whichever that is, and whether it pleases us to know it, or doesn't please us.

CHAPTER 7
A BAD LOT

'There was a man shot in the tram I was in,' said Colm.

'There was a woman shot stone dead on the other side of the street. There's a sniper on the mill all the mornin' and you daren't put your nose out the door.'

Shots crackled fiercely and the man instinctively ducked his head.

'Jesus, Mary and Joseph!' said the woman, blessing herself. 'That's near.'

Michael McLaverty, Call My Brother Back

Violence comes in cycles, say historians. But sometimes it comes *on* cycles.

Harry Tipping

It's worth taking note of the bicycle's role in the business of fostering revolution. All over Ireland, in the years between 1916 and 1923 (say), you might have spotted figures in trench coats cycling in all weathers through boggy back roads or mountain passes, up and down hills, dripping wet, sweltering in the heat, more often than not on borrowed machines with perhaps defective brakes, misshapen saddles or a buckled rim. They were all at it: Tom Barry living, before reliving, his *Guerrilla Days in Ireland*, Sean Treacy veering ahead with the 3rd Tipperary Brigade and going on to die by gunshot in a Dublin street, Dan Breen immersed to the hilt in his *Fight for Irish Freedom*. You had Ernie O'Malley pedalling past demesne walls with thoughts of iniquitous Big House people in his head and Pierce Ferriter's poems in his pocket. Past military road posts and fortified barracks he goes, on and on: east Clare, Waterford, Donegal, Monaghan, all the hill districts and scattered villages of west County Cork. On the roads of Cork, O'Malley might have met the student Volunteer O'Faolain, similarly mounted on a bike, on the same insurrectionary business, undeterred by the noise of machine-gun fire, the prospect of an army ambush or a convoy of Black and Tans careering round the very next bend in the road. And in his pocket, as likely as not, the poems of Yeats.

Sean O'Faolain's first collection of stories, *Midsummer Night Madness* (1932) is filled with the spirit of heroic, brutal and foolhardy undertakings in the name of Ireland free. It has old-style activists holed up in barns and outhouses, digging trenches, gathering information, dodging the enemy, scouting and skiting all over the countryside to more or less encouraging effect. Saturnine Volunteers hunched over handlebars possessed by a steely intent. And it wasn't, indeed, only men, young men, who cycled for Ireland. Carrying dispatches or ammunition, alerting IRA men on active service to dangers approaching, or hastening to lend a hand at some makeshift field hospital: these were ways in which the women of Ireland could involve themselves in the national struggle. Sean O'Faolain's future wife Eileen Gould, for example, was a courier operating between Cork itself and the shifting divisional headquarters in various locations to the west of the city. Cycling skills were required, along with skill at evasion and a steady nerve. And luck – which couldn't always be relied on. Eileen Gould was arrested and imprisoned (briefly) in 1923.

Irish republican women on bicycles might be said to constitute an offshoot, or a specialised section, of the cycling cult which began in the 1890s, and saw the 'New Woman' of that decade carried forward on wheels into a brighter, more expansive future. It required spirit and determination to progress from wobbling to freewheeling, but the end result was worth it. '...On a bicycle you feel a different person; nothing can come near you, you forget who you are. ... It [makes] life an absolutely different thing ...'. Miriam Henderson, in Dorothy Richardson's outstanding series of novels with the overall title *Pilgrimage*, speaks for a whole generation when she lauds the bicycle and its liberating effect. And in early twentieth-century Ireland, its association not only with personal, but with national freedom, gives it an additional éclat.

Sean O'Faolain's friend, fellow-Corkman and author Frank O'Connor, includes in his first collection (*Guests of the Nation*, 1931) a story about an eager girl entrusted with an IRA missive. *Bring your bicycle.* She does, donning gaiters and a stout woollen coat before cycling out of the city and into a warren of muddy back roads clogged with pot-holes. A sodden hay wain, an old woman leaning over a half-door, a boy driving a cart up a boreen: these pass her by like emblems of a country out of time, a country worth fighting for. And she, Helen Joyce, has a part to play in the fight. True, when Helen delivers her dispatch it's accepted off-handedly, as something of small consequence. But what odds — she's in great company, sitting in a 'safe house' by a blazing fire and listening to tales of blown-up bridges and hair's-breadth escapes. But then reality breaks in, in the form of a dead young Volunteer, shot through the chest and stowed in a car outside.

When I was sixteen or seventeen, I lapped up all such stories and reminiscences. The O'Connor/O'Faolain brand of realism, though, may well have sparked a misgiving or two in my head. Though I relished the artistry of their fictions — who would not? — and pungent Irish atmosphere, I'd have felt that the freedom fighters among their characters were entitled to rather more reverential treatment. No 'impossible young fellow[s], ... playing about with guns and explosives, ... letting on [they were] somebody of importance' would do me, thank you very much. No jeers and sneers and 'delight in devilment'. 'Two fine young fellows kilt outright — they're picking up the bits of them still.' 'Our cause is just' was more in my line — and any attempt to temper, or tamper with, the appropriately elevated tone, was flawed in my view from the word go.

But what did I mean by the 'just Irish cause'? As I've already made clear, I saw it — the glorified purpose — as an unassailable entity, allowing no scope for degrees of commitment, or differing forms of interpretation. It was embodied in resistance to injustice, pure and simple, injustice inflicted on the native Irish through eight centuries of misrule. Well, that was all I knew about it. I had the story of Ireland in outline, from Dermot MacMurrough on, and it was always and ever a question of might versus right. There was always a side to revere and a side to deplore, and I knew which was which. It was perfectly straightforward. Even when Irish patriots separated themselves into different categories, one of these categories remained head and shoulders above the others. It was a matter of fidelity to the truer objective, the undiminished ideal. Had I been alive in the early part of the twentieth century (say), I'd have followed the insurgents of Easter Week (or at sixteen I certainly believed I would), not the Redmondite British Army recruits. And after 1921 I'd have thrown in my lot with the anti-Treaty, not the pro-Treaty, faction.

When Frank Tipping came home following his years of service during the First World War, it didn't take him long to exchange his British soldier's khaki for a uniform more in keeping with his background and beliefs: that of an Irish Volunteer.[1] Frank's younger brother Gerry, late of the 2nd Royal Irish Fusiliers, followed suit. It was 1919, and the War of Independence was under way. The country, everyone agreed, was in a shocking state. The hopes of various factions, in the wake of the Great War, were far from being realised. A general election at the end of the previous year had seen Sinn Féin winning all before it in the South, unionists holding on in the North, and a cut-off portion of the country looking very much on the cards. In the effort to get things sorted out (an impossibility), frantic negotiations between all parties were taking place.

At 76 Edward Street, Lurgan, an intensely Irish atmosphere prevailed. It was high-minded, up-the-rebels territory. Four Tipping brothers – Henry and Mary Anne's sons Matt, Frank, Gerry and Jimmy – were full-fledged IRA men, adamant about the proper line to take. It had something to do with the way the country was run, with long-ago massacres, pikes-in-the-thatch, mass rocks, hedge schools, baton charges, guns, and shouts in the street. They were firmly in favour of their own wronged people. The youngest brother, Bertie, had joined the cadet branch of the Volunteers, the Fianna; and one sister, Lily, was in the women's section, the Cumann na mBan. All of them rode about on bicycles on republican errands as circumstances dictated, though other forms of transport weren't excluded from the picture, as we shall see.

Lily Tipping was brainy and go-ahead, and in later years enjoyed a successful career in various branches of nursing – medical, surgical, fever, etc. She had strings of letters after her name. Lily was enrolled with the Royal Rhodesian Medical Corps between 1939 and 1944, and won an international Red Cross medal for services to nursing. She'd trained as a basic nurse at Lurgan Hospital, completing her course in 1917, and then went on to secure all kinds of advanced professional qualifications endorsed by certificates. She became a midwife and a district nurse. But before credit and renown overtook her, Lily demonstrated her full endowment with Tipping mettle by devoting herself to the national cause. 'Nurse and gunrunner', articulated with a certain ironic admiration, is an appropriate tag for Lily in the eyes of her family-historian nephew Harry.

'Enterprising' is another word. Those were dangerous days, with – in Ireland – a plethora of wars to command people's allegiance and harry their nerves. Picture a spring morning in 1919 – say – and a couple of sturdy girls on the platform at Lurgan station awaiting the Dublin train. They are wearing, perhaps, high-waisted, belted, three-quarter-length coats over tailored blouses and navy serge skirts ending just above the ankle. Perhaps felt hats and walking shoes. And carrying canvas holdalls. They're not the chattering kind. A somewhat keyed-up air surrounds them, a sense of urgency. They are Lily Tipping and her friend Elizabeth McCusker of Brown Street in the town. ... The train judders up to the platform, Lily wrenches open the door of the nearest carriage, and the two of them step on board. As they settle themselves, rows and rows of backyards glide slowly past, washing strung on clotheslines blowing in the wind, then flash away into the distance as the train gathers speed. A moment of apprehension occurs at Portadown, perhaps: dear God, are these plain-clothes policemen getting on? *Who* is that military looking man on the platform who seems to be staring at us? Or later along the route: why is the train stopping in the middle of nowhere? But soon it jerks forward again, getting into a steady rhythm: past apple orchards filled with blossom, through the countryside where fortified bawns were built and atrocities committed, where detachments of ancient soldiery roved intent on badness. Past the aloof facade of Carrickblacker House, where direct descendants of Lily's direct ancestors lived their lives, and where bullets were fashioned in a time of disturbance to aid the Orange cause. On and on ... the Gap of the North is coming up, Slieve Gullion to the west, the Carlingford hills on the other side, all the wild and rugged terrain of south Armagh. Newry, Dundalk, the Boyne Bridge, Drogheda ... then Amiens Street station and running the gauntlet of beggarly children with their Dublin whines. On, at a steady pace, to where they've arranged to go, to collect what they have come to collect. ... Some hours later, purpose fulfilled, the two young women alight at Lurgan, the morning's innocent holdalls crammed with service revolvers, spare parts and ammunition, with maybe a cardigan or jumper folded on top to allay suspicion. These girls are part of a Cumann na mBan detachment whose work for Ireland is to fetch and carry home arms from Dublin – easy to get away with in the pre-border era, but nevertheless requiring a steady temperament, an ability to stay unfazed in the event of coming up against the Royal Irish Constabulary. To unsuspecting eyes, it must seem at the time that the town is filled with young day-trippers who have nothing better to do than travel back and forth between Lurgan and Dublin on the train.

I was determined to get Lily Tipping on to a bicycle, and – lo and behold – here she is on one, undergoing a nightly trial of strength by cycling between Bessbrook and Omeath (a journey of about ten miles), where a couple of wounded IRA men are dependent on her nursing proficiency. This clandestine engagement goes on for about two weeks. Lily's daytime job, at the Sisters of Mercy Convent in Bessbrook, keeps her busy ministering to ill nuns and malingering boarding-school pupils: when on earth, one wonders, does she find time to sleep? Skill and determination, the national cause and gritted teeth, I imagine, keep Lily going. Whatever the hardship to her, she'd tell herself, the two men in her care have worse, much worse, to endure.

The men are survivors – just – of the 'Egyptian Arch' debacle of 13 December 1920. A two-part operation was planned for that date, involving about two hundred IRA Volunteers: first one lot was detailed to burn the RIC barracks at nearby Camlough, and the second set to wait in ambush at the 'Egyptian' railway arch at Newry for army and RIC reinforcements rushing to the barracks' aid. It's the night of 12/13 December, dark and foggy and filled with intense activity. Trees are felled on both sides of the railway embankment to make a road block, and once that's done, selected Volunteers, poised to do killing, take up a firing position along the top of the arch. They are armed with guns and hand grenades, but only a limited supply. The bulk of their equipment rests out of reach in dumps on the south Down side of Newry, irretrievable at the necessary moment due to frequent RIC searches in the area. It's not an auspicious start to the night's work.

The 'Egyptian Arch' near Newry, where an IRA ambush was foiled in December 1920

Back at Camlough, Volunteers succeed in setting fire to the barracks,[2] but the fire is quickly extinguished and Verey lights set off to alert the Newry garrison (as the Egyptian Arch contingent had anticipated) to serious trouble in the village. South Armagh Commandant Frank Aiken calls off the barracks attack and commandeers a donkey to carry away an associate wounded in the leg. (I hope this useful donkey is well looked after.) At the same time, armoured cars and Crossley Tenders are speeding past the Egyptian Arch when the IRA roadblock stops them in their tracks. Grenades rain down on them but fail to explode, or explode uselessly in the roadway. Soldiers and RIC men scramble out of their vehicles and run for cover, dodging bullets coming from the top of the arch and swiftly retaliating with machine-gun fire which kills one Volunteer and seriously injures others. There's nothing for it but another IRA withdrawal, which takes place in difficult circumstances. Two wounded men are carried pickaback across the Cooley Hills (a distance of eight or ten miles) – first being hurriedly tended in a shepherd's hut by a couple of Newry doctors named Flood and Quinn. An appalling journey follows, before they're brought to safety at a hospice attached to the priory of the Charity Fathers at Omeath. This is where Nurse Lily Tipping comes in.

Lily Tipping figured quite strongly in my childhood, as someone approved of and cherished in the family. People talked about her a lot, about her time on Achill Island, County Mayo, as the first district nurse appointed there, about her years in Rhodesia and advancement beyond her stay-at-home siblings, about the pull of home that, nevertheless, brought her back in retirement to set up house with her widowed sister Monny (Lily was the only member of her family who hadn't married, and Monny was the only married one who hadn't had children, so they suited one another: oddities both). Small and sharp and ironical, Lily is a person of consequence and a frequent subject of conversation among her relations. What isn't mentioned, though, is the thing I'd have paid attention to, had I been listening: Lily's days as an out-and-out republican. For my parents' generation, by and large (and for the previous one), the political past is a fraught and dingy place better left unrevisited. We're in the '50s, '60s now, a world more peaceful and hopeful, closer to a fair deal for everyone, old-time grudges and angers fading away (or so it seemed). Fading away – but enough of a residue remains to agitate nationalists and reformists, in whose enlightened company I place my sixteen-year-old self. Continuing injustices stare us in the face wherever we look for them, and all down to the English and Orangemen.

I thought of Lily Tipping as a kind of aunt, but she was, in fact, my mother's cousin (though of an earlier generation). I never bothered to sort out the gradations of Tipping connections. There were so many of them – names constantly on my mother's and my grandmother's lips. I was taken to visit Lily a couple of times when she was old and I was nineteen or twenty – and if I'd had the wit to cross-question her, she, I am sure, would gladly have recalled her rebel days, wild nights in December and cycling through the countryside on a patriotic errand of mercy. Brave young women couriers and IRA auxiliaries I knew from books, but here was one, unacknowledged, on my own doorstep, so to speak.

Lily didn't have to go it entirely alone. Her young brother Bernard (Bertie), a prominent Fianna member at the time, is sent from his home in Lurgan to temporary lodgings in Newry, from which he emerges after dark to accompany his sister on her hazardous nocturnal journeys between Bessbrook and Omeath. It's up to him to see her safely back to the convent, once she's done whatever is necessary for her patients. In one case, Lily's ministrations aren't enough. There's nothing she can do – Volunteer Peter Shields is too badly hurt to survive. He is done for, even before he reaches the sanctuary of the Charity Fathers' hospice. He dies from his wounds on Christmas Day and, like the hero of Corunna, is buried darkly at dead of night. It's a sorrowful and macabre occasion in the hospice grounds, the torch-lit procession, the grave-digging Brothers, secrecy and haste. ... The other Volunteer, William Carr, has a leg amputated but recovers under Lily's care and lives on for many years.

The thing that alarms me most in all of this is Bertie Tipping's age. He is fourteen years old and should be at school, not pedalling all over County Armagh running horrendous risks. Or, if not at school, at least serving behind the counter of his father's shop. Didn't his parents have any say in the matter? I can't imagine his mother Mary Anne being overjoyed to see her youngest son set off on his bicycle for the train station en route to Newry and a dangerous mission. Of course, it is possible the parents were not in possession of all the facts. They may have believed that Bertie was simply paying a visit to his older sister, taking a break from his grocery apprenticeship. If a domestic conspiracy was taking place, though, his brothers were in it. His older brother Jimmy (1899–1976) is commanding officer of the Fianna *Sluagh* (Company) to which Bertie belongs. (Jimmy is interned at Ballykinler camp in County Down at this time – see below – but he'd have been kept apprised of events outside.) And Frank and Gerry are still at home and up to the eyes in subversive activity. Or, I suppose, it is just possible that Bertie went to Newry with his parents' full knowledge and blessing. 76 Edward Street was, after all, well known as a 'safe house' and this would require the cooperation of everyone in it. As a dropping and collection point for dispatches, the location of an arms dump and a temporary place of refuge for men on the run, the house sat there in plebeian Edward Street as a beacon of principled resistance.

And it's true that Bertie is no novice, so he isn't, for all his youth, in the ways of republican agitation. The previous year, 1919, Bertie had joined his brother's Fianna *Sluagh*, acquired a gun and a uniform, and, thus equipped, might often be seen cycling with fellow Fenians, through areas both friendly and unfriendly, as part of an IRA recruitment drive.

Also in 1919, Bertie is present and standing to attention at the great St Patrick's Day rally at Piper Hill outside Lurgan, listening to Darrell Figgis[3] deliver an uplifting oration. 'His noble voice re-echoed o'er the waters of Lough Neagh', avers an anonymous local bard roped in to commemorate the occasion. (Probably Aghagallon man Jimmy Devlin.) He also notes some important participants in the event:

> I saw Joe Burke and Tipping[4] as the first command they
> gave,
> I saw Dan Corr and Joe Maguire in those Irish ranks
> so brave.

By the summer of 1920, Bertie is a veteran of police baton charges and arms raids. He's entrusted with keeping guns cleaned and in working order. Along with his friends in the Fianna, he has attended lessons in the making of gunpowder (whew!), and been shown how to refill shotgun cartridges with buckshot. ... Lily too has acquired experience in secretly tending to the wounded long before her involvement with the Egyptian Arch casualties. People with RIC bullets in their flesh have been carried into her home by the back door, to be patched up by Lily and thereby enabled (some of them, at any rate) to get themselves to a hospital for more intensive treatment. On one occasion, Bertie and two local IRA men accompany one of these bandaged and shaken Volunteers on the train to Belfast and a hospital in the city.[5] Even before he makes the transfer from the Fianna to the IRA proper, which occurs in due course, a lot of responsibility is placed on the shoulders of teenage Bertie.

We're still in the summer of 1920 when Bertie receives orders to present himself at Lurgan station to meet his brother Jimmy coming off the Belfast train. From Jimmy he obtains a small travelling bag and nonchalantly carries it out of the station under the eyes of many who'd have gasped at its contents. (I don't know if Jimmy returns to Belfast straight away, without leaving the station, or if he accompanies his innocent looking brother through Lurgan's inflammable streets.) Is Bertie's heart beating wildly as he goes, for all his unconcerned appearance? Does he understand the risk he's running? In the current state of unrest, police and soldiers are constantly on the look-out for anything untoward, such as one youth picking up a bag from another – and in that particular bag, on that July day, are a couple of revolvers and a supply of ammunition. The revolvers may have come from Cork and are destined for a particular purpose. It is possible that one of these firearms holds a special significance for republicans which I'll recount in a minute. We are now approaching the well-documented Swanzy assassination in Lisburn and its terrible aftermath.

The story has often been told, though aspects of the affair remain surrounded by a certain haze and contradiction. In outline, though, it is clear enough. It begins in Cork,[6] with the murder of Tomás MacCurtain, lord mayor and officer in command of the city's 1st IRA brigade. It's 19 March 1920, the middle of the night. MacCurtain is shot in circumstances of extreme brutality at his home in Thomas Davis Street, in the presence of his pregnant wife Elizabeth and with five young children asleep in bed. (Or not asleep: the banging at the door and eruption into the house of men with blackened faces brandishing revolvers no doubt aroused them into a nightmare – every child's worst, most exorbitant fears come true.) After the killers have fled, the police and army arrive and turn the house upside down in a search for seditious material (weapons and documents). They find nothing. MacCurtain's personal revolver, concealed under the mattress of baby Eilis MacCurtain's pram, is overlooked. It is possibly this revolver, earmarked at once for a retaliatory purpose, that is briefly in the keeping of Bertie Tipping in Lurgan, before it is put to its designated use. Or maybe the story of MacCurtain's gun and its ultimate destination is purely apocryphal.

At the inquest into the death of the lord mayor, the coroner's jury brings in an unexpected and amazing verdict. Indicted on a charge of wilful murder are

> ... David Lloyd George, Prime Minister of England; Lord French, Lord Lieutenant of Ireland; Ian McPherson, late Chief Secretary of Ireland; Acting Inspector General Smith, of the Royal Irish Constabulary; Divisional Inspector Clayton of the Royal Irish Constabulary; District Inspector Swanzy and some unknown members of the Royal Irish Constabulary.

Those named become immediate targets for the IRA, though some are clearly beyond their reach. Of those who aren't, two of the specified 'unknown members' of the RIC are the first to die, shot on a tram car in Cork city. Their names are Garvey and Harrington, and they are popularly believed to be the people who fired the lethal shots into Tomás MacCurtain. The process of revenge is under way. Michael Collins himself, in mourning for his close friend and ally, has authorised these and further executions. District Inspector Swanzy is high on the condemned list, and for his own safety the DI is hurriedly transferred from Cork to Lisburn, a staunch wee Protestant town in the distant north. In the eyes of those facing republican implacability down South, Lisburn would look like a haven of loyalism.

But plans are afoot. Ulster and Munster are poles apart, but the whole of Ireland, between the spring of 1920 and the Truce of 1921, is undergoing 'the full voltage of British military oppression' (in the words of Sean O'Faolain in his autobiography *Vive Moi!*), and a complementary network of republican resistance is operating throughout its length and breadth. It isn't too difficult for IRA Intelligence to track the district inspector to his new posting. Soon the IRA has Swanzy in its sights. The Cork brigade claims the honour of carrying out the sentence, but, as the Belfast IRA reasonably point out, their Cork accents would make them conspicuous in the North. In the event, it becomes a joint operation, though with each party reluctant to accord too much credit to the other. 'This was a Belfast Brigade job,' claimed one of its members, Sean Montgomery, in an unpublished memoir,[7] 'the Cork men were guests.'

The Cork men thought otherwise. They were the primary activists in the business, according to them, with Belfast merely taking a secondary role. It was a Corkman, Sean Culhane, who fired the first shot at DI Swanzy as he left Christ Church Cathedral in Lisburn after attending morning service. The date is Sunday 22 August 1920. The gun in question, as I've indicated, passed into republican mythology as Tomás MacCurtain's own, miraculously undetected during the raid on his home on the night of his murder. (Ironically, the permit for this gun had been signed by Swanzy himself in the mistaken belief that it was going to a 'loyalist' in Cork city.[8]) It is possible that Sean Culhane had carried it with him on the train from Cork – risking its confiscation and his own detainment – or, on the other hand, that it had made its way north some weeks earlier, and been handed to Bertie Tipping in Lurgan to be kept until called for. Bertie has testified that the two guns he collected from his brother Jimmy were among those actually used in 'the Swanzy affair'.

Some time during that summer of 1920, Jimmy Tipping is installed in lodgings in Belfast which he shares with Jack (Sean) Leonard, a taxi driver originally from Sligo, and currently a Volunteer with 'B' Company, Belfast Brigade. The lodging house is in Bedeque Street off the Lower Crumlin Road, just opposite the Mater Hospital. The two young men are deeply involved in preparations for the coming assassination. The first time an attempt is made on Swanzy's life – on 15 August 1920 – things do not go according to plan. The DI gains a week's reprieve.

It's in connection with that first Sunday that differing accounts begin to obscure the actual course of events. But what I think took place was this. A bona fide taxi driver named George Nelson was hired to pick up four men on the Shankill Road and take them to Portadown. One of the men was Jimmy Tipping. The taxi, as instructed, then proceeded up the Springfield Road towards Hannahstown (not the Cave Hill Road as Sean Leonard later recalled it), and at a prearranged spot it was halted by three masked men carrying revolvers who sprang out of a hedge. The passengers then joined forces with the hijackers. Nelson was blindfolded and had his hands tied behind his back; he was then led across some fields to a barn where two men guarded him until it was judged safe to let him go. One of the IRA men standing guard over Nelson was Jimmy Tipping. In the meantime, the commandeered taxi on its way to Lisburn had come to grief: either a wheel flew off (one account), it simply broke down (another account), or the driver from Cork got hopelessly lost among the Antrim byroads. Or, a further account has it, Swanzy simply failed to appear at the appointed moment to be shot. Operation postponed.

Lessons were learned. (That's a joke.) The following week a similar ploy is adopted, but the non-bona fide taxi driver for the occasion is Sean Leonard (why didn't they use him in the first place?). Roger McCorley of the Belfast Brigade is already in Lisburn monitoring events, his colleague Joe McKelvey[9] having reported on the expected movements of the DI. As far as I am aware, Jimmy Tipping does not on this occasion travel with the shooting party to Lisburn, but stays behind in Belfast poised to help construct an alibi for the returning victorious executioners. (I am not sure how this works, but it does, at least for a time.)

Lisburn, Market Square, 1.03 p.m. An instant of shocked silence overtakes the Sunday crowds milling about the town centre as shots ring out, leaving Oswald Swanzy lying dead on the pavement, and his killers making a getaway as panic and confusion swiftly flare up. Shouts and screams contribute to the uproar as pedestrians stumble off frantically in all directions. The IRA men continue firing to ward off capture, like something out of a cops-and-robbers screening at the Diamond Cinema on the Falls Road in Belfast, but the only other casualties are a blackthorn stick shot out of the hand of an outraged pursuer, and the grazed leg of a Miss McCreight, who's managed to get herself in the pathway of a bullet. All the gunmen scramble into the waiting car, with Sean Leonard at the wheel, apart from Roger McCorley who nearly gets left behind in the shambles. He has to make a dive for it and as he does, his gun goes off, driving a bullet hole through the floor. McCorley is hauled to safety by his companions as the car speeds off in a manner not consistent with the rules of the road. Pursuit by police in a taxi is foiled by that vehicle losing a wheel as it goes too recklessly round a corner.[10] (There are a lot of flying wheels and bullets in this story – not to mention spokes in wheels.)

Leaving their pursuers far behind, and speeding out of the town towards the back road home, the exhilarated Volunteers reach Belfast without further ado. At Great Victoria Street station, the two Corkmen in the party board a train to Dublin, where, as arranged, they report to Michael Collins on the outcome of the mission and receive his congratulations. Their Belfast associates, Roger McCorley and another Volunteer named Tom Fox, walk away not too hastily and disappear into a district known to be sympathetic, leaving Sean Leonard still driving the cab in the city centre. As far as I can gather (accounts of the business don't always tally), he drives it to Tates Avenue off the Lisburn Road where a couple of supposed 'fares' – actually, Jimmy Tipping and an IRA man named Liam Devlin – are waiting to be collected and taken to Holywood and Helen's Bay to create a sense of an ordinary Sunday outing. In fact, the guilty taxi cab is flagged down and searched by RIC patrols both on the outward and the return journey, but on each occasion the searchers fail to spot the bullet holes which should have alerted them to something fishy. But the reprieve for a few of the northern Volunteers (like Oswald Swanzy's) is short-lived.

Looking back over what I've written about the Swanzy shooting, I'm slightly dismayed to encounter a certain flippancy of tone, as if the only way to treat the event is to be mildly cynical and sardonic. Is this appropriate? Two things I know, or think I know: had I been present in that street in Lisburn when the DI was gunned down, I'd have been as horrified and shocked by the bloodshed as anyone else. And – conversely – if the planning of this piece of retribution for the awful murder of Tomás MacCurtain had involved my cooperation to any extent, I'd have given it freely, regarding the proposed execution as a brave and necessary act to bolster the republican cause. Then, as now – I hope – I'd have drawn the line at exulting in anyone's violent death (well, apart from droves of Black and Tans or other hoodlum belligerents); but equally, I'd have condoned the tactics of guerrilla warfare or any other form of resistance to the current dreadful state of misery and terror throughout Ireland. Those whom Sean O'Faolain called 'the tremendously gallant few', the Irish freedom fighters, could have counted on my iota of advocacy, had I been there to proffer it. The shadowy allure of gunmen and patriots was a thing well understood by me. And yet – I have to acknowledge an impulse to dissociate myself from violence and mayhem, however appealing the cause (the Cause). At the risk of sounding like 'Outraged of Ballymurphy (or Ballymacarrett)' in the Heaney poem, 'Whatever You Say, Say Nothing' – ' "Oh, it's disgraceful, surely, I agree", / "Where's it going to end?" "It's getting worse" ' – I have to deplore destruction, destruction of life, livelihood, architectural treasures, aspiration for the future, homes, whole towns or anything else getting in the way of an undeviating certainty about a right course of action. But someone, you might argue, has to make a stand against perceived injustice and corruption, whatever it entails. Perhaps it's just a question of bravery and fidelity versus expediency, with myself at present in the middle-aged expediency camp, I don't know. But I do understand Louis MacNeice's interrogation of gunmen,

> ... who shoot to kill and never
> See the victim's face become their own,
> Or find his motive sabotage their motives.

If you take to the gun you can't afford to consider any clashing form of integrity, or allow complications to undermine your total dedication. And if, like Michael Collins, you're setting yourself up for future deification or vilification, it's just a way of perpetuating 'us and them'.

★ ★ ★

One thing the would-be saviours of Swanzy got right when they sent him North: Lisburn should have wrapped itself around the DI like an Orange sash. He *should* have been out of harm's way in a town so Protestant and partisan. And when it turned out he wasn't, all hell broke loose. Lisburn's loyalist population is handed on a plate a pretext for a pogrom against Catholics, all of whom are supposed to be tarred with the Fenian–Sinn Féin–desperado brush. Even as the successful killers, Corkmen Culhane and Murphy, are passing through the town on the Dublin train, they see from their carriage windows smoke rising from the first burnt-out 'Fenian' premises. In the terrible 'Swanzy' riots the town is wrecked and burnt as Protestants run amok, and nearly the whole of the Catholic population is driven out. Desperate Catholic refugees carrying whatever they could salvage make their way on foot across the hills to the (comparative) safety of Belfast – following the route of the getaway car a short time earlier – where St Mary's Hall in Bank Street provides a sanctuary of sorts. Days later, the charred remains of shops and houses, the mutilated streets of Lisburn, give rise to a topical comparison. Like a bombarded town in Belgium, it looks: Mons or Ypres or some other ravaged war zone.

Not all the victims in Lisburn are Catholic, indeed; no one can stop Protestant property from going up in flames in the general conflagration. (A lull occurs while internecine energies are marshalled. The social commentator Hugh Shearman had a memory of himself as a very young child in a car going quickly through the empty streets of the town. It was Monday 23 August. The following day, nearly the whole of Bow Street was burned to the ground.) ... But mob fury is directed against the town's Catholics – all innocent of complicity in the crucial killing – and few Protestant voices are raised in sympathy, or even in acknowledgement of their plight. Among those who do express concern and horror at the escalation of anarchy in the streets are the mother and sister of the murdered Swanzy: they are 'grieved beyond measure' by what has taken place in Lisburn – distraught, indeed, that the death of the district inspector should provoke such excesses of wreckage and infliction of terror. For them, it's an added affliction piled on top of mourning.

In 2008, the novelist Glenn Patterson published a book reflecting the kind of ancestral diversity common to most of us. *Once Upon a Hill* tells the story of his Lisburn grandparents, Catherine (Kate) Logue and Jack

Patterson, who were there in the thick of the Swanzy disturbances, one – perhaps – momentarily moidered and running the streets with the Protestant wreckers and looters, the other (possibly) crouching terrified in a cellar, while the noise and excitement of sectarian venom raged at fever pitch above her. Also in hiding in Patterson's putative cellar are Kate Logue's mother and her five-year-old daughter, the latter born out of wedlock due to Jack's opinionated mother, and her refusal to countenance as a daughter-in-law a mill girl and – worse – a Catholic. Glenn Patterson would like to absolve his grandfather Jack of any involvement in the uproar. He would like to think Jack's attention in the crisis was focused on the safety of his wife-to-be and his daughter. But he can't be sure how his grandfather acted – how anyone would act – in the heat of the moment.

Whatever he did, or didn't do, during those berserk August days of 1920, Jack Patterson was forgiven. Catholic, or half-Catholic Kate became his wife in due course, and their Protestant son, the oddly named Phares, Glenn Patterson's father. Jack described Kate as 'the best little woman in Lisburn', while as far as she was concerned, he was simply 'the best man that ever lived'. These mutual declarations of esteem were made years after the Lisburn cataclysm, when the town had long settled back into its workaday routines. Jack by now has succumbed to an evangelical onrush and got himself 'born again'. I'm not sure what religion, if any, his wife Kate professes – probably a low-key, adopted Protestantism – but she's held on to a remnant of her mill-girl aplomb and enjoys as much as anyone (as much as *my* grandmothers) that novelty of the 1960s home, television.

By bringing all of his novelist's skills and insights to bear on the subject, Glenn Patterson has produced the most vivid account I've come across of the Swanzy shooting and its aftermath. The incident is at the centre of his memoir. 'Love in troubled times' is the subtitle of *Once Upon a Hill*. It is not an overstatement.

> ... Earlier in the day the Belfast [Fire] Brigade had sent some of its units to assist, but it withdrew them again at seven o'clock after their hoses were repeatedly cut. The only check now on the arsonists was their own energy and ingenuity after more than thirty hours of destruction and, in a great many cases,

continuous drinking. On Cross Row ... Phelan's pawnshop was looted and burned ... so too was the ice-cream parlour belonging to Pietro Fusco. ... On Bridge Street McCourtney's confectionery and fancy bakery shop was wrecked. ... All of this though, and despite the enthusiasm with which they went at it, was really just a diversion from what had been the target since the crowd marched out of Railway Street and on to Cross Row the previous afternoon:'Sinn Feiners ... sympathisers of the murderers', or, very simply, Catholics.

Jefferson's timber yard went up in smoke, Glenn Patterson continues, so did Burns's fruit and veg. And adds: 'Poor Burns. Poor Lisburn and its fatal attraction to flames.'

The allusion is to 1707 when Lisburn was all but wiped out in an accidental fire. And back beyond that date to the burning of 1641 when the rudimentary town was under siege and defended against the Irish rebels by – among others – the Tipping sons of the earliest settler John. There were Swansys (sic) about the place at that time too: an ancestor of the murdered DI was christened in Lisburn cathedral in 1666 and went on to fight for King Billy at the Battle of the Boyne[11] (alongside William Blacker? – Ah, suppositions). Tipping, Swanzy, Blacker: 'Each individual's story spins complicated cobwebs of relationship.' I'm quoting here another fine Northern Irish writer, the essayist Chris Arthur, meditating in 'Water-Glass' on his home town, Lisburn. Looking back, he says: 'Before that initial cluster of 250 [i.e. the original seventeenth-century builders of the town] there were others, long forgotten, for whom this place was home. Their lives have vanished, their stories are untold, the chemicals that once constituted their fleshy presence have unravelled and dispersed and melded, wraith-like, with the anonymous substance of the earth they used to tread on long ago. Who knows what ghosts haunt the dust of Bachelor's Walk?'

Who indeed. Chris Arthur's perspective here is a bit too long for my particular purposes, but ghosts I can go along with. The ghosts of Warwickshire settlers revisiting the site of their first Irish dwellings; the ghost of Henry Munro re-enacting his bungled execution. And Oswald Ross Swanzy's wraith hovering over the place of his ancestor's christening and his own death. Ghosts of anonymous people trying to lead decent lives; ghosts of infuriated, intoxicated mobs. Coming up to the recent past and the days following 22 August 1920, Chris Arthur remarks bleakly and accurately: 'The worst violence in modern times was done by Lisburn's own people.'

Late in the afternoon of 22 August, taxi man Sean Leonard is arrested in Belfast in connection with the shooting.[12] Two weeks later, at his home in Lurgan, it's the turn of Jimmy Tipping. Charged in the same connection, 'he was subsequently removed under escort, and at a special court in Belfast was remanded on the capital charge,' the *Lurgan Mail* reported solemnly. In fact, no charge is brought against Jimmy (for lack of evidence) and he's dispatched back to Edward Street, only to be promptly rearrested and then interned without trial at Ballykinler camp in County Down. Here Jimmy sits it out for the next fifteen months, until, in December 1921, republican prisoners and internees are released in a general amnesty consequent on the Anglo-Irish Treaty.

A family myth, when I was growing up and beginning to take an interest in such matters, was that one of our Tipping relations was solely responsible for the assassination of DI Swanzy. He had fired the fatal shot. And the same relation, I believed in a vague but adamant way – I hadn't got the Tipping contingent at all clear in my head – had been tried and convicted and was actually languishing (I'm sure the word languishing came into it) in the condemned cell awaiting execution when – miraculous day – the Treaty supervened. I don't know when or how the truth got magnified, whether I did it subconsciously myself, or if it was somehow conveyed to me in this exaggerated form, aggrandisement having occurred spontaneously with the passage of time. Certainly I latched on to the Tipping/Swanzy overstatement. With a name like Craig, I needed all the republican clout I could get.

There were four strands to my family, indeed (taking grandparents into account), but the Wexford Letts only got a look-in, in those besotted days, due to a story of rather less substance than the Swanzy enlargement mentioned above. I cannot get it corroborated from any source I've consulted, but long ago when I was going about waving a green flag, I had a picture in my head of some innocent cousins on my father's side, bowling along a country lane in a pony-and-trap, and being shot dead by trigger-happy Black and Tans for whom *any* native Irish were suitable targets. Unlike the bedraggled Protestant refugees of 1798, whom yeomen took for insurgent-affiliated due to their unkempt appearance, these Wexford cousins weren't given a chance to proclaim their support for the British connection. If they existed, which I now think is doubtful. But where did the story come from? I can't have concocted it entirely out of thin air. Of course, there were many such incidents –

> From Cork on to Limerick, Clare and Mayo,
> Lies a trail of destruction wherever they go –

On the Limerick road, wrote Ernie O'Malley,[13] 'Three lorries of Tans and R.I.C. came up. They were shouting, singing and shooting off their rifles.' This was normal behaviour. And it is possible, I suppose, that those hypothetical Wexford Letts (or whatever their name was) were victims of this kind of lethal exuberance. Possible, as well, that the Protestant side of the family would wish, in the future, to dissociate itself from any alignment with rebel grievances.

For me, of course, the opposite was true. If – and it's a large if – the Black-and-Tan incident really happened, I could use it to reinforce my claim to an Irish identity. I could follow John Hewitt's take on the death of his Protestant great-grandmother in County Armagh, as recounted in his poem 'The Scar': she handed a crust of bread to a starving beggar during the Famine and, he says, for this act of charity, 'accepted in return the famine-fever'. And, he goes on, 'that chance meeting, that brief confrontation, / Conscribed me of the Irishry for ever'. The point being that the whole nation was subject to the same unifying calamity, with consequent undermining of sectarian differences. Well, that was a natural standpoint for a liberal humanist like Hewitt. But how you regarded the great issues in Ireland, of nationality, religion, allegiance and so on, was still for most people a matter of inheritance as much as instinct.

The Wexford Letts. But now another version of that apocryphal Black-and-Tan shooting has come to my attention, and it turns the whole business on its head. In the first place, it has nothing to do with the Letts. In the second place, the shooters in question were IRA Volunteers. ... You will remember my great-grandmother Marie Heller (see Chapter Five) and her employment by the upper-crust Mays of Belfast and Dublin. Marie had died back in 1891, but her children, including my grandfather William Craig, would have gone on taking an interest in the grand family with which their mother's fortunes were intertwined. A great-niece of the family named Winifred Barrington, a granddaughter of Olivia May's brother, was a casualty of the War of Independence. She was shot and killed while travelling incautiously in a car beside a Black-and-Tan officer.

The place was Coolboreen in County Limerick (*Cul Bothairin*, literally: small back road), the date was 14 May 1921, and the merry party, consisting of three young men and two girls, was returning in high spirits from a fishing expedition when the ambush occurred. The car, with a hated Black and Tan in the driver's seat, was sighted by an IRA man who alerted others to its probable route and sent them scurrying to the spot armed with rifles and shotguns. Winifred, wearing a riding outfit and an officer's cap, and looking game for anything, was seated next to the driver and actual IRA target, twenty-six-year-old Inspector Henry Biggs. By all accounts a bit of a tomboy, a VAD recruit during the Great War, and liked by everyone in the district – though no one, after her death, was going to say otherwise – pretty, twenty-two-year-old Winifred took a bullet in the chest and died shortly afterwards from shock and haemorrhage. She had tumbled out of the car and fallen into a ditch. Inspector Biggs, shot in the throat, fell out on the other side and lay in the road, dying. Further shots were fired into him before the Volunteers took to their heels. The three in the back of the car escaped more or less unhurt. It was later claimed that Winifred Barrington was mistaken for a man, due to the way she was dressed. When her identity was disclosed, one Volunteer shouted, 'If the bitch hadn't been in bad company, she wouldn't have got shot' – in other words, slap it into her. But the general feeling in the area, after her death, was one of sadness and dismay at the craziness of the world people inhabited and the tragedies it created. There was jubilation over the execution of Biggs, notorious for brutality and horrors of every kind inflicted on the Irish, but it was tempered by regret for the accompanying death of lovely, lively young Winifred Barrington of Glenstal Castle.

So: a fatal shooting during the Black-and-Tan war, an innocent victim, a distraught family, a Catholic church bell tolling mournfully as the funeral cortège passed by on its way to the Abington Church of Ireland cemetery. ... The event, widely reported, would soon have reached the ears of my grandfather's family in the North, and struck them forcibly due to their slight personal connection with the Barringtons. At the very least, they'd have been well informed about Winifred's antecedents. The

Coolboreen killing, at least for a time, would have loomed large among their preoccupations.

And as it faded, did a whiff of the surrounding shock and outrage get transmitted to me, a long way into the future, and in a distorted form? More likely I'd have effected the transformation all by myself. I'm reminded of Tom Dunne's relative pointing to Scullabogue as the site of a Cromwellian massacre of Catholics (see p. 80). Whatever horror had taken place, in whatever circumstances, it was down to annihilating enemy tactics, never a product of honourable Irish resistance. Or so we – Irish nationalists – were programmed to think. So I may have manufactured a spurious connection to *Irish* victimhood on the part of my Protestant family, out of the bare bones of Coolboreen. I don't know. It is at least a possible explanation for the supposed Black-and-Tan atrocity which no one among my father's relations will corroborate.

During the War of Independence and then the Civil War, things were different in the North. It's necessary to bear this in mind. Sean O'Faolain's 'tremendously gallant few', the rebel soldiers of the Limerick, Cork and Tipperary Brigades (among others), enjoyed a resource unavailable to their northern counterparts:

> The fight was carried through by those tremendously gallant few, darting here and there for an ambush, folding back into their 'normal' lives until they could get another crack at the enemy. They could not, it must always be said, have done anything without the silence, patience and loyal help of the whole people.

But for those operating from Belfast, say, more than half the people had placed themselves at the furthest imaginable remove from the republican ideal. It wasn't only the British who were the enemy, but the Orange population of the North – and for latter-day adherents of Wolfe Tone's philosophy it was important, and often impossible, not to be seen as a factionally motivated force. In the eyes of their enemies, Sinn Feiners were Catholic gunmen out to shoot Protestants, not soldiers of a putative republic defending their communities against loyalist incursions. Despite the example of Protestant nationalists like Bulmer Hobson and others, the old divisions would not go away; and at street level they assumed their most basic and virulent form: Prod versus Taig. When Bertie Tipping, for example, recalled cycling in his Fianna uniform 'through very unfriendly areas' of Lurgan, we understand the hazards he and his fellow-republicans faced on their way to and from political gatherings. Name-calling was the very least of it. And it's axiomatic that the threat to their safety didn't come from St Peter's parishioners.

In the city, 'the noise of shooting, / Starting in the evening at eight, / In Belfast in the York Street district' (Louis MacNeice's words) was a regular cause of alarm – and not only in York Street. People with miserable standards of living in acres of streets all over Belfast, each defined by its place of worship, had almost incessant bloodshed, assault and apprehension imposed on top of their everyday aggravations of poverty and exhaustion. The place was in turmoil. The years between 1917 and 1924 were marked by riots, raids and reprisals. Bigotry and discrimination on one side bred anger and disaffection on the other. It is hard to envisage the scale of the violence and vehemence, and consequent destruction, afflicting Belfast's more volatile quarters – or at least it was hard, during the relatively undisturbed middle years of the century, before the most recent phase of 'Troubles' brought it all sweeping back again, in an even more cruel and chaotic way.

A massive battle with paving stones, the death toll rising, St Matthew's chapel blazing, snipers sniping, this was Belfast in the early 1920s. 'The violence finally petered out ... eighteen people had died, about three hundred were wounded and there was a serious refugee problem. Most of the deaths had been as a result of shooting by the military. ... Ten of the dead were Catholic and eight were Protestant.'[14] All over the city, arms and ammunition are deposited with sympathetic households – in one instance, a Mills hand grenade sits boldly beneath a hat on a sideboard, and is still there at the end of an RIC raid, giving a literal application to 'keeping it under your hat'. There are hair-raising retreats over backyard walls, fake priests escaping with their lives in borrowed clerical garb, bicycles commandeered from passers-by – whether willing or unwilling – to carry handguns away in the aftermath of an ambush. To complicate matters, you find republican fellow-travellers among members of the RIC itself: those willing to pass on crucial information and even, on occasion, ammunition.

In Lurgan, the Tipping residence at 76 Edward Street is subjected to frequent raids by unambivalently orientated police and military. In

September 1920, for example, just after Jimmy's removal for internment, the house is raided once again – and once again reluctantly accorded a clean bill of compliance with regulations. Arrangements – Bertie Tipping's guarded expression – arrangements are always in place to safeguard any wounded Volunteer being treated by Lily, and any arms or documents secreted about the house, once word of an imminent raid is received. It is all very urgent and mysterious. Constant vigilance is necessary. Lower your guard for an instant, and horrors may happen. A neighbour, for instance, standing at the Tippings' door, and mistaken for one of the family, is shot and seriously wounded by an Orange sniper. Desperate times. The Sisters of Mercy Convent, just across the road from 76, is under threat from loyalists, and a nightly patrol, including one or two Tippings, is formed to guard the premises. They spend the hours of darkness being sniped at from an Orange quarter behind the convent, and never hesitating to return fire. The nuns in their beds have cause to be grateful for the shooting skills of their night watchmen. My mother, seven or eight years old at the time, is a primary school pupil attending the convent during the day. No doubt she gains kudos among her peers from pointing to her relations in the armed guard.

The life of those days, all its upsets and stresses, took its toll on the health of the mother of the Tipping family, Mary Anne Dowds. She died aged sixty in 1926. Five of her six sons,[15] and one daughter, were active in the republican movement, upholding all attendant forms of insubordination and exposing themselves to constant danger. From time to time, the sons would quietly interrupt their grocery work to engage in Sinn Féin business. Cutting telegraph wires to disrupt communications, holding up trains, raiding for arms, setting fire to bread vans ... all these form part of the learning process of soldiering for Ireland. Utterly divested of their anti-social aspect in the prevailing conditions, these activities contribute to the message being transmitted to the authorities: republicans mean business. Acts of destruction that would, in normal times, engender outrage in the naturally law-abiding (among whom I would place the Lurgan Tippings – well, most of them), are instead regarded as ethical strikes against a hated system – a system that deforms and derails the lives of ordinary people. The times aren't normal at all, and the naturally law-abiding are provoked into anarchy by having no democratic laws to abide by.

The Tipping brothers, apart from one, all saw the inside of prisons or internment camps. Matt, the oldest – born in 1890 – went to Scotland after the war. He got employment in the Glasgow shipyards; and while he was there, true to the family tradition, he joined the Glasgow Battalion of the IRA and quickly rose to prominence in it. (His future wife Jean Rice was already a member of the Govan Cumann na mBan.) I've mentioned above the miniscule overlap between my (peripheral) family history, and Glenn Patterson's – and I'm about to pinpoint an intriguing instance of a similar kind of convergence. There's a point at which the Tipping story intersects with that of another writer I esteem enormously – the novelist, essayist and critic Andrew O'Hagan.

Andrew O'Hagan's great book *The Missing* is an account of various kinds of disappearance, from his grandfather reported missing in action during the Second World War, to the girls enticed away and killed in Gloucester by Fred and Rosemary West. It's also a memoir of a Glasgow/new town childhood, and it takes in aspects of an older city and a way of life experienced by O'Hagan's recent forebears. The early-twentieth-century O'Hagans were Catholic and – with that name – of Irish descent. Some of them gravitated naturally towards Sinn Féin. 'The history of Sinn Féin in Glasgow,' he writes, ' – that sometimes boiling community of Socialist-Catholics and Ulster Orangemen – has, for the most part, been erased from the city's account of itself. In the twenties, it was much more than a matter of one or two households and the zealous machinations of the families within. It was a faith – a bitter creed for some – scribbled into the very pavements around St. Mary's.' Not too far in spirit from Lurgan or Belfast, then.

In May 1921, O'Hagan says, 'something happened in the Calton, something involving the chapel of St. Mary's, and guns, and Sinn Féin, my grandfather and his uncle Francis, a confectioner.' What happened was an attempt to extricate a couple of high-ranking IRA prisoners, one of them a seasoned gaol-breaker, from a black van, heavily escorted, on the way to Duke Street Prison. The driver of the van was a Constable Thomas Rose.[16] His colleagues were named Stirton, MacDonald, and Johnston. Suddenly, like something out of a cowboy film, groups of men erupted from alleys and closes, firing revolvers; Inspector Johnston was hit and died on the spot; Stirton received a shot to the wrist and dropped his gun. Pandemonium overtook the streets. The IRA men might have brought it off, but failed in the attempt because the van doors jammed, securing the prisoners inside. Everything depended on split-second timing: no scope for snags. They abandoned the operation and scattered in all directions. 'It was a matter of seconds, that's all it was, and they'd all disappeared.'

O'Hagan goes on: 'There was one young man, a witness observed, a stout, dark-haired fellow stuffing a revolver into his pocket as he strode away. He was as pale as a sheet. Very white, this young man, as he made his escape. He got away through Cats' Close, a thin, uneven passageway which cut through the tenements behind High Street.' I have it in my head that the person he's describing here is Matt Tipping, Matt who led the unit involved in the fracas, and fired the shot which struck Constable Stirton in the wrist, disabling him. Later in the afternoon of 4 May the arrests begin, and Matt is rounded up along with others; so is Andrew O'Hagan's great-great-uncle Francis. Matt is held in prison for three months but never charged, and on his release – having lost his job – he returns to Lurgan with his wife Jean. They set up a grocery business of their own in Edward Street, and – in 1929 – become the parents of my cousin Harry Tipping.

On 4 September 1921 Michael Collins is in Armagh city addressing a huge rally of his constituents[17] and assuring them of his opposition to any expedient leaving northern nationalists in the lurch.[18] At the same time, he attempts to play down the fears of unionists by telling them they won't be coerced. I am not sure how he reconciles the two assertions. As he leaves Armagh, his car is stoned by Orange diehards who clearly don't believe a word of it. Throughout the day, Collins is protected by a guard of honour, made up from active service units in the district. It includes a couple of Tippings. Perhaps it's one of these who itches to respond to the Orange provocation by firing shots above the heads of the stone-throwers, and has to be restrained by Collins: I don't know. The entire Lurgan Company is present for the occasion and entrusted with the roles of bodyguards, escorts, sentries and so forth. They're in the thick of it. Cumann na mBan is well represented too. Lily Tipping is in the crowd with her box camera, and gets a good shot of Collins as he engages in his customary oratory. (Lily's photograph eventually finds its way to the National Museum in Dublin, where it still is.)

A Tipping *not* in the middle of the Armagh rally is Jimmy, whose sojourn at Ballykinler camp has another three months to run. It is making him a veteran of rough treatment. A book on internment in Northern Ireland, by the author and civil rights activist John McGuffin, was published in 1973. McGuffin spent a lot of time in Lurgan talking to Jimmy about things the ex-internee recalled from the fraught 1920s, his time in that grim enclosure of barbed-wire fences and manned sentry boxes, of poor food and constant aggravation. And republican camaraderie of course, with parades, exercise and education classes geared to reinforce ideological commitment – all organised by the prisoners themselves. For all the details he supplied, though, Jimmy isn't named in McGuffin's book; no doubt he chose to remain anonymous, at a time when ancient conflicts were undergoing a horrific replay. Jimmy's lawless past, had it been raked up in public, might have endangered the quiet days of his seventies, adding to the agony of seeing the whole bloody business start up again. Jimmy had done his bit for Ireland and possessed three medals awarded by the government of the Republic to prove it: Na Fianna Éireann Jubilee medal, Truce Commemorative medal, and Irish War of Independence service medal with bar.[19] (Two of his brothers, Matt and Gerry,[20] were similarly honoured, and granted small military service pensions following De Valera's Irish Constitution of 1937.)

In the enterprise of keeping down the Tippings and their ilk, the British government is succeeded in 1921 by the new Unionist administration which quickly passes a Special Powers Act enabling it to carry on interning.

In the early hours of 26 January 1923 comes a loud persistent hammering on the door of 76 Edward Street. It's the RUC on the trail of the Tippings. The whole street is roused by the disturbance. Sleepy faces appear at upstairs windows; some neighbours give a weary shrug and go back to bed, while others stand at their front doors in a hostile mode taking note of aggressive goings-on. Special constables stomp through the Tipping house while the rudely awakened family emits defiance in the front kitchen. Present in their night clothes – or wearing hastily donned shirts and trousers – are all six of the brothers, along with their parents Henry and Mary Anne, and their sister May. It's not, indeed, the first time the house has been raided – successfully or unsuccessfully – but on this occasion, they all maintain at the time and later, there is nothing untoward in any corner of the premises.

The RUC has a different story. Policemen pounce on a round of .455

revolver ammunition stowed in a pocket of Henry's overcoat hanging in the hall. Henry, open-mouthed, has no idea how it got there. Nor has anyone else. Some seditious papers are then spotted poking out from behind a row of books in the front room. 'What's this? What's this?' Everyone denies all knowledge of these items, provoking derision in the searchers. Mission accomplished, the police snap a pair of handcuffs on the wrists of brothers Frank and Gerry, and bundle them into a waiting Crossley Tender. 'Dear God,' murmurs distressed Mary Anne once again, falling back on a Lurgan mantra, 'Dear God this holy day and hour.'

Arms and ammunition were distributed among sympathetic households in the town, including my grandmother's. She kept a supply of weapons in a sideboard in the kitchen, and breathed a sigh of relief each time a detachment of police officers passed her front door by. It didn't always happen that way. Once, alerted by some sixth sense to an impending incursion, she mustered sufficient presence of mind to dump the things into a shoe bag and hang it from a nail outside a back window, saving the stash for future use and herself from a load of trouble.

The family at 76 had considerable experience in keeping their own arms supplies from falling into the wrong hands, so it seems odd they'd have been so careless at the time of the January raid. Of course, they insisted the items were planted by the raiding party, but whether or not this was so is impossible to tell. You can take your choice about whom to believe: the police seeking a pretext to detain the Tippings, or the Tippings wishful to cast the RUC in the worst possible light.

The police under Lurgan District Inspector P.J. Ferriss achieve their purpose, whether legitimately or fraudulently, with regard to at least two members of 'this very undesirable family'.[21] Frank and Gerry are on their way to the cheerfully named Larne Workhouse Internment Camp. Gerry, never the most robust of the brothers, falls ill with rheumatic fever in this terrible place, and is moved to a hospital attached to the Crumlin Road gaol in Belfast. After a month or so of hospital treatment, he's released unconditionally on medical grounds, but worries that people may think he signed some kind of undertaking renouncing his republican beliefs. 'I suppose there will be terrible rumours about how I got out,' goes a rueful letter to Frank at Larne Workhouse, 'but my answer to them all is: our cause is just and holy; yield not to coercion; our day shall come;[22] and God is with us. Take out of these lines what you like and they are the terms I brought to freedom with me.' No tergiversators among the Tippings.

In July of that year, Frank is transferred to the prison ship *Argenta*, where his brother Jimmy is already ensconced in one of the eight metal cages which form accommodation on the boat. The *Argenta*, moored near Carrickfergus, makes the workhouse seem desirable. Potato skins are mentioned in several accounts as a main part of the diet there. Meals, such as they are, are eaten by inmates sitting on the floor. Tables and chairs are banned, lest they should get smashed up for makeshift weapons. Whatever nightly escape routes the prisoners envisage evaporate with the coming of day. As in Ciaran Carson's poem, 'The Ballad of HMS *Belfast*', which ends:

> And then the smell of docks and ropeworks. Horse-dung.
>   The tolling of the Albert Clock.
> Its Pisan slant. The whirring of its ratchets. Then everything
>   began to click:
>
> I lay bound in iron chains, alone, my *aisling* gone,
>   my sentence passed.
> Grey Belfast dawn illuminated me, on board the prison
>   ship *Belfast*.

How did Jimmy Tipping arrive on the prison ship *Argenta*? An incident of 23 May 1923 provides the answer. On that Sunday morning flames are spotted rising from a building near Derrytagh South Bog not far from Lurgan. Also spotted at the same time are seven or eight young men cycling for dear life away from the scene of the outrage. The unoccupied building set alight, supposedly earmarked for a new police barracks, is the property of a family named Turkington. Towards it, under cover of darkness, had come the same young men on bicycles laden with petrol cans, guns and homemade explosives. Despite this dangerous equipment rattling along the rough road, no one gets hurt, or at least hurt very much. According to a report in the *Lurgan Mail*, Mrs Turkington and her son, who live nearby, are held at gunpoint while the burning operation goes ahead. It can't have been pleasant for them, but their new building doesn't suffer irreparable damage and they don't die of fright. Asked to attend an identity parade some time later, the Turkingtons fail to recognise anyone in it – although, says J.P. Ferriss apropos Jimmy Tipping, 'I am satisfied the Turkingtons knew him if they wished to say so.'

They don't wish to say so, but it makes no difference as far as Jimmy's presumed guilt is concerned. Picked up in yet another night raid on 76 Edward Street, along with his young brother Bertie, Jimmy is taken away in police custody en route to the *Argenta*. 'He is undoubtedly a leader, and a dangerous one, and should be interned,' the grim Mr Ferriss states unequivocally in his report to the Minister of Home Affairs, Sir Richard Dawson Bates. At the same time, sixteen-year-old Bertie Tipping finds himself summarily installed in Derry gaol. 'He [Bertie] seems to be about the worst of the lot,' goes another withering note to Dawson Bates, who perhaps by this stage has had his fill of the family. But he hasn't heard the last of them.

The *Argenta* internees latch on to anything and everything to keep their spirits up. As Jimmy writes to his brother Gerry (still in hospital in Belfast):

> Frank is transferred here and is my bedmate on this old boat. All the boys are delighted to hear of you getting on so well. Frank and I are doing our best to get Bertie here and expect to succeed. I can see you at your breakfast 'Moyah', it must be great. Tell the Miss Tennysons they have my best regards. – With best love from your brother Jim.

But despite their efforts Bertie stays where he is, and an alternative plan on the part of the authorities, to dispatch Frank and Jimmy to Derry – '[They are] both dangerous men – they would be safer in an ordinary prison' – is vetoed because 'it would make a large collection of this very undesirable family' in the one spot. Concern for Bertie's well-being continues – even his father Henry writes a letter pleading for clemency on account of the boy's age, and his usefulness as an assistant in the grocer's shop – but nothing comes of it. The next thing is a postcard from Jimmy addressed to his sister May in Lurgan, which sparks a slight panic among the prison authorities, sending a flurry of communications flying back and forth at every level. After thanking May for a parcel she'd sent – most of whose contents had reached him, he says, bar an item or two confiscated by the censor – and requesting his usual 200 cigarettes and a string of rosary beads, Jimmy wonders if anything has been heard from Bertie. Then comes the sentence causing alarm and affront. 'The Governor of Derry Gaol should be notified,' writes Jimmy, 'to the effect that, should Bertie be ill-treated in any way, he will not be forgotten.'

Jimmy's postcard is read with horror by the warden on the *Argenta*, who promptly dispatches it to the Ministry of Home Affairs. Did Jimmy really write it with his own hand ('It would be well to obtain a specimen of this internee's handwriting', goes a solemn suggestion), and is the implication really as sinister as it seems? Letters go forth to the Derry governor warning him to be extra vigilant, to the inspector general of the RUC, to the county inspector, Armagh, to the sceptical DI Ferriss in Lurgan – who at last gets the thing in some kind of proportion. 'I have no reason to fear that any of the Tipping family at present at large would molest the Governor of Derry Prison,' he assures his superiors shaking in their shoes. 'No doubt the Tippings are a bad lot, but in my opinion the reference ... to the Gaol Governor is a bit of bluff.' His opinion is listened to. The postcard finally reaches its addressee. No action is taken against Jimmy on account of it. But all three of the Tipping brothers are kept in custody until December 1924, and then only let go when a general release of internees is decreed.

Things are changing in the world of Irish affairs, or at least the emphasis is shifting. With De Valera's about-turn in the South, and the 'Protestant State' consolidated in the North, the nationalist population of towns like Lurgan continued to seethe, indeed, but seethed more quietly. Fewer eruptions of fighting occurred in the small rough streets. Worn out, perhaps, with all the rioting and destruction of the early 1920s, rival factions snarled and grimaced, but kept their distance from one another, on the whole. Threats to 'burn out' this or that sectarian quarter mostly came to nothing.

At the same time, the causes of disaffection were, if anything, on the increase. It was hard for northern Catholics and nationalists to be happy with their lot. They were constantly told they were rogues, dupes and outsiders. Forms of social, religious and indigenous inferiority were pasted over them. Nevertheless – harking back to the seventeenth century – they believed the country was rightfully theirs.[23] They subscribed to a highly charged version of history. It was, of course, a story of wrongs inflicted and – in the teeth of persecution – patriotic values upheld. The republican Tippings (and others) saw a certain kind of moral obligation staring them in the face, and acted upon it. Not to have done so would have branded them as spineless and spiritless. If their actions brought down an old house on their heads in the form of internment and other tests of endurance – well, so be it, they would grit their teeth and endure the lot. There were side benefits, of course: exhilaration, a terrific sense of purpose gingering up the prosaic side of life, being in the thick of things as they slipped away from weighing tea or totting up bills to subvert the state.

Perhaps the instinct to engage in undercover activity was imprinted in their genes. Before they were Protestant, some of the English Tippings were Catholic and imprisoned in the Tower on account of it,[24] 'comitted,' a contemporary report goes, 'uppon Suspition of treason'. Plots and counter-plots fizzed about their heads in the pungent Elizabethan underworld of conspiracy and duplicity. A James Tipping crops up in the 1580s taking a minor part in the Babington affair, and in another, stillborn endeavour to shoot a poisoned arrow into Queen Elizabeth as she walked in the garden. The removal of Elizabeth was essential to the plans of English recusants. James Tipping and his brother John, three centuries and more before their Lurgan namesakes, believed in the possibility of a different kind of social hierarchy, the overthrow of Protestantism and restoration of the Catholic nation, and risked their lives in the effort to achieve it. They held a genuine belief in the justice of the Catholic cause, unlike the many government agents who infiltrated the cabals to the detriment of the plotters. Torture and imprisonment loomed, a consequence of double dealings on the part of informers. The Tower, the *Argenta* ... here comes a cliché but I can't resist it: *autre temps, autre moeurs*.

John Tipping ... hmn. What if – and *here* comes an enormous speculation – what if the husband of long-ago Katherine Rose was not a Stratford man at all, but an ex-conspirator on the run from London to Warwickshire? All right, he'd have had to be nineteen or twenty years older than his bride, but that's not an impossible circumstance. (Or perhaps he had a son, another John.) And yes, I know it's ridiculous to conflate the Babington conspirator and the cutler, on no firmer evidence than the coincidence of their names, but I offer this bit of nonsense for what it is worth.

In twentieth-century Lurgan, time is passing. The leaves of the trees in Lurgan Park turn golden-brown and russet, and then the trees are bare. The lake freezes over, and children slide and slither with enjoyment along North Street. Spring: cherry blossom, daffodils, balloons and hop-scotch. In summer comes the smell of new-mown grass, hay wains and endless sunny days, and a cool breeze blowing from Lough Neagh. ... All of the Edward Street brothers marry and raise families, and over the years enjoy considerable prestige in the locality on account of their darkly glamorous, freedom-fighting past. Republicanism didn't go away, and never would go away, but old-style republicanism was on the wane – though it had a burst or two of reinvigoration before the end of the 1950s (when I was affected by it).

In Lurgan, for example, partisan passions were reignited in the run-up to the general election of 1935. Electioneering meetings, the *Lurgan Mail* reported in its strange decorous prose, 'were full of interest'. So they were. One (unionist) in Market Street, was addressed by the Conservative and Unionist candidate Sir William Allan to the usual cheers and boos. Another (republican) drew an equally large and voluble crowd to Edward Street, where the speakers included 'Madame Gonne MacBride' in her old-fashioned attire. After the meeting, on Tuesday 12 November, Maud Gonne is hastily spirited away to Bertie Tipping's house in Lake Street, where she's arranged to spend the night.

In the early hours of Wednesday morning, something occurs. Police and B Specials surround the house. By crossing the border, Maud Gonne has contravened an exclusion order made against her some time ago (I'm still quoting the *Lurgan Mail*). Roused up by the furore, Bertie and his wife attempt to instil a sense of urgency into their distinguished (and blasé) visitor, but the doughty veteran of many republican campaigns simply snaps her fingers at the RUC and all its works, turns over in her bed and goes back to sleep. It's some time before the recently wed Tippings can get her out of the bed and into her clothes. Her stately descent to the hallway is no doubt a cause of relief to the somewhat nonplussed constabulary, who haven't the knack of dealing with female firebrands and muses. Politely conducted to a car and driven to Newry under police escort, Maud Gonne – not yet exactly old and grey and full of sleep, despite her early rising (and although she's not far short of seventy) – is then safely deposited on the proper side of the border. (On her journey north, Maud Gonne had cannily bought only a one-way ticket, knowing she could rely on the RUC to see her safely home.)

On polling day (Thursday 14 November), says the *Lurgan Mail*, 'there were large numbers of voters waiting to record their votes, including a large contingent of people who had been at early morning Mass in St Peter's Church'. Ho-hum. At the town hall, the report goes on, somewhat cryptically, 'it was alleged that a young man, a supporter of the unionist cause, interfered with some girls and excitement ensued'. In the ensuing excitement, 'the police found it necessary to draw batons and chase a crowd of about a thousand up High Street'. Here you have an instance of bitter Lurgan recidivism. It's no good expecting elections to be conducted sedately. The unionist candidate will win the day, of course, but Sinn Féin means to give him a run for his money. Think Belfast in the docks area in 1857, the Brickfields in 1864, the streets filled with noise and fear. Heads struck with bottles and batons, seasoned rioters dispersing and disappearing, weary policemen slumped over their riot shields at the end of the night ... all these features of endemic instability make an Ulster picture to dishearten ameliorists. 'From every entry and from every lane, / The brickbats and stones in showers they came.'[25]

The Orange young man who 'interfered' with the – I assume green – girls turns up in Edward Street being battered by a mob: from this predicament, I am pleased to say, he is extricated by Gerry Tipping who finds himself unable to stand idly by while harm is done to a fellow human being, of whatever colouration. Gerry, by some means or other, gets the offending youth to the safety of the tally rooms in Jordan's Factory (the property, you will remember, of Gerry's grandmother's relations – though I doubt they'd be falling over themselves to acknowledge the kinship). Ructions over, 'by 11 p.m. the crowd had dispersed and the usual normal conditions prevailed'. Whatever 'normal' means.

Jimmy Tipping – ex-felon – at various times is host in Lurgan to General Tom Barry of *Guerrilla Days in Ireland* fame (an old friend), and to Major Vivion de Valera, oldest son of the Irish president. The days of real poverty, recklessness and raids-by-night are over, for some of the family at least. They just get on with their lives. All prosper, to varying degrees. Photographs from the summer of 1935 show a merry quartet,

Jimmy, Bertie, Bertie's wife Annie and a friend, on holiday in Kerry, all looking at ease on horseback as they trot exuberantly through the Gap of Dungloe. Back in Lurgan, Frank invents an automatic egg-packing device and patents it (not that it nets him a fortune, alas). And when the time arrives for Matt, Jimmy and Gerry to apply for formal recognition of their services to the Republic, they are able to muster a lot of support from people willing to speak on their behalf. All the relevant documents are in the military archives in Dublin, and I don't propose to quote from them – well, apart from the following exchange, which I include as a riposte to the unionist view, the 'troublesome youths', 'bad lot' assessment of the authorities:

Q. They were a great family, the Tippings?
A. They were.

CHAPTER 8
THE IMPORTANCE OF
LOCAL KNOWLEDGE

... Never go by Cupar Street, my father would warn me, and I knew this was a necessary prohibition without asking why, for Cupar Street was one of those areas where the Falls and Shankill joined together as unhappy Siamese twins, one sporadically and mechanically beating the other round the head, where the Cullens, Finnegans and Reillys merged with Todds and Camerons and Wallaces.

Ciaran Carson, 'Question Time'

A time arrives when the fatherless Brady family of Lurgan receives a boost. Nora becomes a day girl at a top-notch convent. She is plucked out of her primary school classroom, where rote-learning, chilblains, snatters and blockheadedness are the order of the day, and deposited on top of a hill, in the select surroundings of Cornakinegar, and with optimum advancement anticipated. She can't believe her good fortune.

It's 1924 or 5, and a one-time industrial school for boys, formerly an imposing Victorian mansion called Irishtown Hill House, has changed its function once again and opened its doors to fee-paying, day- and boarding-pupils. Girls this time, of impeccable Catholic standing, better-than-average brains, and (it is hoped) susceptibility to the school spirit.

The elevated setting reflects its upward orientation in terms of social class and holiness. Our Lady's Secondary School, soon popularly known as Mount St Michael's, Lurgan.

The school's earliest intake isn't quite sufficient to meet Ministry of Education requirements, so to bump up the numbers a year's free tuition becomes available to poor, or poorish, primary school pupils of an appropriate disposition and intelligence. Some of these extra pupils are recruited from the convent in Edward Street, and a shining light among them is champion speller, grammarian, reader and general knowledge wizard Nora Brady, a child so good at answering she's got beyond her primary-grade teachers. When Nora's mother is summoned and the proposition put to her, she grasps it with both hands: *anything* to prolong her youngest daughter's schooling is a godsend. She's not the kind of mother who hurries her children into paid employment to enlarge the family income. Education is the key to a brighter life, she knows that, but until this moment advanced education has had no more relevance to her own situation than pie in the sky. Now, at last, it seems, the pie is in a dish and being borne towards her. And really, it's no more than her due. The Bradys, like the Tippings, think well of themselves, they always have, but scrimping and saving has imposed a kind of martyred aspect on them. And my grandmother understands that it's not enough just to trudge through life, taking blow after blow and still find the heart to laugh and joke – you need some extra ingredient, some source of grace or well-being, to balance the hard times.

So here is Nora in her navy-blue-and-white Mount St Michael's uniform – acquired at goodness knows what cost in exertion or privation – plus all the grammar-school accoutrements: satchel, lesson books, hockey stick, sheet music, drawing block, pens and pencils and what-have-you. And so much invested in the probable outcome of all this! The whole family rallies to make the most of the opportunity, for Nora and themselves. Those already working help with additional costs. As she leaves the house each morning, stepping out buoyantly for her new school, Nora carries the weight of everyone's expectations on her unassuming and unbowed head.

The pressure is enormous, but what makes it bearable, more than bearable, elating and enchanting, is the way she fits into the new environment, like the subject of a restored birthright in a fairy tale. From the minute she sets foot in Mount St Michael's, Nora has a sense of being in her element. It was the biggest thing that could happen to her. The little world of classrooms, corridors, bells, nuns, lessons, japes, bosom friends, games, nature study walks to the shores of Lough Neagh; the glorious convent grounds complete with lawns, fir trees, pines, beeches, hockey pitch and tennis courts ... all this enfolds and sustains her. It's a place apart from rainy, sect-ridden Lurgan, a refuge from a home still reeling from the death of Lily, and attendant sorrows. ... Her charming, tentative sister Kathleen, who married after the war and made a new life for herself in the south of England, was loth to recall those days of the 1920s and 30s, summing up the whole period as 'not a very happy time'. That was all she had to say about it. But for Nora it was different. Nora is going places – or so they all believe – and everything is geared to help her along the way. She is shielded, as far as possible, from the effects of depression and deprivation – just as I, in my turn, am shielded from harsh realities such as a less than adequate household income, and intermittent parental discords.

When I was young and unaccustomed to proper seaside holidays, my mother and I would often go to Dublin on the train. She had cousins there of whom she was very fond, the Ellen Brady tribe whose Lurgan childhoods were entwined with hers and her sisters'. They, the cousins, had migrated southwards with their family at the start of the 1930s, and at the same time my grandmother, with *her* family, had upped sticks for Belfast. What provoked this double exodus in opposite directions from Lurgan I don't know. (The Tippings stayed put.) But contact between the scattered cousins was maintained at a high level. When it came to our Dublin trips, my mother's and mine, in the late 1940s and '50s, it might be just a day's excursion, or we might stay overnight with Josie, Anne, Clare or Maureen; or even as long as a week. And every time the train from Belfast slowed on the outskirts of Lurgan, my mother would raise her arm and point to a four-square, grey building atop a hill, 'That's my old school.' A jumble of emotions including pride, affection, wonder, reverie and wryness were intermingled in that simple statement. It is heartbreaking now to contemplate. I had no idea. I'd nod and smile, without paying too much attention. It was no big deal. Everyone of our sort[1] had an old school somewhere. Didn't they? At five or six, enclosed in my nutshell world, I was as ignorant as could be of the vast implications surrounding my mother's status as an old Michaelonian.

An old Michaelonian – but hold on a minute. Didn't I say my mother's scholarship was only tenable for a year, just long enough to give her a taste of heady grammar-school life, before the prize was snatched away, and her pre-Michaelonian destination of mill or factory reinstated? Yes, but Nora did so well at the school that the nuns were reluctant to lose her – a shame to curtail a promising academic career – and prayers were offered up for a way round the impasse. As a consequence – perhaps – *someone* had a brainwave. The suggestion may have come from the school, or my grandmother may have thought of it herself, but the upshot of all the cogitations on Nora's behalf was the widow Brady getting into her best clothes and marching her daughter Nora, in her trembling-in-the-balance Mount St Michael's uniform, off to the High Street offices of the fledgling British Legion.

The British Legion came into being in 1921 to help ex-servicemen, war widows and their dependents. It was funded partly through the 'Poppy Day' appeal, and high on its agenda was the education of dead soldiers' children. And here was one who fitted the bill, stepping smartly into the office with all her glowing recommendations accompanying her. An unassertive but steadfast child, she must have made a good impression on top of her mother's resolute, no-nonsense demeanour. Between the two of them – and with Nora's teachers' strong backing – they make out a good case. The British Legion officials agree to shoulder the burden of Nora's school fees.

So she's back at the school on the hill for the start of the autumn term of her second year (Form C1). Hardly anyone knows what a close-run thing it was, how easily young Nora might have vanished into a different milieu of factory hooters and boisterous behaviour in the street. Her place in the class is assured, and her essays go on being read aloud by the English teacher as models of composition and insight. All she has to do to keep educationally afloat is to pass her Junior, and then her Senior Certificate examination in every subject – which she does, though not without fuss and anxiety surrounding the maths papers in both exams. If no one twits Nora on account of her scholarship status, it's possibly because her friends are not aware of it: I've written elsewhere[2] about the kindness of nuns who included Nora in the bill-distributing ritual at the end of term, to save her embarrassment, having carefully placed inside her envelope a slip of paper with the words 'No charge'. I think it's unlikely, indeed, that a gulf was apparent between the few scholarship pupils and the rest of the school: whatever their backgrounds, these were *all* provincial Catholic girls, all more or less unworldly and uncouth, vigorous on the hockey field and unabashed by their County Armagh accents and country faces. It wasn't uncommon for one or two to appear in the classroom in twisted black stockings or a slovenly gym-tunic, and come in for a wigging on account of it.

It's true that my mother, like the scholarship heroine of Winifred Darch's *Heather at the High School*,[3] might have based her anticipations of her new life on the treatment meted out to Lancashire ex-council schoolgirl Betty Barton (in the weekly paper *The Schoolgirl's Own*) on her arrival at snooty Morcove ('Scorned by the School' was the title of the opening episode). Also like the eponymous Heather, she'd have found the reality to be different. But a wish to remain securely one of a group, not differentiated from her peers in any way, would have kept my mother silent about her home circumstances.

There were, of course, other reasons besides a fear of snobbishness for keeping the British Legion connection dark. The word 'British' didn't go down too well in republican Lurgan, with its illicit tricolours and Easter lilies as emblems of disaffection. I'm not sure how much of the true state of affairs was divulged by my grandmother to her Tipping relations (some of whom, as we've seen, were interned for anti-government activity around this time). Two of these, indeed, were themselves ex-servicemen; but all that, Salonika and Sud-el-Bar, was obliterated by subsequent overwhelming, countervailing commitments. They, the Tippings, might have taken a critical attitude to *any* dealings with the British. On the other hand, they could have understood that something was owed, and could legitimately be claimed, by Irish families bereaved by the First World War. 'Good for you – take whatever you can get' might have been uttered, commending my grandmother's gumption. Or: 'You'd no call to go crawling to those imperialist bastards.' One or the other, I can't say which.

But no ideological considerations can deflect my grandmother's drive to secure the best possible outcome for her daughter Nora. Whatever needs to be done, she will do it, and reconcile in her own mind any conflicting obligations arising from her actions.

As for Nora – her romantic nationalism survives the acquisition of a non-Irish source for her school fees. And at the same time, her romantic

'Great War' obsession flourishes. 'If I should die, think only this of me ...' runs through her head — though perhaps with 'Ireland' substituted for 'England' in it. It doesn't matter very much; it's the slant of the poem that's important, the high-flown self-sacrificial stance, not the specifics. Also, Brooke's poem chimes with the notion of self-suppression, the unimportance of the individual, purveyed by nuns — one reason why it's taught in Form C1's English class.

The Mercy nuns of Our Lady's Secondary School aren't greatly perturbed by the state of the country. Violence and alarms in the streets hardly impinge on them in their house on the hill (unlike their counterparts in the town centre). They like being Irish, of course, but only in so far as Irishness is conflated with Catholicism. They bask in their remoteness from pagan ways. And the aim is to instil in every pupil a similar aspiration to Hibernian holiness.

Every facet of the social world of Mount St Michael's is bolstered by religiosity. Hymns in the morning, hymns in the afternoon, prayers before class, holy water fonts all over the place, 'Tantum Ergo' in the school chapel, 'pious objects' in everyone's possession, Missionary Society, sodalities of all sorts, virtue and modesty, the Blessed Virgin Mary, Benediction, the annual Retreat, lectures by priests on 'The Suffering that Mortal Sin Gives to God'. A garden party for past and present pupils begins with everyone kneeling on the ground, nuns, teachers, visitors and all, heads bowed, to receive a blessing from a local Monsignor wearing a kind of fur-trimmed cape over a short white muslin dress with a deep lace border, and a long black skirt buttoned down the front. And a silly hat on his head to boot. And an intense solemnity surrounding the proceedings, with never a maverick schoolgirl to nudge the person next to her, causing the both of them to choke back an irreverent outbreak of giggles.

Well, as far as I know. I'm envisaging a deferential gathering here. If all the pre-war girls of Mount St Michael's were bursting with suppressed rebelliousness, they'd have controlled themselves and put up a front of angelic behaviour. It was what they were trained to do. The whole Holy-Father-Reverend-Mother-Corpus Christi-Virgin-Mary gallimaufry had worked its effect on them. It would be the most shaming thing in the world to be taxed with a spiritual deficiency. They had all been got before the age of seven and had swallowed the Church and all its ploys and edicts. The Catholic way of life could hardly have been more fundamentally taken for granted.

(Taken for granted: but quite a high proportion of the school community has a name suggesting a different ancestry and affiliation. Holmes, Rodgers, Harrington, Berwick, Black, Walls, Forrest, Warren, Hinds and – yes – Tipping.[4] And many others to offset the *fior-Gaedhalach* contingent, the O'Boyles, O'Hagans, Raffertys, McQuillans. And all of them lumped together under a cloistered designation. Products – like all of us – of ancestral mixing-and-matching, these girls have all come out unequivocally in a sectional mould. ... Take any classroom in the North, for that matter, and no doubt you will find a similar denominative mix. My own class at St Dominic's High School in the 1950s, I remember, contained Waters, Commerton, Drummond, Buckley, Glover and so on, alongside O'Callaghan, Caffrey, O'Hagan, Devlin, Quinn, Mageean.)

And these particular Mount St Michael's lambs of the flocks of Catholic Ireland are immensely privileged, so they're told, by being in receipt of an education extended well beyond the official school-leaving age of fourteen. They're assured of it over and over, and they believe it wholeheartedly. They are being prepared for a life of service to God (eyes turn upwards and hands are pressed together prayerfully at the idea) – ideally, as nuns or missionaries or something ostentatiously vocational; or more likely – second-best – as Catholic housewives and mothers in some substantial Ulster suburb of new-built houses with garages and lawns. Whichever it is, underpinning the rest of their lives on earth will be that unassailable faith acquired at birth and cultivated thereafter as assiduously as Lord Emsworth's prize-winning pumpkin.

A full immersion in Catholic immaculacy will make each Mount St Michael's girl a better person, and the social ethos of the school will make her a better class of person. (So the received wisdom goes.) She's in a position to look down her nose at the brawls, shawls, catcalls and all the bitter routines of the streets. Walking home in the centre of a group of mildly sky-larking friends, through the gathering dusk of a winter's afternoon, light fading across the rooftops of Lurgan, my mother can feel secure about her place in the world. And, later, she can reminisce self-deprecatingly about those charmed days, inspired, maybe, among other things, by that fleeting glimpse of the sacred spot from the Dublin train, 'There's my old school.'

None of this, the nuts and bolts of a Mount St Michael's training, is very much in the spirit of interdenominational accord. Catholic exclusiveness, like its Protestant counterpart, is a strong feature of the times, the period between the early 1900s and the 1960s (say). Despite the measure of inadvertent integration mentioned above – Harrington/O'Hagan – the integrated school is a thing of the future, as every sect holds fast to its own version of divine revelation.

They know they are right. And no school rebel arrives out of nowhere to pose a challenge to the system, or disrupt the decorum of highly regulated corridors and classrooms. They are all good girls at Mount St Michael's. They are silent at times when silence is enjoined on them, and meekly proceed in crocodile formation to wherever they're summoned by a ringing bell. My mother in particular conforms to the school code and sails through the whole five- or six-year course. ... Move forward thirty-odd years, and you find the same is not true of her only daughter whose career as a Dominican schoolgirl in Belfast can be summed up in a storybook title complete with exclamation mark, *Expelled*! But that's a generation closer to the inevitable undoing of the convent system, and an event which in some ways prefigures the last gasp of nunly autocracy. My mother shows no comparable tendency to look for trouble – at least, until she suddenly throws caution to the winds and marries a Protestant (albeit a convertible Protestant). Ah – you can hear the Sisters of Mercy sigh – here comes an infusion of bad blood; and so it is proved, with regard to the daughter of the marriage. But Nora still has quite a way to go before this impulse of exogamy overtakes her.

She has a whole university course to get through. Her amazing progress doesn't stop at Mount St Michael's. Queen's beckons, though not without an obstacle or two along the way. First come the dreaded maths papers – scraped through, with a sigh of relief. Then, having moved from Edward Street to North Street in Lurgan (some time after Lily's death), my grandmother – as I've said – for some reason gathers up her family and sweeps them north to Belfast, to a dingy house in a street off the Stranmillis Road called Sandhurst Gardens, one of a group collectively known as the River Streets. The phrase 'damp Lagan fogs' comes to mind, again, courtesy of Maurice James Craig[5] and his poem imploring the Lord to be kind to Belfast. These Stranmillis streets slope down to the Lagan and consist of small terraced red-brick houses with miniscule gardens in front and back yards running along an alleyway behind. Indeed the new habitation is very convenient for Queen's

University once Nora gets there; but first comes her final year at school and an arduous train journey every morning from Great Victoria Street station all the way to Lurgan, and back again in the afternoon. (I don't think boarding was an option for her, and neither was a change of school at this late stage.) Some pressing reason must have underlain the leaving of Lurgan, no doubt about it, but what it was I have no idea. The two families, as I've said, the David Bradys and the William Bradys, decamped southwards and northwards at the same time. It didn't have a beneficial effect on Nora's school career, but neither did it knock her off-course entirely. More work, more adjustment, greater concentration, that's all there is to it. She sits her Senior Certificate examination, passes it, and is accepted by Queen's.

This was a vastly more significant achievement than it is at present. Nowadays, third-level education is a right of everyone; but university students were a privileged minority, in those intoxicating, irrecoverable inter-war days. They were a small, high-spirited, but basically hard-working and tractable group, which suited my mother down to the ground. It was a wonderful time for her. She brings to Belfast her notebooks filled with cherished verse, and her tentative self-assurance (assurance nurtured in Lurgan by nuns more helpful than those of my experience). The gracious and expansive university milieu seems like an extension of the well-sited, well-loved school on the hill. Both are, and aren't, Nora's natural habitat, and gain in piquancy from the anomaly. It's just a short step from each, no more than a mile or so, to the crowded and straitened family home with its tiny scullery and mangle in the yard.

And here is Queen's in all its splendour, a refuge of calm in the heart of unruly Belfast. Its carved stone, diamond-pane windows, its buttresses and battlements, all suggesting permanence and pageantry, a ceremonious attitude to life. Looking ancient – though it is, of course, only Victorian. Here are the lawns, the quadrangle, the panelled Great Hall, the gowned figures lending an air of formality to the scene. And here is Nora-from-North-Street acquiring a university sensibility, with her books tucked under her arm and her air of purpose. Here she is during a break between lectures, seated on a bench in the cloisters with a bunch of male and female friends around her, and a medical student – I'm sure he's a medical student – acting the clown in the background. Girls are at a premium at Queen's in the 1930s, when they make up only a quarter of the student population, and hence come in for a lot of gossip and joking attention. Especially if they're at all pleasing in appearance.

My mother led an active social life at Queen's. This is plain from a clutch of letters from admirers which she kept to raise her spirits in grimmer post-war days. Jack, Joe, Jim, Sean and Frank were the writers – all unknown, all vanished into the maw of time. She'd sometimes mention, in sorrow and disbelief, a handsome university friend – maybe one of the above – who ended life with his head in a gas oven. But sorrows and tragedies were figments of an unimaginable future, back in the charmed '30s with its Shakespeare and Keats, its dress patterns garnered from magazines and run up in cheap material to wear at the weekly 'hop', its lovely Queen's Elms building where women students congregated. Unlike her contemporary John Boyd, or the slightly later Robert Greacen, my mother was not dissatisfied with Queen's. She was not disposed to criticise its professors. The need to take notes during lectures didn't aggravate her. Professor Savory wearing riding breeches under his academic gown was not a figure of fun as far as Nora was concerned. She hung on his every word. Everything to her was new and exhilarating then: autumn leaves swirling round her feet in the Stranmillis Road, the steamy Palm House in nearby Botanic Gardens, the keyed-up atmosphere of the examination halls.

The Boat Club Hop, a 'rugger' match, a dance 'up Islandmagee way', a 'Happy Tea' – whatever that is – Rag Day, the student magazine *PTQ*: all these are entered into with gusto. 'I hope you were not scolded for staying out late on the night of the dance,' writes Jack (or Jim). And again: 'I am glad you suffered no ill effects from your "debauch".' The mind boggles: whatever can he mean? This is my stainless mother he's addressing, she of what he calls 'the supercilious eyebrows'. 'Debauch', indeed. Did Nora drink a glass of Babycham? I refuse to entertain the possibility of any more exorbitant impropriety. During my own inflamed student years (and later), I had to protect my mother from the things going on in my head (and not only in my head). Hers was a more innocent generation (or so everyone likes to believe about their predecessors). It was infinitely more shockable. So – no debauched goings-on in those days, thank you very much.

But the wretched Jim (or Jack) won't leave off. 'I'm sure we could do famously if we were laid out somewhere along the Lagan,' he suggests. Well! I had thought the Lagan towpath as a venue for wanton behaviour was a discovery of myself and my contemporaries. And here it is fulfilling the same function back in the days of (supposed) piety and decorum. ... Does Jack's Lagan idyll ever take place? I don't know – well, I assume it does, but my mother at twenty or twenty-one is really an unknown quantity to me. As for Jim/Jack: his medical student bawdiness keeps bursting out (so to speak). In his letters to Nora he alludes to the John Donne poem, 'On His Mistress Going to Bed', and at the same time hopes to provide her – if she'll let him – with abundant saucy anecdotes to entertain her grandchildren. And adds: 'You'll never know how near I was to writing 'our' grandchildren.' What I know is how near he came to writing me out of existence in the process.

But what went wrong between my mother and her undergraduate suitor (and other suitors about the place)? That's a story that can never be told: the facts are missing. For all her relish for learning, Nora becomes an exile from academia, by her own act and choosing. When she comes to marry, some years on, she opts for a person adept in banter and gregariousness, a singer in the John McCormack mould, of a lively temperament and unexalted means of livelihood (he works for the Ulster Transport Authority fitting together parts of trains). Against the odds, it proves a happy alliance in many respects. ... It's just my grandmother I can't help feeling sorry for, with another thundering disappointment to add to her life of hardship and stress. After all the sacrifices, all the aspirations invested in Nora, she has *not* fulfilled her unspoken obligation of marrying into the professional classes, and thereby bumping up the Brady family's social position. Not that her mother, my grandmother, holds this dereliction against her. Whatever Nora decides is right in her mother's eyes; or so she persuades herself. (This attitude, transmitted to the following generation, prevails in relations between my mother and myself, possibly to the detriment of my behaviour. Many actions of mine that should by rights have infuriated her, are excused or even applauded due to her absolute commitment to my well-being – lovely for me, of course, if not ultimately conducive to a sterling character.)

I don't know why my mother's university sojourn didn't lead to a different outcome. The social life of Nora and her sister Kathleen is centred on Queen's for a time ('Remember me to K. and tell her how nice I thought she looked on Friday night last,' writes J.), and then it isn't. They go their different ways. Nora is the first to marry, followed by Kathleen who meets an Englishman, a soldier stationed in Northern

Ireland during the war, at my Craig grandparents' house at Dunmurry, and with whom she emigrates to Wickford, Essex, settling in a bungalow the newly-wed pair calls Lismoyne, in honour of the location of their first encounter. In the meantime, I have come on the scene and am growing up to question none of the choices made by my elders, none of the circumstances of my intriguing life (intriguing to me). It is just the way things are. It takes a long time for the thought to enter my head that my parents are perhaps not entirely on the same wavelength, despite a shared sense of humour and a good many friends in common. It's something to do with one being a reader and the other not, one committed to sociability and the other more to social responsibility. Does the Protestant/Catholic divide come into it? Not at a fundamental level, I think, but perhaps the differing traditions and family settings do in some way work a bothersome effect. I'm not complaining: the marriage endows me, I believe, with an ancestry which is, at the same time, implicit in most of our Northern Irish backgrounds, and unusually explicit in my own case. ... But I wonder a bit about the paths my mother *didn't* take, the kind of life she might have led with someone of a comparable upper mobility, a co-religionist or a fellow schoolteacher.

Like one of those besotted Queen's undergraduates, for instance. 'It was very pleasant to hear that both you and I had passed that Scholastic Philosophy examination,' writes another of Nora's holiday correspondents (more sedate than Jim/Jack, who jokes in one letter about getting drunk and proposing to a barmaid in Derry, while on a mission to offload the magazine *PTQ*). Scholastic philosophy – hmn. The phrase ushers in a fact of university life at the time. Religious segregation. Students were either Protestant (overwhelmingly) or Catholic, and a minimum of intermingling occurred. My mother, of course, knocked around with a 'Catholic' set: a Celia Lenaghan, Frances Kelly, Maureen McKavanagh, Maureen McKenna, Maureen Harbinson, Honoria Smyth, whose future thankless task is to teach *me* arithmetic at St Dominic's High School, Maire Casement, another future Dominican teacher whose English lessons will constitute the highlight of my dodgy school career.

The scholastic philosophy course was available to Catholics only.[6] The department, says Marianne Elliott, had come into being 'in response to a successful campaign to create separate Catholic teaching programmes in controversial subjects'.[7] In the 1930s, scholastic philosophy was the province of Father Arthur Ryan (later Monsignor Ryan), an amiable and cultured professor by all accounts. Many of the current batch of undergraduates would end up as teachers, and the aim was to make them fit to teach in Catholic schools – and thereby perpetuate religious differentiation. Ah me. Few integrationist voices were raised at the time.

The blame for this situation need not be apportioned solely to Catholics. Take Riddel Hall. This otherwise admirable hall of residence on the Stranmillis Road was unambiguous about its orientation. When it opened its doors in September 1915 – incidentally, the year and month of my grandfather William Brady's death in the Dardanelles – it might as well have placed a banner across its seemly facade bearing the words 'No Taigs'. It was set up explicitly to make a home-from-home for female *Protestant* students and teachers of Queen's University, Belfast. ... Have I struck a note of criticism here with my outraged italics? All right, I know in one sense I'm applying standards of the present to institutions of the past. I know they did things differently then, and that it suited each sect to adhere to its own network of ideology, support and social organisation. I'm aware that in ordinary people's minds, attachment to one sect, and repudiation of the other, was bound up with integrity, not bigotry. Bigotry was an attribute of the back streets, the very stupid, or those in high places with an axe to grind (e.g. the 'Protestant' government of the day). For everyone else, it simply made for an easier life to abide by the rules – the 'Protestant' rules, or the 'Catholic' rules, whichever you'd been born to. Abide by the rules – and never bother about contributing by your line-of-least-resistance to the upkeep of apartheid.

Hindsight, that useful commodity, may allow us an amended moral attitude, but it shouldn't encourage automatic condemnation of people who actually did a lot of good, like the two Misses Riddel (though I've got another bone to pick with them, or their relations, in a minute). This pair of well-off, high-minded sisters put up the money to build and endow Riddel Hall, thereby aligning themselves with the cause of women's education in Ireland, and saving generations of clever young women from the miseries of bleak bed-sitting-rooms. Yes, indeed, only good Protestant girls from the country need apply for Riddel Hall accommodation – nevertheless, at the time, the new hall of residence represented an amazingly enlightened and generous action on the part of the two old benefactors (aged 84 and 78 in that year, 1915). We can credit the sisters with a feminist, or proto-feminist, attitude of mind, if not with ecumenical leanings.

But who were these Riddels? Miss Eliza and Miss Isabella[8] were among the youngest of the ten children born to a Belfast hardware merchant named John Riddel and his wife Annabella Charley (yes, of the same linen family that employed my grandfather William Craig as a groom, and founded the school attended by his children in the 1920s). John Riddel had died in 1870, but his sons took over the business and prospered and at some point the family acquired a substantial mansion called Beechmount House. The odd thing about Beechmount House was that it was on the Falls Road. Well, not the historic Falls of popular imagination, with its down-at-heel terraced rows of houses, its cobbles, backyards, factories, street games and disaffection. Beechmount House stood well back from the redoubtable road itself, on high ground in the shadow of the Black Mountain, the Cave Hill clearly discernible to the left, the whole of Belfast spread out beneath it, stretching away in the distance to the shipyard gantries. (It still stands in the same spot, but its function has changed, as we shall see.) ... Or maybe the eponymous beech trees screened out the view of grim glum Belfast, I don't know. Here the very plain looking, unmarried Riddels lived on and on, in elevated style, until the last of them, Eliza, died in 1924.

If you'd lived in the district around the turn of the twentieth century, you might have seen, like an image from another world, Samuel Riddel and his sisters driving down the Falls Road in an open carriage, clip-clopping along while you drew your shawl more tightly around you against the japs from the gutters, or raised your dingy old cap from your uncouth head. There they went, noses in the air, 'like proper royalty', as it seemed to local footsloggers at the time, awestruck by the unimaginable luxury of *Protestant* existences. ... When the people impressed by Riddel hauteur were themselves old, in the 1950s, they'd talk about elements of the past, including Beechmount House and its occupants, and captured the interest of Ballymurphy boy Joe Graham (a future local historian[9]). The phrase stayed in his mind.

Beechmount House, for all its seclusion, wasn't happily situated. It *was* the Falls Road. Isabella Riddel missed the worst of the flaring 'Troubles' by dying in 1918, but the last years of her sister Eliza were filled with distress and apprehension, fear of what the world was coming to. Terrific skirmishes, violence, shouts in the streets. The news is appalling, day after day. And some of it very close to home. For instance: in May 1921 an ambush of police and B Specials takes place near the Ballymurphy brickworks on the Springfield Road. Fourteen men of D Company, armed with handguns and grenades, wait behind a hedge in anticipation of a police tender. ... Here it comes, round a bend, the IRA men open fire, the police retaliate, the ill-prepared Volunteers run out of ammunition. A quick getaway is in order, and the keyed-up republicans go tearing and stumbling across a succession of fields, over a stream, past a clay pit, skirting a small council estate, through a gap and into the private grounds of Beechmount House, out of breath, dodging behind the trees and heading pell-mell for the Beechmount Drive entrance, past the gate lodge and so out on to the safe haven – comparatively safe – of the main Falls Road. And Miss Eliza and her servants cowering in the drawing room. We're reminded of the moment in Elizabeth Bowen's novel *The Last September*, located at the other end of the country, near Mitchelstown in County Cork, when a man in a trench coat, intent on Ireland's business, hurries past the heroine Lois in her own demesne. It's 1920, the Black-and-Tan war is under way, and nineteen-year-old Lois is susceptible not to the romance of the republican cause, but rather to the allure of the great house (a stand-in for Bowen's Court).

'Demesne': it's too grand a word for the grounds of Beechmount House, all thirty-one acres of it notwithstanding. You can't altogether detach the house from its environs, the dusty, rundown terraces, street lamps coming on in the evenings and a fine rain falling on patches of waste ground, the pigeon-fanciers' lofts, the mongrel dogs, the fifteenth-of-August bonfires, the front-parlour shops selling honeycomb and yellowman, the pubs with spittoons and sawdust on the floor, the Mountain Loney with the wee tin church halfway along it, the Brickfields and back fields and sectarian murders perpetrated up sinister alleyways, the half-built houses at the top of the Donegall Road drawing swarms of Catholic refugees. The last intimidated out of their homes in 'mixed' areas, and not lending an uplifted tone to the mid-Falls district. And people in Catholic dress all over the place, priests and nuns and first communicants and what-have-you. And the future Father Ryan of the Scholastic Philosophy Department at Queen's University growing up in a three-storey house on the front of the road, with iron railings separating it from the street, and large bay windows with looped lace curtains proclaiming an attachment to the middle-classes.

As we've seen, the Riddels drew the line at Catholics, so they did. Well, we shouldn't blame them too much for failing to rise above the orthodoxies of the day. It's different, though, when a piece of prejudice gets inscribed in a formal document. We've all heard of clauses in wills prohibiting a person of this or that persuasion from acquiring some specified property at the legator's disposal. It seems the deeds of Beechmount House contained a similar proviso against a future Catholic ownership. The estate was never to be allowed to fall into Papist hands. ... At any rate, this was the received wisdom at Catholic-street-level. It was firmly believed all over Beechmount, the Whiterock and St James's. If it's true – a large 'if'[10] – it is uncertain whether the Riddels themselves, or their predecessors, were responsible for the exclusion order. Again, if it's true, the framers of this bit of sectarian baiting had reckoned without Papist astuteness. ... Enter Daniel Mageean, Bishop of Down and Connor from 1929 until his death thirty-three years later. Mageean had long had his eye on Beechmount House, and when it came on the market around 1932, he arranged to buy it for the Church through a Protestant intermediary. Well! If we accept this story, it is hard to decide who comes out worse in the dodgy transaction, the authors of the initial reprehensible clause, or the bishop scheming to overturn it.

The phrase that comes to mind is 'turning in their graves'. Appropriated for Catholic Belfast, the house exists for many years as a hospital-cum-old-people's-home. Eventually it is taken a stage further and gains not only a Catholic, but a Gaelic overlay. At the present time, renamed Ard na bhFea,[11] it is flourishing as an Irish-language school. Alas, the house and surroundings have undergone unsightly renovation. Bits subtracted and added on. Car parks and sports grounds where a shady beech grove once held sway. A 'leisure centre', God help us, in place of the original gate lodge. The trees incessantly sinned against by concupiscent trespassers of the 1940s and '50s – all gone.

The moment of greatest consternation for ghostly Riddels and their ilk occurs in the summer of 1954, at the height of Father Peyton's transatlantic 'Rosary Crusade', when vast numbers of telling-their-beads enthusiasts swarm all over the grounds of Beechmount House in an intense affirmation of Catholic identity. Oh holy, holy, holy, lord. ... And where am I, while a portion of my home territory is thus devotionally deranged? Not on my knees in the midst of the praying Mass going, 'Hail Mary, holy Mary', that's for sure. I am not and never was a shining light of churchly exhibitionism. You would likely have found me in the back garden of 551 Donegall Road reading *The Mystery of the Hidden House* or *The Reluctant Schoolgirl*. Happily – though I accepted the obligations of being a Catholic child – I was not subjected to excessive religiosity in the home. I never knew a thing about the great Rosary Rally going on just a stone's throw away from our sunlit garden, and, if I had, I'd have taken scant interest in it.

What did engage my interest, up to a point, was the high stone wall running along the Falls Road end of Beechmount House grounds, all the way from the Giant's Foot Road to Beechmount Drive. For some reason, I was drawn to oddities and anomalies, and it was certainly odd to find a one-time gentleman's residence, complete with gardens, in this part of Belfast. At eleven or twelve, on my way to and from school, I would pass this wall four times a day. In my mind I endowed the house beyond the wall with a gothic aspect far removed from the plain reality. But I never ventured up the long curved drive to see the place for myself. And once I understood it was an old people's home I ceased to be intrigued by it. By this stage, of course, Beechmount House was well and truly incorporated into the Catholic Falls, with a nunly and priestly aura about it, and hand-wringing and woe for the wraiths of the Riddels.

When Riddel Hall for female students came into being in south Belfast during the First World War, a warden was appointed to oversee its arrangements. The first and most distinctive warden was Ruth Duffin, a relative by marriage of Miss Eliza and Miss Isabella.[13] She was thirty-six years old at the time, and connected backwards through her ancestor William Drennan to the 'United Irish' movement and the entire ethos of liberal, Protestant, nineteenth-century Belfast.

William Drennan. I've referred to him earlier (see p. 93) as an old Irish separatist, but it's possible I was over-simplifying things with this unequivocal tag. Yes, he founded the Society of United Irishmen in 1791; but later in the decade he disengaged himself from conspiracy and rebellion. In the run-up to the 1798 centenary celebrations, Dr Drennan's son, John Swanwick Drennan, co-opted his father for the unionist cause. At the same time, William Drennan remained an object of veneration for the extreme nationalist contingent. And both parties were right, in a way (which tells us something essential about northern politics). It depends on where you place the emphasis.

William Drennan, New Light Presbyterian, United Irishman, author of the stirring ballad 'The Wake of William Orr', had always held a place in the pantheon of radical Irish patriots, as far as I was concerned. He was up there with Emmet, Pearse and Tone. ... Then, towards the end of the 1980s, as a participant in the newly founded John Hewitt Summer School, I sat in a lecture hall at Garron Tower on the Antrim coast, and listened to poet-and-academic Adrian Rice restore a measure of complexity to the ironed-out, romantic-Irish version of Dr Drennan. Ultimately, Rice claimed, Drennan's social ameliorism and egalitarian standpoint had raised him above 'the diehard dogmas' of the factions of Orange and Green. He'd have wanted no truck with any outraged rabble. He was a social reformer, and once certain reforms were enacted he'd have ceased to be an agitator to any degree, and upheld the status quo. That was how it seemed to William Drennan's son (himself a doctor, a poet and a man of eighty-two at the time of the 1798 centenary celebrations). But Irish nationalists and Parnellites (we're still in the 1890s) took a contrary view. Total separation from England, they maintained, 'was the ideal taught by him'.[13] Drennan's own lines, 'The cause it is good, and the men they are true, / And the green shall outlive both the orange and blue', were constantly on their lips. Thus, you had rival factions laying claim to the larger portion of William Drennan. I would like to detach him from both of them, Green and Orange alike, and reinstate him as a symbol of integration. For whatever is or is not debatable about Dr Drennan's political convictions and private beliefs, one thing is certain, he supported full social rights for Catholics, having identified this lack as a grievous abuse of power. He threw his weight behind the cause of Emancipation (and died before it was achieved). A reasonable and moral Presbyterianism – which Dr Drennan[14] professed – precluded going along with any form of discrimination on grounds of creed or caste.

And here is his great-granddaughter,[15] a hundred years on, attached to an institution excluding Taigs from its intake. (I'm sorry to go on about this exclusion policy on the part of Riddel Hall – and I've already acknowledged its commonplace, non-threatening aspect at the time – but there's a certain irony here which I can't resist noting.) However, if she missed out on her ancestor's ecumenicalism, Ruth Duffin inherited something of his poetic ability. With her sister Celia Duffin, she brought out a couple of collections of verse in the 'fairy fiddler', 'quare wee house' mode – the vernacular manner interspersed with some lofty and archaic stuff. There were, at the time (1890s–1920s), quite a few prosperous Protestant women poets – 'Moira O'Neill', Helen Lanyon, 'Elizabeth Shane', Florence M. Wilson, and so on – who found their subject-matter in countryside lore and Ulster folk emblems, homing in on a mythical spot where pagan Ireland and Catholic peasant Ireland joined forces with Ulster Scots. You know the kind of thing – 'He played by the braes o' Comber, / A quare wee lift o' an air; / It stirred the childer from slumber / With its notes so sweet an' rare ...' – verse, according to the critic Terence Brown,[16] that 'treats of an aspect of Ulster rural life that has a significance for many Ulster people's self-understanding'. So it does, or so it did, and occasionally it rises to a stupendous indigenous piquancy, as in Florence Wilson's 'The Man From God-Knows-Where' with its button-holing opening lines: 'Into our townlan', on a night of snow, / Rode a man from God-knows-where'. You have to read on, for the story and the local ideology. The year – the resonant year – is 1798; and then it's 1803 and a crowd has assembled outside Downpatrick gaol to witness an execution. The poem is written in homage to an exemplary *Presbyterian* steadfastness and integrity. William Drennan would have relished its drift, and probably his great-granddaughter did too, though her own verse eschews any political content whatever. The Carbery/ Milligan brand of defiance is as alien to her as a pawnshop on the Lower Falls.

There's a single poem in which Ruth Duffin's literary reputation resides, and it's called 'The Fairy Piper':

> Who hears the fairy piper play
> Beneath the secret hill,
> Though he should wander worlds away
> Shall hear that music still.

This crystal-clear offering makes an appearance in my mother's brown-paper-covered, personal anthology of cherished verse, along with Helen Lanyon's 'The House of Padraig' and Ethna Carbery's 'The Spell-Stricken' (and John Clare and Thomas Hardy and Yeats and Keats and Shelley and Browning and Tennyson and Wilfred Owen ...). But she'd hardly have known that its author was going about her duties as warden of a girls' hostel just across the road from Sandhurst Gardens, in a building housing many of Nora's fellow students – with whom she probably wasn't acquainted. I doubt if she ever set foot in Riddel Hall. Its Protestant ambience (here we go again) would have struck something of a jarring note. But on the other hand, I think, she wouldn't have known or cared about the religious affiliation of any of the poets, local or otherwise, who made it into her hard-backed notebook. ... I find it slightly odd that so many Ulster poets of the day – town-bred for the most part – should wish so much to immerse themselves in the trappings of picturesque Ireland, all bogs and boreens and banshees and baloney. (I'm not trying to strike a superior note here: I lapped the whole lot up, all the holy wells and rushy crosses and boys-from-the-Rosses, no less than any other indigenous-emblem addict.) And the dour Ulster, not to mention manse backgrounds of some, make for an added irony. ... Of course, exponents of an Ulster pastoral verse form were by no means entirely Protestant, or female, or even Big House people: think of Cahir Healey and Cathal O'Byrne, for instance. Or Joseph Campbell, head and shoulders (in poetic terms) above the rest. One of my mother's university friends married a poet of this lilting type, John Irvine, who, like John Hewitt, fell under the spell of local place names: 'Limavady, Cloonnagashel, Donaghedy, Carrowdore ...'. Indeed, I believe the huge black pram from which I surveyed the activities of St James's Avenue and the Donegall Road was a gift to my mother from this Mrs Irvine – but the friendship must have lapsed, for I never got to know the pair. I liked his book *By Winding Roads*, though, with its William Conor dust jacket showing a donkey-and-cart, and lively illustrations. It was bought in Mullan's bookshop in Donegall Place, and it sat on a shelf in our sitting-room for many years. It's on one of my own bookshelves now.

The summer of 1937 comes, and, with it, the chancellor's garden party at Queen's University, a day filled with sunshine and excitements, at which a row of sweet girl graduates is photographed for a local paper. 'Degree day smiles', the caption goes: twelve joyful faces, the whole row linking arms and each of them putting her best foot forward, as if about to break into a triumphant quickstep. Happy days. And my jubilant mother among them, wearing her graduation gown like a badge of honour, all confidence and exuberance.

Graduation day at Queen's, 1937. PC's mother is first left, in the front row

She'd have considered herself enrolled in an up-and-coming minority of women graduates, but alas, the promise of that early hard-won achievement was not to be fulfilled. It had something to do with the times, the years of economic depression, downbeat Belfast, a glut of

Leaving the censorship office at Stormont, *c*.1944. PC's mother is on the right

women teachers on the market, no clerical or professional connections to put in a word. It is distressing to think of applications going out and out from 31 Sandhurst Gardens, and leading nowhere. ... Then, at last, comes a series of ill-paid, stand-in appointments, some as far afield as Ballymena or Ballynahinch. Nora's work is to fill in for a teacher of English indisposed for a term or two, or a nun in the grip of a nervous breakdown. Well, it's a way of gaining teaching experience. ... Then she gets married and cuts herself off even further from the prospect of full-time employment. Once you're married you have to stay at home, says the Catholic church. You have to stay at home and procreate. That is your role in life. But then the war comes, and things change slightly. It's not until 1943, however, that my mother secures a full-time job: in the censorship office at Stormont. Or, the Postal and Telegraph Censorship Department, to give it its full title. 'The work of Censorship has played an invaluable part in the concealment from the enemy of vital plans and preparations, in the detection and suppression of enemy espionage propaganda and other subversive activities, and in the enforcement of the many regulations necessary to sustain and extend the national war effort.' I'm quoting from a certificate of commendation presented in 1945 to 'all ranks of the Censorship staffs' – all now redundant – whose 'zeal, diligence and skill' are duly applauded.

This is my mother's contribution to the war effort: reading soldiers' letters and blacking out bits of them. I think she enjoyed it: the companionship, the sense of national urgency and the monthly pay cheque. And work as easy to her as falling off a form. My father continues in his employment with the Ulster Transport Authority at Duncrue Street. Their gurgling infant, meanwhile, is left in the care of her grandmother and aunt. They have all (myself excepted) lived through the terrible blitz on Belfast of 1941, when huge portions of the city were obliterated and temporary morgues set up in St George's Market and the Falls Swimming Baths, where stunned survivors come to identify the dead. Something happened at Beechmount,[17] I believe: the nearest the bombs approached to the Donegall Road. I can't remember any of it, of course; but I was told stories about the lot of us huddled under the stairs when the sirens went. Or, in summer, joining distraught hordes streaming up the Mountain Loney towards the sanctuary of a hawthorn bush. By this stage in the war it must be plain to all reasonable people that England's difficulty, in this instance, is also Ireland's difficulty, that the hellishness of Nazi Germany is worse than the devilry of Stormont.

This wasn't always the case. The minute war was declared, its bearing on Irish affairs was assessed rather differently by diehard republicans. Stories abounded of lights being left burning deliberately on the Falls Road, in defiance of the blackout, to guide Nazi bombers – proxy Sinn

Féiners in the eyes of some – on the way to wipe out a detested regime. It didn't work out like that, indeed, but the effect of such perverse wisdom was to reinforce Protestant misgivings about the 'loyalty' of the entire Catholic population. It's just another nail in the coffin of interdenominational accord.

'Them sons of whores,' wails a hurt old woman in Brian Moore's 'blitz' novel *The Emperor of Ice-Cream*, 'them bastards done it on purpose. They brought the German.' 'Who?' asks Moore's ARP[18] protagonist, Catholic Gavin Burke, understandably a bit bewildered by this tirade. 'The Fenians, the IRA,' comes the snarled reply. 'Them's the ones who done it. They should be hung, every one of them, aye, and a fire lit beneath them.'

Brian Moore's novel (his fifth) was published in 1965, and it draws very closely on his own experiences as an ARP recruit in the early days of the war. Like Gavin Burke's, his action caused affront to his Catholic nationalist family. 'Gracious God,' (exclaims Gavin's Aunt Liz in the book), 'did I ever think I'd live to see the day when my own nephew would stand in this room dressed up like a Black and Tan.' Immediately – though they're not addressed in the novel – genealogical complications enter in. Pro-Sinn Féin Aunt Liz is an invented character, but Brian Moore's real-life aunts, his father's sisters, were the children of a Catholic convert; the family's ancestry included a strongly Protestant Ballyclare and Ballymena strain. (And the further back you go the more sectionally tangled it gets; but that, as I've reiterated, is probably true for most of us.) By the early twentieth century, though, the Moores had become as Catholic as Corpus Christi. Exorbitantly Catholic, but another twist of fortune had placed them in a house directly opposite the main Orange Hall in Clifton Street, Belfast – giving Brian and his seniors and siblings a grandstand view, each Twelfth of July throughout the 1920s and 30s, of Orange pageantry and braggadocio. And perhaps engendering a soupçon of atavistic empathy, as the Belfast parade in all its pomp assembled beneath their eyes.

The Emperor of Ice-Cream is probably the finest novel to come out of the Belfast blitz, Belfast's encounter with terror and destruction coming in from outside, not – for once – home-brewed. The resulting cataclysm should have fostered solidarity, an all-in-it-together orientation. In some ways it did, while German bombs rained down on Prod and Taig alike. Few on the ground would have demanded information about a bombed-out person's religion before lending a hand. But, instinctively and insidiously, the old sectarian bogey came poking through the new awareness of a common predicament. You get the Clonard and Holy Family parishes, for example, congratulating themselves on counting low numbers of Catholics among the people killed in the April 1941 blitz[19] – the blitz placed fairly and squarely by Moore's old Shankill Road shawlie (above) at the door of the IRA. 'Them's the ones who done it.'

'All very wearisome and very perplexing,' as Benedict Kiely remarked on the subject of Belfast bigotries. Nevertheless – writing in 1945[20] – Kiely sensed the presence of 'new ideas, generous ideas ... ideas as energetic as the inspiration that built the factories, deepened the river, marked the black water with the shadows of tall cranes and leaning gantries.' He was being a bit over-optimistic, but the times allowed it. The war was over. People of a liberal bent held the same belief in a new advancement, a society – at last – decisively non-sectarian. Surely to goodness, thought Brian Moore, the just-past global conflict had put Belfast's squabbles into perspective: how, in the modern world, could the Orange-and-Green monster go on exerting its baleful influence? Alas, we know the answer. The snake was scotched, not killed. Even while he tried to consign it to the past, Benedict Kiely remained miserably conscious of 'an uncouth, vicious thing that comes to life at intervals to burn and kill and destroy'. Inherited spites and hatreds proved as indestructible as Grendel before the advent of Beowulf. Periods of apparent calm and reason were doomed to fall apart, endlessly. As I write, in July 2011, Belfast nights are filled with the noise of petrol bombs, rubber bullets, crashing vehicles, shouts, screams, smashed paving stones, half bricks, broken glass, running feet.

Wearisome is not the word. We've seen it all before, in the Pound, Millfield and Docks area in 1857, Sandy Row, Brown's Square seven years later, the Brickfields, Donegall Street, the Shankill Road, Divis Street, Short Strand, Willowfield, Lancaster Street. The noise of shooting, 'Starting in the evening at eight, / In Belfast in the York Street district', assaulted the infant ears of Louis MacNeice. John Hewitt remembered night after night seeing the sky 'lit with fire'. By 1922, he says, 'We knew of and accepted violence / in the small streets at hand' – as the longed-for, vividly imagined 'tolerant and just society', receded further and further into the distance.

★★★

Wartime members of the IRA were in something of an anomalous position: not Nazi supporters, indeed (unless they were mad), but still implacable opponents of Britain and its Stormont adjunct. Many IRA men chose to ignore the war and its implications as far as possible, sticking instead to the old republican strategies of drilling, parading, attacking police targets and raiding for guns. A lot were rounded up and interned, and for this and other reasons the organisation was not highly effective at this time, or, indeed, greatly revered as a resistance movement. There wasn't, for instance, much sympathy for a Volunteer from Bombay Street who was hanged at Crumlin Road gaol in 1942, following the shooting of a policeman (a policeman bearing the not exactly unionist name of Paddy Murphy).

I don't think my mother experienced any nationalist qualms on account of her war work in the censorship office. To bolster her decision to accept this employment, she might have held in mind an image of her father in the earlier war, a soldier in a British uniform meeting his death in the Dardanelles. She probably had Rupert Brooke or Francis Ledwidge running through her head on the way to the office. (In the days when the office is being wound up, she brings her two-year-old to be admired by her Stormont friends and colleagues. I have no recollection of the occasion.) I am sure she understood that changed circumstances can call for previously unthinkable adjustments to an ingrained set of opinions. In matters of politics or allegiance, she was never inflexible. She had praise for those who acted in accordance with some reasonably formulated principle, like her Tipping relations. Going further back – and if she'd known about them or it – she might even have understood the Blackers' *de haut en bas* commitment to civic order as filtered through paternalistic obligations. Calm, order and good prospects for the future were the breath of life to her.

At some time during 1938, I think, my grandmother had moved house for the last time. With Kathleen and Nora, the daughters still at home,[21] she moves from Sandhurst Gardens to the Falls Road end of the Donegall Road. It is a slight step up in the world. The new house is semi-detached, with two bay windows, a gate and a paved path leading to the stained-glass-panelled front door, over which a sun curtain is suspended during the summer months. The house stands on a corner, and a garden extends round the side and into St James's Avenue. It boasts a privet hedge and iron railings (soon to be requisitioned to help win the war). A gate for tradesmen − coalman, milkman, refuse collector − is let into the side hedge. It is painted green and shuts with a snib. A stub of a long-gone tree still sits in the front garden, and a sally tree grows between the side wall and the hedge. A trellis structure separates the front garden from the side, and to this, in season, is hooked an infant's swing. A yard, a shed and a wooden garden seat on the back lawn complete the lower-middle-class picture. Inside the house, on the ground floor, are three rooms: the front room known as the sitting-room, a living-room called the kitchen, and a tiny kitchen called the scullery. Three bedrooms and a bathroom upstairs represent a new luxury. It seems like a good place to live. The house is rented from a Dan McGinley who, with his brother Joe, runs a grocer's shop at the top of the Donegall Road. It will be my home until I reach the age of twenty and decamp to London.

It's to this house that my mother brings her new young ex-Protestant husband towards the end of 1941. The whole area − St James's, Whiterock, La Salle, Ballymurphy, Rodney Parade − is intensely Catholic, with its focal point in St John's Chapel on the Falls Road. On this place of worship almost the entire population converges on Sunday morning, with Mass taking place at hourly intervals between seven o'clock and twelve. (Only very infirm or lazy people leave it until twelve.) The exceptions to this weekly display of denominational fervour are the few Protestant families dotted about the district who keep to their own devotional routines. These, however, are not otherwise separated from the life of the community. Certainly such families have no interest in presenting themselves as a beleaguered minority. We have two in our avenue, St James's Avenue, Twybles and Smiths, who experience no discord on account of their beliefs. True, they keep to themselves, but then so do most of us. We have pretensions in our area. Some of the younger generation subscribe to the high-quality monthly *Collins Children's Magazine* − which is not to say we'd never be caught taking a sneaky look at the *Beano*. Solicitors and shopkeepers and teachers live here. Neighbours are not constantly in and out of neighbours' houses, after the manner of the riff-raff of the Lower Falls, thank you very much.

Fast forward to 1971 or thereabouts and an appalling phase of the thirty-year 'Troubles'. Some rearrangement of residences has taken place, not for the first time in Belfast's history. Protestants no longer feel safe or comfortable in a Catholic district, or the other way round. A few house exchanges are effected amicably, between acquaintances of different beliefs, but more families of the 'wrong' persuasion are intimidated out, threatened with arson or injury or, at best, ostracisation. Walls are daubed once more with the old offensive slogans: 'Taigs out'; 'Burn all Prods'. It's a bad case of recidivism. After a few – a very few – hopeful years, the sects are once again up to the oxters in vile primordial muck.

Around this time, my father has an alarming experience on a Donegall Road bus. At a certain point beyond Maguire and Paterson's match factory and the old Bog Meadows (recently appropriated for the start of the M1 motorway), the whole St James's Catholic ethos gives way to a pumped-up Protestantism. It's a feature of the area between the Donegall Road and Tate's Avenue known as 'the Village'. Village lads – ha! – for amusement of an evening, assemble at a bus stop below Celtic Park: the first 'Protestant' stop on the route towards the city centre. The assumption is that anyone already on the bus will be Catholic and therefore fair game. My father is caught unawares in this way on one occasion, and surrounded on the upper deck by a gang of youths hell-bent on bodily harm. Where has he come from? Where is he going? Who were his parents? What street is next to Kitchener Street? What team does he support? What flag does he venerate? (Or words to that effect.)

Fortunately he is able to supply the right answers (right for the circumstances). He is coming from the greyhound racing at Celtic Park, he says, and is on the way home to loyalist Dunmurry. He simply walked up, not down, to catch the bus at the closest stop (otherwise he'd have missed it). His name is Craig. In the garden of his house, orange lilies are planted to bloom in season, and a Union Jack is faithfully displayed on the Twelfth. One of his own sisters lives in Tate's Avenue. An uncle was a dignitary of the Orange Order. He gives the name of the lodge: St Nicholas LOL 264. All true – but not the whole truth. He is, in fact, on the way to visit his mother and his sister Ruby who still live at Lismoyne. The flag and the lilies are matters of fact, and so is Uncle Freddie's Lodge. What's expediently omitted from the account, of course, is his marriage to a Taig, his own conversion and actual place of residence just yards away from the priest-ridden Falls. No matter: his Protestant credentials see him through. He's allowed to go on his way unharmed, and is lucky to wangle it, things being what they were at the time.

I'm reminded of the poet Ciaran Carson's 'Question Time',[22] which partly consists of a fraught exchange between the narrator (Carson himself) and a gang of youths (Catholic this time) who intercept him as he cycles into the Falls Road from the direction of the Shankill.

> *You were seen coming from the Shankill.*
> *Why did you make a U-turn?*
> *Who are you?...*
> *You were seen. You were seen.*
> *Coming from the Shankill.*
> *Where are you from?...*
> *What's the next street down from Raglan Street?*
> *Coming from the Shankill ...*

Carson had innocently embarked on a cycle ride through his childhood haunts which included the Shankill Road library with its stock of Biggles books. But that was a different time. The world is now inhabited by vigilantes who perceive any incursion into their territory as a threat. 'Coming from the Shankill' denotes a sinister intent. 'The questions are snapped at me like photographs.' But for Ciaran Carson, an Irish-speaker born in Raglan Street on the Falls, the answers are child's play. (His Orange great-grandfather he keeps under his hat.) Yes, he knows what street was next to Cape Street, and the names of the people who lived there. Yes, he can tell exactly the relation between Stockman's Lane and Casement Park. He's not, after all, a suitable target for assault.

> I am released. I stumble across the road and look back. ... I get on my bike, and turn, and go down the Falls ... feeling shaky, nervous, remembering how a few moments ago I was *there*, in my mind's eye, one foot in the grave of that Falls Road of thirty years ago, inhaling its gritty smoggy air as I lolled outside the door of 100 Raglan Street, staring down through the comforting gloom to the soot-encrusted spires of St Peter's, or gazing at the blank brick gable walls of Balaklava Street, Cape Street, Frere Street, Milton Street, saying their names over to myself.

CHAPTER 9

'THINGS WERE BAD FOR A LONG WHILE BUT NOW WE'VE TURNED A CORNER'[1]

Where can it be found again,
An elsewhere world, beyond

Maps and atlases,
Where all is woven into

And of itself, like a nest
Of crosshatched grass blades?

Seamus Heaney, from 'A Herbal'

The mad, bad times began in earnest in 1969. But things had already been simmering away for five decades and more, while active insubordination on the part of northern nationalists waxed and waned. With the civil rights movement and People's Democracy idealism of the mid 1960s, an interlude of hopefulness occurred. 'And the next thing, suddenly, this change of mood,' wrote Seamus Heaney in his poem 'From the Canton of Expectation'. An exhilarating exercise in social observation, this poem encompasses a new purposefulness which is overtaking the old subdued state of subterranean affiliations and kinship of the disaffected.

> Once a year we gathered in a field
> Of dance platforms and tents where children sang
> Songs they had learned by rote in the old language.

There's a photograph in the Bigger collection at the Ulster Museum of a feis in Glenarm in 1904 which is an exact visual equivalent of these lines; Heaney, as ever, is spot on. He is also, at the same time, harking back to that 'hidden Ireland' of the eighteenth century postulated by Daniel Corkery – the concept of a vanquished people holding on to their cultural resources in their own language, and indeed glorying in the sense of invisibility, or at least inaccessibility, this confers on them, rather like Mary Norton's Borrowers: tiny people living side by side with those of a normal size, and going about their business almost completely undetected by them. The 'subject people stuff' (to quote another phrase of Heaney's) does indeed contain a large element of resignation, or at best a muted defiance, and it's this sense of demoralisation that's about to be dispelled, according to the poem 'From the Canton of Expectation'. It's goodbye, all at once, to 'the guardian angel of passivity', as an age of assertiveness, with demands for fair play, is ushered in. Aside from its universal application, which enables it to be read on more than one level, I take it that this poem has a specific point of reference: to the 1947 Education Act,[2] and the confidence and articulacy it bestowed on many of its beneficiaries. Readers alive to the Northern Irish context to the poem won't be slow to pick up its pungent allusions.

I'm not sure exactly when it was that the opinion first began to circulate about the civil rights movement having its origin in the enhanced political know-how of the first eleven-plus generation. But before long this reading of the situation had become a commonplace among social historians. Ideally (if rarely in practice) education entails exposure to liberal ideas, and a natural corollary of this is commitment to justice in the social sphere – and would-be ameliorators in Northern Ireland in the late 1950s and early '60s didn't have to look too hard at the society they inhabited to identify its more egregious biases and disgraces. Decades of discrimination, the misuse of power, ingrained bigotries: if you possessed the smallest degree of consciousness, these couldn't help but hit you in the face. One of the earliest effects of widespread education was to foster a critical attitude to such enormities, once they were perceived as such, along with the will to do something about them. To place yourself on the side of the angels, you had to be committed to freedom and democracy (however you chose to define these concepts).

It wasn't long before a catalytic alienation, an honourable outrage, was brewing at Queen's University – and spiralling out into the community at large to generate a kind of buoyancy, an anti-sectarian optimism the likes of which had not been seen in the North since the 1790s (though that particular eighteenth-century 'dream of grace and reason'[3] came to a bad end also, as we know). Education, albeit on a smaller scale, was at the bottom of United Irish agitation: the following are the words of the satirist James Porter's[4] 'Squire Firebrand', in a *Northern Star* of 1796:

> O! How times are changed and all for the worse. Your Catholic emancipation – your Sunday Schools – your Charter schools – your book societies – your Pamphlets, and your books, and your one hell or another are all turning the people's heads, and setting them a-thinking about this, that, and t'other.

Thinking about this, that, and t'other is the first stage in devising a programme for reform, and the better trained and informed the thinking activist is, the more forceful and overpowering will that programme be. Among those people conscious of being in a socially disadvantaged position, and not handicapped by any deficiency of intellect, the drive to obtain an education has always been strong – this was as true of bookish English labourers, artisans and the like, as it was of those eighteenth-century Irish pupils coming in winter clutching their sods of turf to keep a fire going as they crowded into one hedge-, barn- or makeshift schoolroom after another; though the latter contingent, no doubt, had the sense of acting in defiance of an unjust authority to bolster them up. If you, as a social group, are actually forbidden an education through an iniquitous edict from above, your natural inclination, if you have any spunk at all, will be to seek one out as assiduously as possible. Hence the innumerable sites of hedge schools all over the Clogher Valley (for instance), dating from Carleton's day – hence too all the classical allusions inserted into Irish-language poems of the eighteenth century: '...Are you Helen for whom many were destroyed, / Or are you one of Parnassus' nine fair maids ...?' etc. Learning so hard-won simply cried out for some form of expression.

Move forward a couple of centuries, and – all over the United Kingdom – hordes of scholarship pupils (myself included) are gaining whatever advantages a grammar-school education can provide. In England, the process contributed to the making of many a socialist and free-thinker; but in the peculiar circumstances of Northern Ireland, with denominational disabilities imposed alongside those of class, the position was rather more complicated. But the upshot in one area, as I've indicated, was a burgeoning radicalism at Queen's University, as eloquent student-protesters-against-the-system, such as Eamonn McCann, Bernadette Devlin, Michael Farrell, John Hume, Austin Currie and others, rose from the ranks. They had all arrived at Queen's via the eleven-plus/university scholarship route.[5]

They had arrived, some with no bother at all, others with more of a struggle as obstacles rose up to confound them along the way. Some, non-arrivals, fell foul of hidden social pressures geared to sabotage the scholarship scheme. If these weren't hidden they were blatant, and might produce a discouraging or, on the other hand, a bracing effect. Defiance was as sterling a way as any of responding to denigration. The eleven-year-old Eamonn McCann, the minute he set foot in St Columb's School in Derry, was cornered by an insolent priest and quizzed about his home address. 'Where do you come from? Rossville Street? Oh yes, that's where they wash once a month.'[6] Seamus Deane, another of the brainy Bogsiders infiltrating St Columb's, encountered a similar superciliousness at the school: 'The welcome was not exactly stunning. I discovered that I was an Eleven-Plusser ... in the opinion of some teachers, a low type.' These two stuck it out, but others, victims of St Columb's 'unofficial but widespread snobbery', threw in the towel.

I was not a victim of snobbery, but of a churchly severity, as I've related in *Asking for Trouble*. Queen's was the place for me, I thought in my eighteenth year; but instead I had been diverted to a different establishment: art college. As a field of study I had life-drawing, etching, illustration, in place of the more appropriate English or Irish studies. But was I downhearted? No. Somehow I adapted to the new routines; well, it was a relief to have done with school, at least a school as uncongenial as my last one had proved to be. And the slightly bohemian art college atmosphere was exhilarating, even if I didn't participate in it fully. If I hankered after Queen's, it was only a peripheral hankering. Art school had its own form of liberal thinking – though it had more to do with style and sex than sectarianism. If I went around asserting my Irishness in the intervals of applying paint to canvas, I don't think too many people were impressed. (They weren't impressed by the painting results either.) They'd have relegated me, on this account, to the fusty, rather than the avant-garde brigade.

I did get acquainted with some Queen's students though, and briefly became a crusader for a type of socialism which seemed to offer a way out of the sectarian impasse we all deplored. Under the influence of Eamonn McCann, I went from door to door in east Belfast canvassing on behalf of the Northern Ireland Labour Party (without conspicuous success); and in his company too I visited the home of ex-shipyard-worker-turned-playwright, Sam Thompson, whose *Over the Bridge*, first performed in 1960, created such a significant brouhaha in Belfast. This play, described by its author as 'a plea for tolerance', was first accepted, and then rejected, by the Group Theatre, as the Group's pusillanimous board succumbed to misgivings about the probable effect in Belfast of its controversial content. *Over the Bridge* concerns trade unionism and bigotry in the shipyards of Harland and Wolff. Bigotry, of course, was not confined to the shipyards, but by focusing on a particular setting, one he knew inside out, Sam Thompson was presenting in a nutshell the city's outstanding defect. (We remember James Douglas renaming Belfast 'Bigotsborough'.) It proved too much to stomach for people blind to its likeness to life. The Group Theatre washed its hands of it; and a spate of resignations followed as the play's supporters got their backs up in their turn. Eventually, *Over the Bridge* was staged at the Empire Theatre, without its fundamental drift being watered down. It was directed by James Ellis, who also acted in the play; and one of the principal roles was taken by J.G. Devlin, father of my old schoolfriend Fiona Devlin (see p. 5–6). The entire cast of *Over the Bridge*, and everyone connected with it, Protestant, Catholic, Dissenter or whatever, could congratulate themselves on upholding the principles of tolerance, verisimilitude and freedom of expression. And, contrary to the Group Theatre's dismal prediction, the play's initial staging didn't cause offence leading to chaos in Belfast. Instead, it proved a tremendous box-office success.

I was not seated in the audience at the Empire Theatre when Sam Thompson's play set people a-thinking about this, that, and t'other.

At the time I was in my last year at school, attending the Assumption Convent in Ballynahinch where I vacillated between different ways of promoting an equitable society, and chafed under the school regulation enforcing scraped-back hair. In my daily doings I assumed the cultural high ground by speaking Irish assiduously; at the school, I took on the mantle of a would-be rebel by earnestly discussing with one or two like-minded girls the possibility of setting up, among the fifth- and sixth-formers of Ballynahinch, a branch of Cumann na mBan (the female section of the IRA). I rather lost heart for this enterprise on learning that my principal, indeed virtually my only, supporter in the plan, had gone away to be a nun. So the only outlet for my clandestine instincts was the collection box for the Political Prisoners' Dependents Fund which I carried through the streets of drab Beechmount and drabber St James's, as an adjunct to the above-board pools-collecting on behalf of Gael Linn, to which I was also committed. You will see that, despite my lack of a religious temperament, a lack I'd been aware of from an early age, I was living and moving and having my being in Catholic Belfast, with its rituals and rigmaroles, its delusions and exclusions and aggravations. I was vehemently on the side of all of us in an inferior position in the unionist state. I was also continuously undergoing chagrin at not being paid enough attention by whatever boy I wanted to pay attention to me at the time. It seemed being Catholic, and semi-fluent Irish-speaking, and up to the eyes in republican dissent, were fixed points in my otherwise fluctuating sense of identity. It took art school, I suppose, to liberalise my idea of liberalism. There was more than one way, it seemed – the Irish-Ireland way – of achieving an advanced persona for yourself. You could adjust your emphasis by going all out to shock hidebound Belfast (the student way), or by enmeshing yourself in international, not just national, causes (the 'Ban-the-Bomb' way). You could exhibit a proto-feminism by refusing to wash up the dishes in male student friends' disgusting flats. You could involve yourself in enlarging the scope of Belfast politics by supporting the non-sectarian Labour Party. I did, as I say, briefly throw in my lot with the last; but it wasn't, for me, a natural departure. The world of politics was not my sphere.

Sam Thompson. When *Over the Bridge*, that polemical play, ran into trouble with the Group Theatre in Belfast, the hero of the hour – one of the heroes of the hour – was actor/director James Ellis. He was there, a driving force, at every stage of the play's rehabilitation. His support for Thompson was unwavering – and it continued after the playwright's death in 1965 following a heart attack in the Northern Ireland Labour Party offices in Belfast. Both the author and the actor had placed themselves within a tradition of dissent in the North running against the sectarian grain. The *Over the Bridge* controversy, with its implications for the future, was a defining moment in the life of Ellis, no less than that of Sam Thompson.

The future. Here is a cemetery-set piece from 2010, which somehow embodies the confusions and crotchets, obstinacies and fiascos of Northern Irish affairs. Picture a pouring wet morning in late July, and a group of about fifty bystanders assembled in driblets under huge umbrellas at the top end of Belfast's City Cemetery. The occasion is the rededication of Sam Thompson's grave, with a new headstone 'erected by his friends', and inscribed with a line from Sam Hanna Bell, 'His was the voice of many men'. Appropriately – as it seems – the now elderly Ellis has been invited over from England to perform the unveiling and deliver a short address applauding the achievement of his long-dead friend.

We are a motley lot, standing in our raincoats waiting for Ellis to arrive and the ceremony to begin. The Black Mountain looms over the scene, with mist swirling about its summit and the Hatchet Field looking within easy walking distance. Forrest Reid, in his novel of 1915, *At the Door of the Gate*, remarked the way the cemetery ground rose steeply, 'its green surface broken by innumerable white and grey monuments, and threaded with dark trim paths'. He mentions how 'the hard silhouettes of a few cypresses, and the softer outlines of the trees in the park alongside, stood out against a pale blue sky'. And beyond (he adds), 'yet quite close, was a dark low range of hills, the air from which blew down, fresh and cold'. Today the sky is overcast, not pale blue, but otherwise the cemetery is much the same as it was in Forrest Reid's day (as long as the late-twentieth-century housing developments remain out of sight). We have, as I say, arrived from all directions, and from all walks of society. Sinn Féin is represented by Danny Morrison who has organised the event as part of the West Belfast Festival, ex-Lord Mayor Tom Hartley, and Gerry Adams himself who draws up at the graveside in a swish black car, and proceeds to hand around sweets from a paper bag. The old Labour movement in Belfast gets a look-in in the person of Brian Garrett – solicitor and Sam Thompson's literary executor – along with my friend

Anne Devlin, daughter of Paddy Devlin the great Belfast socialist and trade union activist. If she's here on behalf of her dead father, though, Anne is also present in her own right as an acclaimed short-story writer and playwright; along with her contemporary and fellow-playwright Martin Lynch, she imports into the gathering a touch of thespian glamour. My other Devlin friend – not related – now Fiona Coyle, also stands obliquely for the world of the theatre (via her father), and at the same time affirms the ethos of the burgeoning Irish-speaking population of Andersonstown. All of us, in our different ways, are here to honour the memory of Sam Thompson and the anti-sectarian ideal he stood for. Some of us are Catholic, by birth or conviction, some Protestant, and more, probably, subscribe to no religion at all.

Standing by the Thompson graveside with its pre-unveiling covering still in place, I'm struck by the way nearly all of the people present can be assigned to various ideological and cultural categories – allowing for overlap and interfusion, of course. And some of these categories are at odds with one another. Gaelic-socialist-republican-integrationist-theatrical-literary. ...The last brings me to the third Devlin present, Marie Heaney, who's accompanied by her Nobel Laureate husband Seamus. The Heaneys are in Belfast because Seamus is performing at the West Belfast Festival later in the day, reading some poems and talking about the headmaster, Michael McLaverty, of the school he, Seamus, taught in, in the days before fame overtook him. And they, the Heaneys, like the rest of us, are in the City Cemetery defying the damp to pay tribute to the author of *Over the Bridge*. His 'plea for tolerance' is in the thoughts of all of us. 'Shipwright, playwright and trade unionist', Michael Longley wrote in his poem 'The Poker' ('In memory of Sam Thompson'), 'Old Decency's philosopher ...'.

Another exponent of 'old decency' is James Ellis, who duly arrives at the microphone set up under a kind of makeshift tent affair. 'I haven't brought any notes or anything,' he begins. 'You'll have to forgive me, this is just an impromptu speech. Off the cuff.' Encouraging murmurs follow this announcement. 'Good for you, Jimmy.' 'You're all right, Jimmy.' 'Yes,' the famous Belfast actor goes on, looking round with an unexpectedly blank expression on his face. 'It's great to be here among so many distinguished people. Especially Seamus Heaney.'

Well, fair enough, I think. Given the occasion, it was Sam Thompson's due to be mentioned first; but clearly Ellis has caught sight of Seamus in the gathering and feels he has to acknowledge his presence. Now he's got that out of the way, no doubt he will get to the point. But it doesn't happen. Slight ripples of unease run through the crowd as we hear a strange assertion coming from the microphone, to the effect that it is an honour, 'a great honour for me to be here unveiling the grave of this famous poet, a Nobel Laureate, the greatest poet Ireland has ever produced. A great prose writer as well ... great eloquence ... I have signed copies of all his books ... a great poet ... Seamus Heaney ...'.

The acclaimed actor is in no danger of running out of words, but he seems to be attending a different ceremony to the rest of us. What is going on? We find out later that James Ellis has a mild condition requiring medication to keep him in a balanced state, and in the hustle and bustle of flying into Belfast that morning the medication was overlooked. Hence the unexpected oration which has us standing transfixed under our dripping umbrellas, torn between embarrassment, bemusement and an urge to burst out laughing (which no one does). Glances are exchanged denoting bewilderment and consternation. The only one who has the presence of mind to do something is Anne Devlin, who bravely steps across to James Ellis at the microphone, takes him by the elbow and apologises for butting in. 'Tell us about Sam Thompson, Jimmy,' she urges. 'It's important to remember that you are here today because you as an actor took Sam Thompson's banned play *Over the Bridge* and fought to get it on. That showed such courage as an actor, to do that for a writer, for a play that was banned. And it inspired me as a playwright, because I learned that culture was a form of resistance. And that is why we are here today.'

She's done her best, and more than any of us, but her intervention produces only a kind of benign puzzlement in the single-track speaker. It required a tremendous effort on the part of Anne to try to save the situation. ('My legs are about to give way under me,' she whispers, resuming her place in the crowd.) But no sooner has she left the enclosure than 'Seamus Heaney' starts up again. 'A great honour ... the eloquence of this tremendous poet ... Seamus Heaney's grave ...'. God knows what is going through the mind of poor Seamus as he stands there having to hear himself being consigned to a burial spot in the City Cemetery long before his time. He catches Anne Devlin's eye and shakes his head. He tries to efface himself behind the broad back of Gerry Adams. Eventually, though, as the inapposite elegy rambles on, he sees there's nothing for it but to intervene himself. He takes the microphone, thanks James Ellis for his comments, and wrenches the ceremony back on track with his customary grace and gumption. James Ellis, still looking not quite himself, apparently sees no discrepancy between the person standing beside him, alive and well, and the 'great poet' he's had dead and buried a minute earlier. He just seems politely bewildered by all these interruptions. And when Heaney, composed as ever but no doubt disquieted by the occurrence, returns to his place in the audience, blow me if James Ellis doesn't start up again. 'Great honour ... the grave of this great poet ... Seamus Heaney ...'. ('Jimmy was not to be diverted,' observes Seamus ruefully, later.) At this point the organisers give up, the dogged Heaney devotee is led away, still muttering, '... great poet ... grave ...', and the show is over. It's not long, however, before Ellis's usual civility and acumen are restored to him. The incident is just a blip in the long and productive association between actor and playwright. It's been unnerving but with an edge of comedy. And the heroine of the hour is Anne Devlin.

Anne Devlin's classic story 'Naming the Names' is the best account I know of the making of a terrorist. Her protagonist Finn (Finnuala) McQuillen belongs to the burnt-out people of the Falls, victims of an Orange onslaught in August 1969. Finn's grandmother is rescued from her house in Conway Street off the Falls Road, carried to safety in the arms of a neighbour, while the houses of other neighbours blaze around her. Stones and bottles are hurled at fleeing 'Fenians' by a crowd of arsonists at the top of the street. Some time later, Finn walks into 'a house in Andersonstown of a man I knew' and asks if there is anything for her to do. 'And that was how I became involved.' Later again, following the murder of a judge's son, Finn is arrested and interrogated in an interview room by members of the RUC. Asked incessantly for the names of her republican associates, she repeats like a mantra instead the street-names of the pungent old, disaffected Falls. 'Conway and Cupar, David, Percy, Dover and Divis. Mary, Merrion, Milan, McDonnell, Osman, Raglan, Ross, Rumania, Serbia, Slate, Sorella, Sultan ...'

This deeply humane story carries considerable resonance. Obliterated streets, mutilated neighbourhoods, harm done, causes good and bad and inescapable, come within its parameters. Who could witness horrors inflicted on unoffending people and not wish to retaliate, as Finn does in the story? And once you're committed, you're committed. Some distancing mechanism from evil effects takes over. ...Where did 'Naming the Names' come from? A work of fiction, it is very far from being Anne Devlin's own story. In 1981, her family unwillingly abandoned the house in Andersonstown where they had lived for fifteen years. Their exodus was due to violence, or the threat of violence, from ruffian elements of the Provisional IRA who disliked Anne's father Paddy Devlin's principled, and outspoken, refusal to condone the hunger strikers in the Maze prison. Hence some of the behind-the-scenes overlap and dissociation prevailing at the City Cemetery gathering, as indicated above.

However, as I've said, everyone attending the Thompson rededication could be classed as subscribing to liberal values, of whatever variety. And what the lot of us were up against, at the time we got going as would-be progressives, was the old inherited, ingrained and iniquitous 'Bigotsborough' mindset. And this mindset was embodied in a big way in an awful autochthonous figure. Here is an image from 1962. A current annoyance of one or two zealots is the notion that somehow the BBC in Belfast has become a hotbed of popeheads. Fuelled by the wrath of God, these religionists assemble in Ormeau Avenue wearing overcoats not designed for aesthetic appeal, and carrying placards alerting passers-by to the fact – which may have surprised them – that the BBC is the Voice of Popery. 'We Protest Against Roman Catholicism in the BBC,' thunders one of these placards, 'In Ordering Refusal of Protestant Protests Against the BBC's Submission to ROME IN ULSTER.' I don't know what brought on this particular choleric outbreak – not very succinctly, indeed tautologically, articulated; but it made an occasion for the Reverend Ian Paisley to leap on a soap-box outside the BBC, and go into denunciatory mode while emulating his roaring nineteenth-century predecessors such as the Reverend Henry Cooke (a bygone cleric every bit as black as he was painted).

Paisley was the new watchword, among us sceptics and reformers, for utterly abhorrent attitudes. Larger than life, a figure of fun, a cartoon Covenanter, yes; but also a purveyor of poisonous doctrines, a dangerous throw-back and demagogue. 'That noisy preacher,' John Hewitt called him, adding another epithet: 'old-fashioned'. Paisley stood for everything that was wrong with Ulster. The travel writer Dervla Murphy, who visited Belfast in the mid 1970s[7] and attended a Sunday sermon at Paisley's 'Free

Presbyterian' church on the Ravenhill Road, felt, as she watched him perform, that she was 'in the presence of pure evil'. And not without cause. 'We must attack the people – the people who represent the anti-Christ in our midst! Be violent for Christ's sake': this was among the calls to arms assaulting the congregation's ears. Incitements to hatred filled the air. Disbelief and despair filled Dervla Murphy.

My friend Douglas Carson, a Protestant liberal soon to become a radio producer with the Taig-ridden BBC, and his friend Erskine Holmes, equally liberal, took one look at Paisley's antics at the time and joined with the bulk of the populace in consigning the blazing cleric to some abysmal realm of sectarian malevolence and indigenous benightedness. Paisley was the millstone round liberal Ulster's neck. He was going, if he could manage it, to drag the whole province down. ...Years later, in a conversation with Douglas, I listened to him express a rueful amusement, shared by me, at the way things unfold. 'Who'd have thought,' he said (or words to that effect), 'that one day Erskine would be driving the one-time bugbear of all of us through the battlefields of the Somme; or that the same Paisley would sit with my wife and myself in our front room drinking tea and talking knowledgeably about art and books.'

Douglas went on to describe an occasion, a funeral at May Street Presbyterian Church, at which Paisley was also present. The one-time scourge of popery, it seemed, was pleased to draw attention to May Street's ecumenical past. It was, he said, the only Presbyterian establishment in the city in which a Catholic Mass had once been celebrated. This happened in the 1920s, when the then incumbent, the Reverend Alexander Wylie Blue, had offered it as a temporary facility to a local Catholic priest whose own church was destroyed by arson. It was a brave and neighbourly thing to do – and the odd thing was that Paisley appeared to approve of the gesture.

At some point – I am not sure when – the Reverend Ian Paisley emerged from his time warp and went from maleficent to avuncular. What brought about the colossal change I don't know, but it's possible that Sinn Féin had a hand in it. Following his very public show of camaraderie towards Martin McGuinness, Paisley could hardly assume the old-fashioned demonic mantle again. Or, as commentators trying to make sense of Paisley in the past had surmised, it may have been a case of a split personality, with the more agreeable portion finally winning out over the rest. He remains larger than life – but perceptions of him have become enlarged in their turn, to take account of complexities and contradictions (my mantra) in Northern Irish life.

Between the innocent ameliorative impulses of the early 1960s and the slaughterhouse strategies of the following decade, a great gulf opens up. An unprecedented change of atmosphere occurred. Violence and the threat of violence underlay everything, and a concomitant laxity in everyday activity came to the fore. While politicians and others in positions of power desperately sought to contain 'the situation', fighters on the ground, fellow-travellers, and, indeed, large sections of the populace, veered between bleakness and implacability, and a full immersion in a kind of dance-of-death furore. A tit-for-tat killing frenzy overtook the North. Housing estates all over the province got into the grip of a pulverisation mania. Things were torn apart. The old Ulster decorum became a laughable figment of an unimaginable past. And the worst occurrence of all was the alignment of paramilitary and criminal activity, to the point where the two became one and the same thing.

The journalist Kevin Myers was based in Belfast during the 1970s, and has recorded his shocking experience of the city in a memoir, *Watching the Door* (2006). It's a vivid account of the badness of Belfast, gangs and bangs and guns and torture and lamentation, with copious sexual shenanigans thrown into the mix. (When churchly restraints went by the board, they departed with a vengeance.) Myers watched Belfast disintegrate around him. His profession sends him hot-foot to the scene of every atrocity, every place of perdition. And he manages to get himself on the wrong side of everyone, so that the whole of Belfast seems out to get him. His book takes the form, by turns, of unnerving comedy, terrorist imbroglio and bedroom escapade. It presents a version of a Belfast gone berserk. And however much he jazzes up its scenes of depravity, Belfast remains for English-born, Irish-affiliated Myers 'an evil place'.

Was this true? Others, like the poet Carol Rumens, came to Belfast braced for the worst, but found instead leafy suburbs, gardens, cedar and larch and fuchsia, places where 'peace, and love, and money, are made'. Places where ordinary people got on with their ordinary lives, disregarding as far as possible the grim backdrop; where burnt-out cars and shattered buildings were emblems only of a distant derangement. Well, fairly distant. There were reverberations. Many standpoints were shaken. The breaking point for a lot of liberal-minded people occurred at the moment when dissent became accommodating of carnage. Republicanism was then seen to have parted company with idealism.

Sometimes a small occurrence was enough to tip the balance in a previous sympathiser. For example, I date my mother's disillusionment with romantic Ireland and its freedom-fighting partisans – I date her disillusionment to the moment when, with disgust and exasperation, she watched a couple of gun-toting whippersnappers, twelve or thirteen years old, hanging around by 551's back gate in St James's Avenue. (She'd gone into the garden to hang her washing on the clothesline.) The two swaggering juveniles were flaunting their weapons and glorying in the sense of aggrandisement thereby conferred on them. 'Mine's bigger than yours,' she may have heard one claim, accompanied by giggles. And, 'That's the IRA,' my mother snorted later, in sardonic mode. (And yes, I'm bearing in mind young Bertie Tipping and his involvement in illicit activity of the early twentieth century – but I believe, or choose to believe, that a structure and discipline existed at that time very far in spirit from the dislocated '70s.)

Imagine you're a Catholic housewife living in Belfast in 1970, and your sense of justice is constantly violated by one instance of discrimination after another. Your children coming home from school are attacked by thugs from a different school, while your co-religionists are burned and blasted out of their homes. You have statistics concerning Catholic unemployment and belittlement at your fingertips. You're Catholic by upbringing, and allied with that portion of the populace nurtured on a litany of wrongs, while actually undergoing ever more colossal wrongs – though your own lineage, if you cared to look at it, is far from being an ethnically unbroken story. ...This, at least, is true of the two young women whose experience of unionist inclemency I'm about to relate. (Not that being Catholic in the church-going sense is paramount in the evolving political standpoint of either. That's not what the conflict is about. It's about social justice, and putting a stop to terror in the streets.)

One of these young women is my cousin Margaret, my Auntie Eileen's daughter, and of all of us Blacker descendants, the one who is most in line with the Tipping tradition. The other, whom I called Olivia[8] in *Asking for Trouble*, is my old school friend and fellow-Dominican-convent-expellee. These two have found themselves living next door to one another in Andersonstown, and quickly become friends. They have in common membership of the People's Democracy student-run body, and a burning aversion to the way the state of Northern Ireland is run.

There are protests everywhere. In the news is the attack on a republican funeral by a Protestant mob who tear the tricolour from the coffin and carry it away in triumph into their own back streets where it's set alight. Police monitoring the funeral move in to make arrests, but not of the aggressors. They swoop instead on young males wearing black berets and what are later described as 'army style' jackets, these garments supposedly proclaiming membership of an illegal organisation. (No one doubts that this is the case, but what gets the goat of concerned observers is the partisan nature of police and army responses.) Black berets, combat jackets: add a guard of honour equipped with hurley sticks, and the thing goes from a funeral to a quasi-military parade. Or so it seems to those who attach a provocative rather than an emblematic significance to the hurley sticks.

Not everyone takes this view. A particular cause of anger is the Special Powers Act and the way it facilitates unwarranted arrests like those noted above. People passionate about justice are constantly inveighing against this Act which is not perceived to operate in an even-handed way. When the black-beret-hurley-stick contingent comes to trial, a 'Special Powers' protest by disaffected women is set to take place outside the Chichester Street courthouse in Belfast. Among those intending to join in the protest are next-door neighbours Margaret and Olivia. In a gesture of defiance against the system, they will wear a version of the jackets invested by the Royal Ulster Constabulary with an insurrectionary significance. A number of hurley sticks, sardonically brandished in the hands of some as 'offensive weapons', will complete the protestors' tableau – though, if trouble ensues as it is almost certain to do, it is possible that this satiric touch will succumb to the needs of the moment and lose its symbolic edge.

Indeed, what Margaret and Olivia find when they arrive at the spot on the appointed morning in February, is a minor riot already in progress. Two rival crowds, mostly women, have assembled on opposite sides of the street. They are Protestants fully in favour of arresting and trying IRA suspects – the more the better – and their Catholic, or quasi-Catholic, counterparts, incensed by the onslaught on their legitimate gathering, and not slow to respond to traditional insults. It isn't long before dirty Fenian gets and bloody fucking Orange bitches are jammed together in a wild indigenous fracas. Police intervention doesn't achieve a lot. Screaming women hurl themselves on two policemen, enabling a few of their captured friends to break free and disappear into the crowd. Another woman being taken into custody is suddenly bashed in the face by a huge white plastic handbag wielded by a roaring opponent, towards whose assault on their captive the forces of law and order turn a blind eye. Olivia and Margaret, looking on with a measure of bemusement and understanding the impossibility of staging the proposed 'peaceful' demonstration, decide to make themselves scarce.

At this point things take an alarming turn. Olivia is carrying a bag containing three hurley sticks which are poking out at one end. A large rough female in the crowd, catching sight of the sticks, starts shouting and pointing: 'There's another couple of them bastard Fenian scum. Tear the fucking faces off them! Don't let them get away!' Before they *can* get away an inspector appears by their side and informs them they're under arrest. A small local drama involving factions and overreactions is about to be played out. The two women are taken to a nearby police station and charged with behaviour contributing to public disorder, and with being in possession of the ubiquitous 'offensive weapons'. Along with twenty-nine of their fellow would-be demonstrators, some of whom are exhibiting a degree of truculence, they're stripped of their outer clothing – clothing retained as evidence, and later described by the trial judge as 'having a military or a paramilitary connotation in the particular circumstances of Northern Ireland' – and, once solicitors have been contacted and bail arranged, sent home without adequate protection against the freezing cold of a Belfast February.

Certain instinctive actions of the Royal Ulster Constabulary were apt to cause outrage in the bitter past, when the force's reputation for impartiality was not high. The way they would jump in any cat-and-dog situation was easily foretold. The courthouse protest and its chaotic outcome was witnessed by a number of lawyers, Protestant and Catholic, who later issued a statement condemning police leniency towards the attacking faction, not one of whom ended under arrest. Indeed, 'the RUC mixed jovially with the unionist crowd',[9] the statement averred. Its conclusion, that 'legislative reforms are but an empty formula when the administration of justice by the police and courts is so blatantly one-sided and unjust', was not referred to during the subsequent trials.

Nevertheless, you can read into this statement the faintest possible note of hope for the distant future – beyond the cataclysm – when a change of heart, or at least a change of orientation, will come into being. The uncouth, vicious thing deplored by the novelist Benedict Kiely (see p. 233), with its *raison d'être* in killing, maiming and destruction, isn't itself quite dead in the North at present, perhaps, but it's only a shadow of its former sectarian self.

Neither my cousin nor her friend believes they will wind up in prison following the abortive courthouse protest. They enter the courtroom, when their case comes to trial, expecting a fine and rap on the knuckles. What they get instead is a sentence of six months in Armagh gaol. The trial has proceeded in accordance with the guiding principles adumbrated above. Why were these women arrested in the first place? Because, said the officer in question, 'in my opinion the hurley sticks were offensive weapons, and in combination with the jackets, likely to cause a breach of the peace'. (Never mind that 'a breach of the peace' was strenuously under way before they came anywhere near the place.) When Counsel for the defence wants to know 'why all the arrests were carried out on one side only', he gets a somewhat evasive reply:

> 'I did not want to escalate the situation so I only made arrests where a breach of the peace seemed likely.'
> 'You did not consider that remarks shouted by the opposite side were likely to lead to a breach of the peace?'
> 'There were slogans and counter-slogans and cat-calls and jeers coming from both sides.'

There were indeed, so there were, but to say so doesn't explain the heavy hand clamped down exclusively on one side of the Chichester Street battleground. And for some of the protestors anyway, 'sides' were beside the point. When it comes to Olivia's turn to give evidence, she is asked straight out: 'Was the purpose of the hurley sticks offensive?' 'Certainly not,' comes the sturdy answer. 'We merely intended to use them as symbols.' 'You did not consider that they might be offensive to the Protestant faction?'

'I was protesting against legislation that affects everyone,' Olivia declares. 'I do not consider that I belong to one particular religious faction.' It's the thin edge of a socialist-feminist-republican wedge, the voice of a new liberal Ulster, People's-Democracy-derived (though not, alas, the voice of *all* the courthouse demonstrators, some of whom are stuck fast in the old denominational sheugh). And much good it does her. 'Six months,' the judge pronounces; and Margaret the same.

Shortly before the end of Margaret's prison sentence, I accompany her father, and my mother, on a visit to Armagh. 'The incongruously handsome women's prison', to quote the poet John Montague[10] is situated in the town itself, on the south side of the Mall.[11] Built between 1780 and 1820, facing Francis Johnston's courthouse, it is one of the great public buildings of Northern Ireland. But architectural concerns aren't uppermost in any of our minds at the time. The building is not looking its best. A few days previously, the Provisional IRA had blown up a couple of cars belonging to prison warders in retaliation, they said, for the ill-treatment of those locked away inside; and broken glass and debris from the explosions are strewn about the place. All the prison windows facing the Mall have boards nailed across them.

The prison's forbidding entrance is furnished with a peephole through which we are scrutinised before being admitted, by a wardress, into a large tiled hall with a number of archways leading off it. Seated on a couple of chairs against a far wall are two impassive fat women wearing bedroom slippers and slowly consuming enormous ice-cream cones. Male warders stand about jangling bunches of keys. 'Surreal' and 'oppressive' are words that spring to mind. The whole interior of the place is dank and gloomy. Whenever we venture a comment during the twenty minutes or so we're kept waiting – which isn't often, as we're somewhat unnerved and apprehensive – our voices resound off walls imbued with extremes of ancient tension and distress. A constant ringing of bells makes you wonder which miscreants are being summoned to perform what punitive undertaking. Well, I'd hardly expected the atmosphere to be encouraging, had I. But I don't like the way you are made to feel you are downgraded as a human being simply by association with your particular inmate. And what makes it all the more aggravating is the fact that our inmate has committed no crime in the first place.[12]

A sour-faced female warder – 'screw' – arrives and conducts us through the hall and into a small courtyard. We walk in silence. Pleasantries are not exchanged. Suddenly Margaret appears from another direction, accompanied by a wardress of her own. My poor cousin is clad in a shapeless green gingham skirt folded over at one side, a pink blouse and a thin navy cardigan. These are prison-issue clothes, distributed to inmates on arrival at the gaol, and after a strip-search has been carried out. Underneath the terrible outer garments are large blue knickers elasticated round the legs, and a patched-up bra with different cup sizes. Black laced shoes and brown lisle stockings augment the austerity picture. Margaret does not seem low-spirited, though, despite the awful circumstances. Her robust approach to life has stood her in good stead. She's been able to shrug and go through the experience, deriving from it whatever benefits she can. Unlike a number of her fellow-prisoners, she hasn't given way to violence (smashing up her cell) or hysteria. She's acquired a certain skill in sewing shirts and mailbags, in wall-, floor-, and lavatory-cleaning. Prison life is just an ordeal to be got through, days ticked off on a calendar pending the moment of release. It is also a republican rite of passage, aligned to the old resistance-and-endurance model which has long kept revolutionary aspirations on the go.

She relates an anecdote. A fifteen-year-old girl on the way to a remand home is offered a cigarette by one of the so-called 'IRA women'. 'But I'm a Protestant!' the girl exclaims, reluctant to accept the gift under false pretences. Makes not a whit of difference, she's assured, as she lights up reluctantly, still nervously anticipating some awful Fenian trick about to be played on her.

Go back nearly two hundred years, and you find Margaret's ancestral connection William Blacker attending a different institution of Armagh – the Royal School, dubbed 'the Eton of Ireland' – and, in accordance with the current system of fagging, being appointed to the role of 'slave or valet' to the future Earl of Longford, then Tom Pakenham, whose shoes he has to keep polished to the nth degree. Polishing shoes, brushing trousers, burnishing buttons, preparing meals, smuggling in ale ... these schoolboy tasks, 'purgatorial' as they were, were nothing compared to a singular bit of horseplay devised by the aforesaid Pakenham and endured by the young Blacker. The former would oblige the latter to sit on the top stair of the main staircase, bind his wrists to his ankles, seize him by the feet and drag him downstairs, bump, bump, bump, step after step to the bottom, whereupon young Pakenham would laugh uproariously

Orangemen waiting to attack civil rights marchers at Burntollet Bridge, 1969

at young Blacker's discomfort. A curious rite of passage – but never mind, William said wryly, looking back on those days in Armagh, such treatment toughened him up for life's assaults and affrays (which would shortly include the famous affray at the Diamond). And, if the flaming 'Orangeisms of after times' were still largely a matter of amorphous stirrings, a distinct political style and anti-democratic bellicosity is getting drummed up at Armagh's Royal School, where teenage William (elevated to head boy) is a leading light of the Loyalty Lads, a school society devoted to all the implications of its broad-orange-ribbon badge. ... A long, long, hell-bent march is getting initiated, and one of its ultimate destinations is a high ridge above the River Faughan near Dungiven in County Derry, where a line of rogue Orangemen, armed with sticks, boulders and nail-studded cudgels, waits to descend like cartoon savages on an unfortunate procession of civil rights upholders on the way to Derry. The date is 4 January 1969, the place Burntollet Bridge, and terrible scenes of mayhem and bloodshed are about to be enacted – all with the connivance of local B Specials and regular police.

The waylaid Derry marchers are battoned, slashed, kicked, pummelled, knocked unconscious and hurled unmercifully down the slope and into the shallow river. Those still on their feet scatter wildly in all directions trying to evade the onslaught. Frances Molloy, who was present at the time, later published a novel[13] (engagingly written in a County Derry dialect) which includes an account of her own experience of Burntollet (via her narrator Ann McGlone):

> As a was lyin' there ... somebody that called me a fuckin' Fenian bastard started te kick me an' rain blows down on tap of me way some heavy implement that a could feel but didn't risk lookin' up at. ... Then somebody musta come te save me ... for a heard another voice, just as the blows stapped, sayin', are ye tryin' te murder hir, ye cowardly bastard ye, can't ye see that she's only a wain? Me attacker then set te the man that was tryin' te save me, an' the man that was tryin' te save me said te me in a wile urgent kine of a voice, if ye can manage te stan', get up now for god's sake ... an' get outta here quick.

She goes on, 'It musta been a miracle, but nobody got killed that day an' soon after we got across the bridge, cars an' ambulances started arrivin' from both directions te help the marchers an' bring the badly injured te hospital.' Nobody got killed, and nobody got arrested either. 'The polis,' says Frances Molloy, 'knew damn well who the culprits were because they could be seen, laughin' an' chattin' te many of them, on the very best of terms, while the ambush was on.'

The verdict on this memorable episode issued by Captain Terence O'Neill, still holding on as Prime Minister of Northern Ireland, is as follows: 'Some of the marchers and those who supported them in Londonderry itself have shown themselves to be mere hooligans, ready to attack the police and others.' Whew!

The people carrying out the Burntollet ambush probably thought they were ingratiating themselves with their hero Paisley – if they thought at all – and also with one of Paisley's henchmen, a Major Ronald Bunting, who stood behind, supported and directed the wreckers and stone-throwers as their vicious project got under way. There is, however, evidence to suggest that Major Bunting cleared a way for some of the injured marchers, once he understood the thing he'd helped to set up was liable to end in murder, and felt his humane instincts kick in, however late in the day. (Better for those to kick in, than brutal, 'Papist-trampling' boots.) Or it may have been thoughts of his son that came into his mind and checked his Protestant militarism, at this critical moment. I don't know if Ronnie Bunting junior was actually among the Burntollet marchers,[14] but he was, at Queen's University, a prominent member of the People's Democracy group; and his subsequent career would take him as far as possible from the loyalist precepts cherished by his father.

Yes, by one of those indigenous twists beloved of historians and others, the younger Bunting was a convert to socialism and republicanism who became a founder-member of the Irish National Liberation Army, and met a violent end in 1980 when a UDA death squad was sent to his home in Turf Lodge, Belfast, to assassinate him. (He himself had been implicated in the London murder of Airey Neave.) He was thirty-two. He is listed on a roll of honour of republican dead in the Springfield Road, Belfast, one of a very small number of 'Protestants' to be so commemorated.[15] But his father, Major Bunting, had him buried in the family burial plot, in a final gesture of paternal affirmation. Poles apart as they were in political orientation, it seems that each of them, father and son, accorded some respect to the principles the other chose to live by. Major Bunting said of his son, 'I saw him as a man who was virtuous and high-minded, and who had a keen sense of social justice and who fought oppression and injustice wherever he saw it.'[16]

What happened at Burntollet Bridge shows sectarian rage running out of control. The Orange assailants − throwbacks − are, in their own view, defending 'their' territory against a flaunting invasion by a crowd of students, 'Popeheads', socialists and republicans. 'Where's your Pope now?' they sneered. 'Get your Pope now and he'll help you.' They believe their actions are justified − but it's not the way the event is seen by the rest of the world, with photographic and eyewitness evidence testifying to an alarming propensity for stoning and beating on the part of certain scions of Protestant Ulster.[17] It's Benedict Kiely's monster springing to life again. It's the clearest possible indication that things will have to change, that abhorrent energies will have to be worked off, once and for all. Not that people really believed, in the midst of the cataclysm, that change would come, but come it did − though only after years of carnage and destruction on a scale unimagined by even the most pessimistic observers of the start of the Northern Irish Troubles.

My wonderfully sympathetic mother had scant cause to be grateful for many of the routes my life drifted into: unapproved byways, cliff-edge paths. If these were at odds with the comfortable and conventional circumstances she'd have ordained for me – if she could – not one word of criticism on account of my waywardness did I ever hear from her. She managed to accommodate, and even to relish, my vintage-clothes mania ('Sure who's like her ...'), my hennaed hair, even my freelance existence and consequent financial insecurity. (I was happy as an occasional author, book reviewer, and flea-market aficionado, and that was enough for her.) Not that anxiety on my behalf ever left her, and I'm now appalled that I didn't take the trouble to present my daily doings as something more palatable than a source of maternal agitation. But one thing, at least, she must have been thankful for: that I was safely ensconced in London and well away from indigenous perils such as the Derry march and its Burntollet outcome. As a person susceptible to the socialist and radical excitements of the day, I might easily (in my mother's view) have opted for any foolhardy and dangerous gesture available at any time to underscore a reformist point. She'd have dreaded to hear I was half-drowned and battered – like some of my acquaintance – or in Altnagelvin Hospital nursing a broken head.

Our house in the Donegall Road, however, was not at a satisfactory remove from riot and disorder. From a front bedroom window we witnessed scenes of disruption, my mother and father and I, as a bus blazed in the roadway before our eyes; as a commandeered car was rammed with shocking violence, back and forth, back and forth, into a factory wall a hundred yards away, until the wall began to collapse; as soldiers erupted on the scene, leaping from their armoured cars equipped with riot shields and tear gas; as all the inflamed of St James's dispersed and regrouped, using local knowledge to good effect. It was early in the morning of Monday 9 August 1971, and we'd been roused from our sleep by an ominous noise: women parading the streets banging bin lids together to alert the neighbourhood to a state of emergency. Operation Internment was under way.

The day was strange. A minor riot continued to unfold on the patch of waste ground backed by the factory wall against which the reckless driver had smashed his stolen car. Unaccustomed noises filled the air: shouts, bangs, clashes, distant gunshots, stones hitting riot shields, pounding feet on asphalt pavements. Two of the last belonged to a young priest in a black soutane, holding up his skirts as he pelted up the road towards the junction with the Falls – 'By jinkers, that fellow can run,' my father exclaimed admiringly – a priest later shot dead in the act of administering the last rites to another victim of the turbulence. The day was strange, and a nervous apprehension held us in its grip as our once sedate neighbourhood succumbed to an access of anarchy. I thought of our quiet avenues, our old neighbours keeping themselves to themselves, cultivating tidy flower beds in their small gardens, library members, car owners, good housekeepers, emerging for Mass on Sunday mornings decently clad in old-fashioned dress. Where had it all gone?

I feel I am a part of the current exorbitant events, and also that I am not. I can watch and deplore the advent of uproar, outrage after outrage, from a good safe distance. Well out of it. Soon I am back in London, my summer holiday over, back with my Welsh-painter husband, my black cat, my stop-gap proofreading job, the Portobello Road, the National Film Theatre on the South Bank. My parents have no such escape route. They have another five years of being in the thick of it, bomb blast and murder and terror and savagery, five years before they will move to a quiet spot on the County Down coast and put a bit of distance between themselves and the maelstrom. And in the meantime, my mother's teaching is constantly interrupted by factors unconnected with the classroom. Bomb scares abound. Large portions of the day (she tells me) are spent standing shivering in St James's Road, as the school is evacuated yet again following another telephoned alert. Once, the army co-opts members of staff to scour the school for a putative explosive device. They're set to searching lockers, cupboards and cloakrooms, not really knowing what they are looking for, or what action to take if they find it. Normal life has to be fitted in around abnormal circumstances. Two of my mother's pupils blow themselves up in separate incidents, when their bomb-making skills prove lethally insufficient. Everyone's nerves are kept at breaking point, with no respite. A car backfiring in the distance is enough to send the whole class diving for the floor, leaving the teacher standing at her rostrum facing rows of empty desks. Topical excuses for failures of diligence are the order of the day: 'Miss, I couldn't do my homework with the bullets whizzing up and down the hall.'

In the summer of 1999 we came to live in Antrim, transferring ourselves from pleasant Blackheath to a hundred-and-sixty-year-old, three-storey stone-built house with an overgrown garden. It was the month of the Long March – implacable Protestant Ulster on the move from Derry to

Drumcree, in support of immemorial 'civil and religious liberties' which seemed in jeopardy once again, and in protest against continuing IRA atrocities. On our first night in the empty house we heard, in the distance, the sound of Orange drums, conjuring up an ancient intransigence and history of bad blood. (Conjuring up for me, as well, at another level, an irresistible ancestral elation.) What had we come to? Just down the road, on the way into Antrim town, was the railway bridge where an earlier march, bound for Derry via Burntollet, was attacked, jeered at and jostled by stirred-up loyalists of the town. In the other direction lay Donegore Hill, an eldritch hill, once the rallying point for United Irish rebels heading for defeat (but what a storied defeat!) at the Battle of Antrim.

Drumcree, in County Armagh, the destination of the present 'Long Marchers', is rich in associations too. It contains a church at which one of those ubiquitous frock-coated overbearing Blackers once served as rector; and it's the place where the notorious Garvaghy Road stand-off testifies to the persisting nature of the Northern Irish squabble. Teeth and claws perpetually at the ready. Orangemen might have agreed not to march down the Garvaghy Road to the annoyance of local residents; local nationalists might have agreed to let the Orangemen get on with it, in a spirit of goodwill. But neither of them does anything of the sort. A chance for the tonic gesture, bypassed yet again.

As I've said elsewhere,[18] our house, Ashville House, was built for a minister of Antrim First Presbyterian Church, a Reverend Charles Morrison, Belfast- or Saintfield-born, Inst-educated, for whom Antrim did not prove a hospitable incumbency. Negative emotions, for the Morrison family, must have been attached to the town. The minister offended a portion of his flock through some unspecified misdoing (sexual or financial), and soon it became expedient for a move to be made. The Reverend Charles was appointed Principal of Arnold Theological College in Hackney, North London, and there, no doubt, life for the uprooted Morrisons assumed a settled and punctilious character, far from the stresses of dour Antrim town.

Back in Ireland, though, was the burial place of two young sons of the family, a circumstance no doubt adding to the country's fraught associations. One of these boys died (here, in this house) in 1846, possibly from some Famine-related illness. Every part of Ireland has its Famine stories, its emblems of historical woe. I think of my infant great-grandmother, Ellen Jordan, wrapped in a shawl and carried in her mother's arms for sustenance to an Armagh soup kitchen; I think of poor John Tipping dying of cholera in his Lurgan Workhouse bed. I think of all the Protestant dead of Tartaraghan. The children lying in the Antrim Presbyterian churchyard would have tethered the Morrisons to the town, whether they liked it or not. Whether the north of Ireland was, for them, a place of nostalgia or good riddance.

Five of the Morrison children survived into adulthood, and the youngest of these, Jane, born at Ashville in 1855, went on to marry, in England, an Andrew Davitt. In due course Jane Morrison became the grandmother of Donald Maclean of mid twentieth-century, Burgess-and-Maclean defector fame. I don't think many people are aware that Donald Maclean's great-grandfather was an Ulster Presbyterian minister who fell foul of his congregation – and I mention the fact simply because it adds a miniscule detail to the web of Northern Irish ironies and interconnections I'm constructing (those that have an oblique bearing on my own life, that is, or on matters that concern me here).

Everyone's life contains copious stories and histories. Throughout this book I've tried to uncover a few from my own life, and tried, as well, to find ways of enlisting these in the service of a broader perspective, and in support of an integrationist overview. I've hoped, from time to time, to light on a true Ulster spirit, a spirit of benevolence and inclusiveness. I'd like to dispel the notions that some people have a better right than others to be in Northern Ireland, that some are native and some are not, or that an eternal opposition exists between two clear-cut sections of our society, with a licence conferred on each to be at the other's throat ad nauseam. Because of our mixed inheritances, the battle of the ideologies boils down to a battle with the self, of which the only possible outcome is self-mutilation, or self-destruction. And so it proved. Anyone who spent any time in the North, in the 1970s or '80s (say), would have witnessed desolation and devastation on a scale to daunt any ameliorative heart. Though many of its inhabitants never wavered in the belief that the north of Ireland is the most beautiful place on earth, they'd have had, with Derek Mahon, to add a rider to that assessment:

> Portrush, Portstewart, Portballintrae,
> *Un beau pays mal habité.*

Those among us distrustful of hopes for the future might continue to stress the *mal habité* side of things. They might point to sinister paramilitary images still disfiguring gable walls (bring back folksy King Billy on his white horse, please), to continuing sectarian murders and other outrages, to horrid habitations and other terrible edifices replacing incalculable losses by bomb, fire, rot and redevelopment. We all have to take responsibility for everything that's happened. We are bound together by a common ancestry, and by our place in the world. Bound too by the whole pungent history of wrongs and suffering and bigotry and poetry and picturesqueness and notoriety and all our shared knowledge of secret local places. If each of us has to be classed under a divisive denominational label – which remains true to some extent, though it carries less weight than it did in the past – our entitlements, and our ghosts, are none the less interchangeable.

Ghosts. I have a whole restive company of these shadowy presences at my back, eager to communicate approval or disapproval, some reproachful about wrong motives attributed, or crucial details mislaid; others livid about traits they've been lumbered with, on scant evidence. ('The dead can't talk,' Douglas Dunn wrote,[19] 'or appear on your doorstep / Or be discovered turning to you from / Beautiful landscapes, wearing smiles of courtship, / Perusals of what you've written about them.') Some may harbour a modicum of assent; but more, I suspect, would vehemently wish to set the record straight, to detach their after-image from lunatic surmise. To these I can only reply that I've done my best to fit each of them into a pattern not outrageously at variance with actualities of the day (their day), and to flesh out just a little – as we've seen – the bare Jacobean, or eighteenth-century, or mid-Victorian bones. Most of these people had to grapple, in one way or another, with forces beyond their control, political, economic, puritanical, above all sectarian forces. ... My own personal ghosts, and others connected to me by a skimpier thread: these were born into wildly differing circumstances, and inherited concomitant stances. All, or most of them, lived according to their lights, and in ways dictated by the times, and I've no argument with them, except to point out a certain blindness in the face of variegation. There were more elements to their identities than some of them recognised.

Skimming through the preceding chapters, I find they embody a kind of edgeways or idiosyncratic approach to aspects of Northern Irish history. Northern Irish – so the title of at least one chapter, 'Scullabogue', is (again) making an ironic point about inclusiveness, and also about invalidating persistent preconceptions.

In May 2010 I was invited to deliver the annual *Irish Pages* lecture as part of the Cathedral Quarter Festival in Belfast. Because *A Twisted Root* was very much on my mind at the time, I decided to talk a bit about the book, mentioning the reasons why I felt impelled to write it, and including a few indications of what it might consist of. A short time later, a friend was attending a social gathering and chanced to overhear a conversation between two men whom she didn't know. One was telling the other that he'd recently attended an interesting talk 'by a republican woman from the Falls Road who discovered that all her ancestors were Protestants'.

Well! I was never a 'republican woman'; during the height of the Troubles I was not to be found anywhere near the Falls Road; and the largest 'Protestant' element in my background I didn't 'discover', having known about it all along. However, the person who summarised my lecture so cavalierly was at least right about the gist of it. The pasts of all of us in this small corner of the world are repositories of apparently shattering, but actually (if you think about it) unifying truths. As another friend put it, considering the events of the seventeenth century and their implications, if the native Irish had been white and the Planters black, our complexions would all by now be a uniform shade.

NOTES

INTRODUCTION

1 T.J. Campbell, *Fifty Years of Ulster 1890–1940.*
2 Note the name.
3 In his novel of 1907, *The Unpardonable Sin.*
4 *Portrait of a Rebel Father.*
5 All right, I admit I'm prone to favour this mode as a narrative strategy.
6 *The Speckled People.*
7 R.F. Foster, *Modern Ireland 1600–1972.*
8 I'm indebted to Douglas Carson for this information.

CHAPTER 1

1 *Shakespeare's Wife*, Bloomsbury 2007.
2 The ancient name for a part of south-east Ulster.
3 I'll enlarge on this subject in Chapter Eight.
4 At the top of the Cave Hill in Belfast.
5 Pen name of the poet and editor Anna Johnston McManus (1866–1902).
6 Only published for the first time in the Victorian era.

CHAPTER 2

1 Robert M. Young, *Belfast and the Province of Ulster in the 20th Century*, Brighton, 1909.
2 'The Oul' Orange Flute'.
3 It is possible that the liberal Brownlows of Lurgan favoured Bryan O'Neill because neither he nor his father Hugh had been implicated in violence against the Planter community.

CHAPTER 3

1 Since writing this, I've come across evidence suggesting that 'The first Lett in Ireland was a Captain in Cromwell's army'. Ah me. And it seems he came from Warwickshire, which loosely ties him in with the Tippings.

2 With one or two exceptions.

3 A fluent-Irish-speaking friend tells me it's more likely to be an adaptation of *Scealbog*, which means, among other things, 'a detached layer of rock'.

4 His grandfather was Charles Lett (they are all called Charles or Stephen or Thomas or William …).

5 Reports following the suppression of the Rebellion claimed that insurgents on the way to slaughter Protestant prisoners at Wexford Bridge carried a black flag emblazoned with a white cross, and the letters MWS – Murder Without Sin – written across it.

6 A biographical note on Barbara Lett which appears in John D. Beatty's *Protestant Women's Narratives of the Irish Rebellion of 1798* claims that Joshua Lett was her father-in-law. But this information is flatly contradicted by Katherine Lucy Lett in her *History of the Lett Family*, written for private circulation in 1925. Barbara's father-in-law was Charles Lett (another one!), says Katherine Lucy. Since she was the family historian, I'm inclined to go along with her version.

7 The third of a trio of brothers alongside William (father of Benjamin) and Charles (subject of the Reverend Henry Lett's biographical account). Whew!

8 I have to add a note about William. Despite his Orange credentials, says the Reverend Henry, William in later life 'became a PERVERT to the Church of Rome' (his outraged capitals). He suggests that expediency, not conviction, was behind it. But here at last is a 'Catholic' Lett to underscore my point about denominational interchangeability.

9 Actually, I can discard this possibility; see note 17.

10 According to Katherine Lucy Lett, the Charles who joined the yeomanry in 1798 did have a son named Thomas by his second wife, whose dates would fit. But alas, no information about this Thomas exists. (It may have been lost when the Four Courts was burnt.) And, since I can't find any reference to Clonleigh or my grandmother's ancestors in any Lett family documents, I think it's possible that my branch of the family stemmed from some illegitimate offshoot, now undiscoverable.

11 'By all accounts, lower-class Protestants were the original aggressors.' Marianne Elliott, 2000.

12 Blacker Diaries.

13 So called because of his campaign against cruelty to animals. He was the principal founder of the RSPCA.

14 Tim Robinson, *Connemara: Listening to the Wind*.

15 Seamus Heaney, 'Station Island', Canto 11.

16 May God have mercy on them all.

17 Another irony: the Irish rebel later joined the British Navy (and died at seventeen).

CHAPTER 4

1 *Contemplations on the Power, Wisdom, and Goodness of God*, Belfast, 1843.

2 Given William Blacker's much

publicised attitude to the Catholic church, it's hard to understand why these were present; but they were.

3 Not only do we have James and John incessantly recurring as family names, but they're attached to the streets and terraces they live in too.

CHAPTER 5

1 Not to be confused with Henry's father Matthew.

2 He was educated at Foyle College, Derry, before going on to Shrewsbury School and Magdalen College, Cambridge. His mother was Elizabeth Sinclair of Fort William, Belfast.

3 *Changes and Chances of a Soldier's Life*, London, 1925.

4 Rimbaud, *Le Bateau Ivre*.

5 I'm aware that Olivia May was dead at this point, but some female relative would doubtless have taken over the management of domestic affairs, at least until Charlotte Olivia, the eldest daughter and Marie Heller's exact contemporary, was in a position to do it.

CHAPTER 6

1 *A History of the Town of Belfast* (1880).

2 Basically, revival.

3 See Marnie Hay, *Bulmer Hobson and the Nationalist Movement in Twentieth-Century Ireland*.

4 George Buchanan, *Green Seacoast*.

5 The Reverend T.L.F. Stack, quoted in James Winder Good, *Ulster and Ireland*.

6 Both descended from a long line of Brookes and Chichesters.

7 He may not have been in the country at the time.

8 I have to be careful here, since my own name suggests an affiliation I'm far from embracing. I'm pointing this out myself before someone else does, and presenting it, moreover, as a corroborating, not an undermining, factor in my basic thesis.

9 Rea is joking, of course, while Whitman wasn't; but underlying the jocular tone is a refusal to concede superiority or unquestionable rectitude to one political persuasion over another.

10 See Len Graham, *Joe Holmes: Here I Am Amongst You*.

11 In the 1940s or '50s, she conducted a correspondence with Bishop Mageean on the subject of his ban on married women teachers, to which she was opposed.

12 I think Catherine inherited these aunts after her husband's death, since my mother in old age occasionally mentioned three old women who lived upstairs in her grandmother's house, and whose identity puzzled her.

13 Stevie Smith, 'It was a cynical babe. Reader, before you condemn, pause / It was a cynical babe, / Not without cause.'

14 W.B. Yeats, 'Easter 1916'.

15 Third son of Henry and Mary Anne.

16 *Forward the Rifles*, 2009.

17 From a cousin. No one who'd experienced it ever spoke to me of Lily's death. I barely knew that an aunt Lily was missing from the roster of my relations.

18 I think by Christmas they had moved from Edward Street to North Street, perhaps to get away from the setting of the tragedy.

19 It bothered some of the latter, like Francis Ledwidge, 'To be called a British soldier while my country / Has no place among the nations...'. (Quoted by Seamus Heaney.)

CHAPTER 7

1 The term 'Irish Volunteers' soon gave way to 'IRA' – Irish Republican Army.

2 Once I understand that the Barracks is a former Georgian house, I feel my conservationist hackles begin to rise in protest. But before the incident is over, police and military have burned and wrecked half the village. In the destruction stakes, the forces of law and order win hands down.

3 Then joint Hon. Secretary of Sinn Féin. He committed suicide in 1925.

4 The Tipping referred to is Jimmy.

5 Probably the Mater, where Dr Moore, father of the future novelist Brian Moore, had recently been appointed senior surgeon.

6 Well, for practical purposes. You could say it begins with the Plantation of Ulster, if you wanted.

7 One of Jim McDermott's sources

for his book *Northern Divisions,* from which I'm quoting.

8 See Lawlor, *The Burnings.*

9 One of these young men later became a commandant in the Free State army, while the other was executed by the Free State government in December 1922.

10 Only one of the subsequent accounts of the shooting mentions RIC men on the heels of the getaway car, with the mishap calling to mind the doings of the Keystone Cops.

11 I'm indebted to Glenn Patterson's book for this information.

12 He is tried and condemned to death, though the sentence is later commuted to twelve years' imprisonment.

13 *On Another Man's Wound.*

14 I'm quoting from *Northern Divisions* by Jim McDermott. This valuable book provides a day-to-day account of IRA active service units and their operations during this period.

15 Only the second son John, a married man with domestic responsibilities, stayed away from active involvement.

16 Note the name, and think of long-ago Katherine Rose uprooted from Warwickshire and planted in the 'boiling' Ulster countryside.

17 He'd been elected to a County Armagh constituency in addition to Cork in the Provisional Government, Dáil Éireann.

18 Thirty-year-old Collins has less than a year to live. The shock occasioned by news of his assassination, in August 1922, would

have been complicated, for the Tippings, by their position vis-à-vis the Treaty. They were among the northern republicans who opposed it, while others were willing to regard it as a means to an end.

19 Indicating active and armed service. In total 15,224 medals with bar were issued, and 47,644 without

20 Appointed Divisional Signaller, 4th Northern Division, in 1921.

21 In the words of an official at the Ministry of Home Affairs.

22 A slogan of the reconstituted, late-twentieth-century IRA. At least Gerry has it in English, not the bad Irish in which it was framed later.

23 There is, of course, quite a large irony here as far as the Tipping family is concerned.

24 On a recent visit to the Tower of London, my cousin Jerome Tipping was intrigued to find the name 'John Tipping' inscribed on the wall of a prison cell.

25 From an anonymous verse written in the nineteenth century.

CHAPTER 8

1 There wasn't much talk of my father's alma mater the Charley Memorial, or his later Lisburn Tech, but that circumstance hadn't particularly struck me either.

2 *Asking for Trouble*, 2007.

3 Oxford University Press, 1924.

4 Two daughters of Henry and Mary Anne's son John Tipping were pupils at the school in the 1930s.

5 No relation. Neither, I am sorry to

say, is the more obscure poet Julius McCullough Leckey Craig, author of the lines, 'On Carrick shore I stood, I stood, / And gaped across at Holywood; / And as I gaped I saw afar/My love upon the Kinnegar.'

6 At least, only Catholics availed themselves of it.

7 Elliott, op cit.

8 One, I would say, rather jolly in a Margaret Rutherford kind of way, the other a bit fluttery and timid (I'm going by their photographs).

9 I'm quoting from an article on Beechmount in his *Rushlight* magazine.

10 I am doubtful about its authenticity, since no one, as far as I know, has actually come up with documentary evidence in relation to the excluding clause.

11 A literal translation of Beechmount.

12 Their niece had married her uncle.

13 Robert Johnston, letter in the *Ulster Echo*, October 1891.

14 I'd like to think that 'Drennan' and 'Thornberry' were different versions of the same name, both derived from the Irish *Ua Dhroighnean*: one translated, the other transliterated. (The Thornberrys, you remember, were Lurgan republican associates of the Tippings.) And Duffin – like Duff – comes from the Irish word for black.

15 John Swanwick Drennan was Ruth Duffin's grandfather.

16 *Northern Voices*, 1975.

17 The district, not the house.

18 Air Raid Precautions.

19 See Stephen Douds, *The Belfast Blitz*.

20 *Counties of Contention*.

21 The other two had married and gone elsewhere.

22 In *Belfast Confetti* (1989).

CHAPTER 9

1 Paul Muldoon, 'The Biddy Boys'.

2 It arrived later in Northern Ireland than it did in Great Britain.

3 Tom Paulin.

4 Hanged in Greyabbey in 1797.

5 It wasn't the only route to success. People who failed the eleven-plus or equivalent examination should take heart from the story of eleven-plus failure Martin McGuinness who, in the course of his upward progress, held the post of Minister of Education, in an inspiriting instance of the 'reversal-of-fortune' parable.

6 Eamonn McCann, *War and an Irish Town*.

7 See *A Place Apart* (1978).

8 Not her real name, but it's as suitable for present purposes as it was then.

9 This was a common observation and it contributed greatly to Catholic disaffection.

10 *Time in Armagh* (1993).

11 The original architect was Thomas Cooley.

12 I should stress that I'm not opposed to prison as a punishment for those who *have* committed crimes.

13 *No Mate for the Magpie*, Virago, 1985.

14 A residual family loyalty, or embarrassment, may have kept him out of it.

15 But the history of Irish republicanism and nationalism is filled with Protestants, as I've stressed throughout.

16 *Lost Lives*.

17 Interesting to find the same surnames shared by marchers and attackers: Moore, McGuinness, for example.

18 *Asking For Trouble*.

19 In the poem, 'Disenchantments'.

SELECT BIBLIOGRAPHY

Bardon, Jonathan, *A History of Ulster* (Blackstaff Press, 1992)

Beatty, John D. (ed.), *Protestant Women's Narratives of the Irish Rebellion of 1798* (Four Courts Press, 2001)

William Blacker Manuscripts, Armagh County Museum

Brown, Terence, *Northern Voices: Poets from Ulster* (Gill & Macmillan, 1975)

Buchanan, George, *Green Seacoast* (Gaberbocchus Press, 1959)

Byrne, John, *An Impartial Account of the Late Disturbances in the County of Armagh* (Dublin, 1792)

Campbell, Captain David, *Forward the Rifles: The War Diary of an Irish Soldier, 1914–1918* (Nonsuch Publishing, 2009)

Campbell, T.J., *Fifty Years of Ulster 1890–1940* (The Irish News Ltd, 1941)

Carr, Peter, *The Night of the Big Wind* (White Row Press, 1991)

Cloney, Thomas, *A Personal Narrative of 1798* (Dublin, 1832)

Colfer, Billy, *Wexford: A Town and its Landscape* (Cork University Press, 2008)

Devlin, Anne, *The Way-Paver and Other Stories* (Faber, 1986)

Devlin, Paddy, *Straight Left* (Blackstaff Press, 1993)

Devlin, Polly, *All of Us There* (Weidenfeld & Nicolson, 1983)

Dickson, Charles, *The Wexford Rising in 1798* (The Kerryman Ltd, 1955; Constable, 1997)

———, *Revolt in the North* (Clonmore & Reynolds, 1960; Constable, 1997)

Donaldson, John, *A Historical and Statistical Account of the Barony of Upper Fews in the County of Armagh, 1838* (Dundalk, 1923)

Douds, Stephen, *The Belfast Blitz* (Blackstaff Press, 2011)

Dunne, Tom, *Rebellions: Memoir, Memory and 1798* (Lilliput Press, 2004)

Egan, Bowes and Vincent McCormack, *Burntollet* (LRS Publishers, 1969)

Elliott, Marianne, *The Catholics of Ulster* (Allen Lane, 2000)

Farrell, Michael, *The Orange State* (Pluto Press, 1976)

Geary, Laurence M. (ed.), *Rebellion and Remembrance in Modern Ireland* (Four Courts Press, 2001)

Good, James Winder, *Ulster and Ireland* (Maunsel & Co., 1919)

Graham, Len, *Joe Holmes: Here I Am Amongst You* (Four Courts Press, 2010)

Hay, Marnie, *Bulmer Hobson and the Nationalist Movement in Twentieth-Century Ireland* (Manchester University Press, 2009)

Hickson, Mary, *Ireland in the Seventeenth Century* (Longmans, Green, 1884)

Hughes, Andrew, *Lives Less Ordinary: Dublin's Fitzwilliam Square 1798–1922* (The Liffey Press, 2011)

Johnston, Sheila Turner, *Alice: A Life of Alice Milligan* (Colourpoint Press, 1994)

Kane, James S., *For God and the King: The Story of the Blackers of Carrickblacker* (Ulster Society, 1995)

Kiely, Benedict, *Counties of Contention* (Mercier Press, 1945)

Lawlor, Pearse, *The Burnings, 1920* (Mercier Press, 2009)

Lett, Reverend Henry, *Memoir of Charles Lett of Balloughton, Kilcavan, Co. Wexford* (Ms. *c*.1871)

Lett, Katherine Lucy, *A History of the Lett Family* (for private circulation, 1925)

Macardle, Dorothy, *The Irish Republic* (Gollancz, 1937)

McCafferty, Nell, *The Armagh Women* (Co-op Books, 1981)

McCann, Eamonn, *War and an Irish Town* (Penguin, 1974)

McClelland, Gillian, *Pioneering Women* (Ulster Historical Foundation, 2005)

McDermott, Jim, *Northern Divisions: The Old IRA and the Belfast Pogroms, 1920–22* (Beyond the Pale, 2001)

McGuffin, John, *Internment* (Anvil Books, 1973)

May, Major-General Sir Edward S., *Changes and Chances of a Soldier's Life* (Philip Allen & Co., 1925)

Molloy, Frances, *No Mate for the Magpie* (Virago, 1985)

Moore, Brian, *The Emperor of Ice-Cream* (Andre Deutsch, 1966)

Murphy, Dervla, *A Place Apart* (John Murray, 1978)

Myers, Kevin, *Watching the Door* (The Lilliput Press, 2006)

O'Faolain, Sean, *Vive Moi!* (Sinclair Stevenson (revised edition), 1993)

———, *The Great O'Neill* (Longmans, 1942; Mercier Press (revised edition), 1981)

O'Hagan, Andrew, *The Missing* (Picador, 1995)

O'Malley, Ernie, *On Another Man's Wound* (Rich & Cowan, 1936)

Patterson, Glenn, *Once Upon a Hill* (Bloomsbury, 2008)

Rice, Adrian 'The Lonely Rebellion of William Drennan'. In G. Dawe and J. W. Foster (eds), *The Poet's Place* (Institute of Irish Studies, Queen's University, 1991)

Rowe, David and Eithne Scallan, *Houses of Wexford* (Ballinakella Press, 2004)

Stewart, A.T.Q., *The Narrow Ground* (Faber, 1977)

———, *The Summer Soldiers* (Blackstaff Press, 1995)

———, *The Shape of Irish History* (Blackstaff Press, 2001)

Witherow, Thomas, *Derry and Enniskillen in the Year 1689* (Wm. Mullan & Son, 1873)

ACKNOWLEDGEMENTS

I am grateful to the Arts Council of Northern Ireland, and especially to Damian Smyth and Craig Corsar, whose award of a grant in 2010 helped enormously in the preparation of this book. I should also like to thank the Society of Authors for much appreciated financial assistance.

A Twisted Root (whose working title was *Scullabogue*), grew out of its predecessor, *Asking for Trouble*, and out of the researches and family papers of two cousins, Harry Tipping (the dedicatee of *A Twisted Root*) and George Hinds, both of whom supplied encouragement as well as practical information. I owe them an inestimable debt.

I am also grateful, as ever, to Douglas Carson who read the early chapters and made valuable suggestions; and, for various kinds of help, to Jerome Tipping, Brian Tipping, Erskine Holmes, Margaret Gatt, Yvonne Lloyd, Sally Craig, Dave Fisher, David Parks, Fiona Coyle, Mary Cosgrove, Polly Devlin, Maire Mac Sheain, Maire Nic Mhaolain, Angelique Day, Derek Mahon, Joe Graham, Tom Dunne, Joan Maguire, George McDowell, Anne Devlin, Jim Campbell, Michael Longley, Val Warner, Naomi May and Patricia Mallon.

I should like to thank Chris Agee who published a version of the Introduction in *Irish Pages*. Thanks are due, as well, to John Killen of the Linen Hall Library, Belfast; to Patricia Walker of Belfast Central Library; and to Diarmuid Kennedy of the McClay Library at Queen's University, Belfast.

I am fortunate in benefiting from the expertise of the inspired and indefatigable Blackstaff team, in particular Helen Wright and Patsy

Horton (and if I haven't always acted on their advice – on my own head be it). No publishers could be more supportive or enthusiastic.

Finally, the project would never have come to fruition without the intellectual sustenance and invigorating encouragement of my husband Jeffrey Morgan. I am grateful for this, and for much else besides.